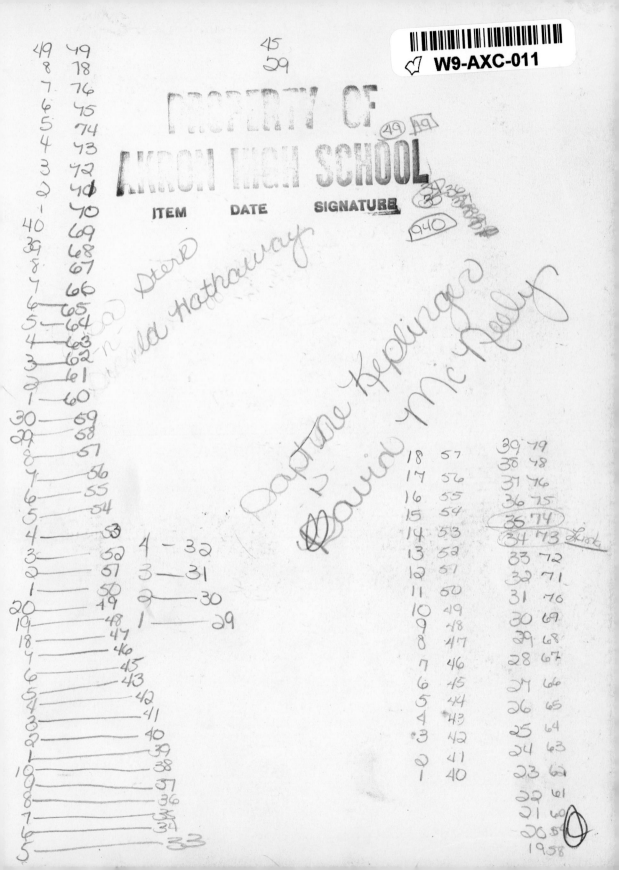

Cammy Kline
-v-
Kim Stevens
(boy)

Experiences with Foods

REVISED EDITION

by L. BELLE POLLARD

Visiting Supervisor of Home Economics for Colleges and Secondary Schools, St. Louis, Missouri
Formerly Supervisor of Home Economics in the Public Schools of St. Louis, Missouri

Ginn and Company

PREFACE

In writing this book the author has been primarily concerned with the growth of the pupil as a person and the achievement of a happy life. *Experiences with Foods* is intended for high-school pupils beginning to study the planning, preparation, and serving of meals. It will be helpful in all types of schools since their programs have a sameness of purpose and procedure.

A wide range of needs has been considered: social needs, from the elementary and simple to the more formal and demanding; budgetary needs, from those of the family of quite limited means to those of the family who, spending generously, could spend more wisely. Resources of both urban and rural communities are recognized. This book provides a practical, well-integrated, family-centered course in foods at the secondary school level.

The present interests and responsibilities of pupils in their home and social contacts have been considered realistically. Pupils should, however, also know the basic principles of nutrition and of cookery, why certain practices are best, and how satisfying results may be accomplished. Making use of such principles and information in a series of carefully planned situations provides high-school pupils with a course that increases both skill and knowledge.

The chapters and the Cookbook are designed to be used together, so that the principles learned may be put constantly into practice. Many cross references, charts, and tables are furnished in the chapters, in the Cookbook, and in the Appendix. Teachers may encourage pupils to bring favorite recipes from home and use many other devices for securing valuable materials from homes, from the school, and from the community, thus giving reality to the pupils' work, ensuring their interest, and gaining the cooperation of their parents and, at times, of community groups. Helping a pupil to assist at home builds competence, as well as cooperation. A sense of integration, whether in cooperative effort or in dovetailing tasks to prepare a meal in a given time, is immensely important to the young person who is learning to plan and accomplish tasks responsibly. Constant emphasis on nutrition, on cookery principles, on the factors of appropriateness, cost, and time is intended to develop such a sense of integration.

High-school pupils may acquire poise in many entertainment situations centered about food. The home, the particular school, and the community serve as a laboratory in which young people develop confidence through the knowledge and practice of correct behavior. Democratic practices which enrich average living are encouraged, and suggestions are made for procedures and etiquette for special occasions. The young person is presented both as host or hostess and as guest. Local customs are distinguished from those universally acceptable.

Since learning becomes meaningful only when applied in many situations, experiences in planning, practicing, and evaluating have been supplied at the close of each chapter. These and other experiences appropriate to the individual school and community will aid in solving real problems in such a way as to promote the pupils' learning. Interested young people can do much to raise nutritional standards and practices in their homes, and in doing so they not only function more positively as family members but are themselves helped to become well-poised, efficient adults. In this way the home-economics program makes its proper contribution to the young person's total development.

The author wishes to express deep appreciation to the many who have helped with the preparation of this book.

L. BELLE POLLARD

CONTENTS

UNIT ONE · Eating Well

Chapter 1. Food Needs of the Body   2

Chapter 2. Preparing Snacks   22

UNIT TWO · Breakfasts

Chapter 3. Fruits for Breakfast   34

Chapter 4. Breakfast Cereals and Breads   47

Chapter 5. Eggs and Breakfast Meats   60

Chapter 6. Breakfast Beverages   72

Chapter 7. Planning and Preparing Breakfast   81

UNIT THREE · Living Well

Chapter 8. The Efficient Kitchen   92

Chapter 9. Planned Spending   114

UNIT FOUR · Luncheons or Suppers

Chapter 10. Types of Luncheons   122
Chapter 11. Meats, Meat Alternates, and Meat Extenders   131
Chapter 12. Luncheon Breads and Sandwiches   142
Chapter 13. Soups and Salads   153
Chapter 14. Luncheon Desserts   165
Chapter 15. Planning and Preparing Luncheon   185

UNIT FIVE · Dinners

Chapter 16. Dinner Meats   192
Chapter 17. Fish and Poultry   218
Chapter 18. Vegetables in the Daily Diet   238
Chapter 19. Dinner Desserts   254
Chapter 20. Planning and Preparing Dinner   262

UNIT SIX · Individual Food Needs

Chapter 21. Helping to Meet the Food Needs of Children   272
Chapter 22. Eating to Control Weight   280
Chapter 23. Feeding the Convalescent   289

UNIT SEVEN · Food Preservation

Chapter 24. Home Preservation Methods   298

UNIT EIGHT · Good Manners and Entertaining

Chapter 25. Table Setting, Service, and Etiquette   312
Chapter 26 Entertaining   333

UNIT NINE · The Cookbook

	PAGE
Introduction	350
Fruits	354
Beverages	359
Cereals	364
Eggs	367
Toast and Quick Breads	373
Soups	384
Salads	391
Salad Dressings	398
Spreads and Sandwiches	401
Cheese	409
Vegetables	412
Sauces and Sirups	422
Meats	428
Fish	440
Poultry	445

	PAGE
Stuffings and Gravies	449
Yeast Breads	451
Custards and Puddings	457
Cakes	461
Cookies	468
Icings and Fillings	473
Pastry and Pies	476
Gelatin Desserts, Ice Cream, and Fruits	482
Candies	488
Canning Fruit	495
Canning Vegetables	497
Freezing Fruits	499
Freezing Vegetables	502
Freezing Meat, Poultry, and Fish	504
Jellies, Preserves, and Pickles	504

Appendix

Table I. Weight-Height-Age Table for Girls of School Age	508
Table II. Weight-Height-Age Table for Boys of School Age	509
Table III. Recommended Daily Dietary Allowances	510
Table IV. Nutritive Value of Foods	511
Audio-Visual Aids	518

Index

520

Alphabetical List of Charts

PAGE

Apples, Uses and Varieties of   39
Basic Four Daily Food Guide   18
Basic Seven Daily Food Guide   19
Beef, Cuts of   194
Cakes and Cookies, Temperature
and Time for Baking   462
Calorie Foods, High, Moderate,
and Low   284
Canning Fruit, Method and
Timetable for   495–496
Canning Vegetables, Methods
and Timetable for   497–498
Cans, Sizes of   41
Cereal Cookery Chart   365
Cereal Grain, Structure and Com-
position of   49
Chickens, Market Classes of   228
Chickens, Three Grades of   229
Crumb Crusts, Varieties of   477
Eggs, Standard for Freshness of   62
Food Combinations, a Guide to   264
Food Equivalents   351
Food Plan for Good Nutrition   116
Freezing Fruits, Directions for   500–501
Freezing Vegetables, Direc-
tions for   502–503
Frozen Meats, Optimum Storage
Time for   304
Frozen Vegetables, Timetable for
Cooking   419
Fruit, Dried, Average Yields   45
Fruit, Fresh, Average Yields   44
Glassware   323

PAGE

Kitchen Equipment, Small   110–111
Kitchen Utensils and Tools   108
Lamb, Cuts of   198
Market-Order Form, a Suggested   267
Meal, Rich, Modification of a   286
Meals, Three, from One Cut of Meat   204
Measures and Abbreviations   350
Meat, Storage Time Limits for   504
Meats, Temperature and Time for
Cooking   429
Menu Chart for One Day   84–85
Menus, Planning, for the Sick   290
Milk as Sold in Various Forms   76
Nuts, Fuel Value of   137
Pork, Cuts of   200
Poultry, Temperature and Time for
Cooking   444
Quick Breads, Baking   375
Quick Breads, Qualities of   57
Sirups for Freezing Fruits   499
Sirups for Fruit Canning   301
Soups, Seasonings for   157
Turkeys, Market Classes of   233
Veal, Cuts of   196
Vegetable Chart   244–245
Vegetable Cooking Chart   413–415
Vegetables, Baked   416
Vegetables, French-Fried   417
Vegetables, Pan-Fried   418
White Sauce   423
White Sauce, Comparison of Meth-
ods for Making   156
Yeast Breads, Baking   451

Experiences with Foods

Eating Well

James Pond, from Shostal

Food needs of the body

you will learn: How food gives energy;
How carbohydrates ensure fuel supply; How fats
are a source of energy; Why proteins are essential
for maintenance, repair, and growth; How minerals
help to maintain health; What the importance
of vitamins is; How water serves many purposes;
The values of a Daily Food Guide

Hunger is one of nature's signals that the body needs food. For fortunate, healthy persons, hunger is a pleasant sensation that suggests a satisfying meal in the near future. For those less fortunate, hunger may become a frightening drive to find anything that can be eaten which will stop the craving and ease the pain of an empty stomach. But inadequate food is not limited to those who are unable to obtain food. Strangely enough, even in the midst of plenty some people suffer from malnutrition because of poor appetite, insufficient food, or an unwise selection of food.

Wild animals, in their natural environment, instinctively eat the kinds of food and the amounts of food that will preserve their health and give them the greatest vigor. Lions, for instance, eat the flesh of other animals, not the grasses that sustain antelope. And wild animals do not eat more than they need.

This instinct that guides the wild animal in his food habits seems, unfortunately, to have been lost to man. As civilization has advanced, more and more foods have become available to man, but often the foods have been so highly refined that many of the nutritive values present in the natural products have been eliminated. Furthermore, elaborate methods of cooking as well as the use of rich sauces and strong flavors have developed food tastes which he insists on satisfying regardless of the nutritional value of the food. Too often he satisfies his appetite but does not really satisfy the needs of his body. And all too often he eats too much. To protect his health and build an efficient body, man needs to give more thought to his diet.

Knowledge of the composition of foods and of the nutritional needs of the body will help you to choose the right foods for promoting good health and vitality. During the past fifty years laboratory experiments and scientific tests have produced much valuable information about nutrition, and we can all benefit from this.

Food is used in your body to carry out three big jobs: (1) Food provides materials for the body's building and repair. These mate-rials are used to make new cells, to build tissues and bones, and to repair cells worn out every day. (2) Food provides regulators that enable the body to carry on its complex operations and to keep all its organs in good condition. (3) Food supplies fuel for the body's energy and warmth.

There is no single food that can accomplish all these purposes. You need to eat a variety of foods to take care of the needs of your body because different foods contain different nourishing substances, or nutrients. Often nutritional fads appear, making false claims concerning certain individual foods or food additives which supposedly can ensure health, cure disease, prolong life, or reduce weight. The Council on Foods and Nutrition of the American Medical Association has stated that there is no single food that can accomplish these goals. A thorough understanding of the principles of good nutrition is your best defense against such mistaken ideas.

The essential nutrients in foods are carbohydrates, fats, proteins, minerals, and vitamins. Besides these, the body needs oxygen and water in order to live and grow. The first three nutrients—carbohydrates, fats, and proteins—supply energy, although protein is also important as a building substance. Minerals, vitamins, and water are regulators and serve a variety of other purposes. In the pages that follow you will learn how these essential nutrients carry out their work.

Food Gives Energy

The primary need for energy in the body is for heat to maintain body temperature and for those inner activities that keep you alive, such as the beating of the heart, breathing, and digestion. The body also needs energy for growth, particularly during childhood and adolescence. Another reason the body needs energy is to enable you to work, play, and exercise.

Food is our only source of this necessary energy. It is somewhat like fuel in a machine. It gives heat and the power to move and be active. No food, however, releases energy as soon as it is eaten; the food must first undergo a series of chemical changes which is called digestion. This process takes place chiefly in the stomach and small intestine. After food is converted into soluble form which can be absorbed into the blood stream, it is carried to the body cells where an intricate system of chemistry is carried on, including oxidation and release of heat. Unabsorbed material is passed on by muscular action of the intestines to be eliminated.

Calories—A Measurement of Energy

Just as milk and sugar and flour can be measured—in pints or cups or pounds—so the heat and energy value of food can be measured. The unit of measure is called a *calorie*. Scientists have experimented with various kinds of food (vegetables, meats, etc.), burning them outside the body under controlled conditions, measuring the heat released by each, and tabulating the released heat or energy value in calories.

Turn to Table IV in the Appendix and look down the first column of figures. There you will find the heat-energy value of many foods recorded in calories. One cup of apple sauce, for example, will give you 184 calories. One slice of whole-wheat bread has 55 calories. How many calories are there in a cup of orange juice? a tablespoon of mayonnaise? a 4-ounce serving of pork sausage?

The calorie value of every food depends on how much carbohydrate, fat, and protein are present. A food that contains lots of these nutrients will be relatively high in calorie value. A food that contains only a small amount of fat or protein or carbohydrate plus a generous proportion of water will be relatively low in calorie value.

When choosing foods for your meals, it is important to think of more than their calorie value. You must also consider their total nutritive value. Otherwise, you can wind up a day having had all the food your stomach will hold but very little nourishment for your body.

Individual Calorie Needs

It is not necessary for everyone to count calories with every meal. If you eat well-balanced meals and maintain normal weight, you probably do not need to worry about calories. When you eat food that supplies the energy you need, your weight remains normal. If the food intake is more than enough to meet the body's energy needs, the excess is stored, chiefly as body fat, and you gain weight. If you do not eat enough to meet your energy demands, you lose weight.

Your age, your body size, and your rate of growth affect the amount of food energy you need. Your activity also has a big influence.

Scientists have estimated the basic number of calories necessary to maintain life at different ages and at different levels of activity. When at rest, a person needs a certain number of calories to take care of the "unconscious" body processes. As activity increases to light, moderate, hard, severe, and very severe work or play, the calorie requirement increases.

Table III in the Appendix will help you to estimate the number of calories you and other members of your family need. In using this table, however, you should realize that the calorie allowances apply to individuals usually engaged in moderate physical activity. And the allowances are only approximate. Adjustments must be made for individual variations in body size and physical activity as well as for the prevailing climate.

Most of our energy requirements are met by the carbohydrates and fats in our foods. For adults, maintenance of body weight at a steady level is the best indication of adequate calorie intake. Children and young people, however, should show a steady weight increase until physical maturity is attained. The weight-height-age tables (I and II) in the Appendix may be used to find the average weight and height ranges for any given age. At the end of these Tables you will find for short, medium, and tall types of persons the average yearly gain in both height and weight. Again, remember that these figures are average and may not apply exactly to you.

Girls and boys of your age need more calories for energy than the typical adult. You are growing, building muscles and more compact bones. As you add inches in height and as your organs and nervous system develop, liberal amounts of food are required. In adult life there is a gradual decrease in need. Girls of high-school age usually grow a little less rapidly in physical stature than do boys. The larger frames of boys must be covered with heavier muscles in keeping with their more vigorous activities. The bodies of girls must build the tissues and lighter muscles that result in an adult figure. To develop into strong adults, boys and girls need to eat enough to support rapid growth.

You can maintain better health by eating wholesome foods, such as milk, fruits, vegetables, cereals, eggs, and meat. Appetites that crave rich desserts or fatty foods should be trained to enjoy more simple diets. If you must have a special diet because of overweight or underweight, you will find suggestions in Chapter 22 of this book.

Carbohydrates Ensure Fuel Supply for Energy

Carbohydrates and Their Function

Sugars and starches in various forms make up a group of nutrients called carbohydrates. Cellulose is also a carbohydrate but has no nutritive value since it cannot be digested. Found in the fibers of all plants—such as the stalks of celery, the skin of apples and potatoes, and the hulls of grain kernels—cellulose serves as bulk or "roughage" and aids in proper intestinal elimination.

The sugars are distributed widely, occurring in the sap of different plants and in the juices of fruits. The most familiar sugar is *sucrose*, a pure carbohydrate. It is used in the form of granulated, confectioners', or brown sugar. Whether sucrose is made from sugar cane or from sugar beets, it is chemically the same product. Many of the common fruits and vegetables also contain some sucrose. *Lactose* is the sugar that occurs in milk.

Other sugars, *glucose* and *fructose*, are found in honey and in fruits and vegetables such as apples, grapes, oranges, peas, corn, and sweet potatoes. Still another sugar, *maltose*, is found in malt products and sprouting grains. Sugars do not furnish any nutrient except carbohydrates.

The carbohydrate *starch* makes up the chief portion of all cereal grains, the tuberous vegetables, and the legumes. Among the many rich sources of starch are corn, oats, wheat, potatoes, beans, and peas. The flour in bread is made from cereal grains, so bread has high value as a carbohydrate food. Since other nutrients which accompany starch in these foods may vary greatly in kind and amount, our starchy foods should be chosen with great care to provide the highest possible nutritive values. The best cereal products are whole or enriched grains. A meal may be very

5

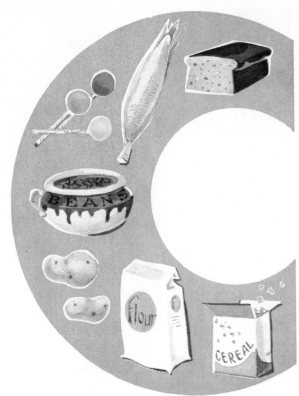

CARBOHYDRATES

easily overloaded with starchy foods. Corn or beans, both rich in starch, may be substituted occasionally for potatoes but not for green and leafy vegetables.

The chief function of carbohydrates in the body is to provide energy. The sugars when oxidized, or burned, yield 48 calories per tablespoon of sugar. All starches are converted, during digestion, into their simple sugar components. These simple sugars can be burned as fuel, and any excess can be stored. Like excess in food intake of any kind—whether carbohydrate, fat, or protein—the excess will be stored in the body chiefly as fat.

Carbohydrates not only supply energy but are essential for the proper use of fat and protein in the body. When there are sufficient carbohydrates and fats in the diet, they, rather than the proteins, are burned for fuel. This leaves the proteins for their essential role in tissue building and the repair of worn-out cells.

Individual Carbohydrate Needs

Although a liberal intake of carbohydrates is advisable to maintain health and energy, there is no definite nutritional requirement for normal persons. Carbohydrates contribute about 50 per cent of the total calories in the diet of most Americans. But in some parts of the world the percentage averages 80. Economic factors determine this situation. The cheapest foods—cereals, dried beans, and potatoes—are mainly carbohydrate. Many families in overcrowded areas of the world, such as China and India, eat great amounts of rice. They have little

6

F A T S

money to spend on food and only small plots of land to plant in crops. Rice and other cereals give a high yield of calories per acre of soil. In some parts of Latin America where poverty is widespread the people depend largely on dried beans as the basis of their meals. Even in our country during a depression many families have to eat greater amounts of bread, dried beans, and potatoes than usual since they cannot afford to buy as much meat or dairy products as they might like to have.

Some care should be taken in eating foods rich in carbohydrates, for some of them affect the teeth. Sticky candy, for example, tends to adhere to the teeth and promote the growth of bacteria in the mouth that may cause tooth decay. When sugars are eaten with meals rather than between meals, less tooth decay is likely to develop. Fruit is better as a between-meal snack. Rinsing the carbohydrates from the mouth after eating can also help prevent tooth decay. It is wise to clean the teeth after each meal.

Fats—Another Source of Energy

Fats and Their Functions

The fats in foods come from both animal and plant sources. Meat is a major source of animal fat, though much of the fat in it is invisible. Other sources of animal fats are whole milk, cheese, and egg yolk. Plant foods, such as corn, nuts, olives, certain seeds and soybeans, contain fats in considerable

7

amounts. The use of plant fats is increasing rapidly. Oils from plants make their contribution to the diet through margarine, salad oils, and cooking oils.

Solid commercial cooking fats may be either animal or vegetable or even a combination of the two. They have been treated by a process called hydrogenation. This produces a creamy, solid product for cooking and prevents the fat from becoming rancid in storage.

Normally the average American eats approximately one-third of his total calories in the form of fat. Fats make eating more pleasurable, for they give flavor to foods, and their relatively slow rate of digestion allays hunger. The feeling of satisfaction lasts over a longer period of time when a meal contains a moderate amount of fat.

When fats are oxidized in the body cells, they yield energy. Fats are more concentrated in fuel value than carbohydrates, giving two and one-fourth times as many calories per unit of weight. However, they are more expensive than carbohydrates. You learned on page 6 that carbohydrates—especially cereals and vegetables—are generally the cheapest energy-giving foods. In many households meat (which contains considerable fat), butter, and other relatively expensive fatty foods must be used sparingly. Because of the concentrated nature of fats, they can easily increase the calorie value of a meal without making the diet too bulky. In addition to providing energy value, fats are needed to enable the body to use the two essential fat-soluble vitamins, A and D.

Food energy intake (whether carbohydrate, fat, or protein) which is in excess of the body's immediate needs is stored as fat. Some stored fat is necessary in the body for a number of reasons. It serves as an energy reserve when food intake does not meet the body's requirements. Fat stored in the connective tissue layers under the skin serves as insulation and conserves body warmth. Stored fat also serves as a support and protector of the vital organs, for example the kidneys. While these are important functions, it must be remembered that fat stored in the body to the point of excess puts an extra burden on the heart and other organs, and it also detracts from personal appearance.

Individual Fat Needs

It is easy to eat excessively of foods that are rich in fat. Overeating of fats often goes along with overeating of other foods. Thus the body weight increases rapidly, as explained in Chapter 22, "Eating to Control Weight." Fried foods, rich gravies and sauces, heavy salad dressings, and pastries not only add body weight but also retard digestion. Because butter, cream, cheese, fortified margarine, egg yolk, salad oils, and meats supply a balanced combination of other essential food elements, they should be the chief sources of fat in the diet.

Proteins—Essential for Maintenance, Repair, and Growth

Proteins and Their Function

Proteins form another class of foodstuffs which are essential for body growth and development. They are important constituents of every living cell in the body and are present in greater quantities than any other one substance with the exception of water. Proteins are part of all the tissues and fluids of the body. Muscles, hair, nails, and skin are largely protein matter. Among the busiest proteins are those in the blood. Hemoglobin, which is 95 per cent protein and 5 per cent iron, constantly carries oxygen from the lungs to the tissues and brings carbon dioxide back from the tissues to the lungs. Other proteins in the blood help a person to resist disease and sometimes to develop immunity to disease.

If proteins are removed from the diet, the tissues slowly starve and waste away. Therefore, the building and repair of body tissue is the chief work of proteins. They contribute greatly to body vigor, strong muscles, and ability to resist infections. Although proteins can be used as a source of energy, it is an uneconomical use. Sufficient carbohydrates and fats should be provided in the diet so that the protein content of the diet will be utilized not to produce energy but to promote proper growth and maintenance of the body.

Some of the proteins found in the daily diet are much more effective than others. The reason for this is that proteins do not all have the same value. They are very complex substances, made up of varying combinations of chemical units called the *amino acids*. The body can make its own supply of some of these amino acids, but the rest of them must come readymade from the food we eat. The kinds and amounts of amino acids in a protein determine its nutritive value.

Proteins from animal sources, as a general rule, supply all of the amino acids in about the same proportions in which they are needed by the body; therefore, they are called "complete proteins." They are rated as having high nutritive value. When you eat meat, fish, fowl, cheese, or eggs and when you drink milk or get it in cooked foods, you supply your body with these complete, or first-class, proteins. Some of these protein foods are needed each day and should be included in each meal.

The proteins from fruits, vegetables, grains, and nuts are "incomplete proteins" because they do not contain all the essential amino acids. Their nutritive value is lower than that of the animal proteins. However, the proteins in some of the legumes—especially soybeans—are almost as good as those from animal sources. Also, incomplete proteins may supplement one another, and when combined with complete proteins are more valuable to the body than when eaten alone. Thus cereals are more nutritionally valuable when eaten with milk, beans when eaten with frankfurters, and so on.

Thus the adequacy of protein foods depends not only on the quality of the protein, but also on the amount contained in an average serving, and on the combination of different protein foods in the diet.

Individual Protein Needs

Children and young people need more protein in relation to their size than older people. Moreover, this substance must be supplied regularly by the diet. If each of your three daily meals contains protein in some form, and if one of the proteins in each meal is of high quality, you will attain your quota easily.

To supply protein economically, remember that the less expensive cuts of meat have as much protein as do steaks and chops. Preparing the less expensive cuts appetizingly and attractively offers a challenge to the cook.

As one matures and ceases to grow, the need for protein decreases somewhat. Sufficient proteins for the average adult will be ensured if at least two glasses of milk, one egg or a serving of cheese, and one serving of meat are included in the daily diet, along with grain products and vegetable foods. Men and women who have been seriously ill with continued fever or severe tissue damage should usually have higher allowances.

PROTEINS

Minerals Help to Maintain Health

Minerals and Their Function

Minerals are inorganic, or nonliving, substances, and, although present in many foods, do not furnish energy to the body. They are used as building materials for bones and teeth, as constituents of blood and tissues, and they promote health in other ways.

There are more than twenty different minerals bound up in the structure of your body or used in carrying out its essential activities. The most important are calcium, phosphorus, iron, and iodine. Each has a special function in your body.

Some minerals occur in large amounts. For example, your body contains about three pounds of calcium, more than 90 per cent of it in your bones and teeth. Some minerals occur in such tiny amounts that they are called trace elements. Scientists have not yet determined the functions of all the trace elements. Some minerals are effective only or usually in combination. For example, calcium and phosphorus combine to form strong bones and teeth.

People found out about the need for certain inorganic elements, or minerals, in the diet when they saw that some deficiency diseases in livestock and in human beings could be treated by giving large doses of a specific mineral. For example, when cattle and sheep in several areas of the world began to suffer loss of appetite and waste away, it was discovered that the deficiency, or lack, in their diet was a mineral called cobalt. To prevent

MINERALS

the disease the animals were given salt that contained cobalt.

Since the early 1900's scientists have conducted many experiments with animals and have made complicated studies of human nutrition in an attempt to determine just how much of each mineral is needed, how the minerals function in the body, and what foods supply them. Some of these questions have not yet been satisfactorily answered, and further research is being carried on. The minerals discussed here are considered the most important in our diet and are, for the most part, the ones about which the most is known.

Individual Mineral Needs

Calcium is one of the most important building materials of the body. Combined with phosphorus, calcium gives rigidity and hardness to the bones and teeth. During the first year of life the amount of these minerals in the body increases faster in relation to size than at any other time. The calcium content of the body continues to increase during growth through childhood and adolescence. Even when physical growth is completed, the adult must have a constant dietary supply of calcium to meet the functional demands of the body and to maintain normal health.

The process of building bones and teeth requires other nutrients besides calcium and phosphorus, particularly vitamin D, which you will learn about later.

Gains in calcium and phosphorus content depend on an adequate supply in the diet and the ability of the body to use the supply for normal growth. The best source of calcium is milk. It is very difficult to supply the amounts of calcium that are needed unless milk in some form is consumed daily. Cheese, like cheddar and "American" cheese, is another excellent source and should be eaten frequently. Cottage cheese and cream cheese, however, are relatively poor sources of calcium.

Most teen-agers can drink 3 or 4 cups of milk a day and have plenty of room for other needed foods. Younger children need about the same amount, but a five-year-old, if given much milk at the start of a meal, may drink so much that he has no appetite for the rest of the meal. Therefore, for young children some of the milk may be supplied in cooked foods.

Calcium serves other purposes in the body besides giving strength and firmness to bones and teeth. It is necessary for the clotting of the blood. Calcium in the blood is also needed for the sending of millions of messages per day along the nerve fibers.

If a child does not get enough calcium in his food, his bones may be smaller and less rigid than they should be and he may have poor teeth. Severe deficiencies can cause permanent stunting of size and malformations of bones and teeth. Older people who have not kept an adequate supply of calcium in their bodies may have thin, brittle bones that break easily.

Fluorine is another mineral that helps build good teeth. It makes the tooth enamel harder and apparently prevents decay. In areas where fluorine is not naturally present in the drinking water, it is sometimes added to the water supply.

Phosphorus is an essential part of every cell in the body. It takes part in the many vital chemical reactions with carbohydrates, fats, and proteins to give the body energy and vital materials for growth and repair. Phosphorus helps the blood in its functions and,

with calcium, is necessary for the work of the muscles and for the normal responses of nerves to stimulation. Phosphorus and calcium are of equal importance in building strong bones and teeth.

The danger of deficiency is not so great for phosphorus as for calcium. Phosphorus is found not only in milk and cheese but also in other protein-rich foods, such as meat, fish, eggs, and poultry. A diet that provides enough protein and calcium will very likely furnish enough phosphorus as well. And for the average person the phosphorus intake should be about equal to that of calcium.

Iron is vital for the development and functioning of the blood pigment, hemoglobin. Hemoglobin is a compound of iron and protein which makes it possible for the red corpuscles to carry oxygen from the lungs to all the tissues of the body. Unlike many other minerals, iron may be stored in small amounts—in the liver, spleen, and bone marrow. This reserve may be drawn on during periods of illness but should not be relied upon to replace the recommended daily supply. (See Table III in the Appendix.)

Iron deficiency may be caused by incorrect diet or loss of blood, but if food is selected sensibly there is no difficulty for most people in securing the generous amounts of iron their bodies need. Although varying amounts occur in many different foods, the chief sources of iron are meats, eggs, and leafy green vegetables. Of the meats, liver is an especially rich source. This accounts in part for the frequent use of liver in baby feedings when semi-solid foods are introduced. Cooked oatmeal and molasses are also good sources of iron.

Iodine is necessary for the thyroid gland to function properly. A deficiency of iodine in the diet may lead to an enlargement of this gland, a condition known as goiter.

12

In areas near seacoasts, iodine is contained in the water and in the soil, and therefore in the vegetables and fruits grown in the soil. Goiter is not a frequent ailment in these parts of our country. But in some other areas, notably the Great Lakes area, the western plains, and the mountain valleys, the amount of iodine in the soil and water is inadequate. Since foods grown in such areas cannot supply the necessary iodine, the people use iodized table salt for the prevention of the thyroid condition. Sea foods are a good source of this mineral, but they are not always available in abundance in inland areas. In Canada the addition of iodine to table salt is compulsory.

The Importance of Vitamins

Vitamins and Their Function

About fifty years ago scientists discovered that proteins, fats, carbohydrates, minerals, and water are not the only essential elements in foods. There is something more that is necessary to maintain life—and that something is vitamins. Vitamins are organic substances present in very small amounts in natural foods, and sometimes produced within the body. Scientists learned in their studies and experiments that if a certain vitamin is lacking in the diet, a person or an animal becomes ill. When that vitamin is added to the diet, the sick person or animal gets well.

If you eat a variety of foods every day, you are almost sure of getting the assortment of vitamins you need. A well-balanced diet that includes sufficient amounts of milk, fruit, vegetables, eggs, meat, and whole-grain or enriched bread and cereals usually provides an adequate supply. Yet in some climates and at various stages of growth, people may have to pay special attention to their diets to see that they are eating foods that contain special vitamins essential to their health. Each vitamin has a specific role to play in the functioning of the body.

Vitamins are usually classified in two groups: those that are soluble in fat and those that are soluble in water. This is significant because foods containing fat-soluble vitamins do not lose their vitamin content readily in cooking with water. Vegetables containing water-soluble vitamins should be cooked quickly in a small amount of water. If any cooking water is left, it should be used in soup, sauce, or gravy.

The fat-soluble vitamins that we know most about are vitamins A and D. The most important water-soluble vitamins are certain B vitamins and vitamin C. An understanding of their individual functions will show you why they are essential to your health.

Vitamin A helps to keep the skin and the linings of nose, mouth, throat, and inner organs in good condition. If these surfaces are weakened, bacteria can invade more easily. Vitamin A is also necessary for normal vision, especially in dim light. When a person does not have enough vitamin A, his eyes adjust slowly to changes from bright light to dim light. This difficulty is called "night blindness." You may have trouble trying to see in a dark theater when you come in from the brightly lighted lobby or street outside. If you have sufficient vitamin A, your eyes adjust quickly to the dim light so that you can see people and objects around you.

Before we knew about vitamin A, night blindness was frequently found among fishermen of Newfoundland and Labrador who worked in open boats in bright sunshine and

13

exposed their eyes to the glare on the water. There was an old belief that if a man could not see at night, he could restore his vision by eating the liver of a codfish or a sea gull. Now we know that he was meeting his need for vitamin A, and people are being taught the importance of butter and whole milk and cheese as well as oil from the liver of salt-water fish as sources of vitamin A.

Vitamin A occurs only in foods of animal origin. However, all yellow and green plants contain a yellow pigment, called *carotene*, which the body can change into vitamin A. It is estimated that about one-half of the vitamin A requirement in the average American diet comes from the carotene in yellow and dark green vegetables and yellow fruits. Examples of these are carrots, pumpkin, sweet potatoes, spinach, beet greens, peaches, apricots, and cantaloupe. The other part of the vitamin requirement is provided by the vitamin itself present in foods of animal origin, such as whole milk, butter, eggs, liver, and kidney.

Since vitamin A and carotene are fat-soluble, they are stable during ordinary cooking and food-preservation processes. There is no loss by extraction during cooking. Exposure to air or oxygen, however, especially along with extreme heat, causes destruction of both vitamin A and carotene. When foods such as eggs and vegetables are air dried, there is a considerable loss of vitamin A. Vacuum drying prevents such loss.

Vitamin D, also a fat-soluble vitamin, is especially important to the young, because it works with calcium and phosphorus to form strong bones and sound teeth. A deficiency of vitamin D causes rickets, a disease in which the bones do not harden properly and may bend and twist into abnormal shape. A long time ago babies and children in northern European countries suffered from rickets.

14

Cod-liver oil was used to treat and then to prevent the disease, but the reason for its effectiveness was not known. In the 19th century, when many industries sprang into existence, rickets became a common disease of children in cities. In London and Glasgow at one time a third of the children of poor families had rickets. The cause was thought to be their lack of sunshine.

Not until the 1920's did scientists show definitely that both exposure to sunlight and the use of cod-liver oil in the diet would prevent rickets./ The ultraviolet rays in sunlight shining on the bare skin change certain substances in the skin to vitamin D. Cod and other fish store vitamin D in their livers.

An insufficiency of vitamin D also affects the teeth. Without vitamin D the teeth are likely to come in irregularly and to have poorly calcified enamel, so that they decay easily.

Very few foods contain significant amounts of vitamin D. Exposure of the skin to sunlight is the way Nature evidently intended us to get enough vitamin D. If you live in a northern climate, however, and wear heavy clothing during the winter, the sunlight cannot do its work. Children and teen-agers who live in smoky, cloudy cities miss the benefit of daily sunshine. Some other source of vitamin D is therefore advisable. Doctors usually prescribe cod-liver oil for babies and small children. In many areas milk to which vitamin D has been added is available.

The B vitamins form a large group, in which thiamine, riboflavin, and niacin are the most generally known and best understood. They are important in converting fuel in foods into energy and in building up and maintaining the cells and tissues of the body. An adequate supply of the B vitamins in food helps to promote normal appetite, good digestion, steady nerves, and good morale.

VITAMINS

Few foods contain a real wealth of the B vitamins, but in a varied diet many foods contribute some and so build an adequate supply. One way of maintaining a high vitamin-B level is to use regularly bread and flour made from whole or enriched grain.

Thiamine, also known as vitamin B_1, is found in the brown outer coats of rice, wheat, and other cereal grains. A deficiency of thiamine causes a disease called beriberi. For many years the disease was common among the rice-eating people in China and Japan and other countries. The sick people felt unable to do anything, and their feet and legs eventually became paralyzed. A Dutch doctor, Christian Eijkman, noticed that beriberi attacked those whose main food was polished white rice, but people who ate unpolished brown rice were well. He discovered the cause of beriberi—a lack of some nutrient in the outer coats of unpolished rice—but it was later scientists who identified the substance as vitamin thiamine.

While a large section of the world's population is dependent on rice for thiamine, this is not true of people living in North America. They get some thiamine from cereal grains, to be sure, but also from meat, milk and cheese, potatoes, and other vegetables. Since thiamine is water-soluble and in some foods is destroyed by heat, overcooking food or cooking in too much water may cause large amounts of the vitamin to be lost.

Riboflavin helps in oxidation processes in cells of many kinds. It is a water-soluble, yellow pigment found in many foods of plant and animal origin. The two outstanding sources of this vitamin are milk and liver.

15

Riboflavin is relatively stable in heat but is destroyed by exposure to light.

A deficiency in riboflavin may result in soreness of the tongue and lips and cracks at the corners of the mouth. The amounts of milk recommended to supply sufficient calcium, along with other foods, will usually meet riboflavin requirements.

Niacin, or nicotinic acid, is known as the pellagra-preventing vitamin. Pellagra is a disease that was common in the 19th and early 20th centuries among poor people who lived mainly on corn bread and fat salt pork and was recognized as the "corn-eaters' disease." The victims of the disease suffer from skin rash, disturbances of the digestive tract, and psychic changes such as anxiety and depression.

After many experiments scientists found that pellagra was due in part to a lack of the vitamin niacin, which is not present in corn. There are still many uncertainties about this disease. Fortunately it is not prevalent today. A diet that is well-balanced with adequate amounts of meat, vegetables, and whole-grain cereals will supply niacin in sufficient quantities.

Vitamin C, or ascorbic acid, is essential for human beings to promote and protect various body processes. It is generally thought that this vitamin forms a cement-like substance that helps to hold the cells of the body together, but there is some doubt about exactly how it does its work.

The main function of vitamin C that has been proved beyond any doubt is that it prevents scurvy. This disease was once common during famines and wars and among sailors who ate little except bread and salt meat on long voyages. The victims of scurvy suffered from spongy gums which bled easily and from loose teeth. Often small blood vessels burst under the skin. Lack of appetite and laziness were minor symptoms. Thousands of sailors in the exploration of the New World became ill with scurvy on their voyages lasting many months. Many died as a result of the disease.

Naval doctors conducted thorough investigations of causes and remedies for scurvy. They learned that eating fresh fruit, especially citrus fruit, and some vegetables can prevent the disease. In 1795 the British Navy ordered all its ships to carry adequate supplies of lemons or limes to be eaten by the sailors during the voyages. This accounts for the fact that British sailors even to this day are called "limeys." Since then, scientists have discovered that the all-important substance possessed by citrus fruits is ascorbic acid, or vitamin C.

Scurvy is no longer a threat to us. Most people get some vitamin C in their food, for there are small amounts in a variety of fruits and vegetables. However, to be sure of enough they should include some citrus fruit in their diet every day. One orange or half a grapefruit—or a corresponding amount of juice from these citrus fruits—supplies most of the vitamin C needed for the day. Other good sources of this vitamin are tomatoes, raw cabbage, spinach, turnips, and potatoes cooked in their skins.

Vitamin C, more than any other known vitamin, tends to be destroyed when we prepare foods that contain it. It is soluble in water and dissolves out of food. The destruction speeds up as temperature increases and as it is exposed to the air. Thus it is important to store foods rich in vitamin C at low temperatures, to prepare them just before they are to be served, and to avoid lengthy cooking. The best methods for cooking vegetables are discussed on pages 249–250. Generally, we get more vitamin C from fruits and vegetables when we eat them raw.

Water Serves Many Purposes

Water makes up about one-half of your total body weight. If you weigh 90 pounds, about 45 pounds of your weight is water. The water consumed by the body is not changed or broken down by digestive juices as foods are. Since water is a part of the digestive juices, of all other fluids, and of all cells of the body, it is essential to every body process. Water has no food value, although most waters contain mineral elements, such as calcium (see page 12).

Water is more immediately necessary to life than food. You might live weeks without food but only a few days without water. It serves as a carrier, transporting, by means of the blood stream, nutritious substances in solution to all parts of the body. It is estimated that about three quarts of water continuously circulate as part of the blood. Water carries dissolved waste materials through the body and aids in their elimination through the lungs and the skin, the kidneys, and the intestines. Water is essential in the regulation of body temperature through evaporation via the skin and lungs. Water is second only to oxygen as a constant body need.

When the balance between water loss and water intake is upset, you get thirsty. Thirst is the best guide to the amount of water you need. You can quench your thirst by drinking water, fruit juice, milk, or some other beverage. But water is present in practically all foods. Ice creams and gelatin are converted into liquid form in the stomach and add to the liquid content of the body. Watermelon, strawberries, lettuce, and tomatoes are all very high in water content. Even cereals and other dry products contain as much as 6 per cent water.

When you are very active at work or play in hot weather, the water lost in sweat should be replaced as soon as possible. It is important to maintain the body's water content throughout any period of exposure to heat, especially if hard physical work is done at the same time.

A Daily Food Guide for Meals

You have learned that the body needs various nutrients for growth and repair, for protection and regulation, and for energy. Most foods contain more than one nutrient. No single food, however, contains all the nutrients in the amounts that we need. In planning menus for each day, therefore, it is wise to choose a variety of foods that together will supply all the nutrients required for a well-balanced diet.

Food guides from the United States Department of Agriculture provide a practical and quick method for making adequate food selections for nutritious daily meals. On page 18 a Daily Food Guide is presented. It shows how foods of similar nutritive value can be grouped together. Everyone needs some foods from each group every day. Choices may be made within each group to give variety to meals. The minimum number of servings specified in the food guide will provide most of the nutrients necessary for the body.

The number of servings recommended in each group applies to an average adult. As a general rule, except for milk, young children need less of all foods than adults. Older children need about the same amount as adults. Teen-agers and very active adults require more of most kinds of food.

DAILY FOOD GUIDE

1 MILK
CHEESE,
ICE CREAM

CHILDREN, FOUR CUPS MILK DAILY; ADULTS, TWO CUPS

2 MEAT
POULTRY, FISH,
EGGS, DRIED PEAS
AND BEANS

TWO OR MORE SERVINGS DAILY

3 BREAD—
CEREALS
GRAINS (WHOLE
OR ENRICHED)

FOUR SERVINGS DAILY

4 VEGETABLES—
FRUITS
ALL KINDS

FOUR SERVINGS DAILY, INCLUDING ONE CITRUS FRUIT
AND ONE GREEN OR YELLOW VEGETABLE

Milk Group

Milk, as you have already learned, is a leading source of calcium, which is essential for the development of bones and teeth and required for other body functions. In addition, milk contributes riboflavin and high-quality protein and also provides many other vitamins and minerals, as well as carbohydrate and fat. Cheese and ice cream, which are milk products, supply these nutrients, too, but in different proportions.

Milk is counted on to furnish the major portion of the daily needs for calcium. Everyone should have milk each day, either as a beverage or in cooked foods. Teen-agers as well as children should have at least 4 cups daily. Other foods, chiefly vegetables, fruits, breads, and cereals, will supply calcium also and add to the daily intake.

Meat Group

The foods of the meat group are important for the amounts and quality of the protein they provide. Remember that protein is vital as a tissue builder. In addition to protein, many of the foods in the meat group supply considerable iron, thiamine, riboflavin, niacin, and varying amounts of fat.

18

Milk Group

Meat Group

A DAILY FOOD GUIDE

(Choose your food every day from these four groups.)

Vegetable-Fruit Group

Bread-Cereal Group

Notice that the chart recommends two or more servings a day. The best choices are meat, poultry, fish, and eggs, because they contain all the essential amino acids in the proportions needed to support growth and maintain health. Dry beans, dry peas, and nuts, however, may be used as alternates.

Bread-cereals Group

The importance of the grain foods in the diet is that they make many-sided nutritional contributions at relatively low cost rather than large contributions of one or two nutrients. In addition to some protein, breads and cereals that are whole-grain or enriched furnish thiamine, riboflavin, niacin, iron, and other vitamins and minerals.

The four servings a day recommended in the chart could include any of the following foods *if they are whole-grain or enriched*: bread, cooked or ready-to-eat cereals, crackers, macaroni, noodles, spaghetti, and rice. Baked goods, such as muffins, cakes, and cookies, made with whole-grain or enriched flour may also be counted in this group.

Vegetable-fruit Group

Vegetables and fruits are valuable because of the vitamins and minerals they contain and for the roughage they provide in the digestive tract. They are also valuable simply because they add interest to any meal, not only in their taste but in their colorful appearance.

Citrus fruits, you learned, are a leading source of ascorbic acid, or vitamin C. Your daily glass of orange juice or tomato juice is really important. Can you tell why?

Dark-green and deep-yellow vegetables are noteworthy for vitamin A, which is needed for healthy skin and good eyesight. Some of the dark-green vegetables also provide considerable vitamin C, iron, riboflavin, and calcium.

The four daily servings of fruits and vegetables make similar nutrient contributions, but vary in the amounts of nutrients in each serving. That is why it is important to eat a variety of fruits and vegetables each day.

To Complete the Daily Meals

The foods suggested in the Daily Food Guide (page 18) provide the *foundation* for an adequate diet. If you have the minimum number of servings specified from each food group, you will get most, but not all, of the nutrients needed for good nutrition. Some foods are not included as groups in the Daily Food Guide. These are butter, margarine, oils, sugar, and unenriched refined cereals. The reason they are not included is that such foods usually appear in meals in combination with the specific foods shown. Fats and oils, for example, are added to many foods in the cooking or preparation process and at the table. Sugar is often used with such foods as breakfast cereals, some fruits, and desserts. Both fats and sugar help to make meals flavorful and satisfying and they also supply calories. It is believed that sufficient amounts of these foods will be provided without special emphasis in the Daily Food Guide.

A varied diet is the best assurance you can have of obtaining all the nutrients essential to good health.

¶ *Understanding:*

1. What are the three big jobs that food has to do for you?
2. Name the essential nutrients. Which two are most valuable in supplying energy?
3. What are calories? Why do teen-agers need more calories than most adults?
4. When your food intake is more than enough to meet your energy needs, what happens?

5. What two kinds of foods are carbohydrates?

6. What are the two sources of fats?

7. What is the primary function of protein?

8. Explain why the body needs adequate amounts of calcium; phosphorus; iron; iodine.

9. What are vitamins? Explain the functions of vitamins A, C, and D.

10. Name some foods rich in vitamins A and C.

11. Why is thiamine an important vitamin?

¶ *Planning:*

1. Choose a school lunch which is adequate in calories and provides proteins of high quality. Which of these foods are good sources of vitamins and minerals?

2. Plan a meal to include protein foods of low cost. Plan one of moderate cost.

3. Improve two meals high in carbohydrates by substituting foods rich in proteins and vitamins.

4. Plan a day's meals for a teen-age girl, based on the requirements of the Daily Food Guide.

5. Revise a dinner menu to include foods less rich in fats. Check for calorie content.

6. Plan a day's meals adequate in calories for you. How can you modify this day's meals for an additional 500 calories? for 250 fewer calories?

7. Plan balanced meals for a day for a 6-year-old child. Check by the Daily Food Guide (page 18).

¶ *Practicing and Evaluating:*

1. Alter a meal for a greater variety of foods, keeping approximately the same food values.

2. Keep a record of the approximate amount of water you supplied for body needs on one certain day. What sources outside of simple drinking water did you use?

3. Compare the cost and protein value of ¾ cup of cottage cheese and one deviled egg.

4. Evaluate a day's meals for calorie values. Suggest ways to decrease the calories.

5. Keep a record of all foods eaten for two days. How should your meals in the future be planned to meet your calorie needs?

6. Check several days' menus for their mineral content.

7. Consult your grocer on the enriched foods stocked and the extent of their enrichment. Include several of these in the family menus.

8. Observe meals chosen at a cafeteria or restaurant. Show how you could have made better choices.

¶ *Reading Further:*

Food, the Yearbook of Agriculture, 1959. U. S. Department of Agriculture, Washington, D. C.

Food for Family with Young Children, rev. ed. 1962. Superintendent of Documents, Washington, D. C.

LEVERTON, RUTH M., *Food Becomes You.* University of Iowa Press, Ames, Iowa.

Nutrition and Healthy Growth. U. S. Department of Health, Education, and Welfare, Children's Bureau, Washington, D. C.

Nutrition . . . Up to Date, Up to You, GS–1, rev. ed., 1960. U. S. Department of Agriculture, Washington, D. C.

Nutritive Value of Foods, G–72, 1960. U. S. Department of Agriculture, Washington, D. C.

Personality "Plus" through Diet—Foodlore for Teenagers. Public Affairs Committee, Inc., New York, N. Y.

Principles of Good Nutrition, Bulletin 162 (1960). U. S. Department of Health, Education, and Welfare, Washington, D. C.

You and What You Eat, 1960. University of California Agricultural Extension Service, Berkeley, California.

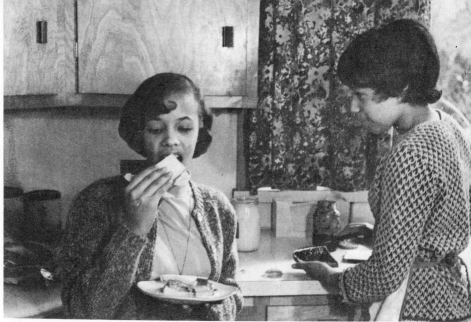

Ginn, (Frank D. Lucas)

Preparing snacks

you will learn: How the good manager works;

How to prepare a simple snack;

How to care for the kitchen after snack preparation;

How to plan snacks for home guests

Your mother, who has made a career of homemaking and whose efficiency in the kitchen you may well admire, knows that real talent and capabilities are needed, and that skill in this field, as in any specialized field, comes only with practice. She knows too that the career of homemaker offers rewards and satisfactions that no other type of work can duplicate. One important phase of homemaking is the planning, preparation, and serving of meals. Certainly, the gracious homemaker and hostess who gives her family and their guests nutritious foods, well cooked and attractively served, has accomplished something well worth while.

Kitchen skills are not mastered all at once nor in a haphazard manner. Your mother's efficiency and good management were learned with patience and practice. So will you, too, in your turn learn the same skills.

22

The Importance of Snacks

One exciting way of becoming acquainted with the kitchen is to prepare snacks there. Whether you prepare a tasty between-meal snack hurriedly from tidbits in the refrigerator, or serve more carefully prepared refreshments to guests, you will be developing the graciousness and poise that characterize a charming hostess.

Since snacks are really little meals, the calories they supply must be counted in the tally of daily food. Weight watchers may have an occasional snack provided it supplies few calories, or provided the same number of calories is omitted from the next meal. For the underweight, snacks are an easy way of adding food in small amounts to the diet. Some people include snacks in the diet regularly to prevent fatigue and hunger.

The following plan shows how snacks may be integrated into a day's menu for a boy or girl who is active in sports.

Breakfast
Sections of One Orange
Dry Cereal   Whole Milk
Egg in Toast Cup
Cocoa

Morning Snack
Tomato Juice
Crackers with Peanut Butter

Lunch
Cheeseburgers
Green Salad   French Dressing
Whole Milk

Afternoon Snack
Hot Spiced Apple Cider
Cream Cheese on Raisin Bread

Dinner
Ham Pineapple Ring
Glazed Sweet Potatoes
Green Beans with Croutons
Perfection Salad
Biscuits   Butter or Margarine
Tapioca Pudding
Whole Milk

Study these menus and show how they furnish the necessary nutrients for growth, repair of the body, energy, and general health as advised by the Daily Food Guide on page 18.

How the Good Manager Works

Good management enables you to accomplish more in less time and with less effort. Bringing several needed supplies from the storage area on the same trip, saving yourself from wiping up spills by not filling utensils too full, and handling sharp knives carefully to avoid cut fingers are simple ways to save yourself work. Moving a flour or sugar canister to the work area instead of making several trips for the needed amounts is another way. Using a tray or utility cart to set the table saves time.

But efficiency in the kitchen is important not only in saving yourself work but also in developing poise and self-confidence. If you have planned a menu that is easily workable, placed necessary equipment within easy reach, and made a time schedule for your work, you can carry out the preparation of the meal with self-assurance.

You become a good manager, not by chance, but by learning all phases of the task. The important things to learn are listed in the left column on the next page.

Thorough washing of the hands with soap is one of the most important preparations for cooking

or apron made from washable fabric. Bib aprons, wide at the side, afford the best protection. Confine your hair with a net, pins, or ribbon. Before beginning work with food you should wash your hands thoroughly with soap, making sure that the nails are clean. Dry hands on paper towels or hand towels, not on dish towels. Even with these precautions, hands should not come into contact with food when knives and forks can serve the same purpose. Teach younger helpers in the family to scrub their hands carefully and to handle food properly.

Working on trays or on waxed paper on the counter tops will keep the area neat. Spills of dry foods can often thus be returned to their containers. Other spills can more easily be cleared away. Discard or cleanse thoroughly anything dropped on the floor.

Safety in work is another important factor in the kitchen. Meet these requirements:

1. To plan wisely for the food needs of the group

2. To buy adequate food within the budget

3. To use food supplies, equipment, energy, and time economically

4. Within a limited time to prepare food well and serve it in an appetizing manner

5. To care properly for the kitchen and its equipment

The Well-Managed Kitchen

There are two basic requirements to keep in mind—cleanliness and safety.

Cleanliness is absolutely essential in the kitchen. Before beginning your work, make careful personal preparation. Wear a dress

1. Learn to operate your gas range safely. To light the oven, first find where the match should be applied. Strike the match, turning your face away from the oven door. If the burner should not ignite, turn off the gas immediately, wait a full minute, and repeat these steps. In using automatic and electric ranges follow the manufacturer's directions.

2. Keep handles of utensils toward the center of the range to prevent accidents caused by brushing against them or catching them with your sleeves.

3. Handle electrical equipment carefully. Be sure your hands are dry when you touch an electric switch or appliance. Standing on a wet surface when handling electrical equipment may cause a bad shock or even death.

4. Prevent dangerous falls by wiping up water or any spilled foods immediately.

5. Discard broken or chipped dishes and kitchen equipment which might cause injury.

Weak stools, ladders, or chairs can result in bad falls.

6. Put away sharp knives, peelers, and choppers as soon as you have used them.

7. Avoid crowding the work space. Confusion causes spills, splashes, and accidents.

8. Keep dish towels, cloths, and curtains far enough away from heating units to insure safety from fire.

9. Throw away worn pot holders which might cause serious burns. Make sure the ones you use are well padded, or use two or more at a time. In handling hot utensils keep a tight grip on them and protect your hands and arms from steam.

Working Efficiently

Planning is the first essential of efficiency. The following suggestions apply in the school kitchen as well as the home kitchen.

1. Plan your work to dovetail tasks; pouring juice, for example, while toasting bread is an efficient practice.

2. Assemble materials and equipment before starting to work.

3. Share responsibilities when working with others.

4. Keep work surfaces orderly. Arrange utensils conveniently, washing used ones promptly or putting them to soak. Collect peelings on paper or in a utensil. Lay used spoons, forks, or tools on a small tray for later washing.

5. Leave all work spaces clean and orderly.

Accuracy in the use of recipes and directions is necessary for success in food preparation, whether you are preparing snacks or more elaborate meals. Recipes tell you exactly how to proceed. Since the recipes have been tested, you can be sure that the measure-

H. Armstrong Roberts

Good management in the kitchen · This girl has assembled the essentials for her recipe and the necessary equipment. She is following the recipe carefully step by step

ments of ingredients to be used are accurate and correct.

These general suggestions from efficient homemakers will help you:

1. Use standard measuring cups and spoons. The 8-ounce measuring cup should have an added space above the one-cup line. Other lines indicating $\frac{1}{4}$-, $\frac{1}{3}$-, $\frac{1}{2}$-, $\frac{2}{3}$-, $\frac{3}{4}$-, and 1-cup measures should be clearly indicated. Glass cups, because they are transparent, are preferable for measuring liquids. For measuring dry ingredients standard individual cups make accurate measurement easier.

25

Standard measuring cups and spoons · The glass measuring cup is intended for liquids. The space above the level of one cup allows liquids to be handled without spilling. The metal measuring cups and the fractional cups, as well as the spoons, are all filled full and leveled carefully with a knife

They are usually made of aluminum or plastic. Standard measuring spoons, also preferably of aluminum, should be used. They come in $\frac{1}{4}$-, $\frac{1}{2}$-, and 1-teaspoon, and in 1-tablespoon sizes.

2. Measure liquids carefully. Measurements in the glass cup should be taken at eye level; setting the cup on a level surface will help to ensure accuracy in reading. Thick, sticky liquids that "pile up" should be measured so that the container is not overfilled. When emptied, the container must be scraped with care to prevent significant loss.

3. Use proper methods in measuring dry ingredients. Overfill the individual cups and level them off with a spatula or other flat edge by cutting across the top of the cup. For the most accurate measurement of one cup, use the 1-cup measure rather than the

$\frac{1}{2}$-cup measure twice. For $\frac{3}{4}$ cup use the $\frac{1}{2}$- and $\frac{1}{4}$-cup measures once instead of the $\frac{1}{4}$-cup size three times. Standard measuring spoons should be overfilled and leveled off.

a. In measuring shortening, use the product at room temperature and pack it firmly into the measure, or use the water-displacement method. For example, if $\frac{1}{2}$ cup of shortening is desired, fill a 1-cup measure with water to the $\frac{1}{2}$-cup mark. Then add shortening until the water reaches the 1-cup level. Drain well. Use standard measuring spoons for less than $\frac{1}{4}$ cup of shortening.

b. If sugar is lumpy, press it through a coarse sieve, heat in a 250° to 325° F. oven, or crush the lumps with a rolling pin before measuring. Then place it in the measuring cup and level it off with a spatula. Recipes usually indicate that brown sugar should be packed into the cup. Confectioners' sugar should be sifted before measuring.

c. To measure flour, sift once, then measure. Spoon the sifted flour lightly into an individual measuring cup until slightly overfilled; level with spatula.

Preparing the Snack

People everywhere enjoy snacks. The Scandinavians like fish tidbits and rich pastries, the English and Scotch serve crumpets and scones, the Germans pretzels and *wursts*. Americans enjoy hamburgers, though nowadays the vogue is to make use of frozen foods and package mixes. Frozen pastries, lemonade, and pizza vie with package mixes used in making angel, orange, or chocolate cake, delicate cookies, and feather-light rolls.

The snack you choose depends upon the locality in which you live and the amount of money you can spend. If you want a snack that is easy to prepare, try cream-cheese-and-olive sandwiches or tuna boats.

Suppose you decide to serve tuna boats and a carbonated beverage with sherbet. With your menu in mind, plan your marketing and preparation. You will need wiener buns to scoop out for boats. (These will be toasted in the broiler 3 inches from the heat for a few minutes. The centers of the buns will be scooped out with a fork, and saved for bread stuffing or meat loaf.) For a filling for the tuna boats consult the recipe for stuffed rolls on page 404. If you want to

Assembling supplies and equipment for cream-cheese-and-olive sandwiches

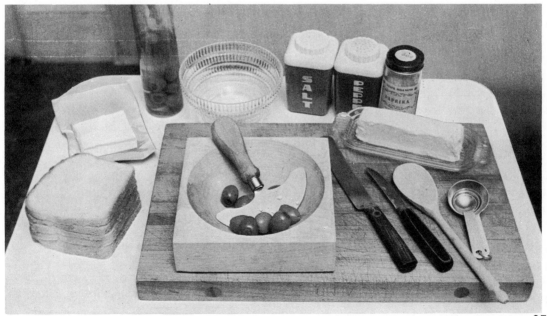

garnish your boats with hard-cooked eggs or sliced stuffed olives, find out whether these are on hand or should be added to your market list. Decide what flavor of sherbet will complement the tuna, and what beverage. Lime sherbet in lemonade, which comes frozen in cans, is good. What items are on your list now?

To Market

Shopping for food requires planning. Examine the supplies at home before shopping for more. A homemaker who goes to market without a list may find that she has not thought of everything, or she may buy items which she cannot use. Anyone working on a budget will find that buying must be planned or more money will be spent than necessary.

Most grocers offer several brands of each food. Individual taste, ease in the use of the product, and its price are points to consider in making choices. The labels on packages will be a guide as to the amount of food contained or the number of servings per package. For further information consult a sales person or the manager in your grocery store. After you have made your selections, check your list. Have you purchased everything needed? Are you sure that the food you have selected will serve your guests generously?

In the Kitchen

To prepare an appetizing snack, such as tuna boats, you should proceed in this way:

1. Use the index in this book to find the recipe for stuffed rolls. Read the recipe and the directions carefully.

2. Plan the work to be done, listing the following:

   a. Food supplies needed

   b. Equipment needed

   c. Approximate time required for preparation

3. Carry out the plan as follows:

   a. Make personal preparation for work.

   b. Place your work plan and recipes within easy reach.

   c. Assemble the supplies needed:

Buns	Seasoning
Tuna	Celery
Onions	Stuffed olives
Eggs	Carbonated beverage
Mayonnaise	Sherbet

   d. Assemble the utensils needed:

Measuring cups	Chopping knife
Measuring spoons	Mixing bowl
Mixing spoon	Cutting board
Rubber spatula	Waxed paper
Fork	Paring knife

   Bowl for bread centers
   Baking sheet for toasting buns
   Plates for tuna boats
   Glasses for sherbet and beverage
   Paper napkins

   e. Prepare the food:

   (1) Follow the recipe and the directions carefully. Measure ingredients accurately and combine properly.

   (2) Practice good standards of work. (Review pages 24–27.) Use food, utensils, and heat economically.

   (3) To insure delicious food, follow the cooking processes carefully. This requires alert attention.

   (4) Check finished products for appetizing appearance.

   (5) Arrange tuna boats attractively on plates; put sherbet in glasses; pour beverage.

   (6) You are now ready to serve your snack. See Chapter 25.

SUMMARY OF PREPARATION EXPERIENCE

1. You worked toward a specific goal.
2. You made a plan of work.
3. You worked efficiently to carry out the plan.
4. You served your snack graciously and expertly with justifiable pride.

Jane and Steven Coons

Rinsing and stacking dishes efficiently

Careful washing of dishes in hot water · Each dish is rinsed under the hot-water faucet before being placed in the rack

Wiping dishes · Glassware and silver may be wiped with a clean towel

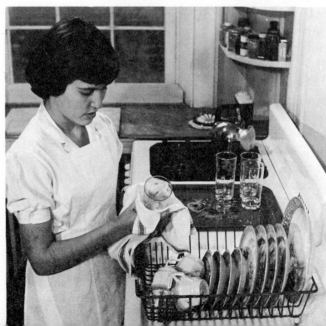

After the Snack

If the kitchen is to be a pleasant place in which to prepare food, it must be kept clean and well organized. After each meal, dishes and utensils that have been used must be washed. To avoid damage and breakage, handle them with care.

When using an automatic dishwasher, rinse both dishes and utensils before arranging them on the racks. Cleansing compounds designed especially for use in dishwashers are required. Certain plastic articles, fragile china, and glassware are more safely washed by hand.

For efficiency in washing dishes by hand, arrange the dishes and other articles conveniently, remove all food, rinsing if necessary, and follow a planned routine:

1. Stack articles at the right of the sink (if you are right-handed).

2. Place garbage in a disposal unit or covered container.

3. Wash the dishes in hot water with a good cleansing agent; protect glassware, china, and enamel from breakage and marring by handling a few articles at a time.

4. Rinse articles well with hot water and drain in a rack. A germicide recommended by the health department may be added to the rinse water in school kitchens.

5. If you prefer to wipe glassware and silver, use a clean, lintless cloth.

6. Dry tinware and cast-iron utensils over low heat to prevent rusting. Dry wooden utensils to prevent warping.

7. Return clean equipment to its proper location.

8. Use a fine cleanser and plenty of hot water to keep porcelain, enamel, and metal-alloy sinks clean. Occasionally use a strong alkali in the drain. If you keep food particles and other refuse out of the sink, little special care of the drain will be necessary.

Planning Snacks for Home Guests

Practice in preparing snacks in the home kitchen can soon add to your poise and to your efficiency in pleasing your family or in entertaining your friends informally after a game or a school program.

Combinations in great variety are possible. Include one substantial item, one lighter food that is colorful, sharp, or sweet, and a beverage which is appropriate to the menu and the season. Minimize labor and time by careful planning and good work habits. Once you have learned to manage without upsetting routines, you will find your family co-operating gladly and welcoming your crowd warmly.

Suggestions for snack foods and their serving are to be found in Chapter 25, and there are recipes in the Cookbook. Some sample menus may fire your imagination.

1. Pineapple upside-down cake
   Milk

2. Popcorn balls
   Milk
   Apples

3. Sandwiches
   Carrot curls
   Hot chocolate

4. Pizza
   Carbonated beverage

Planning Your Work

When preparing snacks, the use of a work plan saves time. The following suggestions will help you in making a work plan:

1. List all tasks, with those dishes requiring the most time at the top.

Raiding the "ice box" is a speedy way to get a snack ready for lunch hour at school. Tomatoes and lettuce or the universal favorite—peanut butter—make tasty sandwiches to go with a thermos of milk and some fruit

Hamburgers and corn on the cob fill the bill for teen-agers when they want to prepare an after-the-movie snack, a quick lunch for unexpected guests, or an easy dish for a television supper

31

2. Include in the plan all details, such as heating the oven, stirring and seasoning food, and setting the table.

3. Dovetail preparations when possible, allowing some extra minutes.

4. Utilize the time of your helpers. Allot them specific duties. Do not expect them to finish your work.

5. Your teacher and classmates will help in evaluating the worth of your work plan.

Serving Snack Meals

Refer to Chapters 25 and 26 for help in serving and enjoying snack meals. A suggested menu and work schedule follow:

MENU 5

Grilled Hamburgers on Bun
Onion Rings
Milk Shake

WORK PLAN FOR MENU 5

3:30 P.M. Make personal preparations. Heat oven. Assemble meat, buns, onions, and cooking and serving equipment.

3:36 Shape hamburgers and place them on grill. Season them, if desired.

3:40 Clean and slice onions into rings. Arrange onion rings on individual plates.

3:45 Turn hamburgers.

3:46 Prepare milk shakes.

3:51 Drain hamburgers and place them in buns on plates.

3:52 Serve.

¶ *Understanding:*

1. Why should you be clean and orderly in using equipment for food preparation?

2. In what ways are snacks as important as other meals?

3. What work and safety habits did you learn in preparing the snack?

4. What is the importance of practicing good work habits in the kitchen?

¶ *Planning:*

1 Plan several work techniques which will improve neatness and orderliness in the preparation of snacks.

2. Plan two snacks: one to be served in the kitchen, the other in the living room.

3. Plan and rearrange measuring and mixing equipment for safe and more efficient use.

4. Plan steps for washing dishes at home and interest your mother in your plan.

¶ *Practicing and Evaluating:*

1. Make a record of the things you need to learn to be more efficient in the kitchen.

2. As you observe your mother prepare a meal, which of her methods do you think would help you to improve your work?

3. Prepare a snack at home. In what ways was your mother pleased with your management in preparation? in cleaning up?

4. Collect and file snack menus and their recipes for home use.

¶ *Reading Further:*

DeLeeuw, Adele, *It's Fun to Cook.* The Macmillan Company, New York.

How To's for Barbecues. Iowa State Extension Service, Ames, Iowa.

Quick Snacks and Suppers, Food for the Gang, Bulletin 538. Washington State College Extension Service, Pullman, Washington.

Teen-Ways with Food, Bulletin 313. Montana State College Extension Service, Bozeman, Montana.

UNIT TWO

Breakfasts

Fruits for breakfast

you will learn: The value of breakfast;
The importance of fruit in the diet; How to choose and
care for fruit; How to make the best use
of fruits; How to cook fruits

After you have fasted twelve hours or more, it is important to eat breakfast in order to give your body energy to start the day's activities. The person who begins the day without eating is likely to be sluggish and irritable, and probably will not work or play as well as the person who has started the day with an adequate breakfast.

It is important, too, to eat the right kind of breakfast. Often custom dictates the foods for this meal. The English, for instance, prefer a menu which includes not only porridge (cooked cereal) and bacon and eggs, but dried fish, or deviled kidneys, or a combination of sausages and tomatoes. The American breakfast, equally hearty, customarily begins with fruit and usually includes a hot beverage for adults and milk for children. Bacon and eggs, or fried mush or cereal with cream, or sausages and pancakes, or biscuits with marmalade are used according to the needs of age, health, and the type of work to be done.

If you have slept eight hours in a well-ventilated room and have risen half an hour before breakfast, you are almost sure to have a good appetite. Scheduled exercises and a quick bath will make you even more ready for the morning meal.

It is almost impossible to skip or skimp breakfast and still meet the food needs for the day. Studies show that breakfast should have the same emphasis as other meals in planning and preparation. From one-fourth to one-third of the day's food allowance should come at breakfast. A breakfast rich in protein, minerals, and vitamins gives a person rewards in energy, efficiency, mental alertness, and general good health. If no breakfast, or too little, is eaten, body tissues will be burned to supply the energy needed, and midmorning hunger and fatigue will result. Continued failure to eat the amount and kinds of foods needed will result in an undernourished condition (see page 281).

Yet in spite of the importance of breakfast to health and efficiency, you will sometimes hear people say that they don't eat breakfast because they "don't like it" or because they "don't have time." A little thought will show that neither of these reasons is very good, whether applied to breakfast or to any other meal.

Making Time for Breakfast

Breakfast is a valuable time for a family get-together. This may be especially true on Saturday and Sunday, but with good management it can be a daily occurrence. This may mean rising a few minutes earlier, but time for eating is as necessary as time for getting dressed. Conversation should be pleasant and the discussion of family problems postponed to another time. This will help to avoid the rushed feeling so often responsible for the eating of an insufficient breakfast, and will, moreover, give a pleasant start to the day.

You can do your part in getting your family off to school or to work well fed and happy. As a willing assistant you can set the table, make toast, prepare fruit, and pour milk. On days when you do not go to school, you can help wash the dishes and straighten the kitchen. You can also do your part by being prompt in coming to the table and by being courteous. Being grouchy at breakfast is nothing but an unpleasant habit.

Even when you are trying not to gain weight, eat a good breakfast daily. It is wiser to reduce the calories a little in each of the three daily meals than to omit an entire meal. The fruits and eggs served at breakfast are among the most important and yet the least fattening of foods. (See pages 283–287 for diets for overweights.)

Enjoying Different Kinds of Foods

Mealtimes are times to enjoy. The time spent around the table with family and friends is more pleasant when the food is appreciated. To like many different kinds of food, with their varied flavors, odors, and textures, will add a great deal to your pleasure. Those who like to eat almost anything usually enjoy their meals wherever they are. By your enjoyment you will give pleasure also—to your hostess, to your mother, to whoever has prepared the food.

Food dislikes, with most people, are more a matter of emotion or of habit than of anything about the food itself. Habits are a strong force in determining what you eat. They are based on past experiences or examples set by others. Perhaps, for some

35

A good start with a good breakfast

Ewing Galloway

you may have observed that they sometimes refuse food to get attention, that is, to make themselves seem important. Or they may refuse to eat because they are annoyed with your mother and are trying to make her unhappy. This childish behavior should be outgrown with childhood. When you are tempted to refuse a dish or to complain that a meal does not please you, examine your motives. Be sure that you are not behaving like a young child. Refrain from being selfish enough to think that each meal should be planned to please your particular taste. You can correct poor eating habits. For every wholesome food that you teach yourself to eat, you are gaining in maturity.

Your reward in learning to be an appreciative eater will not be limited to your enjoyment. You will also have better health. The eating of nourishing meals of varied foods meets the body's demand for many kinds of nutrients. Adequate meals will help you to make greater progress in school work and to have more fun playing games. You are more attractive when you are nutritionally fit, and you cannot be nutritionally fit on a diet that is limited to a few foods. Your parents probably learned long ago that their maximum production of work is largely due to their stamina and that stamina results to a great extent from eating three well-balanced meals a day.

long-forgotten reason, you refused oatmeal when you were a child—and continue to refuse it now without actually remembering what the taste is like. Try it again. You may be surprised to find it delicious. In any case, you can learn, if you are willing to try, to eat it without expressing dislike.

If you have younger brothers and sisters,

The Importance of Fruit in the Diet

Fruits should be eaten daily because they supply many important food values. Their flavor, texture, aroma, and color stimulate the appetite. Fresh fruits in season make a pleasant change from frozen, canned, or dried fruits. The inclusion of fruits in the breakfast menu is one of the best ways to

make sure that the daily diet will provide fibrous content, or cellulose. Cellulose serves as bulk or "roughage" and aids in proper intestinal elimination.

Fruits are a pleasant way to begin to meet the day's requirement of minerals, vitamins, and sugar. They are one of our richest sources of vitamin C. Orange juice and lemon juice are about equal in vitamin-C value. Grapefruit juice is also a rich source. Since these fruits lose vitamin C quickly, their juice should not be allowed to stand before it is drunk. You will have to drink three times as much tomato juice as orange juice to get the same vitamin-C value. Pineapple juice contains less than one-third as much vitamin C as orange juice. There is a wide range in the energy value of fruits; for example, one large orange contains 106 calories, one large banana 119 calories, one-half avocado 279 calories (one-fourth cup, 93 calories). Although fruits may be considered expensive, they represent a wise expenditure because of the return they make in the day's food values and the body's general well-being.

The Choice and Care of Fruit

Fruits for the family breakfast may be purchased fresh, frozen, canned, or dried. Choice will depend on the quality, cost, use, and storage space. You will choose fruit more wisely after you learn to judge the quality of the product.

Fresh Fruit

Rapid transportation and refrigerated cars make it possible to transport perishable foods a long distance without spoilage; consequently, fresh fruit is available throughout the year in almost all parts of the country. Because transportation and careful handling are expensive, fruit that does not have to be shipped long distances is more reasonable in price.

In choosing fresh fruit the degree of ripeness, the color and firmness, and the freedom from decay help the purchaser to judge its quality. The largest fruit is not always the best; it may lack flavor and juice. Neither is the least expensive variety always the most economical, because it may not be as edible. Only by experience will you be able to find out whether the larger, more expensive fruit in your community actually gives you more for your money than the smaller, less expensive fruit. Your decision will depend in part on how you intend to use the fruit. Oranges used for juice need not be large. If, however, they are to be served individually, large ones will help to ensure that each person gets an adequate amount of the food values needed. Beware of bargain prices in fruit; they may mean overripe or partly decayed fruit, or defrosted frozen fruit.

Citrus Fruits

The best citrus fruits are well shaped and heavy for their size. The skin of juicy citrus fruits is generally fine-grained and thin. Most citrus fruits are graded as to size. There are several sizes of grapefruit, lemons, tangerines, and oranges. The largest fruits are usually highest in price. When citrus fruits are artificially colored, the words "color added" must be stamped on the skin. Coloring is harmless and is permitted by the government if it does not conceal inferior fruit.

Oranges of different varieties are grown in different parts of the country and they vary greatly in flavor. The navel orange has a rich, sweet taste. It is seedless and a deep yellow in color with a medium-thick skin. Other oranges generally have seeds; their skin varies in thickness from medium to thin, and their color ranges from bright orange to russet. Perhaps you have always thought a good orange should be brilliant orange in color, but russet-brown oranges are equally good and are frequently less expensive. Do not choose oranges which are pale green in color, or which have cracks or soft spots in the skin, or which look shriveled in appearance.

Grapefruits that have clear yellow or russet skins are equally good. Both the fruits with white and pink meat should be a bit springy to the touch. Reject puffy grapefruit or those with very coarse skin and soft decayed areas near the stem end.

In choosing *lemons*, examine them at the stem end for decayed areas. Other citrus fruits are *tangerines*, *tangelos*, and *kumquats*. When shriveled and flabby, they are tasteless. *Limes* are green in color. Those turned yellow are not acid enough for good flavor.

Citrus fruits keep best in a cool place. If the fruit is underripe, store it on a rack where the air circulates freely. Such fruit must be examined daily in order to use it before spoilage takes place.

Orchard Fruits

These fruits are best when they are firm but not hard, when they are plump and have their natural fruit color. The best-flavored and most economical fruits are free from decay and woody spots. They are well shaped, smooth surfaced, and free from insect bites.

Apples, if grown locally, are the most commonly used orchard fruit, and since a few varieties are shipped to all parts of the country, they are used to some extent in nearly all localities. Apples of medium size are generally cheaper than large ones. Those coming before the season, as listed in the following chart, do not keep well and should be purchased only for immediate use. Late apples may be purchased by the box, peck, bushel, or even barrel. In purchasing small quantities, it is better to buy by weight. A chart on page 39 lists the varieties of eating, baking, and cooking apples and the months when they are available.

Reject apples that have a heavy brown-tinted irregular surface. This defect is called scald and occurs during storage. Slight scald affects quality very little. Apples that are overripe, frosted, dull in color, bruised, or shriveled are not good buys.

Peaches grow in many sections of the United States but some of the most delicious varieties are not firm enough to ship. The Elberta is the leading commercial variety. Peaches vary in color from cream white to deep yellow and may be either clingstone or freestone type. Choose peaches that are mature and free from cracks, bruises, shrivel, or soft spots. Peaches are marketed in baskets of several sizes and vary in degree of ripeness. Select only the ripe ones for immediate use and store the others in a cool place to ripen. They must be carefully sorted about every twelve hours because they ripen and spoil quickly.

Pears are best when ripened in storage. They have to be sorted frequently to remove the ripe ones and those that begin to show signs of spoilage. The Bartlett is the most used market pear and the Keiffer, a good cooking and canning pear, is second. Choose pears that are mature, smooth, and free from decay. Pears are marketed in baskets, boxes, or crates, or may be sold by the dozen.

Apricots and *nectarines* should be golden yellow and ripe but firm and free from blemishes. They average twelve to fourteen per pound and are sold by the dozen or by the basket.

Plums with unbroken skins that are plump and slightly soft are the ones to choose.

USES AND VARIETIES OF APPLES

EATING	Baldwin (Nov.–Apr.); Red Delicious (Oct.–Apr.); Golden Delicious (Oct.–Mar.); Grimes Golden (Oct.–Feb.); Gravenstein (Jul.–Aug.); Jonathan (Oct.–Feb.); Northern Spy (Oct.–Mar.); Winesap (Jan.–May); Yellow Newtown (Feb.–June)
BAKING	Stayman (Nov.–Apr.); McIntosh (Oct.–Jan.); Winesap (Jan.–May); Rome Beauty (Nov.–May); Wolf River (Sept.–Dec.)
COOKING	Ben Davis (Nov.–May); Maiden Blush (Aug.–Nov.); Wealthy (Aug.–Dec.); Rome Beauty (Nov.–May); Stark (Dec.–May); Wolf River (Sept.–Dec.)
DRYING	Rhode Island Greening (Sept.–Dec.); Yellow Transparent (Dec.–May)
JELLY	Crab Apples Dolgo (early Sept.), Hyslop (Sept.–Oct.)

Plums or prunes with a brownish color on the side show sunburn and are poor in flavor. Plums are sold by the dozen, basket, or bushel.

Cherries, quinces, and *persimmons* should have a full fruit color and bright, fresh appearance. Good quinces are hard and greenish yellow. When cherries and persimmons are juicy or moldy, hard or cracked, reject them. Avoid bruised cherries or cherries with brown circular spots on them.

Orchard fruits must be carefully washed to remove the residue from sprays that have been applied to destroy insects. A brush is handy for scrubbing fruit. It is necessary to sort orchard fruits frequently in order to use the ripened products and to remove fruits showing signs of spoilage.

Tropical Fruits

From the tropics come such fruits as bananas, pineapples, and avocados.

Bananas of the common variety are entirely yellow or mottled with brown spots when fully ripe. They should be bought by weight and, if necessary, ripened in a cool place but not in a refrigerator. When kept too cold, they do not ripen properly and have a poor flavor. Reject bananas that are soft or mushy or that have black or moldy areas.

Pineapples should be heavy and fragrant with an orange-yellow color, and the eyes should be flat. Pineapples are plentiful in spring and early summer. Choose a pineapple without soft watery areas on the surface or dark areas at the base or around the

39

eyes. Immature fruit is dull, has a lifeless yellow color and eyes that are only partly developed and pointed. Light areas on the side indicate sunburn and the fruit will be pithy, dry, and hard.

A less common fruit, used in salads and as a spread for bread or crackers, is the *avocado*. It is a green, pear-shaped fruit with yellow-green meat and a large nutlike pit. For salads, the fruit should be firm but not hard and immature. For a spread, select a fruit which has ripened to a softer stage. As they ripen further, avocadoes will become blackened, mushy, and undesirable for use.

Vine Fruits

Grapes and *melons* belong to this group. The best grapes are well attached to the stem and have a high natural color. They are purchased by the basket or by the pound. Each variety should be purchased with the idea of immediate use. Reject grapes that have a whitish or shriveled appearance or that are moldy and decayed at the stem end. Grapes should be stored in the refrigerator. Ripe cantaloupes, honeydews, and muskmelons have a characteristic aroma and yield slightly to pressure at the stem end. Cantaloupes and muskmelons have a heavy surface netting that is corky and yellowish-green in color. Muskmelons may have either green, pink, or salmon-colored meat. Store these melons at room temperature, 70° F., to ripen. Honeydews have a smooth, cream-colored surface. Casaba and Persian melons are available in late summer. The casaba, similar to the honeydew, has a rougher, slightly darker skin than the honeydew and the meat is yellower. The Persian melon has a heavy greenish skin, knotty or warty in appearance, and is like a honeydew in size and shape. The meat is similar to that of cantaloupes. A pronounced yellow may indicate

overripeness in cantaloupe or muskmelon. A greenish-white color and hardness show immaturity in honeydews. Watermelon that is firm with a fresh good color and a yellowish lower side should be good. A thin surface skin that scrapes off easily is another indication of a good watermelon. Overmature watermelons are dull in appearance and springy to the touch.

Small Fruits

Berries of all types should be solid, plump, clean, bright, fresh, and full-colored. Strawberries should have their caps attached and be a bright, clean, solid red color. When their caps cling tightly, the berries are underripe. Berries are packed in standard pint or quart baskets and shipped in crates. If berries are graded, they are uniform in size; otherwise only the top layer may carry large berries. Avoid buying overripe berries which are dull in color, soft, or leaky. By careful handling, baskets can be tipped enough to see whether the berries are of uniform quality throughout. Strawberries that are small and misshapen with hard green areas have a poor flavor.

Soft fresh fruits, such as berries, *cherries*, and *plums*, must be handled gently and should never be stacked. They may be spread on a tray for storing. Although such fruits should be placed in a sieve and washed carefully before eating, they need not be washed before storing in the refrigerator. If they are allowed to stand in water, good food value and, in some instances, texture is lost.

Garden Fruits

Tomatoes and *rhubarb* are often considered garden fruits. Tomatoes should be firm, evenly shaped, free from cracks, and bright red. As a breakfast fruit, tomatoes are most often used for their juice. Fresh rhubarb will be firm and crisp with thick stalks. It should be tender and red or pink in color.

Canned Fruits

Canned fruits make it possible to enjoy a wide variety of fruits regardless of the season. Canned fruits are convenient to keep on hand because they take up little storage space and require little preparation for serving. Containers are made of glass or metal. When glass jars are used, the purchaser is enabled to see the product. However, light changes many food colors and destroys riboflavin. Metal when lacquered prevents discoloration of food. Cool and dry storage is required for canned foods. Freezing does not affect canned foods greatly, except for some breakdown in texture.

Canning companies are required by law to use informative labels. Purchasers should read them carefully to learn the amount and quality of the product. Required information includes weight, number of servings, style of pack (whole, halves, sliced, etc.), type or variety, sweetness of sirup, and added seasonings or other ingredients. A federal grade on the label indicates that the food has been packed under federal inspection. Federal grades are A (Fancy), B (Extra-standard, or Choice), C (Standard), and D (Substandard). Grade variations are based on color, uniformity of size, and absence of defects. Some packers use different brand names for fruit of different qualities. They may also add voluntary information about the size of the fruit and the method of processing, or give suggested recipes and ways of serving.

Choice of which grade to buy will depend on the price and on how the fruit is to be used. Grade B fruits may retain their shape better than Grade A since they are less fragile. Grade C is perfectly adequate for

SIZES OF CANS

SIZE	AMOUNT IN CUPS	SERVINGS
8 oz.	1	2
10½ oz.	1¼	2 to 3
No. 300	1¾	2 to 4
12 oz.	1½	4
No. 303	2	4
No. 2	2½	5
No. 2½	3½	7
46 oz. (juices)	5¾	11
No. 10	12–13	24

many cooking needs, and Grade D is the best buy for pies and cobblers. All grades compare favorably in nutrition.

A dented can is not a sign of spoilage unless the dent has caused a leak. Neither is rust on the can dangerous unless it has penetrated the can and made a leak.

Grades of canned foods · Read the labels on canned foods to learn the grades. For some purposes Grade B or Grade C may be more suitable than Grade A

United States Department of Agriculture

Frozen Fruits

Frozen fruit can now be widely used because of facilities for storage in freezing compartments in home refrigerators, in home freezers, or in local freezer lockers. The quick-freezing process makes available all the year many different kinds of perishable fruits, such as strawberries, peaches, cherries, and fruit juices. The cost is usually higher than the cost of canned or in-season fresh fruit, but not if the time to prepare and eliminate the waste of fresh fruits is taken into consideration.

Standards for most frozen products have not yet been set up by the government or packers. Frozen fruits have a fresh taste but the consistency is somewhat softer than that of fresh fruit. They must be kept frozen until used, as partially defrosted foods are not only unattractive but less flavorful. The best temperature for storing is between 10° and 0° F. Though frozen fruits are used for breakfast and for luncheon or dinner desserts, the frozen juices are more common. United States standards for frozen orange-juice concentrate are in use: U. S. Grade A, or Fancy; U. S. Grade B, or Choice; and U. S. Grade D, or Substandard.

Dried Fruits

Dried fruits sealed in packages are kept fresh and clean, but the food value is no greater than that in the fruit which is sold in bulk. Unpackaged dried fruit should be washed; if it is to be eaten raw, it should be dipped quickly into boiling water and dried with a towel. Some of the commonly used dried fruits are apples, peaches, apricots, pears, prunes, raisins, dates, and figs. Packages of mixed dried fruits are available.

Making the Best Use of Fruits

Care must be taken in the preparation of fruits to conserve the nutrients, flavor, aroma, and appearance. Fruit should be prepared just before it is served to avoid losing vitamins. Fruit should also be served unpared or very thinly pared because the skin contains valuable minerals, vitamins, and cellulose. If freshly chopped fruit cannot be served at once, it can be kept from darkening by brushing it with a citrus fruit juice, pineapple juice, or a commercially available ascorbic acid and sucrose product. Some pared fruits, such as apples, will not discolor if put under water until ready to cook; but most should be cooked at once. Berries may be prepared the night before if covered tightly and refrigerated.

Fresh juices prepared ahead and covered tightly in small containers which eliminate air can be refrigerated for several hours without losing large amounts of vitamin C. Shake the fruit juice just before serving. Canned or bottled fruit juices taste better when poured from one container to another several times to aerate them. Commonly used juices are prune, grape, pineapple, orange, grapefruit, cranberry, and apple.

Opened cans of fruit or fruit juices may be stored safely in the original containers, provided the cans are kept covered and cool. Many people, however, prefer transferring fruit, such as pineapple, to a glass or plastic container, because tin cans may impart a metallic flavor.

Interest and attractiveness can be added to breakfast by variations in serving fruits and juices. For instance, chilled berries in grapefruit halves add variety to a breakfast

Grapefruit for a festive breakfast · Not only have the sections been carefully separated, but a festive touch has been added with the maraschino cherries and cress

R. Day, from F. P. G.

meal. They may be topped with crumbled maple sugar, powdered sugar, or brown sugar. For Sunday morning breakfast, try serving orange sauce on griddle cakes or waffles. Combinations of fruit make tasty servings. Expensive strawberries may be extended with less-expensive rhubarb in a cooked sauce. Pear and quince may be cooked together. Mixed dried fruits add interest to a dish of cooked cereal. A slice of lemon, or grated lemon or orange rind, added to prunes gives them a pleasing flavor. Combined fruit juices can provide a beautiful and colorful punch for parties or special occasions. If a red punch is desired, use red- or blue-colored juices and add lemon juice.

Cooking Fruits

It is important in cooking fruits to use a low heat and to keep the fruit from being exposed to the air. Vitamins and minerals are lost because they dissolve in cooking water and also because vitamins are destroyed by high heat. When fruits are served with the juice in which they were cooked, this loss is reduced.

There are several advantages in cooking fruits:

1. Cooking brings out flavor and may make the fruit easier to digest. Green apples, for example, taste delicious when made into sauce and they digest readily in this form because the cooking process helps to change the starch to sugar.

2. Cooked fruit adds interest to the breakfast menu. Broiled grapefruit halves with bacon or sausage make a tempting combination. Canned fruit simmered in its own juice may be served hot or chilled.

3. Preservation of fruits through the canning process or by freezing makes them available throughout the coming year.

Suggestions and directions for the cooking of both fresh and dried fruits are given on page 44.

43

AMOUNT of FRESH FRUIT	YIELD
1 lb. apples	3 medium apples
1 lb. apricots	8 to 12 apricots, 5 servings
1 lb. avocado	2 avocado, 4 servings
1 lb. bananas	$2\frac{1}{4}$ cups, sliced; 3 to 4 medium bananas
1 qt. blueberries	6 servings
1 qt. cherries	2 cups, pitted
1 lb. cranberries	4 cups
1 grapefruit (medium)	2 servings
1 lb. grapes Concord	1 qt., or 4 servings
Tokay	$2\frac{3}{4}$ cups, seeded
1 doz. lemons (medium)	2 cups juice
1 doz. oranges (medium)	4 cups juice; 3 qts., diced
1 lb. peaches	4 servings, or 4 medium peaches
1 lb. pears	4 servings, or 4 medium pears
1 pineapple (medium)	6 servings, or about 3 cups
1 lb. plums	4 servings; 8 to 20 plums
1 lb. rhubarb	2 cups, cooked; 4 to 8 stalks
1 qt. strawberries	4 servings

FRESH FRUITS

1. To ensure a soft texture and the best flavor, cook the fruit at a low temperature with little sugar. When fresh fruit is cooked in plain water, the structure of the fruit is broken down to make a sauce. Water passing into the cells of the fruit bursts them. Apples for sauce are cooked by this method.
2. To retain the shape of the fruit, use a higher temperature and cook in a sirup. If too much sugar is used in the sirup, water will pass from the fruit into the sirup leaving the fruit shrunken and tough.
3. To purée fruit, cook in water and force through a sieve. Add sugar later.
4. Baking fruits with sugar and other seasonings gives a change when the same fruit is used often. Apples, pears, and peaches are favorites for baking. Sugar and seasoning should not be used in such quantities that they detract from the natural fruit flavor.

FRUIT	YIELD
1 lb. dried apples	10 cups, cooked
1 lb. dried apricots	5 cups, cooked
1 lb. candied cherries	$2\frac{1}{4}$ cups, whole
1 lb. dried citron	$2\frac{1}{2}$ cups, sliced
1 lb. currants	3 cups
1 lb. dates	$2\frac{1}{2}$ cups, pitted (60 dates) 3 cups, chopped
1 lb. figs	3 cups, cut fine (44 figs)
1 lb. crystallized ginger	$2\frac{2}{3}$ cups, diced
1 lb. dried peaches	6 cups, cooked
1 lb. dried prunes	4 cups, cooked $2\frac{1}{4}$ cups, pitted, uncooked
1 lb. raisins (seeded)	$2\frac{1}{2}$ cups
1 lb. raisins (seedless)	3 cups

5. Grapefruits, bananas, and pineapples are delicious when broiled under a flame or electric unit. Pineapples and apples may also be fried in a small amount of fat in a frying pan.

DRIED FRUITS

1. The cooking of dried fruit in simmering water or by pressure cooker produces a firm, plump, sweet-flavored product. The pressure method lessens the time of preparation, which is important in a busy household. The use of tenderized dried fruits further lessens the cooking time required to ensure a tender product.

2. Whole dried fruits, such as prunes, should be soaked before cooking. Apricots and peach halves, which have part of the surface free from skin, will become plump and tender during cooking without being soaked. Dried fruits take up moisture more rapidly in hot water than in cold. To soak dried fruit, pour hot water over the fruit, using 4 cups per pound of fruit. Soaked dried fruit may or may not be cooked. To cook dried fruit, simmer in a covered pan in the same water in which it was soaked.

3. Dried fruit should be cooked at a moderate rate to keep the pieces whole. It is ready to remove from the heat when it is lustrous and plump as well as tender and when it separates readily from the pit. If sugar is needed, it should be added before removing the fruit from the heat. Dried-fruit juice is delicious as a beverage, when served plain or in combination with other fruit juices. The juices may also be used in gelatin salads or desserts.

¶ Understanding:

1. Why is breakfast such an important meal in your home?

2. What are the main reasons for persons skipping breakfast?

3. What are the values to you of learning to enjoy many kinds of food?

4. Why is it important for a family to include sufficient fruit in the diet?

5. What are the differences in food values between fresh, frozen, canned, and dried fruits?

6. How does the use of fruit at home determine the quality to be chosen? Give illustrations.

7. What qualities will you look for in buying berries, citrus fruits, or orchard fruits?

8. Why is it worth while to do personal marketing for fruits? Give examples from shopping with a family member.

9. Compare the cost of fresh, frozen, canned, and dried fruits commonly used for breakfast.

10. For what reasons are fruits cooked?

11. How should dried fruits be stored in your home? canned fruits? frozen fruits?

¶ Planning:

1. Plan breakfasts which you can prepare using canned and frozen products and packaged mixes.

2. Plan ways to improve your eating habits.

3. Assist your mother in planning two breakfast meals using low-cost fruit, to be prepared and served in attractive ways.

4. Plan a variety of ways to serve fresh fruits for breakfast.

5. Plan means of preserving the quality of freshly prepared fruit until serving time.

6. Plan a home breakfast including dried prunes. Substitute canned pineapple juice for the prunes. What additional food values are needed?

¶ Practicing and Evaluating:

1. Encourage a younger member of a family to eat a food which he does not like. What step processes did you follow?

2. Purchase fresh fruit protected from flies, dust, and handling. What superior qualities does the fruit possess? Compare the price with that of fruit less carefully handled.

3. Prepare rhubarb or applesauce as part of a home meal. Check the product for flavor. How do the two fruits compare in food values?

4. Cook fresh peaches or apples in a sirup for a home breakfast. Check the product for tenderness, shape, and flavor.

5. Bake pears or apples to retain the natural fruit flavor. Compare the cost with that of canned pears or apples.

6. Contribute flavor to cereals or quick breads by the addition of fruit. What are other values of the added fruit?

¶ Reading Further:

Apples in Appealing Ways, Leaflet No. 312, rev. ed., 1959. Bureau of Human Nutrition and Home Economics, U. S. Department of Agriculture, Washington, D. C.

KINDER, FAYE, *Meal Management* (including purchasing guide for fruits and vegetables). The Macmillan Company, New York.

Know the Best Buys in Fruits and Vegetables, Bulletin 197. University of Minnesota Extension Service, St. Paul, Minnesota.

Tips on Selecting Fruits and Vegetables, Marketing Bulletin 13 (1961). U. S. Department of Agriculture, Washington, D. C.

Fruit, Treasure Chest of Health, Bulletin 234. Pennsylvania State University Extension Service, University Park, Pennsylvania.

General Mills

Breakfast cereals and breads

you will learn: The value and uses of cereals;
How to choose and prepare cereals;
How to cook quick breads

Long before he wrote history, man must have discovered that the kernels of grain growing on the end of certain grasses were good to eat. With his teeth he tore the kernels from the stem and chewed them. Later he learned to pound the grain between stones and mix it with water into a mash which, dried in the sun or baked on hot stones, became the first crude bread. A hand mill in which the weight of the upper millstone helped in grinding was known over most of the ancient world. In the Middle Ages nature's power was harnessed in the water mills and windmills for grinding grain. Early American communities had their gristmills where farmers took their corn to be ground or wheat to be cracked. When the Middle West began to thrive as wheat country, the gristmill with its simple, coarse, whole-grain product was almost completely superseded by the great mills that turned out fine white flour by the barrel. Modern mills furnish a wide variety of flours other than white flour and also of breakfast cereals.

47

In the methods of using these products, the world has also progressed. We have learned, for instance, about leavening. The discovery of fermentation as a leavener was probably accidental. A woman who had saved leftover dough may have kneaded it, after it had begun to ferment, into the next batch, and so discovered that fermentation made the loaf larger and lighter and gave it better flavor. Yeast, also a very old leavener, is still widely used, and there are other leaveners which help to make bread palatable. But in spite of changes in methods of production and preparation, grain products are still, as in Biblical times, the basic food of the human race. Bread is still "the staff of life," and breakfast cereals now serve much as the simple porridge of ancient times.

The Value and Uses of Cereals

Through manufacturing processes the seeds of wheat, corn, oats, barley, rye, and rice are converted into cereal breakfast foods as well as into flour. Rice outranks other cereals in use throughout the world. Grown extensively in China and India, it provides the main food of these countries. In the western world wheat is considered the choice cereal because of the fine flours it yields. Flour or meal is also made from barley, buckwheat, and corn. Wheat, rice, corn, and oats are the grains most used as cooked or as ready-to-eat breakfast cereals. Corn products include cornstarch, made from the starch of the corn, cooking oil made from its fat, and corn sirup made from its sugars. Barley, as a whole grain, is often added to soups. Millet and kaffir corn may be used in steamed breads.

Structure of a Cereal Grain

Seeds are the start of new plant life. Nature made them rich storehouses of the food elements needed by living things. Thus cereals are a rich source of nourishment. Though the cereal grains vary somewhat in food values, they are similar in structure. Each kernel has three separate sections and each section performs a special function.

Food Values of Cereals

Cereals are one of the best and least expensive sources of food energy. The high energy value is shown through the relatively small portions sufficient for one serving. In the United States, cereal grains provide approximately one-third of the total calories consumed. However, most of these cereals are highly refined and are composed primarily of the endosperm portion of the grain, which is chiefly carbohydrate in nature.

Carbohydrates, Fats, and Proteins—The carbohydrate of grain is in the form of starch which separates readily from the kernel. Wheat flour is chiefly starch. Cornstarch is made from the endosperm of corn kernels. Oats and corn, the cereals providing the highest energy value, contain the most fat. The proteins of cereals are of low quality and, therefore, need to be supplemented (see page 9). Oatmeal and other oat cereals are the best of the cereals for proteins. When the protein of wheat is combined with moisture and stirred or handled, a substance called gluten is produced. The gluten develops into a meshwork of soft, sticky fibers, or strands. These elastic strands enmesh starch, fat, and other ingredients, giving a firm, elastic-textured bread dough. Over-stirring of bread mixtures can cause over-

48

development of the gluten content, resulting in a tough bread.

Minerals and Vitamins—Whole-grain cereals are far more valuable in nutrients than any of the refined cereals. The bran layers, though low in calcium, are rich in iron, phosphorus, and thiamine. They also contain riboflavin and niacin. The germ of wheat is an excellent source of thiamine and other B vitamins, and contains considerable iron. Cereals are deficient in vitamins A, D, and C, with the exception of yellow-corn products, which contain a good amount of vitamin A. Top milk and buttered toast eaten with the breakfast cereal will furnish the needed vitamin A. Vitamin C can be added to the breakfast by including citrus fruit, and vitamin D by using irradiated milk. (For additional information of the mineral and vitamin content of cereals refer to Table IV in the Appendix.)

Effect of Milling on Cereals and How to Offset It—Refining processes destroy many of the valuable nutrients in cereals. Because

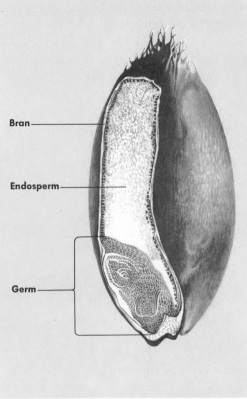

General Mills

A kernel of wheat

STRUCTURE AND COMPOSITION OF A CEREAL GRAIN

SECTION OF THE KERNEL	DESCRIPTION	FOOD VALUES
BRAN	Brown outer covering made of many layers of cellulose	Contains carbohydrates, thiamine, niacin, riboflavin, protein, iron, phosphorus, copper, and calcium.
ENDOSPERM	Central portion of the kernel, the only portion left in highly refined cereals	Made chiefly of carbohydrates and protein. Furnishes food supply to growing seed
GERM	Portion that sprouts when the seed is allowed to grow	Rich source of protein, thiamine, vitamin E, iron, carbohydrates, and fat.

cereals make up a very large part of the daily diet of the average person in this country, millers are required by law in some states to put back into the milled product—flour, meal, rice, or breakfast cereals—some of the most necessary food values which have been removed by refining.

You will find it easy and profitable to buy restored cereal products which contain adequate mineral and vitamin values. In these restored products enough thiamine, riboflavin, and iron have been added to replace a high per cent of what was lost in milling. Flour is enriched with definite amounts of iron, thiamine, riboflavin, and niacin. Calcium and vitamin D also may be added. Always read the labels on cereal products for information about the values contained, and buy to get as much nutrient value as you can for your money.

Restoring or enriching does not injure color, taste, or cooking quality of the cereals, but these products cannot equal whole-grain cereals or whole-grain bread—which should be used whenever possible for nature's complete store of food value.

The effect of milling is clearly illustrated by a comparison of the food values of brown and white rice. Brown rice contains the bran of the grain, and because the important nutrients remain, people who live largely on a brown-rice diet thrive. White rice, however, which is refined, has much of the natural food value removed; for an adequate diet it must be supplemented with food from the other Basic Four or Basic Seven groups.

Refined flours and cereals may be supplemented in various ways. Sometimes the *polishings from rice* can be bought. Many people add these to quick breads and meat loaf because of their high thiamine content. *Soybean flour* and *soybean grits*, made from soybeans, are rich sources of proteins and are good supplements for refined flour and cereals. The protein has qualities similar to that found in meat, eggs, and milk. Soybean foods also contain thiamine, riboflavin, niacin, iron, calcium, and phosphorus. Soybean flour improves nourishment but does not take the place of other flour in so far as starch and gluten are concerned. Soybean flour works best in recipes with finely ground white flour; soybean grits are best when used with coarsely ground meals. Soybean grits may also be used as an addition to cooked cereals.

Care of Cereals

One reason for the wide use of cereal grains is that they are easily stored and transported. Uncooked cereals are best kept if they are closely covered in their original package or in tightly covered glass or metal containers. In such containers they are thoroughly protected from weevils, insects that burrow in the grain to lay their eggs. The presence of the weevil may not be discovered until the eggs hatch into worms. Storage cans or bins must be kept clean and dry and should be inspected often.

Cereals keep well because of their low moisture content. Flour and cereals should be kept in a cool, dry place. Because of their high fat content, products made from the whole grain will become rancid if stored long. Moist heat hastens the process by which the fat becomes rancid. In warm weather, cereal products should be purchased in small quantities and inspected often. If possible, ready-to-eat cereals should be kept near a range or radiator since dry warmth helps to keep them crisp. To restore crispness, pour the cereal into a shallow pan and heat it in a moderately hot oven (350° F.) with the door slightly open.

Your choice of cereal, ready-to-eat or cooked, will depend on the season of the year, on the other foods to be served for breakfast, on the time available for preparing and serving breakfast, and on the budget and the family tastes.

Ready-to-Eat Cereals

Ready-to-eat cereals are made of wheat, corn, oats, rice, or barley, or combinations of them. Sugar, sirup, malt, salt, and honey are added in varying amounts, and the mixture is precooked and processed into many interesting forms, such as flakes, puffs, letters of the alphabet, and circles. Ready-to-eat cereals are available in gay packages of various sizes. Groups of individual servings of different cereals, each in its own box, are also available; however, they are more expensive than the regular and economy-size packages. They are convenient, add appeal, taste, and variety to menus. The nutritional value varies but is usually less than that of cooked cereals and the cost is considerably more.

Cooked Cereals

A serving of well-cooked hot cereal with whole milk helps to prevent midmorning hunger. Raisins or pieces of dates added to the cereal gives increased food value and flavor to the breakfast.

Since cereals contain chiefly starch, they must be thoroughly cooked. Starch granules absorb water as they cook, thus increasing the bulk of the cereal. The water absorbed is converted into steam which bursts the granules, thus thickening and changing the starch and ensuring easy and complete digestion of the cereal. Cereals differ in the amounts of water required for cooking.

Follow directions on the cereal package. Gentle stirring while adding coarse cereal to boiling water is a precaution against lumping. Fine cereal may first be mixed with a small amount of cold water to separate the starch granules. Some stirring may be necessary as the cereal cooks, but overstirring results in a pasty, sticky product.

Leftover cooked cereal may be reheated and served. It is best to use a double boiler for these leftovers but they may be heated over low direct heat. Reheated cereal should not be stirred until it is very warm or it will become lumpy.

Whole-grain cereals require the longest cooking time. Flaked or ground cereals have had the bran layers removed or cracked, so that the cereal will soften and the starch will cook more rapidly. Packaged breakfast cereals that have not been precooked with steam may required a longer cooking time than that stated on the package to bring out the desired flavor. Overcooking, like overstirring, makes the product pasty. Cereals

Cold cereal for a summer breakfast

Kellogg Company

51

which have been steamed during the manufacturing process require a shorter cooking time. These are so labeled and directions are given for cooking. Well-cooked cereal is free from lumps and raw spots, is not too stiff or too thin, and is well flavored with no starch taste. It should always be served hot.

VARIATIONS IN SERVING CEREALS

1. Combine two or three ready-to-eat cereals.
2. Spread flake cereals in a shallow pan, dot with table fat, sprinkle with brown sugar. Heat in a 325° F. oven for a few minutes. Serve at once.
3. Give cooked cereal a crispy topping of ready-to-eat cereal.
4. Add several tablespoons of honey or molasses to the cereal while it is cooking.
5. Add chopped dates to hot farina or granular wheat cereal. Stir well, pour into loaf pan, and chill. Unmold, cut in thin slices and fry in a small amount of fat, turning to brown both sides. Serve hot with sirup.
6. Use alternates for sugar—sliced or diced fresh fruit, dried fruit, maple sirup, molasses, honey, fruit juice, preserves, and jelly.

Preparing Quick Breads

Quick breads are excellent for breakfast, or for any other quickly prepared meal. They provide food values and flavor; most require very little time in preparation. Popovers, muffins, and coffee cake, of course, take longer than toast or griddle cakes.

Ingredients

The basic ingredients for quick breads are flour, leavening, shortening, liquid, eggs, and sugar.

Flours—Wheat is made into whole-wheat flour, which contains all the wheat grain, or it is refined to make white flour, which contains chiefly the starch and protein of the endosperm. Restored or enriched white flour is widely used, making white bread a very good food. Since this enrichment of breads costs the baker very little, the process has become a valuable means of improving nutrition in the United States. Enrichment of white flour restores mineral

The Quaker Oats Company

Baking griddle cakes

and vitamins but not the protein lost in milling. When enriched white flour replaces whole-wheat flour in quick breads, eggs and milk will supply protein.

Flours vary according to the kind of wheat from which they are made. Hard spring wheat and hard winter wheat, grown in climates of low rainfall, produce a flour which forms large amounts of gluten, or strong elastic strands. These strands are the framework for holding together the other ingredients in bread. This flour is called bread flour and is milled chiefly for bakers. It is somewhat grainy in texture and may be either bleached or unbleached. Blends of hard wheat are especially good for yeast breads. This flour is used for most household cookery.

Light, tender cakes, however, require a fine flour with a low gluten content, made from soft wheat. The soft wheat blends— that is, blends of both hard and soft wheats —are also best for quick breads.

All-purpose flour is a mixture of hard- and soft-wheat flours and is suitable for all types of breads.

Self-rising flour made from all-purpose flour may be purchased. Leavening ingredients and salt have been added. Directions printed on the packages of this product should be followed closely. Self-rising flours may have other ingredients added, such as fat, sugar, dried eggs, and milk solids, to produce mixes. Popular mixes on the market are pie crust, cake, quick breads, yeast breads, and griddle cakes.

Leavenings—Quick breads get their name from the quick-acting leavenings used in them to make the product porous and light. The leavenings are usually baking powder, soda, air, or steam. When *baking powder* is combined with a liquid, a chemical action occurs in which carbon dioxide is formed.

53

Assembling ingredients and equipment · Here the flour has been measured and sifted with the baking powder and salt. The milk is measured

Cutting shortening into flour with a blender

Adding the milk

Clabber Girl Baking Powder

This gas expands when it is heated and causes the mixture to rise. The quick-acting tartrate and phosphate baking powders start the chemical reaction as soon as the liquid is added. Breads made with quick-acting powder should be mixed quickly and placed immediately in the oven to avoid heavy loss of the leavening gas. Sodium aluminum sulphate powder, sometimes labeled S.A.S., is a double-acting powder. The gas begins to form at room temperature but does not complete its formation until the mixture is at oven temperature. The number of teaspoonfuls per cup of flour will be stated on the container of each type of baking powder.

Baking soda, when combined with an acid such as sour milk or buttermilk, produces carbon dioxide for leavening. The soda begins to react at once when mixed with the sour milk; therefore, it is necessary to work quickly in getting biscuits and other products mixed and into the oven.

Air as a leavener is introduced into quick breads by sifting the flour through a sieve, by beating the eggs, and by creaming the fat. When the product is heated, the air expands and leavens the mixture. Where the proportion of liquid is high, the large quantity of *steam* produced acts as the leavener.

Shortenings—Fat makes quick breads tender and, in some cases, flaky. Fats also help to produce a velvety crumb and to keep quick breads moist. In choosing fats, read the package label which is required by the Federal Food, Drug, and Cosmetic Act. If the fat is from an animal source, the label must give the standard name of the product, for example, "refined lard." Note whether the label on fats states the addition of an antioxidant to prevent rancidity and other spoilage. The use of protected fats in prepared mixes aids in retaining their freshness. (Review information on fats on pages 7–8.)

Liquids—Liquids are added to quick-bread batters and doughs to form gluten from the protein in the flour and to start the leavening action. The proportion of liquid to flour determines the stiffness of the batter or dough. Milk, the most common liquid, adds both food value and flavor to the product. Dried or evaporated milk can be used satisfactorily. Sour milk, buttermilk, or clabber are sometimes used. Water may be used in place of milk, but the texture of the finished product will be coarser, and a good opportunity to add food value to the diet will be lost.

Eggs Eggs in quick breads serve as a binder to hold the ingredients together. When beaten, eggs also become leavening agents by adding air to the batter or dough. Egg yolks increase the fineness of texture and the

Crisp, evenly browned, hot toast

R. Day, from F. P. G.

54

tenderness of the product. Egg whites tend to produce a harder crust; they also add flavor and food value. Use only the number of eggs the recipe calls for; too many eggs cause a product to be dry and tough by supplying too much protein.

Sugar—Sugar tenderizes quick breads and adds flavor and crispness. It also helps to make the surface of quick breads a golden brown.

Fruits and Other Ingredients—Candied fruit, nuts, cheese, peanut butter, caraway, poppy, or sesame seeds add food value, interesting flavor, and texture to quick breads.

Principles of Cookery for Quick Breads

With a good recipe for a quick bread, careful combining of ingredients, and proper baking, the product should be excellent. Quick breads may be mixed and baked just prior to the meal; or the dry ingredients may be combined ahead and stored, tightly covered, and liquids added just before baking; or completed batters and doughs may be frozen to be used as needed. They may be partially baked before they are frozen, requiring only a quick browning. The advantage of preparing mixtures ahead lies in the saving of time and work.

Ingredients for quick breads should be mixed quickly and only enough to blend. Overstirring toughens the product and results in a coarse texture. Fat may be added to the mixture by two methods (the recipe tells you which one to use). In the first method, the fat is melted before it is added to the liquid. In the second method, the fat is cut into the sifted dry ingredients by using a pastry blender, two knives, or a fork. Do not mash the fat by pressing it down. This mixture should resemble coarse meal or rice kernels.

When combining a liquid with dry in-gredients, you may make a well in the center of the dry ingredients, add the liquid, and mix immediately by stirring. This method is good in making biscuits and muffins. When the recipe calls for adding ingredients alternately, stir after each addition. Flour should be added first and last to prevent curdling. Coffee cake and doughnuts may call for this method.

Eggs may be beaten into the mixture one at a time or all at once. To include air, whole eggs may be beaten, or yolks and whites may be beaten separately, and added to the mixture.

Techniques for Quick-Bread Mixtures

Each of the two basic types of quick-bread mixtures, batters and doughs, requires its own technique of combining ingredients and baking. The *pour batter* is thin enough to flow readily. It is used for several favorite breakfast breads:

1. *Popovers* are made from the thinnest of pour batters. The large amount of liquid makes beating possible without toughening. The two or three eggs used strengthen the walls. The high beginning temperature forms a crust to hold the steam, which leavens the popovers. Reduced temperature after the first 20 minutes prevents excessive browning and sets the walls. Popovers should be baked until they feel firm while still in the oven. Ungreased heavy iron or glass containers are considered best for pop-overs; however, muffin pans may be used.

2. A thin batter produces crisp *griddle cakes*; a thicker batter gives a cake-like tex-ture. For a tender product the thicker batters should be stirred only until dry in-gredients are moistened. Overstirred cakes develop tunnels. Griddle cakes are partially leavened by steam, but baking soda or baking

powder is used as an additional leavening agent. Sugar in the batter is an aid in browning, and fat makes greasing of the griddle unnecessary. Slow baking dries the cakes, making them tough, deeply pitted, and unevenly browned. Quick baking produces light, tender griddle cakes.

3. *Waffles* are crisper if pastry flour (low in gluten) is used. The best texture is obtained by beating yolks and whites of eggs separately and folding the whites into the batter just before baking. Greasing a pretreated waffle iron is unnecessary. Waffles rich in fat and sugar require 2 to 3 minutes additional baking. A stiff waffle batter must be mixed briefly. Follow manufacturer's directions for an automatic iron. For others, put 1 t. water inside iron; close. When steaming stops, iron is ready. A waffle may stick to a too cold or too hot iron. In filling the iron, allow room for the waffle to expand. Rich waffles may seem limp when first baked, but they become crisp in a short time.

The *drop batter* is thick enough to break from a spoon. It is used for muffins and biscuits:

Muffins · Greased pans should be filled about two-thirds full of batter

1. *Muffins* are more tender if made from a soft-wheat flour. Since the batter is thick, overstirring tends to toughen, to produce a waxy interior with tunnels, and to develop muffins with peaks rather than evenly rounded tops. Mix only until the dry ingredients are moistened, then place in pans at once to prevent loss of gas. Dropping the batter stretches gluten, toughening the muffins. Two spoons may be used: the one to hold the correct amount of batter, the other to push it into the tin. Pans greased only on the bottom produce larger muffins.

2. A *biscuit* mixture of drop-batter consistency may be dropped onto a greased baking sheet. For a crisp crust drop biscuits are better than kneaded ones.

Soft doughs are resilient and are easily handled on a breadboard.

1. For flaky-textured *biscuits* the shortening should be cut into the flour. Adding liquid to flour by light tossing with a fork will give a fluffy dough containing the maximum of air. Kneading the dough on a lightly floured board about ten quick strokes develops layers with a fine texture. Kneading produces more volume, mixes ingredients thoroughly (especially important in baking-soda biscuits), and helps to produce smooth, level tops. Overkneading toughens dough and decreases volume. After the dough has been rolled, it may be folded over and rolled again, two or three times, to produce a very flaky texture. Pans used for biscuits, and all quick breads, should be large enough to allow them nearly to double in size while baking.

2. Sweet soft-dough mixtures with the addition of fruits and nuts make nutritious *quick coffee cakes*.

56

TYPE OF BREAD	OUTSIDE APPEARANCE	INTERIOR QUALITY

POPOVERS	Well-popped appearance
	Golden-brown color
		Hollowed interior,
		   slightly moist
		Walls thick and crusty,
		   tender and crisp
		Pleasing flavor

GRIDDLE CAKES	Uniform shape Even, golden-brown color Delicately pitted surface	Light and porous texture Tender crumb Pleasing flavor
WAFFLES	Regular shape Even golden color	Light and tender Crisp crust Slightly moist Mild, pleasing flavor
MUFFINS	Symmetrical shape, Rounded, golden-brown top	Light in relation to size Creamy white interior with even-grained texture Slightly moist, tender crumb Mild flavored
BISCUITS	Smooth-grained appearance Even size with straight sides Level top, golden color Evenly browned bottom	Creamy, light, tender crumb Slightly moist flaky texture and medium-fine grain Good flavor

Qualities of Good Quick Breads

You can be proud of serving quick breads that have good flavor, a tender crumb, moist quality, even grain, and good color and shape. Good quick breads should have the characteristics shown in the chart above.

Quick breads should be served hot. If the baking is well timed, the bread is ready to serve hot with the meal. Using a heated plate, allow one serving for each person. Keep the remainder warm until needed. Leftover quick breads are especially good if split, buttered, and toasted.

Buying Quick Breads

Commercially prepared breads, though considered more expensive than homemade ones, are timesavers for the homemaker. You should read labels for information about weight and enrichment. The product should be properly protected in tins or in waxed-paper or cellophane wrapping. It is interesting to compare the commercial product with the homemade in flavor, texture, keeping quality, and cost. Quick breads may be purchased in several forms which are listed on page 58.

57

Ready-mix: Liquid to be added and dough shaped, then baked

Frozen breads: To be baked before or after thawing

Partially baked bread: Baking process to be completed

Canned prepared biscuits: To be baked before serving

Baked products: Ready for immediate serving or may be heated or toasted

Choice among these products depends on time of preparation, amount of money to be spent, food values gained, and the taste of the family. Be sure to select baked or partially baked quick breads from fresh, carefully wrapped products.

Prepared mixes include a wide range, from griddle cakes to muffins and biscuits. Muffin mixes may include a small can of blueberries to be added. Fruit, nuts, or cheese can be added to enrich other ready-mix batters. Ready-to-serve baked products should be fresh. However, day-old breads, which can be bought more cheaply than fresh, make excellent toast. Toasting does not change the caloric value of bread, and the drying and browning by direct heat makes it more digestible. Plain toast may be varied in interesting ways. The Cookbook gives recipes for French toast, cinnamon toast, milk toast, cheese toast, and others. For added nutrients, plain toast may be served with a variety of toppings appropriate for breakfast. Toast should be evenly browned, crisp, tender, and of good flavor. Buttered and served hot with accompaniments of jelly or jam, it is a very satisfying breakfast bread.

Practically all breakfasts include bread in some form, though in light breakfasts it may alternate with cereals, which have similar food values. Care given to its selection, preparation, and serving is important in supplying the family with an attractive and satisfying morning meal. No one will long resist the fragrance of baking waffles, muffins, or cinnamon toast, and your family will appreciate the effort and skill which produced a tasty quick bread to round out a good breakfast.

¶ *Understanding:*

1. What are the values of including cereals in your diet?

2. What portion of the wheat contains the most minerals? the most vitamins? the most proteins?

3. What are the effects of milling on cereal grains? What are the values of using restored or enriched cereal products?

4. Which cooked cereals are moderate in cost? How may you add to their food values?

5. Under what circumstances will you serve ready-to-eat breakfast cereals in your home?

6. What general information can you find on the labels of packaged breakfast cereals? How will you use this information?

7. What are the characteristics of a well-cooked cereal?

8. How could you store cereals in your home to retain their fresh quality?

9. What values do quick breads add to your breakfast menu that make them well worth the effort of preparation?

10. How may you reduce the time for breakfast preparation at home when hot quick breads are served?

11. Check cooked cereals that have been served for breakfasts at home. Which were moderate in cost? Which were quickly prepared?

¶ *Planning:*

1. Plan the addition of soybean flour or grits to a food for breakfast. What food values will be gained by your family?

58

2. Starting with cooked oatmeal with raisins, complete a breakfast menu for your family. Do the same with hot bran muffins; with nut coffee cake.

3. Plan two breakfasts each including a cereal. Alter the menu in one breakfast substituting eggs for the cereal.

4. Plan ways to vary cooked cereal dishes for your family so as to include additional flavors and textures.

5. In purchasing cereals for your family would you choose the large or the small package? Explain reasons.

6. Plan two breakfast menus that you would enjoy preparing and serving. In one include a moderate-cost hot bread. In the other include a bread rich in mineral and vitamin values.

¶ *Practicing and Evaluating:*

1. Cook a cereal for the home breakfast and serve it hot in combination with a ready-prepared cereal. In what ways were you satisfied with the dish?

2. Mix and bake a quick bread and note the time required. How could you improve?

3. Prepare a quick bread for two breakfasts. In one use a purchased ready-mix; in the other use a homemade ready-mix. Compare the breads in flavor, texture, and cost.

4. Prepare a quick bread at home from a partially baked product and from a frozen-bread product. Compare.

5. Store cereals by the following methods: in a refrigerator container which is tightly covered; on the cupboard shelf in the original package. What are the advantages of each method?

¶ *Reading Further:*

A Basic Breakfast Pattern. Cereal Institute, Inc., Chicago, Ill.

Family Fare, Food Management and Recipes, G–1, rev. ed., 1960. Bureau of Human Nutrition and Home Economics, U. S. Department of Agriculture, Washington, D. C.

How to Make Yeast Breads and Rolls, Bulletin E425. Oklahoma State University Extension Service, Stillwater, Oklahoma.

STEVENSON, GLADYS T., and MILLER, CORA, *Introduction to Foods and Nutrition,* Chapter 6. John Wiley and Sons, Inc., New York.

Yeast Breads and Rolls, Bulletin 888. Cornell University Extension Service, Ithaca, New York.

American Meat Institute

Eggs and breakfast meats

you will learn: The value of eggs in the diet;
How to select and handle eggs; How to use eggs in
the diet; How to prepare eggs for eating;
How to use meats for breakfast

Eggs and meat are essential to a breakfast that is to provide its share of the day's food needs, especially those of protein and minerals. Just as a roll-and-coffee breakfast is a poor meal, so is a breakfast of fruit and toast. Both these breakfasts are deficient in certain food values. A person needs protein and fat from eggs or meat as well as the vitamins from fruit, the minerals and protein from milk, and the carbohydrates from cereals and breads. In addition to supplying necessary food values, eggs and meat taste good and satisfy hunger.

Meat and eggs may be used as alternates for one another in protein values.

The Value of Eggs in the Diet

People everywhere eat eggs because they provide such concentrated food values, being amply supplied with vitamins and minerals, protein and fat. An egg, to most of us, means a hen's egg, but people in other parts of the world enjoy other kinds of eggs also. Sturgeon eggs in the form of caviar are a favorite luxury of the Russians. To the Chinese, turtle eggs are a special delicacy. Eggs of shad and other fish (called roe) and eggs of such birds as ducks, geese, plover, and pheasant are also used as food in this country and elsewhere.

Whatever their cost, eggs should be used generously. They are completely without waste and therefore, even when they seem expensive, may be more economical than other foods which can be bought for less money but which contain considerable waste.

Eggs do not always have to be eaten as eggs, pure and simple, although that is a popular way to eat them at breakfast. They may be used at other meals in custards, sauces, and puddings, and they are appropriate in the main course of luncheons and simple suppers.

The fact that a chick is formed and grows from the contents of an egg is proof that an egg is very nearly a complete food. A medium-sized egg contains 77 calories, which come from the protein and fat. The protein of eggs is of high quality, and the yolks are an excellent source of minerals, such as iron, and vitamins, especially vitamins A and D. The amount of vitamins present is, of course, affected by the diet of the hen.

In children's diets the yolk is especially important. If every child after the age of one month had the yolk of an egg every day, he would probably never suffer from anemia in the course of a long life.

In addition to their high nutritive value, eggs have the advantage, when properly cooked, of being easily digested and used by the body. As compared with such a cooking fat as lard, the fat content, found chiefly in the yolk, digests very quickly.

Each day's menu should include an egg—though, when eggs are expensive, adults may safely limit themselves to four a week. (For detailed information on the nutritive value of eggs, refer to Table IV in the Appendix.)

Selection and Handling of Eggs

Testing Eggs

To be certain that the eggs she serves contain their full vitamin value, flavor, and texture, a wise shopper will insist on fresh eggs. As a simple test, eggs may be placed in cold water. A fresh egg will sink immediately. The commercial test for freshness of eggs is called candling. The testing apparatus is a tube with a strong electric light at one end and a place for the egg at the other. A fresh egg has a transparent look with little or no air space. Old eggs appear cloudy and may have a large air space at the larger end. The term "candling" comes from the fact that originally a candle was used in place of the electric light.

Buying Fresh Eggs

Beware of eggs washed clean and having a glossy, smooth shell. Producers often wash eggs because clean eggs will sell for a higher price. Newly laid eggs have a pro-

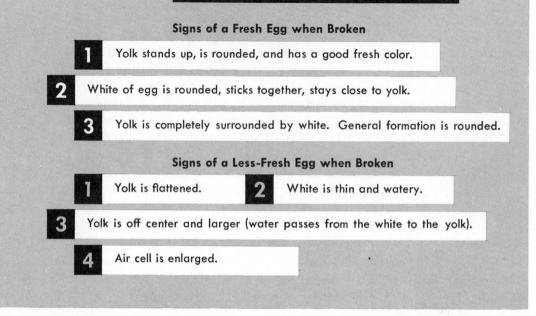

Signs of a Fresh Egg when Broken

1 Yolk stands up, is rounded, and has a good fresh color.

2 White of egg is rounded, sticks together, stays close to yolk.

3 Yolk is completely surrounded by white. General formation is rounded.

Signs of a Less-Fresh Egg when Broken

1 Yolk is flattened.   2 White is thin and watery.

3 Yolk is off center and larger (water passes from the white to the yolk).

4 Air cell is enlarged.

tective covering which seals the pores and prevents bacteria from entering. Washing removes this covering and allows the eggs to absorb odors and to lose their water content. The covering gives eggs a dull-looking shell. On the other hand, eggs which are badly soiled should not be chosen. They show careless handling and may have been gathered from unclean nests. Eggs that have thin or rough shells tend to lose their moisture more quickly. The egg yolk will vary in color from pale yellow to deep orange depending on the diet fed to the hen. Dealers in some parts of the country charge more for white-shelled eggs than for brown ones; in other areas the reverse is true. The color of the shell, however, has nothing to do with the quality, taste, or food value of the eggs.

The ideal eggs to buy are those produced locally, gathered twice daily, and stored in a cool place. Refrigeration helps to prevent deterioration of eggs. Exposure to dust, flies, or heat brings quick spoilage. Eggs left three to four days in a warm store lose as much freshness as eggs kept tightly covered for several weeks in a refrigerator. In home use, eggs should be stored in the refrigerator.

Grades of Fresh Eggs

You may have an opportunity to select eggs graded according to United States Standards. The grades U. S. Special (AA), U. S. Extra (A), U. S. Standard (B), and U. S. Trade (C) depend on size, shell condition, and interior quality. The best grade commonly sold is Grade A. Eggs that are graded A at the source of supply may, because of their perishable state, be only Grade B in quality when used. Eggs graded by the United States Standards are divided by weight into six classes: jumbo, extra large, large, medium, small, and peewee. Not all Grade AA eggs are extra large, nor are Grade A eggs always large and Grade B eggs small. The label tells the grade or quality, the size based on weight per dozen eggs, and the grading date. The grade label on the box is a guide in selecting eggs, but you should judge the interior quality when you break an egg; this will help to guide you in future purchases.

Your choice of grade and size will depend upon how you plan to use the eggs. For poaching, egg drinks, omelets, or angel cakes, eggs of higher quality, such as AA or A, are best. The whites are larger and thicker and the yolk is upstanding. Eggs of the two lower qualities, B and C, do not have thick whites and the egg yolk is flattened (see page 64). Grade B eggs are usually a good buy for general cooking and for combining with other foods. They are good scrambled and in plain omelets. Grade C eggs are seldom on the market. They may be used as thickening or to add food value in quick breads and casseroles where flavor is provided by other ingredients.

Fresh-Egg Substitutes

Dealers often put eggs in *cold storage* when they are plentiful and bring them out to sell when they become more scarce. Only fresh eggs can be kept in good condition in cold storage. The change in flavor is slight and they compare favorably with fresh eggs in food value. You probably will not know whether you are buying cold-storage eggs or not, as in only a few states is the word "storage" required on the package label.

Frozen eggs come in pound cans which are equivalent to about ten medium-sized fresh eggs. Either the whites and yolks are stirred together for freezing or they are frozen separately. They are used largely by commercial bakeries. Frozen eggs probably will increase in use as home freezers and frozen-food compartments in refrigerators become more common in homes and stores. An important precaution to prevent bacterial growth is to freeze eggs quickly after they are broken. Frozen eggs require less storage space and there is no spoilage as long as they are kept frozen. Thawed eggs must be used at once; they must never be refrozen and thawed again.

Dried eggs, either whole, yolk, or white, have about the same food value as fresh eggs. There is probably some loss in vitamins, but the mineral and protein value remains the same. Two and one-half tablespoons of water added to two tablespoons of dried whole egg will give the equivalent of a medium-sized fresh whole egg. Dried egg is used in ready-to-bake products, such as cake mixes, and may be substituted satisfactorily in most recipes. Dried eggs are not expensive—a pound equals thirty-six to forty medium-sized eggs—but they are not readily available to the housewife. To store dried eggs, cover and keep in the refrigerator.

There is also some economy in *home storage* of fresh, clean eggs during the plentiful season. They may be packed away in lime water, wheat, ashes, salt, or waterglass. Eggs kept for several months are better used in cookery. For detailed information on how to store eggs at home write to the Extension Division of your state college.

Caring for Eggs

Eggs are a perishable item and should be given care similar to that given to milk. They should be kept covered and away from strong-smelling food, at a temperature of 45° to 55° F. Cracked eggs should be used immediately. Leftover whites or yolks, if kept tightly covered, may be stored for a

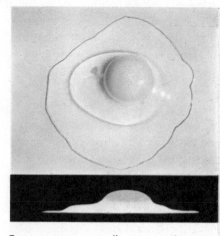

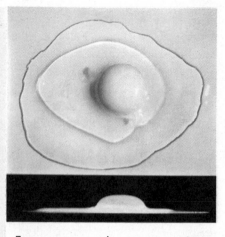

Grade
AA

Grade
A

Egg covers a small area; white is thick and stands high; yolk is firm and high

Egg covers a moderate area; white is reasonably thick, stands fairly high; yolk is firm and high

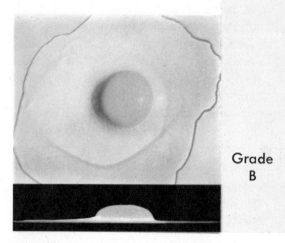

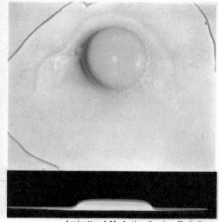

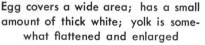

Grade
B

Grade
C

Egg covers a wide area; has a small amount of thick white; yolk is somewhat flattened and enlarged

Egg covers a wide area; white is thin and watery; yolk is flat, enlarged, and breaks easily

few days in the refrigerator. A small-mouthed container is better than one with a wide, shallow mouth as it allows less evaporation and surface drying. Egg whites or yolks become less dry if a thin layer of water, milk, or cooking oil is used to cover them. Yolks are preserved most satisfactorily when

covered with waxed paper or metal foil and frozen in an ice-cube tray. Yolks may also be preserved by dropping them one by one into simmering water, covering, and cooking below the boiling point for 10 to 15 minutes.

Even though eggs have been properly cared for, it is a good precaution to break each one into a saucer instead of directly into a bowl containing other ingredients. Then it is possible to detect any sign of spoilage before the egg ruins a whole mixture. It is easy to slip the egg from a saucer to a mixing bowl or pan.

Uses of Eggs in the Diet

Eggs can probably be used in more ways than any other food. They may be used alone or in combination with other foods. If used alone, they may be poached, scrambled, fried, steamed, or coddled; they may be soft-cooked, hard-cooked, or made into an omelet.

In combination with other foods, they may also be used in many ways, all of which are important in the preparation of tasty, nutritious meals. As *leavening*, one egg may be used instead of ½ teaspoon of baking powder. This is explained by the fact that when an egg white is beaten, a foam is formed that holds many tiny air bubbles. It is this air which expands under heat and causes omelets and cakes to rise, thus producing the same effect as a leavening agent. Because the protein of eggs coagulates when heated, eggs can be used as *thickening*. One egg will thicken as much liquid as 1 tablespoon of flour. This thickening quality also makes eggs useful for *binding* food materials, as in croquettes and potato cakes. Still another use is as a *coating* for certain fried foods, for example, fried eggplant, breaded pork chops, fried oysters, and chicken fried in batter. Egg yolk is used as the emulsifying agent in making mayonnaise. When beaten, egg whites have innumerable uses in the preparation of attractive dishes. Since eggs cook quickly, they are especially valuable for meals that must be prepared in a short time —as breakfasts and emergency meals.

Preparation of Eggs for Eating

In whatever way you use eggs, it is necessary to know certain basic principles about their preparation in order to produce tasty, digestible dishes. These principles are discussed in the next two sections.

How to Beat Egg Whites

The foam formed by beating egg whites depends upon the ability of the whites to stretch and hold air particles. Even a slight trace of yolk will keep the egg white from mounding. The age of the egg, temperature of the egg, and rate of beating are important factors in the foaminess. Fresh eggs, of course, produce the greatest amount of foam. Egg whites at room temperature will produce greater volume than those taken directly from the refrigerator. A small amount of salt, sugar, or acid, such as lemon juice or cream of tartar, will increase the amount of air bubbles which egg whites can hold. Such ingredients give strength to the foam, and therefore less air is lost in mixing. Overbeating will lower the stability of the foam and also cause flakes of protein to separate. Eggs beaten in a flat plate with a fine-wired, flat whisk beater will have larger air bubbles and more volume than those beaten by other means. Rotary beaters, either the hand-operated or the mechanical type, save time and energy for the worker and are successful in producing a foam with fine air cells and good texture.

Beaten egg whites must be used as soon

Caring for eggs · Left-over whites in a small-mouthed, tightly-covered container are stored in the refrigerator

as the beating is completed for the air separates quickly from the liquid. They should be handled carefully. When combining them with foods, fold by cutting down through the mixture, across the bottom of the bowl, up and over the top close to the surface of the mixture Turn the bowl as you work, using a minimum number of strokes, preferably with a rubber spatula.

STAGES OF BEATEN EGG WHITES

1. Slightly beaten egg whites are frothy or slightly foamy. They have large air bubbles, are transparent, and flow easily. They may be used to clear coffee or to coat croquettes.
2. Stiffly beaten egg whites lose their frothy look, have smaller air cells and are very white. They flow if the bowl is tipped, are glossy and moist, and have softly rounded peaks.
3. Very stiffly beaten whites have tiny air cells and are very white. They slip slightly if the

66

bowl is tipped and have stiff, pointed peaks which stand upright. They are still glossy, smooth, and moist-looking.

How to Cook Eggs

Whether eggs are being cooked alone or in combination with other foods, the *correct temperature* is essential to a successful product. The most important thing to remember about egg cookery is that protein foods are more tender when cooked at low temperatures. Eggs cooked at boiling temperature or in very hot fat will be toughened. Also cooking heat must be evenly distributed. Egg mixtures must be cooked at a low 325° F. temperature or a moderate 350° F. temperature so that the air will expand as much as possible before the egg sets. Since egg whites begin to cook at a low temperature, if you combine hot liquid with them, add only a small amount of liquid at a time and beat continuously, as in parfaits, boiled icings, and candies. Since eggs will continue to cook after the pan has been removed from the heat, the cooking process should be stopped a few seconds before the cooking period is completed.

Cooking an egg is simple, but it may take practice before you can fry eggs so that they are lightly browned at the edges and delicately tender, or scramble them so that they are moist and tender. To be sure that your family will enjoy eating eggs, never serve watery scrambled eggs, leathery fried eggs, or greenish hard-cooked eggs. Here are some directions that will help you to make delicious egg dishes.

To prepare *soft-cooked eggs* use either cold or hot water, a pint for the first egg and an additional cup for each extra egg. Follow the directions about temperatures given above. Immediately after the eggs are removed from the cooking water, they should be cooled slightly and opened quickly. These eggs may be served in or out of the shell. To serve in a dish, strike the egg sharply at the center with a blade of a knife and remove the contents into the dish— carefully, to avoid bits of shell. To serve in the shell, remove the shell at the small end and place the egg in an egg cup. A standard product should have a uniformly coagulated white, firm enough to hold shape, yet soft and tender. The yolk should be evenly coagulated and slightly thickened, and should have a fresh-cooked flavor.

To prepare *hard-cooked eggs* that are tender, simmer them just below boiling temperature for 15 to 20 minutes. You may wish to use a double boiler to ensure a simmering temperature. Cool them quickly in cold water to prevent green rings from forming around the yolk and to make them easier to peel. The green ring results from sulphur deposits which collect between the yolk and the white when the egg is hard-cooked. Crack the shell and roll the egg to loosen the shell. Begin at the large end and ease the shell off the egg. Holding the egg under running water aids this process. A hard-cooked egg should have an even, glossy white that is uniformly coagulated and tender. The yolk should be mealy throughout with no dark rings. The flavor should be fresh and delicate.

Before *frying eggs* heat a thin layer of table fat or shortening in a frying pan. Do not let the fat smoke. After breaking the eggs, one at a time, into a saucer, slip them gently into the fat. Cook slowly, dipping the fat over the egg, or add 1 teaspoon of water and cover the pan. Eggs may be turned over to cook the tops, if that is the way your family prefers them. If you prefer your eggs *hard-fried*, cover the pan during the process; increase the cooking time but

67

FRYING EGGS

FRYING EGGS

Slipping egg into pan from saucer

Adding one teaspoon of water when egg whites are just set

Covering tightly with heat turned off to finish cooking with steam

Swift & Company

Scrambled eggs · Beating the eggs with a fork before scrambling

not the temperature. If the fat becomes too hot, the white will be tough, crisp, and hard to digest. In a standard fried egg the yolk is unbroken and thickened and covered by a film of coagulated white. It is surrounded by soft, thick white forming a rounded outline. The white should be tender and free from excess fat. The egg should have a fresh well-seasoned flavor.

For *poaching*, use fresh eggs which have just been broken. Really fresh eggs stay round, and the white will stick together instead of spreading. Adding $\frac{1}{4}$ teaspoon of salt, vinegar, or lemon juice to every cup of water helps to keep the egg white together.

The acid sets the white before it has a chance to scatter. Using an egg poacher will also prevent this loss of egg white.

For an interesting effect, try poaching eggs in a whirlpool of water. Use a shallow pan with enough water to cover the eggs, stir the simmering water briskly, and slip the egg into the whirling center. Cook from 3 to 5 minutes just below the boiling point. Eggs may also be poached in milk or broth, which can then be thickened to pour over the egg.

A standard poached egg has a whole yolk rounded and covered with a film of coagulated white. The yolk is surrounded by thick white which forms a rounded outline. The yolk and white are softly coagulated throughout. The white is tender. The egg has a fresh flavor and is well seasoned.

Scrambled eggs are a general favorite. Avoid cooking them at a high temperature; this toughens them and makes the whites watery. For each egg, as in any cooking process, add $\frac{1}{8}$ teaspoon of salt. One teaspoon of water, chicken stock, milk, or cream per egg improves the product.

Delicious scrambled eggs should have a fresh well-flavored taste. They should be fairly moist, light in texture, softly coagulated, and tender. Like all cooked eggs they must be served hot.

Using Breakfast Meats

Meat served at breakfast is another way of fulfilling the day's protein requirements. People recovering from illnesses, hard-working adults, and growing youngsters who need ample protein in their diet find that meat together with a breakfast egg helps to meet their demand.

Those for whom a medium-sized break-

fast is sufficient will find that an occasional breakfast meat instead of the daily egg lends variety. A serving of breakfast meat is equal to two eggs in protein value. If the meat is liver, it also surpasses the eggs in vitamin and mineral content. (For other food-value comparisons study Table IV in the Appendix.)

Breakfast for company (right) includes a choice of foods and beverages to suit everyone's taste. It is especially inviting when served on pretty china. And for an everyday breakfast what could be more appealing than scrambled eggs and bacon or an omelet hot out of the pan?

H. Armstrong Roberts

Shostal

Poultry and Egg National Board

Bacon is perhaps the most popular breakfast meat. It is a pork side streaked with lean and fat and usually sold cured. Two slices of medium-fat bacon equal 97 calories. It is most delicious when served crisp and hot. Bacon may be pan-fried or broiled. Flavor and texture are improved by draining on absorbent paper after cooking. Canadian bacon is boned pork loin, cured and smoked. It is more lean than regular bacon. Use thin slices and broil or fry like bacon.

Sausage is fresh ground pork which may be bought either in links of various sizes or in bulk (country style). Bulk sausage is formed into patties and fried or broiled slowly until thoroughly cooked. Link sausages are cooked in the same way.

Ham slices provide a delicious meat for Sunday or a holiday morning. When ham is cooked slowly, the full flavor is brought out and the product is tender.

Some people like *codfish balls* for breakfast. The combination of the fish with the eggs and potatoes makes a hearty meal.

Leftover meat may be combined with other foods for breakfast dishes. Minced or chopped meat may be added to scrambled eggs. Leftover pork or beef may be shredded and shaped into a nest in a custard cup or muffin tin. Bits of tomato or cheese or an egg baked in this nest result in an interesting dish.

A full discussion of meat will be found on pages 192–217.

¶ Understanding:

1. What will you receive from the yolk of eggs in the diet? from the white?

2. Describe the characteristics of fresh eggs when broken.

3. How should eggs be handled by the producer to maintain their quality?

4. By what characteristics can you tell whether or not an egg is fresh?

5. What points should you remember in the home storage of eggs?

6. What helpful information may you secure from egg-carton labels?

7. Which grade of eggs will you choose for omelets? for scrambled eggs?

8. When can you substitute dried eggs for fresh eggs?

9. Describe the characteristics of slightly beaten, stiffly beaten, and very stiffly beaten egg whites.

10. What protein foods more economical than meat could you serve for breakfast?

11. Under what circumstances should meat be served for your family breakfast?

¶ Planning:

1. Plan three breakfasts for your family, using eggs in different ways. Explain your selection. What grade of eggs will you use in each case?

2. Plan means of caring for fresh eggs in your home; for egg yolks

3. What guides will aid you in choosing fresh, well-cared-for eggs in the market?

4. Plan a dish for the use of eggs as a leavening, thickening, binding, or coating agent.

5. Plan a baked product in which eggs will be used. What food nutrients will the eggs supply?

6. Plan a breakfast menu including meat. How does the food value compare with that of the same breakfast using eggs instead of meat?

¶ Practicing and Evaluating:

1. Scramble eggs so that they are soft, moist, and tender. Serve attractively with other well-prepared foods for a well-planned breakfast.

2. Fry eggs for a home breakfast to a tender consistency.

3. Prepare an egg dish which includes beaten egg whites. Use correct techniques to include a large amount of air bubbles.

4. Cook eggs in the shell to the soft-cooked stage; to the hard-cooked stage. Check results

by the standards set up in this chapter (pages 66 and 67).

5. Prepare breakfast sausage to achieve a well-flavored product with an appetizing appearance. Should sausage be cooked fast or slowly?

6. Prepare two breakfast menus to include moderate-cost meats.

7. Use a leftover meat for breakfast. What principles of cookery did you follow?

¶ Reading Further:

Cooking with Dried Eggs, A 1.77:50 (1956). Government Printing Office, Washington, D. C.

Eggs: Selection, Care and Preparation, Bulletin 915 (1961). Cornell University Extension Service, Ithaca, New York.

Eggs: Selection, Grades, Care, and Cookery. Poultry and Egg National Board, Chicago.

Grading and Inspection of Eggs and Egg Products, Bulletin 159 (1961). Agricultural Marketing Service, U. S. Department of Agriculture, Washington, D. C.

How to Buy Eggs by USDA Grades and Weight Classes, A 1.35:442 (1958). Government Printing Office, Washington, D. C.

Let's Eat Eggs, Cornell Extension Bulletin No. 915, Cornell University, Ithaca, N. Y.

Marketing Quality Eggs, Bulletin 468 (1960). University of Georgia Extension Service, Athens, Georgia.

Methods of Egg Cookery, Bulletin E–455 (1959). Oklahoma State University Extension Service, Stillwater, Oklahoma.

Meat in Our Meals, Bulletin 9 (1959). Iowa State University Extension Service, Ames, Iowa.

SERANNE, ANN, *The Art of Egg Cookery*. Doubleday & Company, Inc., New York.

6

Jane and Steven Coons

Breakfast beverages

you will learn: The importance of milk;
The market forms of milk; How milk is kept safe;
How to cook milk; How to select and
prepare other beverages

Beverages add enjoyment to meals as well as furnish the body with needed fluid and, in most instances, with food nutrients. Milk, rich in food value, has been an important part of the diet for centuries. Most of the milk consumed in the United States comes from the cow—an animal that is not native to this country but was brought by the early colonists from Europe. The cow, however, is not the only animal that gives milk. People in other parts of the world get their milk from such animals as the llama, sheep, goat, camel, yak, and reindeer. All over the world the herding and raising of milk-giving animals is an essential occupation because milk is such an important food.

Other beverages have their place in the menu, too. Although other drinks may not have as much food value as milk, they are valuable because of their flavor, aroma, color, and stimulating effect.

72

The age of discovery and exploration gave Europe claims to land in the New World and also extended trade into many countries, east and west. Traders brought tea, coffee, and cacao beans (cocoa) back with them, which consequently modified breakfasts, dinners, and suppers of the civilized world.

Each beverage, with its special characteristics, has its place in menu planning because beverages give variety to the texture and appearance of meals. Beverages should never be used to wash down half-chewed food; rather, they should be sipped slowly and enjoyed for their special qualities.

The Importance of Milk

Of all beverages, milk supplies the greatest number of food nutrients. The proportion and qualities of food values in milk are affected by the breed of the cow and by the time of year in which the milk is produced. For instance, when a supply of green foods is available to the cow the vitamin content of milk increases. Milk is one of the best foods you can get. It contains many vitamins and minerals, high-quality proteins, also fat and sugar. Milk is especially important for three nutrients: (1) the mineral calcium, (2) the B-vitamin riboflavin, and (3) protein. Many people get too little of these nutrients for good health, and too little milk is often the reason.

Milk is a most important food in the diet of babies. Growing children should drink milk three or four times each day; and adults need at least a pint every day. That more people are realizing the value of milk is shown by the increased consumption of it. The less expensive forms of milk are real budget savers (see Chapter 9).

Market Forms of Milk

There are several types of milk on the market. The purpose that milk is to serve, the amount of money that can be spent, and the storage methods that are available help determine the type of milk you choose. The Federal Food and Drug Administration has set up standards for milk products to help in regulating the quality. Your state and local standards are probably based on the same definitions. A description of the several types of milk is given in the table on page 76.

Fresh pasteurized milk (whole or skim) and buttermilk are the best selections for beverages. For cooking purposes, you may choose the less expensive (whole) evaporated, sweetened condensed, or skim milk, or dried-milk solids. By adding water, evaporated or dried milk may also be used as a beverage; the flavor is improved if the milk is beaten and then aerated by being poured from one container to another. Fresh skim milk, considerably cheaper than the whole milk, provides both calcium and phosphorus, which are usually difficult to obtain on a restricted budget. However, not all markets carry liquid skim milk because its lower cost makes it unprofitable to handle. Dried skim milk is even less expensive than liquid skim milk, $4\frac{1}{2}$ ounces generally being equivalent to 1 quart of fresh milk. Dried milk is easily transported and stored—a great convenience. These less expensive forms may be used to make the wide variety of flavored milk drinks liked by children and adults.

Bacteria, like people, thrive on milk. From the time of milking to delivery, there are many opportunities for contamination. Diseased cows may infect milk with tuberculosis bacteria or with the bacteria that cause undulant fever. Bacteria may also get into milk from containers and utensils used in handling, from the hands of milkers, from flies and insects, and from dust-laden air.

Because milk can carry bacteria which cause disease, precautions must be taken to keep milk safe. The bacterial count in milk indicates its degree of safety.

When buying milk, make sure that it is clean and of high quality by following these directions:

1. Use milk from cows which have been inspected for disease.

2. Find out whether the Standard Milk Ordinance, approved by the United States Public Health Service, Federal Security Administration, and the Bureau of Dairy Industry, U. S. Department of Agriculture, is in effect in your state and city. Understand the regulations in effect in your locality for the quality and cleanliness of milk.

3. Use milk in which disease-producing bacteria have been killed or weakened by pasteurization. (The flavor of milk is slightly changed by this process.)

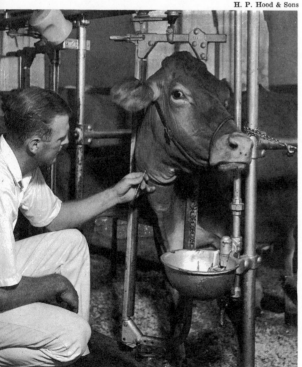

Taking a blood test to see if a cow is free of certain communicable diseases · The health of cows whose milk is sold commercially is carefully supervised by the dairies and by state and local health officers

H. P. Hood & Sons

To keep fresh milk safe at home, use clean containers and store near the freezing compartment in the refrigerator. Bacteria grow quickly in milk and milk products unless they are kept cold. Once bacteria are present, no amount of chilling will kill them. Normally, milk and cream should be kept at 50° F. However, if storage time is 24 hours or longer, the temperature should be about 40° F. Evaporated milk, once the can is opened, requires the same care as fresh milk. It need not be refrigerated until it has been opened. Proteins decompose and produce disagreeable odors and flavors if milk is not kept cold. At room temperature, the sugar in liquid milk changes to acid and produces sour milk. Mixing fresh milk with old milk may spoil the combined product more quickly. Milk, like butter, should be kept tightly covered since it absorbs odors easily.

Milk that is produced and used at home, should meet these regulations:

1. Cows should be tested for disease.

2. Milking should be done in stables kept clean and free from dust.

3. Milkers should wear clean clothes, keep hands clean, and be free from disease.

4. Utensils should be sterilized through boiling, steaming, or exposing to bright sunlight, and kept away from dust and flies.

5. Home-produced milk should be pasteurized.

How to Cook Milk

A scum may form on the top of milk when it is heated for cocoa, milk toast, or white sauce. This scum contains chiefly protein and fat and should be stirred back into the mixture to conserve food values. Formation of scum is hindered by heating milk in a covered double boiler because by using this method of preparation the evaporation which dries the surface of the milk and causes the scum is greatly lessened. Stirring or beating the milk while it cooks over direct heat will also discourage the forming of scum. If cocoa must stand before serving, beat it well to form a foam on top. This foam, too, helps to prevent scum. Since milk, because of its proteins, has a tendency to stick to the pan and scorch, it is best to heat it in the top of a double boiler over hot water.

How to Select and Prepare Beverages Other than Milk

Cocoa and Chocolate Beverages

Cocoa and chocolate are manufactured from the beans of the cacao tree, which grows in tropical countries. Cacao contains theobromine, a stimulant similar to those in tea and coffee. The chief food value of cocoa and chocolate is in their fat, called cocoa butter (50 per cent in chocolate, 8 to 30 per cent in cocoa). Chocolate, as you can see, has more energy value than cocoa.

Chocolate is sold in cakes marked off, for convenient measuring, into ounce or half-ounce squares. Both bitter and semisweet chocolate are available. Semisweet chocolate is also sold in chips or bits. There are many brands, varying in cost, flavor, and color. Price is not a good guide to selection. Fat content, which must be stated on the label, is a better guide.

The fat content makes it necessary to store both cocoa and chocolate in airtight containers and in a cool place. Cakes of chocolate allowed to stand in a warm place may develop white spots. These are caused by the melting of the cocoa butter, which comes to the surface and hardens when the temperature is lowered. However, this change in appearance does not affect the cooking qualities of the chocolate.

In working with *cocoa,* treat it like dry starch. It will lump if combined directly with hot liquids, but because of the low fat content it blends easily with cold liquids. In making cocoa, separate the starch grains of cocoa powder with sugar or a little cold milk before combining with the other ingredients. Cocoa must be cooked to make the starch digestible. Cooking improves the

MILK AS SOLD IN VARIOUS FORMS

NAME ▼	DESCRIPTION ▼
Raw	Fresh, liquid milk which is unpasteurized
Pasteurized	Milk which is subjected to heat long enough to kill dangerous bacteria. There are two accepted methods: the *hold method*, in which milk is held at 145°F. for 30 minutes, and the *flash method*, in which the milk is held at 161°F. for 15 seconds. Pasteurized milk should be cooled quickly to 40°F. or below
Homogenized	Pasteurized milk treated to break up the fat into very small particles of uniform size so that they remain distributed throughout the liquid. Therefore the cream does not rise to the top
Certified	Raw or pasteurized milk produced and marketed under strict supervision. It has the highest rating for purity and cleanliness
Grade A	Milk obtained from cows which must be tested and declared free from disease. It has a specified butterfat content
Skim	Milk from which the cream has been removed to the extent that not more than 1.5 per cent butterfat is left. This milk contains the same nutritional values as whole milk except for lessened calorie and vitamin-A content
Chocolate	Whole milk to which chocolate sirup has been added
Chocolate-flavored	Skim milk with cocoa added
Buttermilk	Churned cream with butter removed
Cultured buttermilk	Buttermilk prepared by lactic culture or citric acid
Sour	Milk that has been soured naturally or artificially
Evaporated	Whole milk homogenized from which 50 to 60 per cent of the water has been removed
Sweetened condensed	Evaporated milk to which sugar up to 40 per cent weight has been added
Irradiated	Milk to which vitamin D has been added. The milk may be fortified with concentrates, or the milk or the cow may be irradiated (exposed to strong sunlight or ultraviolet light)
Dried whole	All the milk solids must be present. There must be not less than 4 per cent butterfat nor more than 5 per cent moisture
Nonfat dried-milk solids or dried skim milk	Skim milk from which all but 5 per cent of the moisture has been removed. Dried milk contains all the food values of liquid skim milk
Malted	A flavored, powdered mixture of dried milk, barley malt, and wheat flour which has liquid added

flavor and also prevents the separation of the cocoa from the liquid. Instant cocoa is made by the addition of a hot liquid.

In cooking *chocolate*, melt it over hot water, or directly over a very low heat, or in a small amount of milk or water. Melted chocolate can be added directly to flour mixtures without lumping because the fat of chocolate separates the starch particles in the flour. Combining a hot liquid with melted chocolate permits the chocolate to blend into the mixture easily. The addition of a cold liquid to melted chocolate may cause lumping and always makes blending more difficult. Chocolate, like cocoa, should be kept over the heat long enough to form a sirup and cook the starch. Correctly made cocoa has no surface scum, ingredients are well blended, and no sediment remains as it is poured. It has a rich brown color and a definite chocolate flavor.

Ginn, (Frank D. Lucas)

Preventing scum on cocoa · Beating cocoa while it cooks over direct heat will help to prevent scum

Tea and Coffee Beverages

Neither tea nor coffee drinks contain any food value except for that in the cream and sugar that may be used in them. It is their flavor and the stimulant in them that make them enjoyable. The heart, kidneys, and nervous system of some persons are affected by the stimulant; those of others apparently are not greatly disturbed. This stimulant in coffee is caffeine, called theine in tea.

Tea may be served at breakfast, but in the United States it is more commonly used at other meals. Tea should be purchased in small amounts because it loses its flavor in storage. Tea bags of cloth or parchment are a convenience. An instant tea is also on the market. However, tea bags and instant tea may add to the cost per serving.

There are several types of tea, each with its characteristic flavor, color, and aroma. Black tea is made from tea leaves that have been fermented by the use of wet cloths spread over them. Green tea is unfermented, and oolong tea is semifermented. Sometimes flowers or spices are added for flavor, jasmine being the most popular flower. Grades of tea, like orange-pekoe, a black tea, or gunpowder, a green tea, are determined by the size and maturity of the tea leaves.

When making tea, use tea that has been stored in an airtight container in a cool place for not longer than 6 or 8 months. Use a china, glass, or earthenware teapot or cup (a metal container may cause a metallic flavor). Preheat the container by pouring boiling water into it and then emptying. Use fresh boiling water; it contains more oxygen than water that has been boiling for some time and prevents a flat taste. Soft water produces a clearer, more sparkling color in tea than hard water. Follow a recipe in the Cookbook carefully. Too much tea

77

may cause cloudiness. Lemon helps to clear tea.

Tea should be steeped by allowing it to stand from 3 to 5 minutes in water below the boiling point. Then serve it at once. Tea should never be boiled or allowed to stand for long. In either case the tannic acid present in the leaves will make the tea bitter and the flavor factor will escape.

Coffee is probably the most popular hot beverage in this country. The coffee bean is the seed of a small tree. Most of our supply comes from South America. Coffee beans are roasted to develop flavor and aroma, and the beans are ground before using.

Since freshly roasted and ground coffee is necessary for a good beverage, only small quantities should be purchased at a time. Ground coffee, especially, loses its flavor and aroma very quickly—in a few weeks— if exposed to the air. All coffee should be kept tightly covered. Some people prefer to store it in the refrigerator.

Coffee may be purchased in various forms. That for home brewing may be bought in the bean or ready-ground. Ground coffee comes in containers of various sizes and may be vacuum-packed in glass or tin to preserve its freshness. In purchasing ground coffee read labels to make sure that it has been ground to suit the method of coffee making that you use. Instant coffee, in a dried form, is packed either in sealed containers or in parchment bags similar to tea bags. It is ready to drink after it has been dissolved in boiling water. Frozen coffee concentrate is also available and is prepared in the same way. Coffee may be purchased with the major part of the caffeine (the stimulant) removed.

To make coffee successfully, the coffee maker must be scrupulously clean, and also the filter cloth, if one is used. The oily film which collects in the maker gives an undesirable flavor. Be sure that you use freshly drawn water, soft if possible. For methods of making coffee, refer to the Cookbook. Serve the coffee immediately, as it loses its mellow flavor, stimulating aroma, and amber color if it stands. Do not boil coffee. In reheating coffee, always keep it below the boiling point. If it is boiled the flavor factor evaporates, and the tannic acid in the coffee gives a bitter taste.

Fruit and Vegetable Juices

Of all the breakfast juices or appetizers, orange juice is probably used the most, but as almost any fruit may be converted into a juice, a wide variety is possible. As tea

From left to right: glass coffee maker; percolator for use over direct heat; electric percolator; drip coffee maker

leaves are blended for flavors, so fruit juices may be blended into delicious combinations. Vegetable juices also are much used for breakfast, especially tomato juice and carrot juice. A combination of vegetable juices may be obtained from the market at moderate cost. When vegetable juices are used for breakfast, be sure to include fruit at luncheon or dinner.

Fruit-juice concentrates are available in powdered, canned, bottled, and frozen forms. Frozen fruit juices are considered equal to fresh juices in food value, flavor, aroma, and color; in some instances they are comparable in cost. Canned tomato juice is as rich in vitamin C as freshly prepared tomato juice.

Of the usual breakfast beverages, coffee gives adults pleasure and stimulation, milk provides adults and children the most complete food, and juices add much in minerals and vitamins along with color for the eye and tang for the taste. Good breakfast planning includes the right beverages for each member of the family.

Pouring orange juice for breakfast

¶ *Understanding:*

1. Of what values in the diet are beverages?
2. Describe the types of milk available in your community. What determines the best type for your use?
3. How must milk be handled at home for safety?
4. How does fresh milk compare with evaporated milk in food value? with condensed milk? with dried milk?
5. What are the advantages of using dried milk?
6. What are some ways of increasing the milk intake of family members at breakfast?
7. How will you cook cocoa and chocolate to obtain satisfactory products?

8. Name fruit and vegetable juices which can be used to create variety in breakfasts.
9. How does orange juice compare with carrot juice in food values?
10. What good manners should you practice when drinking beverages with a meal?

¶ *Planning:*

1. Plan dishes in which dried-milk solids can be substituted for fresh milk. Compare costs.
2. Plan the step processes in making cocoa. Consider utensils needed and time for preparation. Estimate the cost.
3. Plan to use evaporated milk instead of fresh milk in a beverage. Compare flavor. Compare cost.
4. Help arrange for the proper storage of milk at home.
5. Plan a low-cost breakfast including orange juice. Will you use fresh, canned, or frozen juice? Explain.

¶ Practicing and Evaluating:

1. Make cocoa for breakfast and prevent a scum from forming on top. What should be done if scum forms on cocoa? if the cocoa must stand for a short time before serving?

2. Substitute evaporated or dried milk for fresh milk in the preparation of a dish. How much was the cost affected?

3. Compare the flavor of homogenized, Grade A, and skim milk. Compare food values and costs. For what purposes is each well suited?

4. Prepare and serve hot tea and coffee to adult guests. Check for flavor and clarity.

5. Prepare fresh orange juice for a breakfast. Compare as to flavor, color, and cost with canned orange juice. Compare time for preparation with the time for preparing frozen juice.

¶ Reading Further:

Getting Enough Milk, A 1.77:57 (1957). U. S. Department of Agriculture, Washington, D. C.

How to Use Whole and Non-fat Dry Milk, L–275. U. S. Department of Agriculture, Washington, D. C.

LOWE, BELLE, *Experimental Cookery*, pages 308–310. John Wiley and Sons, Inc., New York.

Milk Consumption in the Nation's Schools, A 1.82:284 (1958). Government Printing Office, Washington, D. C.

Non-fat Dry Milk, Bulletin 44 (1960). Iowa State University Extension Service, Ames, Iowa.

STEVENSON, GLADYS T., and MILLER, CORA, *Foods and Nutrition*, pages 153–158 and page 185. John Wiley and Sons, Inc., New York.

7

Jane and Steven Coons

Planning and preparing breakfast

you will learn: How to plan breakfasts wisely;
How to cook breakfasts

The old saying, "He got up on the wrong side of the bed," probably means, in reality, that his breakfast was inadequate, a circumstance too frequent in many families. A good breakfast will provide the spark which makes one alert and cheerful throughout the day. The challenge is to plan breakfasts that are tempting in flavor and aroma as well as adequate. Dull breakfasts are not enjoyed; every effort should be made to vary the foods in taste, texture, and color, and to serve them on an attractively set table. Other factors in getting the day started well are the promptness with which breakfast is served and a pleasant social atmosphere while it is being eaten. Under these conditions breakfast becomes a delightful and valuable meal.

81

Making Breakfast Do Its Share in the Day's Diet

Breakfast must be planned so that it will provide you its share of the daily food needs. When each of the three meals carries its fair share of the day's nutritional quota, no one meal overburdens the stomach. Adequate meals safeguard against hunger before the next mealtime and provide sufficient continuous energy throughout the day to prevent fatigue. According to the Daily Food Guide on page 18, certain foods properly combined in the day's menus will satisfy all the needs of the body. As an illustration of the use of the Daily Food Guide in planning a day's meals, and as a guide to checking other menus, study the menu chart carefully on pages 84–85. Note how foods for breakfast, as well as those for luncheon and dinner, can furnish a complete range of food elements. (For food needs of the body, review Chapter 1.)

Adults need less calcium and protein than these menus call for. They may adapt the menus by drinking a beverage other than milk once or twice daily and by eating smaller amounts of the protein foods.

Adapting Breakfast to Individual Needs

Not everyone needs the same kind of breakfast. However, it is important that everyone eat the breakfast that gives him the right start toward fulfilling his nutritional needs for the day. The calorie content will depend largely on the individual's program of work and play. The breakfast allowances also vary according to age: young, vigorous people need more food than do those who are older (see pages 3–5).

Light breakfasts are appropriate for adults who lead inactive lives. Their food needs, which are not as great as formerly, are satisfied by a meal of fruit, toast, and a beverage, such as milk, cocoa, or coffee. Unless milk is served, light breakfasts are inadequate in protein. The need must be met by the other meals of the day.

Medium breakfasts are required by those who go to school, teach, sell, do housework, or work in offices. Such a breakfast consists of fruit, cereal or egg, buttered bread or toast, and a beverage. The size of servings should be suited to individual needs, as is discussed in Chapter 1.

If you do not enter into active sports you would probably find the following breakfast satisfying:

1 large sliced orange
$\frac{3}{4}$ cup oatmeal with raisins, whole milk, and sugar if needed
1 slice of buttered toast
$1\frac{1}{2}$ cups cocoa (made with milk)

A high-school boy would need a breakfast of this kind:

$\frac{1}{2}$ large grapefruit (with sweetening)
2 eggs
2 slices of buttered toast with jam
2 glasses whole milk

Heavy breakfasts are necessary for laborers, such as shipbuilders, airplane mechanics, welders, miners, farmers, and homemakers doing heavy work. The heavy breakfast includes fruit; cereal or potatoes; eggs; breakfast meat, such as bacon or sausage; buttered bread, biscuits, toast, or hot cakes with sirup; and a beverage.

A heavy breakfast served late in the morning as a combination of breakfast and lunch

82

is called brunch. Brunch is a popular special-occasion meal. Main-dish foods, such as waffles with creamed chicken, mixed grills of lamb chops, chicken livers, or bacon, omelets with cheese or ham, and broiled fish are typical brunch dishes. There is a tendency in some families to serve a heavy breakfast on week ends and holidays because there is usually more time for preparing and serving it. Unless the morning activities of the holiday are going to be as strenuous as those of other days, the breakfast menu should be light. A late and hearty breakfast requires that lunch be light, consisting of such foods as fruit, milk, and perhaps a sandwich, and that a full dinner round out the diet for the day. It is a mistake to serve three large meals on the days when the family is least active.

Staying within the Family Budget

Since families have to spend a large part of their income to meet food needs adequately, it is important to avoid waste and to obtain the most food value for the money spent. Some of the foods commonly served for breakfast are expensive in certain seasons, in certain markets, or in certain forms or grades. Eggs, meats, milk, and fruit are examples of such foods. However, there are many ways in which you, as a food purchaser, can plan your buying to secure the most food value for your money.

An experienced homemaker, like your mother, knows that it is not always more economical to buy the least expensive varieties. In buying prunes, for instance, the cost per pound usually is less for the smaller size of fruit. However, since the proportion of pits to pulp is greater in the smaller size, the larger fruit is the better buy. Through wise planning you will learn to stay within the family budget. (See Chapter 9 on "Planned Spending.")

A small budget requires careful use of food for the day's needs. Breakfast should not be slighted to serve expensive meats or desserts for dinner. The budget allowance for breakfast must provide nearly one-third of the day's calories including the proper proportion of food elements. Wise practices in the use and care of food at all times will help to accomplish this.

Careful storage of fresh fruit, cereals, or eggs, and use of all leftover foods, such as toast, oatmeal, and scrambled eggs, prevent waste. The amount of leftover food can be controlled in most families by preparing only the amount of food needed. The exceptions to this rule are leftovers which have been purposely planned for use in future meals.

Recognizing the Season

The foods served at breakfast should correspond to the season of the year in which they are plentiful and appropriate. Chilled applesauce is delicious with buttered toast on a sultry summer morning. The same fruit, served hot with biscuits and butter, is equally appetizing on a wintery day. When melons are plentiful and inexpensive, they may be made into chilled melon balls for a hot-weather breakfast. Cooked dried fruit is a better choice for a cold day than a hot one as it contains the high-energy value you need in the winter for warmth as well as growth.

Because activities vary with the seasons, the kind and amount of food should vary to fit the activities. When activities lessen in hot weather, energy needs are reduced; therefore foods lower in calories should be served. Although the calorie need is reduced in warm weather, the requirements for protein, vitamins, and minerals remain the same. Wise planning on the part of the homemaker is needed if the diet is to be adequate during hot-weather periods. A breakfast of fruit juice, lean bacon or a poached egg, toast, and skim milk is a good low-calorie meal for such a season, because it includes the needed minerals and vitamins as well as protein. In cold weather, vigorous activities like out-of-door sports, walking to school, and shoveling snow increase calorie needs. A breakfast of baked peaches, sausage, eggs, cooked cereal with cream, a hot bread with butter, and hot chocolate provides enough calories for such strenuous activities. Calorie needs are partly seasonal.

The season of the year influences the kinds of food on the market and their cost. In the cold months, the supply of fresh fruits is likely to be limited, especially in small communities, and the price of these fruits may be high. This may make it desirable to use canned fruits or tomato juice, or frozen fruits and citrus-fruit juices, to supply vitamin C. Much that is lost at breakfast in the day's quota of vitamins and minerals can be made up by green and yellow vegetables served for luncheon and dinner. Only families with a generous food allowance can afford to buy fresh foods out of season. Using seasonal foods protects the budget.

Where summers are especially hot and hurried, food problems increase. There is a tendency to serve too much cold food with the mistaken notion that it reduces body heat. Actually, one or two hot dishes served at each meal stimulate digestion and increase loss of body heat. Freshly baked muffins and a hot beverage are as good for hot-weather breakfasts as for winter ones.

Greater care must be given to foods in hot weather. Breakfast fruits should be prepared and set back into the refrigerator

84

BREAKFAST
SLICED ORANGES

SCRAMBLED EGGS

TOAST
BUTTER or FORTIFIED MARGARINE
MILK

LUNCH
POTATO SOUP

TOASTED CHEESE SANDWICH

LETTUCE SALAD

BAKED APPLE

MILK

DINNER
CUBE STEAK
GREEN BEANS

BUTTERED CARROTS

CRACKED-WHEAT BREAD

BUTTER or FORTIFIED MARGARINE
PINEAPPLE ICE CREAM
MILK

Nutrients Obtained	Daily-Food-Guide Requirements Met
Vitamin C; calcium	Citrus fruit, tomatoes (one or more servings daily)
Protein of high value; iron, phosphorus, vitamin A	Meat, poultry, fish, eggs (one or two servings daily)
Carbohydrate; thiamine, riboflavin, niacin	Breadstuffs, cereals (every day)
Fat; vitamin A	Butter, fortified margarine (some daily)
Calcium; vitamin A, protein, riboflavin	Milk (3 to 4 cups daily)
Vitamins A and C, thiamine, riboflavin, niacin; iron, calcium; carbohydrate	Potatoes, other vegetables and fruits (non-citrus) (two or more servings daily)
Protein of high value; fat; vitamin A; calcium, phosphorus; carbohydrate	Breadstuff, cereals; milk, cheese, ice cream (some of each group daily)
Vitamins A, B, and C; iron	Leafy, green and yellow vegetables (one or more servings daily)
Carbohydrate; vitamins A and C	Other fruits, not citrus (two or more servings daily)
Calcium; vitamins A and D	Milk
Protein of high value	Meat, poultry, fish, etc.
Thiamine, riboflavin, niacin; calcium, phosphorus; carbohydrates	Leafy, green and yellow vegetables
Vitamin A; calcium, phosphorus	Leafy, green and yellow vegetables; butter, fortified margarine
Carbohydrate; thiamine, riboflavin, niacin; calcium, phosphorus	Breadstuffs, cereals
Fat; vitamin A	Butter or fortified margarine
Vitamin A; calcium, phosphorus; carbohydrate	Milk, cheese, ice cream
Calcium; vitamins A and D	Milk

unless served immediately. Only the milk, eggs, and meat required for the meal should be taken from the refrigerator, and any leftovers should be returned immediately. The best of care for food in hot weather safeguards health and prevents loss of supplies.

Judging the Time Required

The time needed to prepare and serve any meal depends on the menu and the efficiency of the worker. Week-day breakfast menus should be simple and the routines of table setting and cooking soon completed. You will be a valuable helper for your mother when you assume such tasks as pouring the milk and setting the table. Perhaps you can relieve her by breaking eggs for an omelet or by watching the bacon, which must be just crisped. These experiences will make you increasingly efficient at dovetailing tasks (cooking one food while preparing another or setting the table) until you can prepare a simple breakfast as quickly as your mother.

Regarding Personal Likes

The importance of learning to eat and enjoy a variety of foods has already been discussed (pages 35–36). Personal tastes should not be allowed to raise the cost of meals above the budget allowance, nor should they restrict meals to low nutritional standards. The family can somewhat adjust their preferences to their nutritional needs, and the homemaker can find ways to add more food values to favored dishes. Often, as with breakfast cereals, there is a wide choice. The addition of sugar and cream or fruit to cereals adds to the nutritive value and attractiveness which will encourage the acceptance of the food.

An occasional new dish will be more readily received when it is served attractively

and when it accompanies foods well liked by the family. In many cases the new dish may become a first choice of the future. Favorites should be recognized and used wisely while new tastes are being encouraged, until the family will choose a wide variety of foods.

You can plan a well-balanced meal around a favorite dish by serving other foods which include the needed food values that the favorite dish lacks. If the family favorite contains a protein of high value, you will not need another protein food in the meal but can serve fruit, cereal grain, a table fat, and beverage. Suppose you serve pancakes with sirup and butter or fortified margarine. Pancakes are mostly flour, with a small amount of egg and milk. Fat is supplied on the pancakes. You will still need a fruit, a protein of high value, and more milk. A selection of a baked red apple for fruit and golden-brown bacon for protein would make an interesting contrast in color, texture, and flavor as well as complete a nourishing breakfast to start the day.

Foods that a family does not like, or that they have tired of, often become acceptable if prepared in a different way. Instead of scrambling eggs, plan a fluffy omelet or shirred eggs, or vary the scrambled eggs by adding chopped bacon. For a brunch you might add a strip of anchovy, chopped parsley, or grated cheese, or make a cheese omelet. Eggs need not always be served for breakfast. Try a breakfast meat or a cereal dish and supplement it to provide a protein of high value.

There are so many delicious combinations of food that breakfast planning should always remain interesting. Ways in which you can vary meals to appeal to personal taste include the substitution of new dishes for overused dishes, the combining of foods, the use of new garnishes, and the trying of new foods on the market.

Judging Your Breakfast Menus

Your breakfast menu should be tested by certain general standards. An appropriate breakfast meets the following requirements:

1. It contains nearly a third of the nutritional requirements for the day.

2. It offers a variety of foods that satisfy hunger, have a good taste, and appeal to the eye.

3. It can be purchased with the money allowed.

4. It can be prepared and served easily and quickly.

Working Ahead on Menus

Planning meals for three or four days, or as much as a week, ahead is standard practice in good food management. Advance planning makes it possible for you to have more adequate breakfasts, to save time and motions, and to spend more wisely. It is easier and quicker to check the meals for several days against the allowances listed in Table III in the Appendix than to check each meal separately.

Though planning meals ahead is both a necessity and a convenience to the homemaker, no plan should be followed so closely that last-minute changes cannot be made. The opportunity to obtain unexpected food items, perhaps at an especially low price, should not be passed by.

Planned meals are usually more interesting than unplanned ones because there is less tendency to repeat foods prepared by the same methods and in the same combinations. Even repeating the same menu once a week for several consecutive weeks is uninteresting. Food on hand, scarce food, or expensive food can be used to better advantage

with advance planning. You have greater poise and peace of mind if you avoid uncertainty about what to serve for the next meal. Through planning you may earn leisure.

Making Out the Market Order

To carry out the week's menus as planned, food must be supplied at home or purchased from the grocer. When food needs are known in advance, buying is easier and better use can be made of the budget allowance. If you know a food will be served more than once a week, you can take advantage of purchasing in larger quantities for less money. A large can of tomato juice is cheaper than the same amount from two or three smaller cans. Planned menus also save trips to the market. Home storage of perishable and staple foods can be better organized. The oven can be used more economically, and leftovers will be better used.

Your mother is repaid for the trouble of keeping a simple market list and shopping periodically by the saving in time and money and by the convenience of being able to get a meal without a special trip to the market. She probably lists breakfast staples for prompt replacement, and notes special needs for the week's menus well in advance. Buying in quantity where storage facilities permit and the food can be safely kept also helps her to cut down the family's breakfast budget. Careful planning well ahead of immediate needs allows her to take advantage of sales and other special opportunities. Perhaps your mother keeps the market order in a convenient spot where she can check it often. Perhaps too her market list carries useful reminders for the other home buyers who must from time to time act as assistant purchasing agents for her. (For specific buying information, see Chapter 9.)

The principles of cooking foods for breakfast have been set forth previously in Chapters 3–6. Additional directions are discussed later in this unit and appear in the Cookbook in the form of recipes, charts of direction, and pictured step processes. By following a carefully worked-out plan, you will learn the best use of effort and time and develop skill in work methods and good management.

Using Recipes

You need recipes as guides for cooking food of high standard. Make a choice from those that have been tested in laboratories, in home kitchens, or in both.

Dependable recipes meet the following standards:

1. They use ingredients and equipment found in most households.

2. They use measurements easily understood.

3. They give full information on procedures.

4. They provide clear and concise directions.

5. They require a minimum of work.

6. They give cooking temperatures.

7. They state the number of servings.

Your success in the use of recipes depends upon food materials, the equipment used, your skill in methods of work, and your ability to follow directions. Accurate measurements of ingredients and of temperatures for food cookery are discussed in Chapter 2 (pages 25–27) and in the Cookbook (pages 352–353).

Planning Your Work

When you prepared snacks, you learned the values of the work plan. (See *Planning*

Snacks for Home Guests, page 30.) Dovetailing tasks helps you to get all foods ready to serve when needed. In the work plan that follows, the setting of the table is completed while the water is boiling for the cereal. While the oven is heating and the toast is being made, the beverages are removed from the refrigerator and poured. When you first prepare breakfast in the school kitchen, the menus should be planned for easy management.

MENU I

Tomato Juice
Oatmeal
Bacon Strips
Buttered Oven Toast   Apricot Marmalade
Milk

WORK PLAN FOR MENU I

The night before	Place tomato juice in refrigerator. Set the table (see Chapter 25).
7:00 A.M.	Make personal preparation. (Wash hands, put on apron and hair net.) Assemble quick-cooking oatmeal, bacon, table fat, bread, and cooking and serving equipment.
7:06	Put water for cereal in top part of double boiler and place over high heat. Put water into lower pan and heat.
7:08	Fill sugar bowl and salt shaker; place on table. Add oatmeal to water in top of double boiler; stir and cook on low direct heat. Spread butter or fortified margarine on bread and place on baking sheet.
7:10	Stir oatmeal gently; place over hot water in lower pan of double boiler. Cover and let cook at medium heat.

7:12   Place bacon in skillet and set on low heat.

7:13   Heat oven to 375° F.
       Remove tomato juice, milk, and marmalade from refrigerator.

7:15   Place toast in oven.
       Pour tomato juice and milk; fill pitcher with milk for cereal.
       Turn bacon.

7:16   Place marmalade in dish; put marmalade, tomato juice, and milk on table.

7:18   Turn toast.
       Place oatmeal in dishes on tray.

7:20   Remove bacon, drain, and place on platter.
       Remove toast; place on plate.

7:22   Serve oatmeal, bacon, and toast.

Here is a menu for a special-occasion breakfast with waffles as the main dish. You may wish to write out the work plan. About twenty-eight minutes is required for the meal preparation.

MENU II

Mixed Fruit Juice
Waffles with Butter or Margarine and Sirup
Link Sausages
Milk

Before you begin work, place the plan and required recipes where they can be used conveniently, and be thoroughly familiar with the plan. Gather all utensils and ingredients together first. A tray or roll cart is a help for this.

Follow the plan closely. Do not attempt to change it at the last minute unless there is an emergency. If you get behind, spill ingredients, burn food or a finger, or find an ingredient spoiled or not on hand, do not become alarmed. Remember that such accidents happen to the most experienced cooks.

Quickly think through your problem to find the best solution or substitute. Do not hesitate to ask for help in such emergencies. When you have finished with your responsibilities, take time to analyze the reason for the emergency so that it can be avoided another time.

If you find that you allowed more time than was needed for any part of the work, use the extra minutes to recheck the table, straighten the kitchen, or wash pans.

Serving

After you have planned and prepared a good breakfast, you want it to look attractive on a well-set table. Table setting and serving at breakfast should become so easy that it can be done almost unconsciously. Because breakfasts are informal, their service should be simple. (See Chapter 25.) Pleasant and stimulating conversation will follow naturally when the family is seated at an attractive table, eating a good breakfast.

¶ *Understanding:*

1. Give several reasons why an adequate breakfast is important to you.

2. In what ways would planning meals in advance help your family?

3. What portion of your daily food allowances should be included in breakfast?

4. What are the values to your mother of having a well-planned market order?

5. How will a plan of work aid in the preparation of breakfast at home?

6. What may be the results when a work plan for breakfast is not followed? What should a good work plan include?

7. How will you care for the quick breads for family members who cannot eat breakfast at the same time?

8. How will you protect breakfast fruits against the loss of food values?

¶ *Planning:*

1. Plan two breakfast meals to include breads which have been partially prepared and stored in the refrigerator.

2. Plan ways to keep eggs and cereals warm over a period of time.

3. Make out the market order and a work plan for a breakfast of fresh fruit, cooked cereal, and milk.

4. In planning a day's meals for four of your friends, find acceptable luncheon and dinner menus and plan a breakfast to complete their nutritional allowances.

5. With your mother, check a day's menus planned for home use. Use Table III in the Appendix. If additions are needed, furnish them by revising the breakfast menu.

6. Help plan your family's weekly market order, keeping within the budget of the week.

7. Plan a table arrangement suitable for a breakfast at which waffles are the main dish and are baked at the table. Complete the menu to provide a well-balanced meal.

¶ *Practicing and Evaluating:*

1. Assist with the purchasing of the fruit needed at home for a week. What guides aided you in making wise choices?

2. Prepare the fruit and beverage for a home breakfast. In what ways could you save time and effort when repeating the task?

3. Cook the eggs for a family breakfast, keeping them tender and having them ready to serve with the meal.

4. Prepare a cooked cereal for a home breakfast so that it has a good flavor and texture and is served hot. On two mornings use the same recipe with different variations.

5. Serve a ready-to-eat and a home-prepared breakfast cereal. Compare in food values, cost, and time for preparation.

6. Assist with the preparation and serving of a breakfast at home to consist of fruit, hot cakes, bacon, butter or fortified margarine, sirup, and milk. Check the breakfast for flavor, appetizing appearance, and length of time required for preparation.

7. Set the home breakfast table for five days. Each day work out means with your mother for improving the process.

¶ *Reading Further:*

Eat a Good Breakfast to Start a Good Day, Bulletin L–268 (1959). U. S. Department of Agriculture, Washington, D. C.

Family Time Meals, Bulletin (1963). Iowa State Extension Service, Ames, Iowa.

It's Breakfast Time, Bulletin 277 (1959). Kansas State College Extension Service, Manhattan, Kansas.

Skillet Skills, Bulletin 43 (1961). Iowa State Extension Service, Ames, Iowa.

Today's Girls—Food and Nutrition, Bulletin 4360 (1960). Iowa State Extension Service, Ames, Iowa.

UNIT THREE

Living Well

Frigidaire

The efficient kitchen

you will learn: How to plan an efficient kitchen;
How to suit the kitchen to family needs; How to
organize work centers; How to select kitchen equipment;
How to care for small equipment;
How to care for the kitchen and large equipment

It is fun to work in a kitchen that is attractive and arranged for efficiency in work. Ideas of what a kitchen should be and what purposes it should serve have varied with the times and modes of living. George Washington's kitchen, where work was done by the servants, was not in the house itself but was connected with it by a covered walk. Old brownstone houses in New York had kitchens and servants'

quarters in the half-basement; food was sent to the dining room on a dumb-waiter, where a second servant placed it before the family and guests. Considerable skill was needed to keep hot foods from cooling. Today homes without servants are common. Homemakers, faced with many tasks and the problem of little outside assistance, must have kitchens equipped and arranged to simplify their work.

Planning an Efficient Kitchen

The New Kitchen

Foresight and careful planning can help to provide a practical, cheerful kitchen. For most families the designing of a kitchen is a long-time process. The plan is revised many times before it begins to promise satisfying results. The completed kitchen must give the homemaker a convenient and pleasant place to work and must provide for other activities which the family expect to carry on there. Having thought out the problem with reference to family needs and budget, you may get excellent help with the detailed planning. University and government services will send free, or at a very small cost, plans made by their specialists, scaled to suit any budget. Some household magazines carry good kitchen plans, pictured as well as diagrammed, with discussion of materials, equipment, and costs. Commercial firms which manufacture kitchen equipment often send out kitchen plans, some provided with cutouts of equipment which can be moved about on their floor plan or on one of your own made in scale with the cutouts.

Keep in mind not only the present needs of the family but those likely to develop. It is wise to plan the purchase of essential equipment of the size and quality to last. Space can be left for additions toward the ideally equipped kitchen. Work with a good floor plan, and cutouts of desired equipment will show what can be done. The kitchen can grow with the budget until you have the kitchen you planned.

The Rearranged Kitchen

One of the advantages of remodeling your present kitchen is that you know what im-provements are needed. The inconvenience of present working arrangements can be corrected. True, you must work within the present walls, but one of three good kitchen plans may be possible by a not-too-difficult or costly rearrangement of large equipment. In the L-shaped kitchen the grouping is along two adjoining walls, leaving the other two free for serving or other activities.

A U-shaped plan is formed when work centers follow continuously along three sides of the kitchen. An important advantage of the U-shape plan is that through traffic is eliminated from the work areas. The rectangular U plan, which leaves a long, narrow space in the center, is desirable. In an especially large room, a U-shaped arrangement which uses only a portion of the floor space may be preferable. Work centers may be grouped on two adjoining walls with the third side of the U created by a low arrangement of base cabinets, or a counter for serving meals, extending out from the second wall. The space not occupied by food units is ideal for play or dining. (See the U plan for a kitchen, page 94.)

The third type of kitchen has its equipment compactly arranged along one wall for the convenience of the worker in receiving food, preparing it, and cleaning up. The one-wall kitchen grouping may be best suited to a small family.

Discuss with your mother what is needed and plan how it can be accomplished. Work from the present kitchen toward a more attractive and convenient one. Though structural changes are costly, an added window, improved artificial lighting over work surfaces, or a different wall and floor treatment may be managed on the budget.

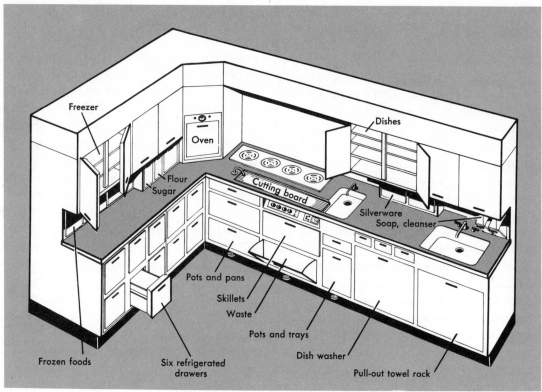

Labels on the image:
Freezer
Oven
Dishes
Flour
Sugar
Cutting board
Silverware
Soap, cleanser
Pots and pans
Skillets
Waste
Pots and trays
Dish washer
Frozen foods
Six refrigerated drawers
Pull-out towel rack

Motion and Time Study Laboratory, Purdue University

An L-shaped kitchen · Notice the efficient arrangement of equipment. The oven at counter level is a great convenience. The position of the top burners at the back of the counter aids safety and releases front space for a cutting board

Motion and Time Study Laboratory, Purdue University

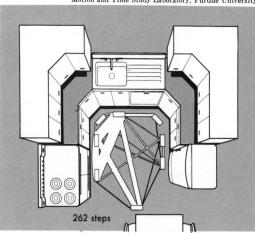

262 steps

A U-shaped kitchen · All the equipment and supplies in this kitchen are arranged along three walls. The width of the different paths across the floor shows the relative number of trips which the homemaker has to make in the preparation of an ordinary dinner. The rectangles in the plan indicate the standing areas most frequently used in getting a meal

Windows and Lighting

Kitchen windows should be located with reference to the equipment which must fit under them, to the placing of wall cabinets, and to work spaces that require light. Above work spaces they not only admit light but may provide a pleasant view. Windows overlooking outdoor play areas enable a busy homemaker to watch over small children while she works. Any undesirable view can be shut out by using opaque structural glass blocks. A kitchen in a corner of the house offers the best arrangement of windows for both light and ventilation. It is especially important that hot air and cooking odors escape. Windows which open from the top are helpful, since warm air tends to rise.

In some kitchens artificial light is needed, even during the day. Fluorescent lighting is considered good because it greatly resembles daylight. Incandescent light may be supplied by a bracket or droplight shaded and placed so that the bulb is not visible to the eye but gives direct light on the working surface. Frosted and shaded electric bulbs help to prevent eyestrain. A semitransparent globe for a light placed near the ceiling will prevent shadows and give a diffused light. Lights placed between wall and base cabinets furnish light for counters. Good ventilation and lighting add to the safety as well as to the convenience and comfort of the kitchen.

Walls and Floors

Wall and floor coverings are chosen for their attractiveness, comfort, and safety. Whatever the materials, beautiful colors can be selected to give your kitchen warmth and charm. Enamel paint is a desirable finish for a kitchen. If walls must be papered, washable wallpapers are best. Tiles, plastics, or glass bricks are ideal. They are durable, attractive, and easy to clean. Other choices for a kitchen wall covering are wall linoleum, plywood, wallboard, and wood paneling.

A kitchen floor should, first of all, be comfortable to stand on. Inlaid cushion-backed linoleum or tiles of linoleum, rubber, plastic, or cork are satisfactory for this. Avoid any slippery surface, for it can be hazardous. Secondly, a housewife chooses flooring that will be an attractive base for the color scheme of the kitchen. For ease in keeping clean, a kitchen floor should have a surface which will not absorb grease or water, or show stains. Printed linoleum cleans more easily and wears longer when protected with varnish or linoleum paint. Inlaid linoleum retains its appearance through long wear. A wooden floor should be treated with hot linseed oil and painted and waxed.

Suiting the Kitchen to Family Needs

A small, compact kitchen large enough to hold only the necessary equipment is limited to the preparation of food. A larger kitchen may allow space for meals. A large family whose life is centered in the home may need a kitchen large enough to allow for various activities without confusion.

The Small Kitchen

A small kitchen may be a model of convenience. With light cool background colors that make it seem more than its actual size, with a compact and convenient arrangement of necessary equipment, and with other space properly utilized for storage, it becomes a

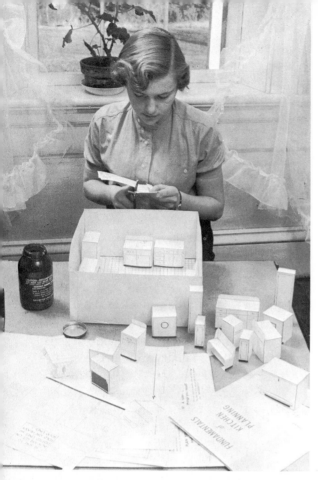

Using a kitchen-planning kit · Here a part of a box has been cut away and a floor plan made to scale has been inserted. On this floor plan, which is divided into foot squares, the various pieces of permanent kitchen equipment are being arranged. By this method a clearer idea can be obtained than by the use of a floor plan with the position of equipment penciled in. Arranging the model and rearranging it as often as the family's ideas change will prevent serious disappointment and expensive alterations after the kitchen is completed

satisfactory workshop for one person. It may have a drop-leaf table which can be used for serving one or two people. Some apartment kitchens are no more than a nook in the wall, hidden behind sliding doors.

96

The needed equipment is there, but you must be precise in returning articles to their assigned places before taking out others. A careful dovetailing of tasks is required to work efficiently in a very small kitchen.

The Kitchen for a Family of Three or Four

The needs of most families are best met by a kitchen large enough to allow some meals to be eaten there. There must be room enough for at least two people, perhaps mother and daughter, to work together comfortably in preparing meals. Wall space must allow for efficient grouping of large equipment and for storage spaces within easy reach for small equipment and supplies. It should easily accommodate large equipment, such as a 7- or 8-cubic-foot refrigerator, a 40-inch range, and a double-well sink. There should be space for wall and base cabinets which, besides storage, will provide 6 to 8 feet of working surface. This kitchen should accommodate a table and chairs.

This larger kitchen will have room for many conveniences not possible in the very small one. A work space dropped low enough for comfortable sitting may have a telephone and other needs for planning menus and ordering supplies. Many tasks will be lightened here. The stool or chair, which pulls from space directly beneath, will provide relief from work which would have to be done standing at higher work spaces. The stool may also be used at an ironing board. Cabinets can be larger than in the small kitchen, with step shelves for spices and for dishes, and racks or other devices for covers and trays. Much time is saved if equipment need not be stacked, and there is less breakage and other damage. Storage of canned and packaged foods in quantity is possible in this kitchen, saving shopping time and increasing convenience. Unquestionably for a family of three or four the larger kitchen can be a satisfactory functional part of the home. When you help to plan or to remodel a house, you should consider the adaptability of the kitchen to the demands which will be made upon it by the family.

The Combination Kitchen

In many homes, the kitchen has become the main workshop and the family center because much of the homemaker's work is there. It may have been well planned to care for the needs of a growing family, including play or study space and provision for hobbies or any other activities more appropriate here than elsewhere in the house. If the activities outgrow the original plan, such a kitchen may be extended by a porch, a terrace, or a play space on the adjacent lawn or patio, which the homemaker can supervise from the kitchen. If a kitchen is to provide a play area for small children, it must have space for a playpen and for suitable toys. The safety of the children at play and of the homemaker stepping swiftly about her work can be assured by keeping the areas well separated. A place in the kitchen for wraps and books might be convenient. Perhaps you can help plan a storage arrangement for toys, books, and wraps.

You and your family may find the kitchen the best place in the house for some of your parties. Refreshments are easily served there. Games can be played, a kitchen radio and record player will get much use, and the floor covering will not be marred by dancing.

There may be advantages in moving the laundry from the basement to the kitchen or to an adjoining utility room. A complete

In this compact kitchen the cook can work efficiently. It's only a few steps from refrigerator to stove to sink and dishwasher. An attractive table may be used for breakfast and for other purposes during the day

Youngstown Kitchens

laundry unit including the washer, dryer, and ironer, when part of the kitchen, will save steps. An all-purpose kitchen may also be a good place for sewing.

The use of kitchens, designed of materials which will stand hard wear, cuts down wear on the less durable furnishings in other parts of the home.

The Farm Kitchen

You may know farm families that enjoy gathering in the kitchen for sewing, playing games, studying, and other activities. Such a kitchen should have 150 to 200 square feet of floor space for the above activities and those connected with the work of the farm. Since the activities relating to farm life should not interfere with preparing meals, extra work surfaces, a separate sink, special storage areas for supplies and for coats and boots, and perhaps a lavatory may be wise additions. Thus a utility area in or near the farm kitchen may provide for activities such as canning, caring for eggs, and laundering.

L-type farm kitchen plus workroom and washroom · Placing the sink across the corner reduces dimensions of the L arrangement. Generous space for meals is provided. Notice how efficiently equipment and storage space have been grouped. The shower stall in the washroom is one of the essentials for a farm family

Adapted from United States Department of Agriculture

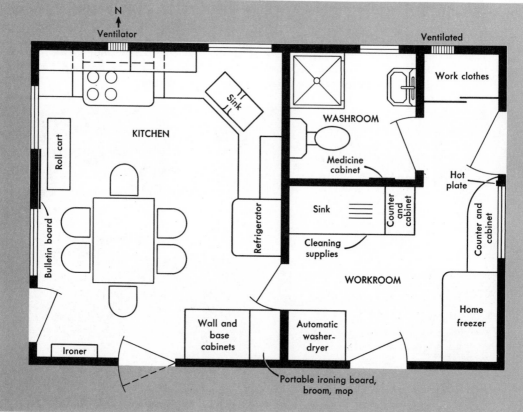

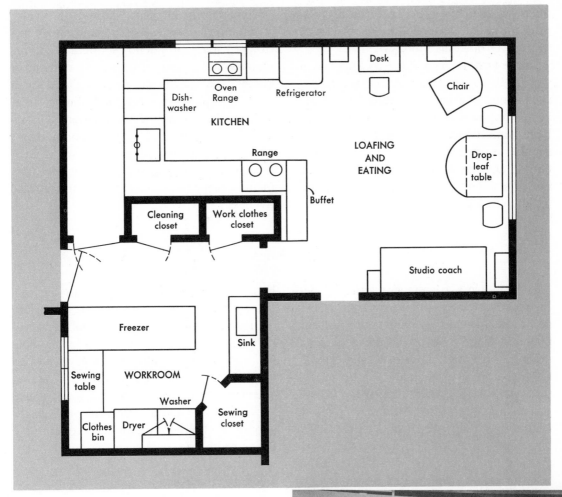

A kitchen for cooking, working, and relaxing ·
Study the plan to discover how carefully this
kitchen has been planned, not only for the preparation of food but for comfortable living. Here the
busy homemaker can relax while she keeps an eye
on the preparation of a meal or while she is wait-
ing for clothes to be washed or dried in the workroom. The combination of the laundry and the
work of food freezing is a particularly good one.
Notice that the workroom, as well as the kitchen,
has its own sink. This, of course, is essential for
the preparation of vegetables, fruits, and other
foods for the freezer

General Electric Co.

Such an area may also serve as a storage place for cured meats, flours, sugar, potatoes, or reserves of canned foods.

In the farm kitchen, large cooking utensils and a 10- to 15-cubic-foot refrigerator are usually needed, since food must be served to farm employees as well as to the family. A large home freezer will help to care for the supplies produced on the farm. As the large farm kitchen serves many purposes, duplication of small equipment needed for activities in different areas will save time and steps.

Some farm kitchens, lacking a utility room, may make use of a pantry as extra storage space for food supplies and for utensils and linens. In some modern farm homes, the pantry has been replaced by a counter between kitchen and dining area, making the serving of food easier. Dishes and other equipment may be stored there. The accompanying diagram shows a farm kitchen and utility area with modern equipment arranged for convenience and attractiveness.

Organizing Work Centers

Kitchen work centers are arranged with the idea that all equipment for a task should be in one area. A receiving center for supplies should be close to the refrigerator and other storage space. Utensils and supplies for preparing a meal should be stored near the work surfaces where they are to be used in cooking, and those surfaces should be next to the range, making a meal-preparation unit. The sink is the center of the cleaning-up unit. The serving space and table for eating make another center. Organization into well-equipped centers results in simplification of the work to be done in the kitchen, shortening the time and reducing the labor.

Regardless of the size and shape of a kitchen or of the simplicity of its equipment, its arrangement into well-organized work centers is important.

Food Receiving and Storage

Food is received, sorted, cared for, and, as far as possible, stored in this center. Some provisions go to the sink for care and are then placed in the refrigerator. Other items may be stored in cabinets, in the home freezer, in the pantry, or in the cellar. If the center is carefully arranged and equipped, a minimum number of steps will be taken in going from the counter or table for sorting to the sink for washing and to the refrigerator and other storage areas. A wheeled cart or trays will save many steps. If there is no sink, a table with pans, water supply, and disposal container could serve the purpose.

Food Preparation

Refrigerator, sink, cabinets, counter space and range compose the food-preparation center. It is convenient to have ample storage space and counter area near the refrigerator for making salads, mixing cakes, and preparing meats. Staple foods and utensils should be stored according to their use in food preparation. As an illustration, baking powder, soda, and cream of tartar are all leavening agents and belong together; sweetenings, such as sugar, sirups, and honey, belong together. Place together the beaters and choppers and the bowls with which they are used. Measuring spoons and cups should be within easy reach. The convenience of

100

An attractive and efficient kitchen · Good counter space, large cupboards, and
carefully designed shelf space make this a pleasant kitchen to work in

having supplies together in a center is worth the work of rearrangement.

Cooking

Locating the range near the sink and refrigerator saves unnecessary steps. Counter space should be immediately adjoining. Hot foods can be served more conveniently if the range is not too far from the dining center. There should be some cabinets near the range to store cooking utensils and seasonings. Cabinets and drawers for these may be above or below counter space, with dishes stored nearby for the serving of cooked foods.

Cleaning

In addition to being used for cleaning vegetables and peeling fruits, the sink and adjacent counters form a cleanup unit. All cleaning supplies should be conveniently placed. Powdered cleaning agents may be kept in decorated cans, which add a pleasing note of color to the center. Soaps, detergents, polishes, and scouring pads should be arranged conveniently. Cleaning utensils, such as brushes, scrapers, and peelers, are easy to find if kept in a sectional box or hung in the storage area beneath the sink. Cooking utensils washed there should be stored near the food-preparation center. Dishes washed and drained there are usually stored in cabinets near the range. Planning can improve the arrangement of utensils and supplies and save much waste motion. Good management here means that you will spend less time in the kitchen.

Serving

Meals will be more pleasant and relaxing if this center is out of the way of work centers and is large enough for comfort. If located close to windows, the area will seem more spacious and problems of light and ventilation will be solved. In a small kitchen there may be room only for a table which opens down from the wall, and which can be returned to its place when the meal is cleared, thus freeing needed floor space. In a larger kitchen, a wide peninsula bar, a partitioned counter, or a table with chairs may be used. A drop-leaf table may be substituted for the dinette table if floor space is needed. Whatever the space and equipment in the dining area, variety in color and design may be used on the walls, in window decoration, and in the linen, china, and glassware (see Chapter 25). The eating center should be so inviting that the family and friends will enjoy meals there.

Selecting Efficient Kitchen Equipment

Many new homes are built so that the kitchen walls will be of the correct length to allow the pieces of equipment to fit exactly into compact groupings. The variety in size and kind of equipment makes it possible to introduce new equipment even into old kitchens without making structural changes. Cabinets, sinks, ranges, and refrigerators should be purchased only after careful investigation. Each piece of equipment should be examined for mechanical efficiency, durability, cost of installation, and, in the case of ranges and refrigerators, cost of operation.

Large Equipment

Cabinets—Both wood and metal cabinets, portable or built-in, are available. Selection

102

EFFICIENT STORAGE OF EQUIPMENT

Efficient storage increases ease and speed of mixing jobs. Notice flour and sugar bins to replace canisters. Above, pans are filed vertically. Measuring spoons and cups are readily accessible. At the left the wall cupboard has revolving shelves. Staples in daily use occupy the outer part of the shelves, leaving room near the center for reserve supplies. Notice also the arrangement of knives, which are both conveniently and safely arranged

Storing bowls and pans efficiently · Place mixing bowls, small pots and pans in easily sliding drawers. Here the backs of the drawers are higher than the front to keep the pans or bowls from sliding off

will depend upon whether the dwelling is owned or rented, upon wall space, upon comparative cost, and upon suitability of the cabinet to the purpose intended. Wooden cabinets, especially the built-in type, may be more expensive than metal ones because of the workmanship required. Enamel painted surfaces are desirable for wooden cabinets because they are easy to clean and durable. Natural wood finishes are also attractive. For families who rent houses or apartments, portable cabinets that may be rearranged easily and inexpensively are recommended. They should be of good material and durable in construction.

Either portable or built-in cabinets are more desirable when they have shelves of good width and depth, pull-out boards and pastry boards, and easy-pulling drawers of convenient sizes. Standard cabinets may be chosen in the width desired. There are several special types: corner wall, corner base, base ends, vegetable storage. Cabinet doors should be narrow to avoid inconvenience in opening and the hazard of a wide swing. Sliding doors of wood, metal, or opaque glass may be more expensive than swinging doors but are desirable where space is at a premium. Cabinets may have rollup doors of wood or metal. All doors should be tested for durability and ease of operation.

Since base-cabinet tops are work surfaces, a comfortable working height is important. This should be determined before the cabinet is purchased. The standard cabinet height is 36 inches, but cabinets 30 and 32 inches in height are available for the shorter person. Equipment that is too high may be recessed in the floor; for the tall person, cabinets may be elevated by a platform. The range and sink may also be elevated. Base cabinets should have toe space

for the comfort of the worker. Knee space should be provided at surfaces where work will be done sitting down.

The top surface of base cabinets, counters, or tables should be of an easy-to-clean, non-absorbent material. Resistance to warping and cracking and to temperatures must be considered as well as price. Linoleum makes a satisfactory work surface if it is cemented to the wood and if the edges are protected by a molding. Linoleum is attractive, easily cleaned, resilient, and reasonably durable. Hot pans will, however, damage it. Pressed wood treated with a protective finish in various colors may also be used as covering. Wood surfaces may be filled with linseed oil or oil stain to make them easier to clean, or they may be treated with waterproof, heat-resistant varnish. Other satisfactory surface materials are hardwood, composition material, enameled iron, formica, rubber tile and tile, monel metal, and stainless steel.

The Sink—A kitchen sink is a great labor-saver. The market affords a wide selection of many types to fit the needs of every family. A choice may be made of a sink complete with its own storage cabinet, a sink built into cabinets, or a sink hung on the wall. The advantage of the accompanying cabinet should not be overlooked.

Sinks are available in standard lengths with one or two basins, and with single left or right, or double drainboards. Most sinks are made of porcelain or porcelain enamel. Those of monel metal and stainless steel are expensive but last a lifetime. The one-piece sink with its splash back, basin, and drainboard all cast from one piece is the most desirable. Faucets made of metal do not break as readily as porcelain ones. Some models have recessed faucets, knee or foot controls, and a spray with special nozzles for cleaning vegetables or pots and pans. A sink equipped

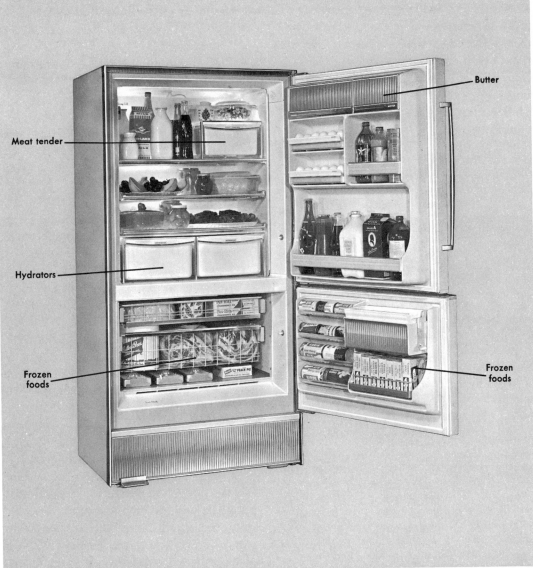

Meat tender

Hydrators

Frozen foods

Butter

Frozen foods

Frigidaire

A modern refrigerator is designed to care for different kinds of food which should be stored at different temperatures. Here the freezer for frozen foods is a separate compartment at the bottom. Its door contains an ice ejector, which pops out cubes at a touch. In the main part of the refrigerator is a meat tender, having its own individual chilling system, in which fresh meats can be stored for several days without freezing. Fresh fruits and vegetables are kept in the hydrators. The storage door has a special compartment for butter, to keep it "spreadable," and a utility compartment for cheese and snacks. Hidden from view is a mechanism which prevents frost from forming, thereby making defrosting unnecessary

105

with a garbage-disposal unit and an electric dishwasher is a modern convenience which aids in sanitation and saves time and work. The garbage disposal, attached to the sink drain, has a mechanism which electrically grinds the garbage. It is flushed down the drain. The process is quick, easy, sanitary. Before selecting a sink consider the following points:

1. Size and style to fit family needs and floor and wall space

2. Comfortable height for the worker,

POTS AND PANS

Top row: 8–10-quart kettle; 4-quart saucepan; 6–8-quart saucepot

Bottom row: 2-quart saucepan; 1-quart saucepan; 3-quart saucepan. The large 8–10-quart kettle is useful for making soups or stews in large quantity, cooking a whole ham, or blanching vegetables and fruits for canning and freezing. The other utensils are used for general cooking

Roasting pans · The roasting pan on the left with cover is used for meats that require long cooking to tenderize. The open roaster on the right is used when a rich brown crust is desired

United States Department of Agriculture

with toe space under the cabinet and a narrow rim at the front of the sink

3. Good hardware—well-located faucets and drain pull

4. Sink and drainboards resistant to stains, scratches, chips, heat, and acids

5. Cost as a long-time investment

6. Color to fit your kitchen scheme

The Range—Choice of a kitchen range is usually determined by the fuel to be used, cost of installation and maintenance, the cooking space available, and the preference of the family. A few decades ago the kitchen range burned wood or coal, and might be replaced in the summer by a kerosene range. These are still useful on remote farms and in camps. But today bottled gas and rural electrification have put modern ranges in farm kitchens. In city homes either natural gas or electricity is supplied.

Ranges are easier to clean when the cooking top and the back splash are constructed in one piece. This prevents food from collecting in crevices. Some models have removable burners to aid cleaning. If the range surface is of porcelain enamel, it should be acid-resistant.

A range should always be well insulated on all sides of the oven and the broiler, and it should bear a stamp of approval from a testing laboratory. Many modern ranges include excellent features, such as automatic ignition and control of top burners and oven (including safety devices), an electric eye, timing clocks, a special lamp to help banish kitchen odors, a divided oven, a built-in barbecue attachment, a built-in French-fryer unit, glass in the oven door, lights on the top of the range and inside the oven.

The very newest range is electronic, using high frequency radio energy, or microwaves, for the fastest cooking yet known. A cake bakes in 3 minutes, potatoes in 8 minutes,

and a five-pound beef roast in 30 minutes. In the oven the only heat produced is in the food. The air in the range remains at room temperature. Non-metallic baking utensils must be used to permit the microwaves to penetrate into the food. A high-speed browning element is used during the last few minutes of electronic cooking to brown the foods on the outside. Experiments are being carried on to refine electronic ranges and produce them at lower cost.

The Refrigerator—Mechanical refrigerators are available in common household sizes varying from 4 to 12 cubic feet. Keeping within the budget but remembering that this is an important purchase, the family will select a refrigerator that covers their needs, fits the kitchen space reserved for it, and operates on the fuel (electricity, gas, or kerosene) available. If the budget does not allow a mechanical refrigerator, a modern icebox will be satisfactory. Fully insulated iceboxes, carefully designed to permit efficient circulation of air, are available today.

Refrigerators are judged by the sturdiness of the cabinet, exterior and interior finishes, resistance to stains, ease in cleaning and defrosting, and size and convenience of the storage compartments. There are many interior conveniences in modern refrigerators. Among them are covered vegetable containers, compartments with low temperatures for meats and butter, and freezers, as the picture on page 105 shows.

The Home Freezer—If the kitchen can accommodate a home freezer next to the refrigerator instead of in the basement or in a utility room, many steps will be saved. The home freezer may have a single compartment for freezing and storage or it may be equipped with both storage and freezing compartments.

Owners of home freezers can often use the processing services of local locker plants. A side of beef or a bushel of peas may be prepared at the plant for the home freezer. The home freezer is valuable equipment if foods are home-produced or can be bought in season for future use, or if work is to be simplified through preparing foods in advance of their use.

Small Equipment

Pots, pans, and tools can be purchased in attractive colors and designs and in many different materials. Although electrical appliances are replacing some of the older-type articles, most housewives still find a need for a Dutch oven, hand beaters, flameproof glass or metal coffee makers, and saucepans and casseroles for oven cooking. Tools or utensils which serve several purposes are most practical. A flameproof skillet with removable handle can double as a baking pan or casserole; a double boiler can be two saucepans. Necessary utensils should be purchased first, and others added only as real need for them is felt.

Materials and Care of Small Kitchen Equipment

Small equipment for the kitchen is commonly manufactured from a variety of materials. None of these is superior in every respect to the others but each has some outstanding qualities.

Electric Equipment

As wiring for electricity has become general, electric roasters, coffee makers, toasters, waffle bakers, and mixers have come into common use. Electric equipment, when

BASIC TOOLS AND UTENSILS

TEA KETTLE
MIXING BOWLS
FLOUR SIFTER
SAUCEPANS

2 covered tightly.......2 to 4 qt.
1 small...............1 to 2 pt.
1 double boiler.........1½ to 2 qt.
1 pressure............4 to 6 qt.

SKILLETS (frying pans)

1 large covered........10 inch
   or twin skillet
1 small...............6 to 7 inch

OVEN UTENSILS

1 large casserole with cover,
   or individual casseroles
1 muffin pan.......6 to 8 to 12 cups
1 pie pan........9 inch
2 layer-cake pans..8 x 1¼ inches, or
         9 x 1½ inches
1 square cake pan..8 x 8 x 2 inches
1 oblong cake pan 10 x 6 x 1½ inches
1 tube pan...10 x 4 inches
1 loaf pan ...8½ x 4½ x 2½ inches
1 baking sheet
1 roasting pan with rack

TOOLS

1 paring knife.....3½-inch blade
1 large knife.......5- to 7-inch blade
2 or 3 mixing spoons
2 long-handled cooking spoons
1 long-handled cooking fork
1 spatula
1 rotary or whisk beater
1 rolling pin
1 kneading board or canvas
1 can opener, hand or wall
1 potato masher
Measuring spoons and cups

SUGGESTED ADDITIONS

Dutch oven with cover

Wire rack for cooling food

Juice extractor

Graters (fine to coarse)

Sink strainer

Dish-drain racks

Saucepans (covered tightly),
   4- to 6-quart

Pancake griddle

Salad molds

Coffee maker

Meat grinder

Meat board

Saw or small cleaver

Electric mixer

Vegetable parer or potato
   peeler

Food thermometer (candy, meat)

Kitchen shears

Lipped ladle for soup or gravy

Tongs for ice cubes or hot foods

Cookie and doughnut cutters

Rubber scraper for cleaning

Food mill, 6-inch diameter

placed conveniently and used wisely, can be a great time- and labor-saver. Each new appliance is accompanied by an instruction book, which tells how to operate and care for it. Paying careful attention to the instructions will save money and time. It is wise to buy appliances only from reliable, authorized dealers and to request a home demonstration. Upon delivery of the appliance, find out whom to call for service.

A *roaster oven* is a good supplementary cooking appliance. It is portable and economical for small dinners.

Coffee makers come in drip, vacuum, or percolator styles. Some coffee makers are automatically controlled.

Waffle bakers that are automatic give uniform products because the grids are heated to the right temperature. Some are a combination of waffle baker and grill.

Toasters which are automatic are time-savers and last for years if well cared for.

Electric mixers reduce the time and effort of preparing foods which require beating. Some have attachments for grinding, chopping, and juicing. A good mixer will have several speeds for different types of mixing and power enough to mix stiff doughs. Rustproof mixers with attachments free from dirt-collecting crevices are desirable.

Electric equipment encourages cooking at the serving table, where attractive toasters, waffle bakers, coffee makers, or grills may occupy a place of honor.

Caring for the Kitchen and Large Equipment

Your mother has learned that consistent cleaning and disposal of waste are required to keep the kitchen clean and orderly. Her well-worked-out plan includes seasonal as well as daily cleaning. You are already acquainted with the daily clearing up after meal preparation and you, of course, put the kitchen in order after your party there. You should learn also the processes of periodic cleaning. Walls, woodwork, and floors, should be washed with hot water and a good cleansing agent. A cloth or sponge is best for oil-painted or enameled walls and woodwork. You must rub hard enough to remove the dirt, then wipe each small area dry with a clean, absorbent cloth. The water should be changed often enough to produce a bright, clean finish. Cleaning from the bottom of a wall up avoids streaking the surface. Any water that runs down the clean surface must be carefully wiped off with a clean cloth. Papered walls may be cleaned with commercial doughlike products, or, if they are glazed, they may be washed. Floors may be washed with a long-handled mop or brush. Applicators are available for waxing a floor. If spilled water and food are always mopped up immediately, floors will be kept in better condition.

Care of Large Equipment

To give its best service over a long period, large equipment must receive consistent care. Your best use of gas or electric refrigerators or ranges depends on operating them properly and on keeping them in condition according to manufacturer's instructions.

The Refrigerator—Care of the refrigerator consists of defrosting with general cleaning. Even if your refrigerator defrosts itself, the weekly cleaning is still needed. Clean the inside of the box and the racks and ice trays

MATERIALS AND USES	ADVANTAGES AND DISADVANTAGES
Aluminum Top-of-range utensils, ovenware, measuring and mixing equipment	● Conducts heat fast, is lightweight, durable (depends on grade), easy to clean ○ Discolors with some foods, darkens with alkalies, does not hold heat
Steel Knives, spatula, shears	● Sharp cutting edge if well tempered
Steel, copper-clad Top-of-range utensils, kettles	● Adds decorative touch ○ Expensive
Steel, stainless Top-of-range utensils, cutlery, sinks	● Does not tarnish or corrode ○ Expensive
Enamelware, sheet steel coated with enamel Top-of-range and oven utensils, mixing equipment, pitchers, ladles	● Not affected by alkalies or acids, easily cleaned, moderate cost ○ Chips easily, cracks in high baking temperatures
Glassware Heat-resistant ovenware and flameware in a wide variety of utensils and measuring and mixing equipment	● Not affected by acids or alkalies, easy to clean, attractive to cook in and serve from ○ Breaks with quick changes of temperature Not easily handled
Earthenware Mixing bowls, oven dishes, bean pots, teapots, crocks	● Resistant to acids and alkalies, easy to clean, does not scratch, holds heat, attractive to cook in and serve from ○ Chips and breaks rather easily
Cast iron Top-of-range utensils, corn-stick and waffle bakers, Dutch ovens, skillets, griddles	● Not affected by acids and alkalies, moderate cost ○ Heavy, rusts easily
Tinware Mixing equipment, ovenware, cookie cutters, graters	● Conducts heat fast, lightweight, inexpensive ○ Tarnished by heat and acids
Plastic Measuring, mixing and storing equipment	● Lightweight, attractive, colorful ○ Loses shape in high temperatures
Wood Bowls, spoons, mallets, boards	● Lightweight, inexpensive ○ Cracks if stored moist

DESIRED STRUCTURAL QUALITIES

1 Pans of size and shape to fit heating unit

2 Handles sturdy, of length and shape to be grasped easily, attached for correct balance; two handles on large kettles, not bails

3 Lips which pour well, preferably on two sides of pan or bowl

4 Flat bottoms and straight sides, lids tightly fitted on saucepans

5 Smooth edges and seams; few seams, or of one piece (muffin or loaf pans)

6 Rounded corners on all ovenware; baking sheet with one edge upturned for easy grasping

7 Steel, tempered to take and hold cutting edge; blades and handles proportioned for comfortable use

8 Flexible steel spatulas of correct length and width

9 Sturdy graters with drilled rather than punched holes for easy cleaning

10 Correct design for tools for specific purpose: curved blade of grapefruit knife, slotted spoon for creaming, six-tined fork for blending, saw-edged bread knife and steak knives, tongs and pan lifters with firm grip

with hot water and a cleaning agent. Rinse and dry. Occasionally, wash the inside with a solution of 1 teaspoon of baking soda per quart of water as an aid to removing odors. Clean the frozen-food compartment as instructed by the manufacturer. In daily care, wipe up spilled food immediately and keep the exterior clean with a dampened cloth. A refrigerator cooled by ice is cared for by the same methods.

Put only clean containers and clean food into the box. Wash milk bottles, fruits, and vegetables thoroughly before storing them. Follow the manufacturer's directions carefully in the use of the refrigerator.

The Range—Grates, burners, and porcelain enamel parts of *gas ranges* should be wiped daily with a damp cloth. Grates can be lifted for an occasional cleaning of the pan below. For a thorough cleaning, scrub the burners in hot water, using a cleaning agent and a stiff brush. Rinse and dry the grates before replacing them in the range. *Electric-range* units will burn spilled foods. When the unit cools it may be cleaned with a stiff brush and fine steel wool. The burners of *kerosene ranges* must be kept clean to prevent smoking. Wicks should be brushed at least once a week. They require frequent replacement.

The film that accumulates in a range oven can be removed by scrubbing with a cleaning agent and hot water. An occasional use of fine steel wool may be necessary. Broiler pans should be cleaned after each use. Pour off the fat, wipe with soft paper, scrub with a cleanser and stiff brush, using hot water. The lining of the broiler oven needs an occasional scrubbing.

Ashes and soot must be removed periodically from *wood and coal ranges*. Iron surfaces of the range may be cleaned with steel wool and washed with hot water and a

Caring for the refrigerator · Some modern refrigerators do not require defrosting. Others must be defrosted only once or twice a year. After defrosting they should be carefully cleaned

Care of Small Equipment

The small equipment in an efficient kitchen may represent nearly as great an investment as the large equipment. That it be conveniently arranged and in good condition when needed is essential. With proper care kitchen utensils and tools will give excellent service for many years. Every meal requires the use of bowls, spoons, egg beaters, paring knives, and many other small pieces of equipment, as well as griddles, coffee makers, saucepans, and mixers. The chapter on "Snacks," pages 22–32, gives information on cleaning up after the meal. Electric equipment should be cared for according to the manufacturer's directions. The booklets should be kept in a convenient place and reviewed now and then for directions on cleaning and for replacement of parts which wear out. Repair of electric equipment is expensive but the expense can be kept to a minimum by good care and by making simple replacements at home.

Other small kitchen equipment needing care consists of dish towels, dishcloths, pan holders, mops, and dustcloths. Here cleanliness and order are most important. Materials must be able to stand hard wear and repeated laundering without losing body or color. You should know current laundry methods for keeping kitchen linens clean and attractive. Of necessity, special cleaning agents and modern processes of washing and drying will replace the older methods of boiling linens or hanging them in the sunshine. Before storing mops, cleaning cloths, or dustcloths, make sure that they are dry and clean. Keep all equipment ready for use. Good management in the kitchen requires consistent care of all its equipment so that it may have long usefulness with a minimum of expense, repair, or replacement.

Because of your interest in the home

cleaning agent and dried quickly before rusting begins. As a preventive of rust and to improve appearance, polish may be applied.

If you will learn the following good habits in the use of the range, you will avoid much difficulty:

1. Control the spilling and splashing of food.

2. Wipe up spilled food before it hardens or dulls the surface.

3. Prevent foods from boiling over by using a large enough pan and centering it over the heat unit.

4. Follow manufacturer's directions for operating ranges.

kitchen you·have found ways of improving it as an important family center and are trusted with the use of its equipment and tools. You are aware that careless handling of equipment is damaging, even dangerous; that intelligent use and care protects and preserves its appearance. You share your mother's pleasure and pride in working in an efficient kitchen.

¶ Understanding:

1. What is one way in which you can make work in your kitchen easier, pleasanter, and less time-consuming?

2. What facilities could be wisely provided in your kitchen for family activities?

3. What kinds of wall and floor finishes would you like for your kitchen? Why?

4. What features would your family desire in a kitchen range?

5. What suggestions have you for reorganizing a work center in your home kitchen? How would the work be simplified?

6. What are the advantages of aluminum utensils? glass? stainless steel? earthenware?

7. What structural characteristics in utensils promote safe handling and easy cleaning?

8. What could you do to keep the linen supply for your kitchen in good condition?

¶ Planning:

1. With the help of your family, plan an improvement in your kitchen to save motions in work; to add to kitchen attractiveness.

2. From a sketch of your kitchen show how equipment can be better arranged in work centers. Suggest ways to achieve more effective lighting; more effective ventilation.

3. Find pictures in magazines to aid you in planning a kitchen which would meet the needs of your family.

4. Plan ways of extending a small kitchen to accommodate activities other than food preparation.

¶ Practicing and Evaluating:

1. Share in the preparation of breakfast for your family. What changes in your kitchen would make meal preparation more simple?

2. Sketch a kitchen floor plan to include laundry equipment. Check your placement of this equipment for convenience.

3. Time dishwashing in the school kitchen. Suggest changes in the location of utensils and supplies, and time the activity again.

4. Relocate a piece of kitchen equipment for convenience so that it will be used more often. What are the advantages of the new location?

5. Evaluate the placement of frequently used articles in your kitchen cabinets. Make suggestions for their relocation.

¶ Reading Further:

Better Kitchen Storage, Bulletin 47 (1961). Pacific Northwest Cooperative Extension Service, Oregon, Washington.

Handbook of Household Equipment Terminology (1960). American Home Economics Association, 1600 Twentieth Street, N. W., Washington 9, D. C.

Home Freezers—Their Selection and Use, Bulletin 48 (1961). U. S. Department of Agriculture, Washington, D. C.

Improve Your Kitchen Storage, Bulletin 365 (1959). Michigan State University Extension Service, East Lansing, Michigan.

Kitchen Cabinets for Convenience and Appearance, FS–855 (1960). Iowa State University Extension Service, Ames, Iowa.

PEET, LOUISE J., *Young Homemakers' Equipment Guide*. Iowa State University Press, Ames, Iowa.

Shopper's Guide to U. S. Grades for Food, Home and Garden Bulletin 58 (1961). U. S. Department of Agriculture, Washington, D. C.

Monkmeyer Press Photo Service, (Hilda Bijur)

Planned spending

you will learn: How to spend food money wisely;
How to use food economically

A hundred years ago the rural family went to a small store that carried general merchandise, to trade eggs or other produce for sugar, coffee, and other staples. Very probably the choice of food products was limited and the money allotted for food purchases, scarce. Most of the food eaten in those days was produced at home. Nowadays, changes in industry and in the home have brought about a change in the purchasing habits of nearly all families. We buy much of what we eat and are constantly having to decide what to buy, and how to use the product to the best advantage.

114

By careful planning it is possible to spend wisely and save money. The majority of families must extend moderate incomes to supply their needs, and planned spending for food is essential to ensure that the requirements of daily nutrition are met.

When families make their spending plans, they must allow an adequate amount of money for food. Generally more than one-fourth of the income is necessary, but the required amount varies slightly with family needs, the availability of foods, and current prices. Many families could reduce the amount spent for food by planning and buying carefully and by eliminating waste.

Consumers are buyers of products and services. They are concerned with getting the most for their money with a minimum of time and effort. The homemaker, spending a high per cent of the family income, has a special responsibility; she must learn to plan wisely and to spend the family food dollars with utmost care.

In planning a food budget, you will have to estimate the amount to allow for the different types of food. A regular record of how much food was bought and how much it cost will help in making buying plans in the future.

What to Buy

Knowing what to buy is one of your mother's most challenging problems because the many grades and qualities of food vary in cost. For some purposes, the higher qualities of food should be chosen; for others, the lower qualities are suitable. Grade A corn might be purchased to use as a buttered vegetable; Grade B might be used in a casserole, and Grade C for cream-of-corn soup. Similarly, considerable saving

in the family's milk bill can be effected by knowing the kind of milk to buy (see Chapter 6). Frozen foods, because there is no waste, may be more economical than fresh foods. You must learn to compare the prices of different forms of food to estimate which is the best to buy. Wise consumers buy first such necessary items as milk, eggs, meat, fruit, vegetables, and whole-grain cereals. The budget may then provide sweet rolls, ice-cream sundaes, and other luxuries. The chart on page 116 suggests minimum amounts of the basic foods which must be included in the diet to provide well-balanced meals.

How to Stretch the Food Dollar

An intelligent consumer knows the difference between merely satisfying the appetite of the family members and giving them adequate and nourishing meals. She does not buy beyond the estimated needs and budget, and at the same time she is aware of the many buying economies which enable her to use her budget to the best advantage. She knows the signs of quality in all kinds of food. She may compare prices at several stores to get the best buy—a few pennies saved on several items may total several dollars a month. However, since this method of shopping consumes time and energy, and requires transportation, the buyer must weigh the value of this practice. Buying at sales may or may not be economical. Damaged or inferior foods or items that a shopper does not need are never a bargain. Consumers always should compare sale prices against regular stock prices. Through continuous study of food qualities and prices the intelligent consumer learns to make wise choices within his budget.

115

KIND OF FOOD	QUANTITIES FOR ONE WEEK*		
	FOR CHILDREN UNDER 12 YEARS	FOR GIRLS 13 TO 20 YEARS	FOR BOYS 13 TO 20 YEARS
Leafy, green and yellow vegetables	2 - 3 lb.	3½ lb.	3½ - 4 lb.
Citrus fruits, tomatoes	2 - 3 lb.	3 lb.	3 - 3½ lb.
Potatoes, sweet potatoes	½ - 2 lb.	2½ lb.	3½ - 4½ lb.
Other vegetables and fruits (not citrus)	2 - 2½ lb.	3½ lb.	3½ lb.
Milk, cheese, ice cream	6 - 7 qt.	6 - 7 qt.	7 qt.
Meat, poultry, fish	1 - 2 lb.	2½ - 3 lb.	3 lb.
Eggs	6 to 7 eggs	7 eggs	7 eggs
Dry beans and peas, nuts	1 - 2 oz.	2 oz.	4 - 6 oz.
Baked goods, flour, cereals	1 - 2 lb.	2½ - 3 lb.	4 - 5 lb.
Fats, oils	¼ - ½ lb.	¾ lb.	1 - 1½ lb.
Sugar, sirups, preserves	¼ - ¾ lb.	1 lb.	1 - 1½ lb.

*Adapted from Family Fare No. 1, United States Department of Agriculture.

Buying in advance often saves time and money. Canned vegetables and fruits are sometimes sold at lower prices during the season when the fresh products are available, and this is the best time of year to purchase them. Such quantity buying need not strain the family budget if money has been set aside for this purpose over a period of several months.

Purchase of foods may be reduced by home production of fruits, vegetables, meats, and bakery products. Time and energy are factors to consider in determining the worth of home gardens. Sometimes it is advisable to grow only what can be eaten fresh. On the other hand, enough extra may be produced to fulfill a family's needs all through the winter in canned, dehydrated, or frozen form.

A good home freezer is an economy in storing fresh foods, home grown or purchased in season for future use. Families will save on home-baked foods by preparing them in quantity and placing them in the freezer. Freezing leftovers will practically eliminate day-to-day food waste because better use can be made of such leftovers if they are well spaced in future meals.

For families without a home freezer a large refrigerator often proves advisable. Leftovers can be kept better and longer, and purchases in larger quantities become possible. The refrigerator which holds a week's groceries saves the family's shopping and meal-preparation time.

Where to Buy

Select a market that operates with fair prices and practices. It should ensure the cleanliness of workers and merchandise. Consumers can help to improve standards of cleanliness by buying only from places that use sanitary methods of handling food and that comply with local, state, and national food regulations. Services furnished by a market raise the price of the merchandise, for such services require additional personnel. If your family chooses to buy in a supermarket, they select their purchases, pay cash, and carry the groceries home. They may find it necessary to use a store where they can maintain a charge account, order by phone, and have purchases delivered. Most shoppers believe that personal selection secures the best food for the money.

When to Buy

Purchase food when it is fresh and at its lowest cost. Usually, perishable foods are freshest in the morning or on those days of the week when such foods are regularly delivered to the retailer. Frequency in buying

Produce from the home garden · Families that live in the country or in the suburbs with a large enough plot of land frequently grow most of their vegetables that can be eaten fresh. Other families with more time and land raise enough fruits and vegetables to meet some of the winter's needs in canned or frozen form

Better Homes & Gardens

depends on the facilities in the home for food storage. When menus are planned a week at a time, most of the supplies can be bought at once, necessitating only one or two quick trips later for perishables.

How to Buy

A carefully planned *market order* prevents forgetting needed items; it should also curb the desire for luxuries, since thought has been given to the necessary purchases. The order should show current needs and list alternate choices which may be lower in price or provide better quality yet serve the same purpose. (Market orders are discussed on page 87.)

Personal shopping permits comparison of price, quality, and quantity, and enables the shopper to get the most for her money. Costs should be figured per measure or weight. Two packages of the same product, such as dried beans or fruit, priced differently, should be compared in measure or weight. Often the larger has a lower price per weight unit than the smaller. Use your table of weights and measures to help determine the best buys. A study of labels when purchasing food helps in choosing a product suitable to its purpose and so saves unnecessary expense (see page 41 for specific information con- cerning labels). The Federal Food, Drug, and Cosmetic Act ensures the truthfulness of label information. The personal shopper can note waste in food. For example, low-priced meat with a large amount of fat and bone may actually be more expensive than higher-priced meat with less fat and bone. Likewise vegetables such as cabbage should not have loose or damaged leaves included in their weight, and easily perishable fruits such as bananas should be chosen to avoid waste.

In many markets special salespeople are trained to assist in making selections. If you will choose a salesperson and establish a courteous and friendly relationship, shopping will be more pleasant and satisfactory. When you help to buy food for the family, you are trusted with budget funds. It is your responsibility to get just value for what you spend. You must observe the weighing of such foods as meat or cheese. Only a layer of thin paper is necessary beneath the product being weighed. Scales should have a seal attached to indicate that they are tested regularly. They should also have two-way vision so the buyer can see the weight recorded. Often you can weigh fruits and vegetables to make your own calculations. When your bill is tabulated, make sure that the adding-machine tape has a star at the

A. Devaney

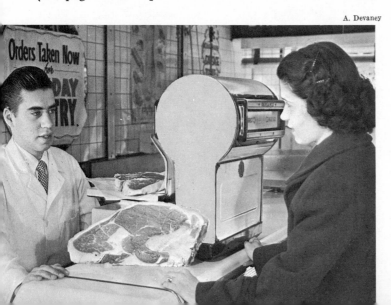

Meat being carefully weighed

top to ensure the clearance of other shoppers' listings. You should add food bills before paying them. Before you pocket your change count it. It is as important for the consumer to use good business methods as for her to expect them of the grocer.

Ordering by telephone may be satisfactory for busy persons, invalids, or parents of small children who have limited opportunity for marketing. Staple goods are more satisfactory purchased in this way than perishable products. However, even fresh fruits and vegetables may be ordered from a trusted grocer.

Advertisements are helpful as buying guides when they provide basic, accurate information, but it is necessary for consumers to learn to evaluate them. The consumer must look objectively at advertisements for facts about quality, size, quantity, and price. Many times quality cannot be determined until the buyer can test the item himself.

The price of a food cannot be used as the only measure of its quality. Value may be determined not only by inspecting foods and perhaps by testing them but also by comparing your experience with what advertisers have to say about them in newspapers and on radio and television programs.

Using Food Economically

Your family's responsibility for careful spending does not end when the food is delivered at home; it is necessary to use the purchases wisely.

Families must learn which dollar-stretching methods are true economies and which mean lower nutritional standards. With knowledge and experience, it is possible to extend the flavors of foods, to make substitutions without loss of food value, to utilize lower grades in cooking, and to avoid wasting anything edible. You can learn not only to balance a meal nutritionally but also to balance expensive dishes in a meal with less expensive ones to keep within the food-buying plan. Skilled buyers know which less expensive dishes are nourishing as well as satisfying. Heavy soups, stews, goulashes, and scalloped potatoes may be true economies. Macaroni is not always a wise choice as an economical dish because it contains a protein of low quality and is relatively low in mineral and vitamin values; these nutrients must be added in other foods, such as milk and cheese.

In planning economical meals you face the problem of varying menus sufficiently to maintain family interest. You can use the same inexpensive foods repeatedly if you vary the recipes and use different garnishes or accompaniments. Potatoes need not always be boiled; and chopped meats in other combinations than meat loaf may be more acceptable. There are endless economical casseroles, to which may be added such leftovers as a spoonful of scrambled eggs or broccoli, a strip of bacon, or a little cooked cereal. Mashed potatoes can be combined with meat leftovers into patties or croquettes. With experience you will become skilled in combining bits of fruit or raw vegetables into salads. Vegetable tops, if vegetables have been chosen with this in mind, can be used as cooked greens, in salads, or as garnishes. Nothing edible need be wasted. Potatoes may be steamed with the idea of using them in potato salad for a second meal. The food loss will not be great if they are tightly covered, stored in the refrigerator, and used within a few hours. For further economical practices in storing and using specific foods, refer to the index for chapter discussions. Good management of the family food budget includes these practices in economical use as well as carefully planned spending.

¶ Understanding:

1. What can families gain by planning their food expenditures?

2. What determines the amount your family should spend for food?

3. Why do markets differ in the prices they ask for foods? What besides prices determines your choice of a market?

4. When and how will you purchase staple foods in your locality? perishable foods?

5. What are the advantages and disadvantages of ordering food by telephone?

6. How should the proposed use of the food determine the grade chosen? Give an illustration.

7. In planning what to buy, which foods should you consider first?

8. What helps can you rely on in purchasing food?

9. How can you cut down waste through careful choice of foods?

10. What are some ways in which food waste in your home can be eliminated through better food care?

¶ Planning:

1. (a) Plan the amount of green and yellow vegetables and milk, cheese, and ice cream needed by your family for a week. Use Table III in the Appendix. (b) Plan where and how to buy moderate-priced meat for your family dinner.

2. Help plan a family market order of meats for a week, and keep within the budget. Include a cut of beef which may be used for several different meat dishes.

3. In menus using out-of-season fruits and vegetables, substitute lower-priced foods without sacrificing nutritive value.

4. Plan several specific ways to stretch food-budget dollars. Which of these will not affect nutritional values?

5. Using your knowledge of different grades of canned goods, plan economical purchasing of vegetables for a salad and a casserole and of fruit for a salad and for sauce.

6. Plan a snack meal which makes use of two of your mother's suggestions for the economical use of food.

¶ Practicing and Evaluating:

1. Evaluate at least three markets in your community for cleanliness and for freshness of perishable foods.

2. In selecting food for a meal what helped most in making choices?

3. Select sale foods to stretch your budget dollar. What saving was made? What made your purchase a true bargain?

4. Buy foods, using the label as your chief guide. What information helped in your choices?

5. Observe a shopper making food choices. What buying guides were used? What additional guides would you have used?

6. Discuss food-buying practices with three homemakers. Which practice seems to you the most economical of money, time, and effort?

7. Prepare a simple luncheon, demonstrating methods of eliminating waste in the use of food.

¶ Reading Further:

Family Meals at Low Cost, PA–472 (1962). Agricultural Marketing Service, U. S. Department of Agriculture, Washington, D. C.

Food Shopper's Guide, Folder F–306 (1961). University of Michigan Agricultural Extension Service, East Lansing, Michigan.

Money Management—Your Food Dollar (1960). Household Finance Corporation, Chicago, Illinois.

Read the Label on Foods, Drugs, Devices, Cosmetics, and Household Chemicals, FS 13.111:3. Government Printing Office, Washington, D. C.

UNIT FOUR

Luncheons
or Suppers

Types of luncheons

you will learn: How to plan casserole luncheons; How to combine foods for plate luncheons; How to achieve variety in packed lunches; How to make use of the hot lunch at school

The type of luncheon best suited to the need of individuals in families depends on the activities in which each is engaged and the place and circumstances of eating. By lunchtime most families are widely scattered. The lunch hour is too often a scant twenty or thirty minutes and the food is anything available which will satisfy hunger. Luncheon may be eaten in the school lunchroom, from a lunch box, at the

factory, or at a crowded lunch bar. Knowing how to adapt lunch habits to these circumstances is important. Each person should consider his own problem and plan with the homemaker the type of luncheon he should have. Does the school lunchroom supply you with a complete lunch, such as a casserole which can be supplemented with carrot sticks and milk? What plate lunches are available and what additions can be chosen?

Perhaps certain foods must be brought from home. The factory worker may need to carry a complete packed lunch. The office worker may decide that the food bar is poor economy in time and money and that the tension of the noon-hour rush is disturbing. He may have a tendency to choose foods which are too rich. The business person's too-hearty lunch, hastily eaten, has often been cited as one cause of physical breakdown.

The homemaker has a responsibility in teaching the members of her family that correct food choices for the midday meal are important and that quiet relaxation while eating is a positive health measure. If the family lunches at home, she must master techniques of planning and preparation which will produce an adequate and satisfying luncheon, served promptly, and eaten under the best possible conditions. Since she too is a busy person, this task will require foresight and expertness. Time, as well as economy and good nutrition, has been considered in the luncheon dishes described here and in the packed luncheons for absent members. For lunch you should eat nutritious and easily digested foods, sufficient to satisfy hunger, and eat them unhurriedly.

Planning Casserole Luncheons

The casserole is a main dish prepared by baking a combination of foods together, usually in a white sauce or gravy. A successful casserole is appetizing, suited to many occasions, quickly and easily prepared, and supplies essential food elements. A casserole dish is a convenience when other household duties require unusual time and effort. The success of a casserole depends upon combining foods to produce adequate nutrition plus a pleasing blend of tastes and textures. Some crispness is desirable.

A well-planned, nutritious casserole may need no accompaniments other than bread and a beverage. A macaroni-and-cheese casserole, a green salad, beverage, and fruit dessert may be served. Baked beans with pork in a casserole can be supplemented with Boston brown bread, carrot strips, fruit, and a beverage. A casserole of ground meat, sliced potato, and onion, served with Harvard beets, whole-wheat muffins, milk, and a fruit cup with sugar cookies is a good luncheon combination. These menus provide satisfying, well-balanced luncheons.

There is no better way to use leftover foods than in casserole dishes. A vegetable combination of leftovers to which sea food, cheese, and a white sauce or soup is added makes a delicious main dish, rich in food values. The casserole is one of the most economical main dishes for luncheon. In this kind of dish the flavor of expensive meat, poultry, fish, and cheese is easily extended by using them with less expensive, high-energy foods. (See Chapter 11 for meat extenders.)

Another advantage of casserole cookery is that, by this means, food less liked by the family can be camouflaged by combining it with a more favored one of pronounced flavor. If, for example, onions are enjoyed more than eggplant, their flavor can predominate in a casserole of eggplant, crackers, and onion. A taste for okra, green pepper, or other food may be encouraged through combining them with the more familiar tomatoes or potatoes as ingredients in casseroles.

Similar to the meat casserole are several

other nourishing dishes appropriate for luncheon—stew, meat pie, and goulash. Any combination of small pieces of meat and vegetables, such as potatoes, carrots, celery, and onions, cooked on top of the range is called a *stew*. *Meat pie* is a stew with a pastry or biscuit topping. A *goulash* is a thick meat stew, sometimes thickened with browned flour and served on rice or noodles. Celery, carrots, and green peppers may be added for flavor. For the best flavor, meat for all these dishes, including casseroles, should be browned with sliced onion in a small amount of shortening.

Plate Luncheons

Whether a plate luncheon is hot or cold depends upon the season of the year, and the time and effort required in meal preparation. Hot foods are stimulating to the appetite and digestion and are enjoyable the year round. On winter days, in addition, they make the body feel warmer. A hot meal may require no more effort than a cold one.

Meat or Meat Alternates with Combinations

The plate luncheon may consist of meat with vegetables or fruits or both. Ground beef or chicken croquettes with white sauce, green beans, whole-wheat bread, baked apple, and milk are typical of a combination plate of meat, vegetable, and fruit. Meat alternates may be used as a protein dish (see pages 133–139).

Vegetable Plates

This type of luncheon is usually less expensive than the luncheon with meat as the main dish. For a plate combination select vegetables which contrast with one another in flavor, food values, color, and texture. Compare the two luncheons below for nutritive value and attractiveness.

Browning meat for stew

LUNCHEON I

(A Well-Planned Menu)

Scalloped corn with buttered crumbs
Buttered asparagus
Sliced tomato on lettuce leaf
Graham muffin with butter
Fruit cup
Peanut-butter cookies
Milk

LUNCHEON II

(A Poorly Planned Menu)

Mashed potatoes
Mashed turnips
Celery sticks
Biscuits and butter or fortified margarine
Rice pudding
Iced tea

These luncheons differ greatly in their protein values. Luncheon I is a satisfactory choice because it offers a good supply of proteins. It supplements proteins of low value with proteins of high quality. Luncheon II is a poor choice, offering insufficient proteins. The second meal also lacks variety in flavor, texture, and color.

In proper combinations, vegetables for a plate luncheon will provide the main protein dish of the day. However, since soybeans are the only vegetable of relatively high protein quality, most vegetable plates must be supplemented with such high-quality protein foods as cheese, milk, or eggs. Luncheon I has the low-quality protein of corn, asparagus, tomato, and graham flour supplemented with the high-quality protein of milk, used in the scalloped corn and the graham muffin and as the beverage. The peanut butter in the cookies also provides some protein. In Luncheon II the proteins of low value are not supplemented sufficiently by the amount of milk used in mashed potatoes, biscuits, and rice pudding.

Fruit Plates

Fruit plates are especially attractive and refreshing in warm weather, but fruits alone are not nutritious enough to make an adequate meal. They need to be supplemented by high-calorie protein and fat foods, such as cheese balls or cottage cheese; nuts; finger sandwiches with meat, fish, or poultry fillings; or rich buttered breads. The fruits used should provide variety in texture, color, and flavor. Fresh fruits are especially desirable for fruit plates and when they are in season are usually more economical than preserved ones. Frozen, canned, and dried fruits, however, may be used for contrasting colors and food values. They also add interesting contrasts of texture.

In experimenting with fruit plates, use the diversity of shapes, sizes, and colors to make an attractive arrangement. Every fruit plate should have a center of attraction with the other fruits grouped as pleasingly as possible around it. Bananas coated with peanuts make an interesting base for a fruit luncheon. Grapes, melon balls, and canned grapefruit sections, with mayonnaise, whole-wheat bread, and honey-butter sandwiches provide a filling and satisfying meal. Canned pear halves may be filled with cottage cheese and surrounded by dried apricots stuffed with chopped raisins and peanut butter. The meal may be completed with cinnamon rolls and a dessert of soft custard, topped with beaten egg whites or whipped cream.

Fruit plates must be served cold to preserve their texture. All fruits should be chilled 2 to 4 hours before serving. Plan to drain and chill canned fruits several hours before arranging them on the plates and keep the plates in the refrigerator until ready to serve. (The selection and care of fruits is discussed in detail in Chapter 3.)

Packed Lunches

Packing a lunch every day is a challenge to your imagination and ability to plan. The packed lunch should be attractive, satisfying, easy to eat—and within the food budget. A variety of foods is possible and desirable in a packed lunch, for repetition of the same items day after day may result in a lack of interest in eating. The use of appropriate utensils for the packed lunch makes it possible to include many different kinds of food.

125

Plate lunch · A well-balanced and satisfying lunch

Better Homes & Gardens

Paper cups with tight-fitting lids or other food containers may be used. Glass or plastic jars also are helpful if it is convenient to take them back and forth from home to school or to work. (Juicy or soft-textured foods, of course, require special care in packing.)

The place where the lunch is to be eaten should be considered by the planner. When any one or more of such facilities as eating utensils, a sink, a range or a hot plate, or a refrigerator are available, more foods can be included than otherwise. But even without these facilities, with the exception of the few foods which cannot be left unrefrigerated for 3 or 4 hours, the variety in packed lunches may be nearly as great as that for the home luncheon.

Foods to Include

The packed lunch must include its share of the day's food needs. There should be protein, carbohydrates, fats, minerals, and vitamin foods. Very rich or highly seasoned

126

foods should not be included in lunch menus because they are likely to create a drowsiness or thirst which may interfere with working efficiency. Highly seasoned foods may also leave an offensive taste. A packed lunch menu is more delicious if it includes a variety of sweet, tart, crisp, and soft foods.

For a packed lunch hot *soup* or a hot *beverage*, such as cocoa or hot tomato juice, may be carried in a vacuum bottle. A hot drink stimulates the appetite and is very relaxing. Cold milk drinks and cold fruit juices are acceptable in hot weather.

Sandwiches (see Chapter 12) are usually the basis of packed lunches. For those who need a heavy lunch, two or more kinds of sandwiches may be required, some of protein and some of vegetable or fruit combinations. The use of a variety of breads as well as of fillings helps to prevent monotony.

It is not always necessary, however, to serve a sandwich; salads, soups, fresh vegetables, and desserts can provide the necessary food values and offer a change of menu.

Salads can be packed in lunches if they are put into containers with tight-fitting lids. The lunch box is an excellent means of serving the daily allowance of *vegetables* and *fruits*. Cucumber, cauliflower, tomatoes, green peppers, and turnips may be used. It is important to wrap uncooked vegetables carefully while still moist so that they will retain their freshness and crispness. Fresh fruits of all kinds and dried fruits are appropriate in packed lunches, as are frozen and canned fruits. These latter should be packed in the same way as salads.

Cookies, candy, doughnuts, and cakes are good *desserts* for the packed-lunch menu. Semisolid desserts, such as a custard pudding, can be carried safely when covered tightly in a sturdy container.

Packing the Lunch

Paper bags, cardboard or plastic boxes, or light metal lunch boxes may be used for carrying lunches. Before they are used, all plastic or metal containers should be thoroughly washed and aired until they have a fresh clean smell. Upon being emptied, vacuum bottles should be rinsed with cold water, washed carefully in warm water with a cleansing agent, and rinsed. Before they are used again, they should be aired and again rinsed. Wrappings should be moisture-proof and strong; waxed paper, metal foil, or plastic bags are suitable. Wrap all foods separately for cleanliness and to keep their flavors and odors distinct. Separate wrapping also preserves the freshness of crisp vegetables and fruits. Lettuce remains more crisp if wrapped alone and added to the sandwiches just before they are eaten. Paper napkins should be included in every packed lunch. A napkin on the lap saves clothing and catches crumbs for disposal; for personal cleanliness in eating, a napkin is necessary.

Hot Lunches at School

The school lunch is a valuable part of the school's contribution to good nutrition and health protection. Ideally, every pupil should be able at school to select a lunch suited to his needs. Some schools can make this possible; others are able to provide only a hot dish to supplement the lunch brought from home, or to serve fresh milk to the pupils. Some school systems publish weekly menus as an aid to the home planner in providing well-balanced meals for the whole day. School lunches are comparatively inexpensive because they are provided on a nonprofit basis.

Hot Dishes to Supplement Cold Lunches

Among the nutritious hot dishes prepared at school may be soup, cocoa, or a vegetable. The hot dish usually becomes the main dish in a school lunch. The home planner should build the supplementary lunch around the hot dish. On the days when steamed rice or any cereal is to be served, less bread should be used in the packed lunch. Hot vegetable dishes provided at school make it unnecessary to pack carrot strips, lettuce, or cabbage wedges. The hot vegetable should, rather, be supplemented by such foods as meat sandwiches, fruit, milk, and a dessert. Cocoa served at school may take the place of milk from home, and cream soups at school may replace both milk and a main dish from home. When meat, egg, cheese, peanut butter, or soybean dishes are provided at school for a hot main serving, the packed lunch needs bread and butter, fruit, a vegetable, and milk.

Besides making a lunch more nutritious, a hot dish encourages slower eating and stimulates the digestion. Furthermore the supplemented lunch links the school and home programs through their cooperative efforts to provide a good lunch for the pupils.

Complete Meals
from the School Lunchroom

Some schools are able to provide a complete lunch prepared in their own kitchens.

Packing a school lunch · Hot soup has been placed in the thermos bottle; bread-and-butter sandwiches have been made; cookies have been selected; and Jane is now cutting up celery for her tuna-fish-and-celery salad, which she will pack in the plastic container

Jane and Steven Coons

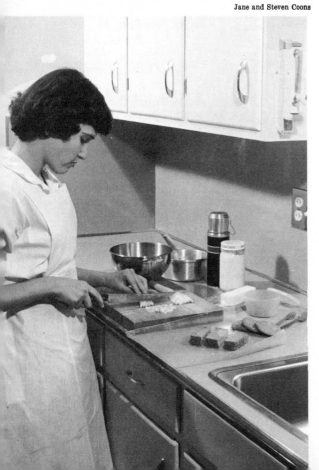

This makes it possible to offer students an appetizing meal with contrasts in flavors and in textures. For example, soft, crisp, and firm foods may be provided in a lunch of tuna fish and noodles, chopped fresh-vegetable salad, fruit cup and cookies, and milk. Variety of flavor and of flavor intensity is also important. A meal composed entirely of mild-flavored foods is dull; a meal containing too many strong-flavored foods is unappealing. Flavors should not be repeated in the same lunch; for example, spiced peaches and spice cake should not be served together.

A GOOD CONTRAST

Lamb patty
Buttered potatoes   Pickled beets
Peach cobbler
Milk

A POOR CONTRAST

Creamed eggs
Scalloped potatoes
Baked custard
Milk

Conditions for Preparation and Serving

Absolute cleanliness of person and clothing should be required of all food handlers in lunchrooms. The equipment should be kept scrupulously clean, should be well stored and efficiently used for the quick and safe handling of food. The room or rooms should be orderly, quiet, airy, and free from flies and dust. The service of food should be prompt. It is the pupils' responsibility to wash their hands before eating, to waste no food, and to leave the table and surroundings neat and orderly. Young children can learn to refrain from noisy talking and laughter and to chat quietly when they are

Choosing a lunch at school

in surroundings that make for pleasant eating and good digestion. The school lunch-table atmosphere need not differ greatly from that at home.

¶ *Understanding:*

1. Show on a chart the chief food values of meat, cheese, or fish casseroles.

2. In what ways is the serving of casserole luncheons an advantage to your family?

3. Find ways of keeping down the expense of casserole dishes.

4. What characteristics would you look for in a nourishing and appetizing vegetable or fruit plate?

5. Suggest ideas for controlling the cost of vegetable or fruit plates.

6. What are the qualities of a satisfactory packed lunch?

7. What standards of food service should a school lunch program be expected to maintain?

8. How can you help to make the school lunch program a success?

¶ *Planning:*

1. Plan foods to accompany a macaroni-and-cheese casserole for a balanced luncheon meal for a family of two adults and two preschool children.

2. Plan a vegetable casserole adequate in calories for a main dish. Introduce a less-liked vegetable.

3. Plan ways to add extra food values to casseroles.

4. Choose two casseroles and plan the accompanying foods which would make up adequate meals for your family.

5. Using in-season fruits, plan a plate luncheon for a group of your friends. Include a beverage and dessert which will be appropriate with the fruit plate. Estimate the cost of the meal.

6. Plan foods suitable for a vegetable-plate luncheon for your family. Choose a nutritious dessert to serve with the meal.

7. Creamed cabbage and Waldorf salad are available in your lunchroom; plan foods to be packed at home for completing an adequate lunch.

¶ Practicing and Evaluating:

1. Prepare a casserole for a luncheon or supper, using only leftover foods. Check the casserole for flavor and appearance.

2. On a busy day at home prepare a casserole to serve to your family. Include all the food values possible.

3. Select and prepare vegetables for a plate luncheon. Practice saving time and effort when preparing vegetables for cookery.

4. Using precautions to preserve color, texture, and food values, prepare fruits in advance for a plate luncheon.

5. For a member of your family, pack an appropriate lunch which includes sandwiches, a hot drink, salad, and dessert. Use methods which will conserve food values, flavors, and textures.

6. Choose a meal in the school lunchroom, using basic nutrition information to get all the food values possible at a minimum cost. Discuss how the choices could have been more appropriate.

7. Pack three lunches, one to include a hot food or drink, one a salad or a custard, and the third a crisp vegetable and soft cake. Check your menus by the Basic Seven Food Guide.

¶ Reading Further:

ANDERS, NEDDA CARSON, *Casserole Specialties*. Hearthside Press Inc., New York.

Barbequing Poultry, Bulletin 200 (1961). University of Minnesota Extension Service, St. Paul, Minnesota.

BEAN, RUTH, *All-in-One-Oven Meals*, M. Barrows & Company, New York.

Delicious Kentucky Barbequed Chicken, Bulletin 535 (1960). University of Kentucky Extension Service, Lexington, Kentucky.

It's Cookout Time, Bulletin 4–H163 (1961). University of Missouri Extension Service, Columbia, Missouri.

ROBERSON, JOHN E., and ROBERSON, MARIE N., *The Casserole Cookbook*, Prentice-Hall, Inc., New York, N. Y.

ROSS, E. L., *Small Meals for Company*. Hearthside Press Inc., New York.

American Home Foods

Meats, meat alternates, and meat extenders

you will learn: How to choose meats for
luncheon; How to use meat alternates;
How to extend meat in meals

Meat is the flesh of animals. Usually domestic ones are raised for the purpose of supplying man with food. People eat more meat in those countries where the meat production per capita is the largest. Argentina, New Zealand, Australia, Uruguay, Canada, and the United States are among the great meat-producing meat-eating countries of the world. Americans have always liked meat because of its excellent flavor and satisfying quality. The protein of meat is especially needed after a severe illness or surgery to rebuild muscles which have lost much of their protein.

131

Kinds of Luncheon Meats

Cured meats, such as sausages, wieners, cold cuts, dried beef, smoked or pickled fish, smoked turkey, ham, pickled pork cuts, and Canadian bacon, provide high amounts of animal protein and varying amounts of fat, mineral, and vitamin values (see Table IV in the Appendix). Some sausages, wieners, and even cold cuts contain carbohydrates from other foods such as cereals.

Among the *canned meats*, *poultry*, and *fish products* on the market are stew combinations, meat balls, corned beef, pork and gravy, liver paste, sliced chicken, tuna fish, salmon, sardines, and anchovies. Canned meats, poultry, and fish foods may be served in many forms, such as casseroles, soufflés, and salads. Although canned meats may seem expensive, they have no waste and are usually ready to serve except for heating.

Little preparation is needed for *leftover meats*. We should attempt to plan our marketing and preparation so that the same cut of meat can be used in several different dishes. A roast of veal, pork, or chicken may be sliced and served cold on a luncheon plate or in a sandwich, or it may be diced for a salad or casserole. Yesterday's steak or stew is a good basis for savory hash or scalloped dishes. There are so many ways of using leftover meat that none should be wasted. Turning leftovers into tempting new dishes affords opportunities for a free use of imagination.

Selection, Care, and Cookery of Luncheon Meats

Meats you purchase should have been kept refrigerated and protected from flies, dust, and handling by customers. The clothing and hands of those who sell should be clean, and all equipment should be sanitary.

Cured meats, packaged in a variety of ways, provide many interesting flavors. In selecting meats, consider their cost in comparison with that of other meat products. Some of the cured luncheon meats are relatively moderate in price and compare favorably in protein content with many of the expensive fresh meats. For example, a pound of bologna has as much protein as a pound of smoked ham or a pound of beef with a moderate amount of bone and fat. A choice between cured ham or fresh pork depends on the flavor preferred, the time the work, and the fuel needed for preparation, and the cost of the product itself.

Canned products may well be purchased if they are nourishing and economical as well as appetizing. Cans of meat may be had in different sizes for small or larger families or to suit recipe requirements (can sizes are discussed on page 248). Labels on canned meats should carry the words "Inspected and Passed by the Department of Agriculture." They should also give the approximate content in weight, the number of servings or slices, and adequate directions for serving.

Canned meats should be stored in a dry, cool, dark place. Moisture will cause damage to the rubber rings which keep glass jars airtight and to the labels on these and other containers. Keep canned meats on low shelves where the air is cooler than on higher ones. Cover cured and cooked meats tightly with waxed paper to prevent the surface from drying, refrigerate, and use within two or three days. Pickled meats and fish must be kept tightly covered in a cool place.

Luncheon main dishes of cured, canned, or leftover meats are endless in variety and dependable for furnishing the meal's protein. In preparing them you should follow the principles of protein cookery: a low temperature and a short cooking period. Those which have been precooked require only to be heated thoroughly before they are served. Other foods to be combined with these meats, such as rice or macaroni, are usually cooked first to avoid overcooking the meat. The tenderness, flavor, and juices of meats which have not been precooked should be protected according to the basic principles of meat cookery as discussed in Chapter 16, pages 206–211.

Meat Alternates

A substitute food for meat must include a protein of high quality. Dishes with high milk or egg content are excellent to replace meat because the protein of each contains the necessary high-quality protein for growth and maintenance. Eggs as a protein are discussed in Chapter 6 and milk in Chapter 7. Cheese is one of the most popular alternates for meat. It is made by separating the curd of milk from the liquid or whey. This solid curd is known as casein. The casein may be seasoned and served fresh, or ripened for cheeses of widely varying flavors and textures. Ripening is a process of storing the cheeses with various molds, yeast, or bacteria under controlled conditions for months, or even years, to bring about a mellowing of flavor and texture. Cows' milk is used in the United States for cheeses. Certain other nations also use milk from goats, camels, reindeer, and buffalo.

Cheeses

The characteristics of individual cheeses are determined by the kind of milk used (usually cow or goat), by the butterfat content (of skimmed, partly skimmed, or whole milk, or of milk with cream added), by any other ingredients, and by the method of manufacture.

Kinds of Cheeses—Unripened *soft cheeses* are the cottage and cream varieties. Cottage cheese is the curd from milk, seasoned and served fresh. It is on the market in several forms: large-curd, creamed, and sometimes with such additions as pineapple or chives. It is sold in bulk or in labeled cartons. Cream cheese comes from milk curd processed into a soft, smooth, milk-flavored product which is white to cream in color. Cream cheeses lend themselves to a variety of flavorings. They are sold in 3- or 6-ounce packages or by the pound. Neufchâtel, an unripened cream cheese, originally from France, is an example of a mild-flavored soft cheese.

Among the ripened soft cheeses of French origin is Camembert, which has a strong, pronounced flavor. It is creamy yellow inside with a brownish-gray crust. Liederkranz is a soft cheese which is a golden yellow inside with a russet surface and a strong flavor. France's soft Brie cheese is sharp in taste.

The *semisoft* to *semihard ripened cheeses* are numerous in variety. Roquefort, imported from France, and Gorgonzola, of Italian origin, are sharp cheeses, semisoft in texture with blue veins. Blue cheese, made in Denmark, Argentina, and the United States, resembles Roquefort. Brick cheese, a semihard

133

cheese of American origin, has a mild to sharp flavor. Stilton, a sharp-flavored, semihard cheese imported from England, has a green mold and a wrinkled surface. Other semihard cheeses are Gruyere, Muenster, and Limburger. Gruyere, a light-yellow cheese, is similar in flavor to the hard Swiss cheese, and originates from France and Switzerland. Muenster, a German cheese, is creamy-white inside and yellowish outside, and has a sweetish flavor between that of brick and Limburger. Limburger originated in Belgium and Germany. It has a strong flavor and odor and is creamy white inside.

Hard cheeses may have gas holes resulting from the action of bacteria. Cheeses of this type are Swiss, mild to slightly sharp in flavor, and Parmesan, which is of Italian origin. Parmesan, one of the hardest cheeses, is grayish white inside and green on the outside. Edam is of Dutch origin and is like Cheddar in flavor. Covered with a red waxed surface, its interior is yellow. Provolene, a sharp, smoke-flavored cheese from Italy, is sold in packages of various shapes. The much-used Cheddar cheese is slightly sharp in flavor, white to orange inside, and waxed outside. Although Cheddar was first made in England, quantities are now manufactured in the United States.

Process cheese is a pasteurized product made by blending one or more different kinds of cheeses under controlled heat. It is mild in flavor and soft. Among the natural cheeses used are Cheddar, Swiss, brick, and Camembert. Process cheese is sold by the pound or grated and packaged.

Cheese spreads are any soft cheeses or cheese foods that spread at room temperature. Pimento, olives, pickles, or onions may be added to either the cheese spreads or process cheeses.

Cheese foods are usually produced by adding whey, milk, or cream to process cheese. Cheese foods are sold under trade names and not as cheese because of the regulations of the Federal Food, Drug, and Cosmetic Act.

Nutritional Value of Cheese—Cheese is excellent for food values and flavor. Its protein compares with that of meat and eggs for tissue building and repair. Approximately eleven ounces of American Cheddar cheese has the same protein content as a pound of cooked beef without bone. Since cottage cheese is less concentrated than Cheddar, about twelve ounces of cottage cheese equals a pound of cooked beef. About six ounces of American Cheddar cheese contains as much calcium as a quart of milk. Since cheese, like milk, is low in iron content, a green vegetable may accompany a cheese dish to supply the iron. The energy value in cheese varies with the amount of fat it contains. American Cheddar cheese furnishes 113 calories in a one-inch cube. The fat in cheese is finely divided, and although it is digestible, its high concentration tends to increase the time needed for digestion. Nevertheless the ability of the body to use cheese compares favorably with its ability to use other foods. (For additional information on the nutritive value of cheese, see Table IV in the Appendix.)

The United States Department of Agriculture has set up grades for American Cheddar cheese to indicate the quality in terms of flavor, body, and color. The cheese grades, A, B, or C, are placed on the rind or package. Cheese marked "no grade" may have an off flavor and color.

Selection and Use of Cheese—Since cheese is a concentrated product, the food value per dollar is high. A little goes a long way in adding nutrients and flavor to bland vege-

STEPS IN MAKING SWISS CHEESE

1. Milk is stirred slowly while heating

2. The curds are broken up with a cheese "harp"

3. The curds are lifted in heavy cheesecloth by a block and tackle

4. In a wooden press water is squeezed out of the curds, which are wrapped in heavy cheesecloth inside a press

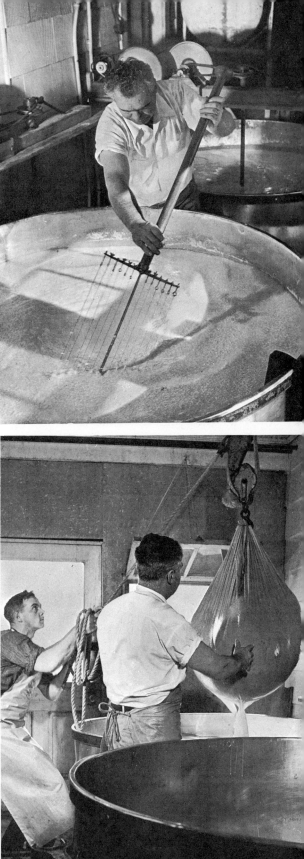

tables and grain products. In cooking cheese with other foods select mild varieties that will bring out the natural food flavors. Strong cheeses are best used in small quantities. Sharp-flavored cheese served at the beginning of a meal is a good appetizer. Or, at the close of a meal, cheese may be used in place of a richer dessert. Cottage cheese, rich in protein, if served with crackers and fresh fruit, makes an inexpensive, nourishing, and appetizing light meal. Attractive arrangements of various cheeses on a tray will appeal through color, texture, shapes, and flavors. Cheese adds greatly to a meal.

Cheeses may be used in sauces, on toast, as a topping, or as an important ingredient in main dishes. Before being combined in cookery, hard cheeses should be grated or thinly sliced. The softer process cheeses and cheese foods melt quickly. Food value and flavor of many dishes are improved by the addition of cheese.

For sandwiches and cold-plate servings, cheese takes its place along with sliced ham and other cold cuts. Both brick and Swiss cheeses are favorites to use in this way. Cream cheese and cheese spreads are excellent for cold sandwich fillings and as frostings for sandwich loaves. For toasted sandwiches a variety of cheeses may be used for flavor.

Many cheeses are appropriate in salads or as salad accompaniments. Cream or cottage cheese is good for stuffing fresh fruit or dried fruits, and, when well seasoned, for stuffing celery stalks. Cream cheeses are important ingredients in certain salad dressings. In French dressings cheeses of the Blue type are often used. Cheese may serve as the main food in gelatin or frozen salads. Cubes of Swiss, Muenster, or Edam, or crumbled pieces of Blue, Roquefort, or Gorgonzola may be used in tossed salads. Wedges of Camembert, Gruyère, Brie, or Cheddar,

along with crackers, are often served with salads.

Grated or crumbled cheese may be sprinkled over soup or added to hot vegetables just before serving.

Care of Cheese—Cutting off only as much cheese as is needed is a way to preserve the quality and avoid waste. Soft cheeses must be treated like other perishable foods: wrap the cheese or cover it tightly to prevent drying, and refrigerate. Hard cheeses become dry and moldy unless covered and stored in a refrigerator. One way to keep loaf cheese from drying out is to save the end piece and replace it on the cut side. To keep cheese moist wrap it in a cloth wrung out of a solution of 1 tablespoon of vinegar to $\frac{1}{2}$ cup of water. Then cover the whole with waxed paper. Leftover bits of cheese may be stored in a tightly covered container and refrigerated. Metal foil, if available, is a good wrapping to keep cheese fresh. Other suitable wrappings are waxed paper, cellophane, oiled silk, and plastic cloth.

Preparation of Cheese Dishes—Understanding the effect of heat upon cheese is important in preparing cheese dishes. Cooking temperature affects the protein of cheese much as it affects the protein of eggs. Because this is true two precautions should be observed:

1. Cheese must not be cooked at too high a temperature or for too long a time or it will be lumpy, tough, and rubbery. A low temperature will melt cheeses smoothly, after which they should be served at once.

2. Blending cheese with white sauce makes it combine more easily with other ingredients, such as macaroni.

Legumes

Legumes, such as beans, peas, and lentils, are sources of protein, yet with a few exceptions they are not true alternates for meat unless they are supplemented, in the same meal, with animal-protein foods. If legumes are used as a main luncheon dish, such foods as cottage cheese, cheese soufflé, or a custard pie should also be served to complete the protein requirement of the meal. Adding milk to bean or lentil soup gives a high-quality protein combination. Beans combined with corn provide protein of excellent quality since the proteins of each supply the kinds of proteins lacking in the other.

Among the dried varieties of *beans* are navy, kidney, chili, pinto, lima, and soybeans. Navy, lima, or soybeans may be baked for an excellent luncheon main dish. Boston-baked beans are a well-known favorite. Canned baked beans are available and may be seasoned as desired and baked again for a short time. Baked beans may also be used in chili con carne, sandwiches, and croquettes, and as the basis of a soup.

Soybeans and *peanuts* are the only legumes containing high-quality protein. Therefore, they are protein alternates for meat. To obtain high nutritional value for your money, you may like to try using soybeans in main dishes instead of the more usual navy or lima beans. Soybeans may be used green as a vegetable, sprouted for salads or casseroles, or shelled for baking; soybean grits can be combined with ground meats; soybean flour or meal may be used in baked products and gravies; and the whole bean may be roasted and served salted as an accompaniment. Like milk and eggs, soybeans help complete the proteins found in flour and other cereal foods. When a half cup of soybean flour is added to nine cups of an all-purpose flour, a combination of proteins superior to those found in whole-wheat flour is produced. This percentage of soybean flour in baked products not only improves protein value but adds flavor and keeping quality. Care should be taken, however, not to use too much: more than 10 per cent of soybean flour used with wheat flour alters the flavor and texture of the product unfavorably.

Since the proteins from peanuts, like those from soybeans, compare favorably with animal proteins, peanuts may be used to enrich salads, or in meat loaves and in casseroles. A favorite use for chopped peanuts is as topping for cake, bread, or cream soup.

The dried *pea* legumes include green, black-eyed, chick-, and cowpeas. Green peas are used in split form for soups. Adding milk gives the soup a protein of high quality. Green split peas may cost less than navy beans but there is slightly more protein per pound in navy beans. Black-eyed peas baked with pork provide a substantial luncheon main dish. The protein of chick-peas and cowpeas is adequately supplemented if meat, cheese, or milk is served. Lentils may be baked but are used mostly in soups. The dried-pea legumes are served creamed, buttered, and in stews.

FUEL VALUE OF NUTS		
KINDS of NUTS	AMOUNT	CALORIES
ALMONDS	$\frac{1}{4}$ c.	424
CASHEWS	1 oz.	164
COCONUT	$\frac{1}{4}$ c.	86
PEANUTS	1 T.	50
PECANS	1 T.	52
WALNUTS	1 T.	49

Assorted cheeses · How many kinds of cheese can you identify here?

Legume foods are important in low-to-moderate-cost diets. For example, if you are using navy beans supplemented with pork as a main dish, you may find the cost only about two-thirds as much as that of an equal amount of protein provided in lean stewing beef. Protein and carbohydrate content make legumes rich in fuel value. With the exception of soybeans and peanuts, legumes are more than half starch. The low starch content of soybeans makes them desirable for overweight diets. Legumes are also valuable as meat alternates because of their calcium, phosphorus, and iron content. They are good sources of thiamine, ribo-flavin, and niacin, and sprouted legumes form an important source of vitamin C. Dried legumes are bought by the pound or in packages. Some packaged beans come

partly precooked. Ready-to-eat legumes are available in cans.

Except for bean sprouts, legumes are always cooked before eating. Uncooked bean sprouts are easier to digest and more readily used by the body than cooked ones. Soak dried legumes in about three quarts of water to each quart of legumes until they double their bulk, then cook them until they are about three times their original bulk. Allow 3 hours soaking in warm water, or overnight soaking in cold water. Cook the beans in the soaking water after adding salt. The protein of legumes is more tender when cooked at low heat until their skins are soft.

For soups, legumes may be mashed or strained after cooking. Cook the shelled beans until just tender. Properly cooked green soybeans have a clear color, firm texture, and a pleasant, nutty flavor. Serve them buttered with salt. They may be used in any way that you would use green peas or lima beans.

Nuts

Like legumes, nuts add protein to meals. They make excellent contribution to baked foods, salads, and desserts. Nuts are very rich in fat. The high protein and fat content of nuts gives them high fuel value.

Nuts may be bought either shelled or unshelled. Because of their high fat content, they spoil easily. Shelled nuts should be covered and kept in a refrigerator. Unshelled nuts should be kept tightly covered in a cool, dark place.

Meat Extenders

Many nutritious low-cost foods may be combined with meat to extend meat flavors, to make the dish more filling, and to add food values. Such cereal products as macaroni, cracked whole wheat, and bread crumbs added to meat balls of beef or sausage make a satisfactory substitute for steak and chops.

Soybean flour or grits added to sausage in the proportion of 2 to 3 tablespoons per pound of meat will greatly increase the total protein content without affecting the flavor. When a cereal like mush, cracked whole wheat, or bran is also added, the meat flavor is extended and food values are added. This sausage may be formed into cakes or it may be spread on bread dough, rolled like a jelly roll, and baked. It thus provides a less expensive protein main dish than sausage used alone. Cereal products generally cost one-third as much as meats.

Another appetizing, nourishing dish is chow mein, made of pork, bean sprouts, water chestnuts, and vegetables. (For recipes, refer to the Cookbook.) Baked vegetables may be stuffed with leftover meats. Cooking meats with rice or noodles or with vegetables as stews or goulashes, or serving them with gravies are additional means of extending meat flavors.

Florence Stove Company

Baked beans served in the pot which they were baked

The flavors of poultry and fish may also be extended by combining them with other foods. Dishes are enriched and cost lowered when fish and noodles are baked together, or when chicken is combined with vegetables for a chicken pie. Creaming fish or chicken and serving it on toast extends the dish in food values and makes the servings more economical. A knowledge of how to extend meat by using less expensive foods with it enables one to enjoy it without exceeding the budget.

¶ *Understanding:*

1. Which of the luncheon meats will you choose if preparation time is limited? if your food budget is limited?

2. How must you care for leftover meats?

3. In what ways could you use leftover meats in a luncheon or supper meal?

4. What foods will provide the same quality protein as that contained in meat?

5. What are some alternates for meats? How do they compare with meat in food values? in cost?

6. How may you use cheese in your luncheons?

7. How do cooking temperatures affect cheese protein?

8. What cheeses would you choose for cooking? Explain your choices.

9. What are the values of combining other foods with meats?

10. How can a leftover roast be used for three different main dishes?

¶ *Planning:*

1. Make suggestions for including more protein in the family luncheons without increasing the total cost.

2. Plan a home luncheon which includes an inexpensive meat as the main dish. Write out the work schedule for preparation of the meal.

3. Plan meat-combination dishes and the foods to serve with them for two quickly prepared luncheons.

4. Plan a meal including chicken potpie to be served to your parents. Plan one to be served to a family with two preschool children.

¶ *Practicing and Evaluating:*

1. Prepare a leftover meat dish for a home luncheon. How much time did the use of leftover meats save in meal preparation?

2. Melt and blend cheese into a sauce for toasted bread.

3. Prepare a macaroni-and-cheese casserole; combine the cheese so that it remains tender and of a creamy consistency.

4. Help in the purchase and preparation of a classroom luncheon using a meat alternate. Evaluate for flavor and cost.

5. Purchase the meat and help with the preparation of a meat-extender dish for luncheon.

6. Prepare a tray using cheeses and canned meats in sandwiches for an after-game snack.

7. Check on the amount of high-quality protein in a day's meals planned to include meat alternates.

¶ *Reading Further:*

A Shopper's Guide for Meat, Bulletin 288 (1962). Iowa State Extension Service, Ames, Iowa.

Beef in the Family Menu, Bulletin 259 (1960). Arizona State University Extension Service, Phoenix, Arizona.

Buying Meat, Bulletin 352 (1961). University of Idaho Extension Service, Boise, Idaho.

Cheese Buying Guide for Consumers, A 1.95:17. Government Printing Office, Washington, D. C.

Game Foods, Bulletin 539 (1960). Washington State University Extension Service, Pullman, Washington.

Know Your Meat, Bulletin 63 (1959). Kansas State University Extension Service, Manhattan, Kansas.

Lamb Dishes for Variety, Bulletin 279 (1960). University of Arizona Extension Service, Phoenix, Arizona.

Let's Cut Meat, Bulletin 1053 (1961). Cornell University Extension Service, Ithaca, N. Y.

Meat for Thrifty Meals, Bulletin No. 27 (June 1953), Bureau of Human Nutrition and Home Economics, U. S. Department of Agriculture, Washington, D. C.

Selected References on Nutrition and School Lunch, FS 5.228: 28004. Government Printing Office, Washington, D. C.

SHERMAN, HENRY C., *Food Products*, 4th ed., The Macmillan Company, New York.

STANLEY, LOUISE, and CLINE, JESSIE ALICE, *Foods: Their Selection and Preparation*, rev. ed., Chap. 9 ("Cheese and Cheese Cookery"), and Chap. 18 ("Dried Legumes and Nuts"), Ginn and Company, Boston.

Venison, Bulletin 253 (1960). Michigan State University Extension Service, East Lansing, Michigan.

12

R. Day, from F. P. G.

Luncheon breads and sandwiches

you will learn: How to select appropriate breads
for luncheon or supper; How to prepare yeast breads;
How to prepare sandwiches

The idea of leavening bread is so ancient that it is mentioned in the Bible. Down through the centuries various means have been used to leaven homemade bread. Before yeast was prepared and sold by the grocer, it was bought at a brewery or made at home. The hop plant used in yeast making was introduced into England in the sixteenth century. In seventeenth-century America

your many-times-great-grandmother probably made her own yeast, and she may have grown the hops for it. Rye or corn meals, and sometimes potatoes, and a cupful of yeast saved from the last bread were used to start the yeast growing in the new dough. The Southern cook, famous for her hot biscuits, depended on beating to make them light. She beat the dough with a paddle for

142

an hour until air was in every pore. Her biscuits, pricked on top and baked, were delicious, and "beaten biscuits" are still a favorite in the South.

By the nineteenth century, almost all Northern towns had bakeries. While many American families continued to bake their own bread, cakes, and pies, there were enough people not interested in making bread, or without facilities for baking, to support a bakery. Today bakeries use modern equipment to knead and bake dough. Bakers have learned the trade and are able to solve problems connected with bread and yeast. Bread production is now a big industry and by buying bread the homemaker is saved hours of kneading and baking. The art of making bread at home is not, however, a dead one. Although most of the bread is usually purchased, a good cook prides herself on her ability to make yeast bread or rolls as a delicious accompaniment for family and guest meals.

Selecting Appropriate Breads

Bread is a nourishing, satisfying food which generally is served at all meals. One of the foods highest in energy, bread also serves as a good source of minerals and vitamins when it is made from whole-wheat or enriched flour, milk, and eggs. The flour proteins are low in quality but can be supplemented easily at a meal with milk, eggs, meat, or other high-quality protein foods. Breads made from white flour are the most used in this country. The eating of whole-wheat, cracked-wheat, soybean, oatmeal, and whole-rye breads should be encouraged because of their high nutritional value.

Enriched yeast breads, rich muffins, or waffles are high in calories and food values. Any of these breads served with such foods as peanut butter, cottage cheese, or creamed vegetables, or with hot chocolate made with whole milk, provides an adequate light luncheon. Many foods, such as fruits, nuts, coconut, honey, chocolate, cheese, crumbled bacon, and cracklings, may be used in luncheon breads to increase their food value and flavor.

Luncheon breads serve also as pleasant supplements to other main dishes. Meat, cheese, vegetables, or fish dishes may be accompanied either by quick breads, like biscuits or muffins, by steamed breads, such as brown bread, or by yeast breads. Corn bread is appetizing with bean, pea, or meat soups.

Soda, soybean, or cheese crackers, shredded-wheat or rye wafers, small biscuits, rolls, muffins, toast, and bread sticks are suitable for serving with soups and salads.

Before you select a bread for luncheon, consider the flavor and texture of other foods in the menu. Nut muffins are delicious when served with fruit salad but are too rich to accompany a main dish of macaroni and cheese. You should also choose bread to supplement the day's requirements of food values. If a meal is low in carbohydrates, cinnamon rolls or raisin bread will supply the need.

The choice of breads is governed further by the time required for their preparation and by their expense. Rich quick breads may contain costly ingredients although they require a minimum amount of time to prepare. Yeast breads, on the other hand, take two or more hours to prepare but may be less expensive. Both types of bread should be familiar to the homemaker. She will find that each one is suitable for certain menus.

The homemaker should not shrug off the art of making yeast bread as a slow, old-fashioned process associated only with grandmother's day. On the contrary, making yeast bread has been so simplified by modern methods and equipment that bread can be made at home quickly and economically. Nothing can compare with the flavor and aroma of fresh bread just out of the oven.

The busy homemaker or career person will, of course, find it advantageous to buy at least part of her yeast bread. But many new mixes, frozen products, and partially baked breads allow her the pleasure of homemade bread with the minimum of time spent in preparation. Such mixes and frozen products include rolls, coffee cakes, buns, and bread loaves. Each can be used appropriately for luncheon. Mixes come with the ingredients already measured. All that is left to do is to dissolve and add the yeast and liquid and set the dough aside to rise. Frozen products leave nothing to be done but the actual baking. Rolls can be bought which are partially baked and need only the last few minutes of browning.

If a family wishes to be economical, they can prepare their own mixes for homemade bread. These should be tightly covered until used. They can make large batches of dough, bake only the rolls or loaves immediately needed, and freeze the rest. Breads can also be completely baked and stored in the home freezer. All that is necessary before serving is thawing and, possibly, reheating. Or they may be partially baked and quick-frozen in a refrigerator freezing compartment or home freezer for later use. Cooking today for tomorrow is a great convenience.

The Qualities of Yeast Breads

Because the action of the yeast takes several hours, yeast breads are not classified as quick breads. However, the actual mixing of ingredients and the baking is no more difficult or time-consuming than for making quick breads. Yeast, which causes the bread to rise and is responsible for the texture, is a plant organism. It feeds upon the starch and sugars in the bread mixture and gives off carbon dioxide, which expands the gluten meshwork of the dough (see page 53). This process is called fermentation. Yeast leaves no aftertaste and is a rich source of thiamine, riboflavin, and niacin.

There are three forms of yeast on the market:

1. *Compressed yeast* contains many active yeast plants and must be kept refrigerated. Fermentation begins as soon as the yeast comes into contact with sugar, moisture, and warmth.

2. *Dry-yeast cakes* are made of dried yeast mixed with corn meal. This kind of yeast

Ready-to-bake bread foods · These salt sticks have been carefully prepared and were ready for the oven when they were frozen. Taken from the freezer and put into a 400° oven, they should bake for about fifteen minutes

Pepperidge Farm

THE PREPARATION OF BREAD DOUGH

1

When an irregular ball has been formed and the dough comes away from the bowl readily, turn it out on a lightly floured breadboard

2

Fold the dough toward you with a rolling motion, using the fingers of both hands

Push the ball of dough away from you, using the heels of your hands

3

4

After kneading approximately five minutes as before, you should have a softly rounded, spongy mound of dough. Return the dough to the greased mixing bowl

5

When two fingers are pressed deeply into the dough and the holes remain, the dough has doubled in bulk and is ready for the next step

At this point the dough should be punched down to release some of the gas, thus speeding fermentation by accelerating yeast activity

6

keeps longer than others but also takes longer to ferment. Because of this slower fermentation, bread made with hard-wheat flours has a very fine texture when this yeast is used.

3. *Fast-rising granular yeast* is a dried yeast packaged in powder form. It keeps without refrigeration, dissolves easily, and works quickly. Dried granular yeast acts more quickly when mixed with a little lukewarm water before it is added to the liquid. A package of this stabie, active, dry yeast may be used in any recipe which calls for a cake of yeast.

Regular makers of yeast bread sometimes save a portion of the sponge to start fermentation. Sugar is added for the growth of the yeast until the sponge is used in the dough for the next baking. The process can be repeated indefinitely.

The Ingredients in Yeast Breads

Flour, liquid, salt, fat, sugar, and yeast make up the basic dough. *Flour* has been discussed in Chapter 4. Hard-wheat flour is especially good because of its high gluten content which makes a dough strong and elastic and allows the volume to double. With soft-wheat flour more yeast and sugar and less liquid are used. Dough made with soft-wheat flour requires rapid fermentation and less kneading than that made with a hard-wheat variety. The amount of flour needed is not definite in most recipes since it depends on the kind of flour used. Sufficient flour is needed for the dough to be easily handled.

The *liquid* may be water, potato water, or milk. Potato water gives a distinctive flavor and stimulates the yeast growth. Mashed potatoes added in small amounts help to keep the bread moist. Milk, a good liquid

for yeast growth, adds nutritive value. It also furnishes flavor and color, gives a finer grain, and improves the keeping quality of the bread. Fresh milk must be scalded before it is used (heated to 160° to 180° F.) to destroy microorganisms which might interfere with the yeast growth or produce undesirable flavor. Diluted evaporated milk or dried milk need not be scalded.

Sugar is an important ingredient in yeast breads. It serves as food for the yeast plants, helps to make the bread tender and crusty, and adds flavor. It also causes bread to brown quickly. An excess of sugar retards yeast growth.

Salt brings out the wheat flavor of bread. Without salt, fermentation takes place too rapidly and gives the bread a coarse texture. Too much salt slows fermentation too much and produces a compact, heavy bread.

Any bland *fat* (that is, one without pronounced flavor) may be used to make yeast breads. Fat gives flavor, tenderizes, makes a soft crumb, and helps to keep the bread moist.

Eggs, in the richer doughs, give protein of high quality. They add color and flavor and help produce a velvety texture.

Fruits, nuts, seeds, or flavorings may be used for special and unusual breads. Caraway, sesame, or poppy seeds are desirable for this purpose. Usually, they are sprinkled over the surface of the shaped dough before it is baked.

Combining the Ingredients

Though the ingredients of yeast breads may be combined in several ways, there are two general methods. In both, the kneading, rising, and shaping of the dough, and the baking are the same. If scalded milk is used, it must be cooled to lukewarm before it is added to the yeast as yeast plants are killed

Yeast breads and rolls; casserole bread (upper right); yeast raised muffins; white bread; whole-wheat rolls; cinnamon buns

by high temperatures. A small amount of sugar hastens fermentation.

In the *straight-dough method* all ingredients are combined in a single mixing process. This is the quickest method of making yeast bread. The *sponge method* is always used with dry yeast, which requires a long fermentation period. The time can be shortened by using more yeast. Compressed yeast may be used in the sponge method. The yeast is dissolved in lukewarm liquid. Then it is combined with the remaining liquid and half of the flour. This mixture is covered and set aside at room temperature until it becomes a frothy sponge. Then the salt, sugar, fat, and the remainder of the flour are mixed into the sponge to form a stiff dough.

Kneading the Dough

After the ingredients are mixed, the dough is turned out on a floured board and allowed to rest for 3 to 5 minutes—dough that stands a few minutes is more easily kneaded. Before kneading the dough, flour your hands just enough to prevent sticking. Push the center of the dough down with the heel of your hand, keeping the fingers curved around the dough. Double the dough over with the fingers and give it a quarter turn with the same movement. Repeat this process quickly, with a light, rhythmic touch, until the dough is soft, satin smooth, and elastic, with blisters under the surface. Heavy pressure is not needed. Hard-wheat flour requires more kneading than soft-wheat flour. Kneading develops the gluten and allows it to take up more moisture for further expansion. It also helps blend the ingredients.

The Rising Period

After you have kneaded the dough, grease the top lightly to prevent drying and allow it to rise in a covered greased bowl.

Too much fat will cause streaks to show up later in the bread. A waxed paper over the top and a tight cover help to control the temperature and protect the dough from dust and drying. In the first rising the dough should double in bulk and should spring back quickly when pressed with the finger. At the end of the first rising, punch the dough down and knead it lightly to allow the gas to escape. Rolls or soft-wheat breads may be shaped at this time.

A second rising period is desirable with hard-wheat flours to make a fine-grained bread. When the dough has been punched down after the first rising, turn it over in the bowl, cover, and set aside to double again in bulk. Kneading the dough between risings will improve the texture. The second rising should not take as long as the first. The second kneading will not require additional flour and can be done quickly.

Shaping the Dough

To shape the dough into loaves, divide it into balls of equal size and allow it to rest for 10 minutes. Then flatten the dough and fold lengthwise. Stretch the dough to three times the length of the pan. Fold ends to center and press down to seal. Roll by hand into the shape of the pan. The dough should fill the pan half full. Grease the top lightly. Rolls are shaped either by breaking off small lumps of the dough and shaping them individually by hand, or by rolling out the dough and cutting it into the desired shapes with a sharp knife or biscuit cutter. Both rolls and loaves should be handled with a light touch. The tops may be brushed with melted fat or milk. Grease roll or loaf pans lightly on the bottom and sides. Cover the pans with a towel or waxed paper and allow the shaped dough to rise again until double in bulk before baking.

148

Baking the Bread

Your yeast breads are ready to bake when they have attained the required lightness. For a pound loaf, 385° F. is a desirable temperature to stop the growth of the yeast plant. Unless the oven bakes very evenly, loaves should be turned around after they have been in 15 minutes. The oven temperature should then be lowered. In the use of a wood or coal range the temperature at the start should be 400° F. Baking will require 45 minutes to 1 hour. Rolls require a high temperature and a short time for baking (see baking chart, page 451). You will know that yeast bread is done when you hear a hollow sound on tapping the loaves, and when the bread shrinks slightly from the sides of the pan. In the last few minutes of baking, bread loaves may be brushed with milk to improve their color and give a glossy tender crust. Mixtures of milk and sugar, or of table fat, sugar, and cinnamon make good finishes. Properly baked loaves and rolls are evenly grained with a tender, soft crumb. They are moist and springy to the touch and golden brown in color.

Caring for the Baked Bread

Remove bread from the pans as soon as it is taken from the oven to prevent the crusts from steaming. Place the loaves on a rack or crosswise on the top edges of the pans to cool thoroughly. They should never be covered while warm. After the bread is cool, it may be wrapped in waxed paper and stored in a breadbox or in the refrigerator.

Preparing Sandwiches

Sandwiches, made by spreading various fillings on sliced bread, may be used as main luncheon dishes if they are rich in food values. Smaller, less-rich sandwiches are excellent to accompany soups, salads, or desserts for luncheon. You may also enjoy sandwiches as nourishing between-meal snacks (see Chapter 2).

Main-Dish Sandwiches

Some luncheon sandwiches are more savory when served *hot*. Protein foods are usually the fillings for these hot sandwiches, and gravy or sauce often is served with them. Toast, bread slices, or a split roll makes a good sandwich. Fillings may be spread on two bread slices or between three or more slices. Three layers are, however, difficult to assemble and hard to eat, even when held together by skewers or toothpicks. Hot sandwiches are eaten with a fork.

Meat or poultry served with gravy on bread or toast makes a pleasing open sandwich. A hot sandwich made with a meat filling on French bread, toasted, is also an appetizing variation. (For further suggestions, refer to the Cookbook, pages 401–408.)

Other sandwiches for serving as hot dishes include the following:

1. Sliced roast beef or pork on bread or toast, with a large serving of hot gravy

2. Broiled or fried ground-meat cakes served between plain or toasted bread slices or on a bun

3. Hot cheese sauce, seasoned, and served on toast

4. Slices of hard-cooked egg served on toast with a generous amount of white sauce

5. French bread, toasted, with meat-salad or poultry filling

6. Toasted, buttered bread with fillings of green vegetables and meat slices or cheese

Two types of *toasted* sandwiches are suitable main dishes. In one, the filling is placed between buttered bread and toasted. Made with cheese and served with sliced tomatoes and green olives, it is a satisfying luncheon dish. In the second, the bread is toasted first; then the sandwich is made. This method is appropriate for fillings containing lettuce, other greens, and raw vegetables. Toasting the bread adds flavor and makes the sandwich easier to eat.

The following combinations of fillings and breads offer you a wide variety:

1. Slivered cheese, pickles, on toasted bread strips
2. Chopped dried fruits, lemon juice, on toasted nut bread
3. Grated raw carrots, chopped raisins, on toasted cinnamon bread
4. Chopped nuts, honey, on toasted cracked-wheat bread
5. Deviled ham, slivered olives, on toasted split biscuits
6. Chopped crisp bacon, raw apple, on toasted rye bread

Cold sandwiches that are sufficiently rich in calories for main dishes are made chiefly of protein foods. They may be served with a green salad on which an appetizing dressing is used. Adding a vegetable and a beverage makes a complete luncheon meal. With a cold sandwich as the main dish, a hot vegetable adds contrast to the menu.

Suitable meats to use in cold sandwiches are sliced roast beef, pork, ham, tongue, corned beef, and bacon. Finely cut meat, poultry, hard-cooked eggs, or fish, combined with pickles, seasonings, and dressing, are good sandwich fillers. Other protein foods to use in main-dish sandwiches are cheese and nuts. Raw vegetables, with or without meat, add flavor, food values, and texture to

sandwiches. Lettuce, spinach, parsley, grated carrots, chopped celery, onions, cucumbers, and red and green peppers may be used in combination with hard-cooked eggs, cheese, or nuts. The following rich fillings and breads are among the main-dish sandwich combinations that are appetizing served cold:

1. Sliced roast meat, green pepper, horseradish, and mayonnaise or cooked salad dressing on rye or cracked-wheat bread
2. Tuna, chopped apple, celery, lemon juice, and mayonnaise on whole-wheat bread
3. Shredded cabbage, dried apricots, walnuts, and mayonnaise on white bread
4. Swiss cheese, bacon, tomato, and lettuce on rye bread
5. Chopped hard-cooked egg, canned tongue, grated cheese, mustard, and mayonnaise on whole-wheat rolls

Cold main-dish sandwiches may be garnished as a means of adding food value. *Garnishes* should be eaten with the sandwiches. Among those quickly prepared and served are the following:

1. Dill, sweet, or cucumber pickles
2. Pickled onions, beets, or beans
3. Ripe, green, or stuffed olives
4. Cucumber sticks or rings
5. Slices of radish, tomato, green pepper, or onion
6. Carrot, celery, or radish curls

Accompaniment Sandwiches

Smaller cold sandwiches are served with soups or salads at luncheons. You can make an almost endless variety of these smaller sandwiches with a filling between slices of bread or spread on one piece of bread. Appropriate fillings may be made from finely chopped cooked meats or flaked fish (canned

Sandwiches for parties · Using cookie cutters of different shapes adds interest to a sandwich tray. The possibilities of sandwich fillings are as wide as your imagination

products may be used). Fruits, either dried, candied, canned, or fresh, make interesting sandwiches. Carrots, tomatoes, celery, lettuce, and other greens are good vegetable fillings. Olives, pickles, coconut, and nuts give flavor and texture contrast. Suggested garnishes to accompany these sandwiches are: small bunches of grapes, sweet cherries on stems, cheese cubes on toothpicks, salted nuts, chocolate-covered raisins or nuts, gumdrops, candied orange or grapefruit rind, stuffed fruits, radish roses, and celery hearts.

Making Sandwiches

You should choose breads for sandwiches for their flavor and value in food combinations. If the filling is to be rich or well seasoned, an enriched white bread or whole-wheat bread is desirable. Certain fillings, such as tomatoes or bananas, are best on nut, rye, or other bread with a distinctive flavor. The bread for sandwiches should be fresh. For cold sandwiches, day-old bread may be preferred. Drying is eliminated and the sandwich is kept firm when the crust is left on. Matched bread slices make neater sandwiches.

Sandwich fillings should be made from products that are fresh, of excellent quality and flavor, and should be appropriately seasoned. Several thin slices of meat instead of a single thick one make a more delicious and easy-to-eat sandwich. Fillings of correct consistency do not ooze from sandwiches or cause bread to become soggy. Buttering or coating both slices of the bread with cream cheese or peanut butter helps to prevent the filling from soaking through and also keeps the bread moist. You should spread fillings to the edges of the bread and should use generous enough amounts to give a flavorful and adequate serving.

Storing Quantities of Sandwiches

Ingredients for sandwiches (except fresh fruits and vegetables) may be combined a few days before using if they are kept tightly covered and refrigerated to prevent loss of food value. In this way, two or three fillings can be kept on hand to vary the kind of sandwiches served during a week. Breads of all varieties will refrigerate or freeze satisfactorily. Most fillings or the completed sandwich may be frozen and kept in the

151

freezer compartment of the refrigerator for a week or stored in a home freezer for several months. Waxed paper or heavy cellophane or metal foil are satisfactory wrappings. Protein foods for sandwiches freeze successfully except for egg whites, which may become tough. If mayonnaise is to be used, it should be added to foods that have been frozen after they have been thawed—it separates when frozen and will soak into the bread. Salad greens or tomatoes should not be used in any sandwich which is made in advance.

¶ Understanding:

1. How may breads be made to contribute more generously to your diet?

2. When you make yeast bread by the sponge method, what kind of yeast and flour will you use? Describe the steps you will follow.

3. How may a busy homemaker serve freshly baked yeast breads with the least time and labor for herself?

4. What are the advantages of making bread at home? Do they outweigh the disadvantages?

5. How should bread be cared for in the market? at home?

6. How will the kind of bread used for luncheon affect the choice of other dishes?

7. What will be your guides in buying bread?

8. What is required of main-dish sandwiches for luncheons? of accompaniment sandwiches for soups and salads?

¶ Planning:

1. Plan two luncheon meals in which you will include breads. Show what nutritional values you will introduce into the diet through each bread.

2. Plan two sandwich fillings. Which kind of bread will you use for each, and why? What other foods would be necessary to serve with each sandwich in order to make an adequate, well-balanced meal for your family?

3. Plan a sandwich which can be served hot for the home luncheon or packed cold in a lunch box.

4. Plan two meals to include different sandwiches. Make sandwiches the main dish in one meal.

5. In a luncheon menu substitute white bread for whole-wheat bread. Adjust the menu to give approximately the same food values.

¶ Practicing and Evaluating:

1. Make a bread using the straight-dough method. Check for flavor, texture, and color.

2. Make a bread from a packaged mix. Compare its cost with that of bread bought ready baked; with that of bread bought partially baked.

3. Prepare a main-dish sandwich for luncheon, observing the precautions necessary for a fresh, appetizing sandwich.

4. Prepare a nourishing, inexpensive toasted sandwich. What are appropriate accompaniments?

5. Store whole-wheat bread in the refrigerator; in a bread box; and in cloth wrappings. Compare the quality of the three after one day; after three days.

6. Interest the family in trying two or three new breads. Assist with their purchase.

7. Purchase the breads for home use for two days, using as a purchasing guide the information provided by the labels. What other helpful guides did you use?

8. Shape dough into rolls and loaves. Bake, keeping a moist product with tender crust.

¶ Reading Further:

HALLIDAY, EVELYN G., and NOBLE, I. T., *Hows and Whys of Cooking*, Chapter 6, University of Chicago Press, Chicago.

Yeast Breads and Rolls, Bulletin 541 (1960). University of Kentucky Extension Service, Lexington, Kentucky.

Yeast Breads and Rolls, Bulletin E–888 (1961). Cornell University Extension Service, Ithaca, New York.

13

Soups and salads

you will learn: The kinds of soup and their uses;
How to prepare and serve soups; The kinds of salads and
their uses; How to prepare and serve salads;
How to select and make salad dressings

To many people soup is an everyday dish, furnishing pleasant warmth to a chilled body or quick nourishment in a snack meal; few associate it with imagination and romance. But at least one romantic story is centered about soup. In the sixteenth century, in the household of Pope Leo X, a cook created a savory Lenten soup which so delighted the Pope that he gave his cook the surname Careme (meaning "Lent") and raised his salary to five times that of the highest-paid cook in the land.

While a delicious soup may not bring such a reward to the present-day cook, it is still the result of imagination and skill. It deserves the appreciation of those to whom it is served, either as a delightful introduction to a meal or as the main dish with tasty accompaniments. Give your soup the thought and care which will merit the family's pleased "This is different! What herb did you use?" The seasoning chart, on page 157, also suggests appropriate garnishes.

153

Kinds of Soup and Their Uses

Soups, because of their almost endless variety in content and nutritive value, can be fitted into luncheon or dinner menus to serve different purposes. Thin soups, such as bouillon or broth, when given a distinctive flavor and served with an attractive garnish, are commonly used to stimulate appetite for the rest of the meal. They are usually served in cups. Such soups are an excellent way of giving nourishment to small children or to persons unable, for any reason, to take solid foods.

Heavier soups, the thick cream soups and the meat soups containing vegetables and cereals, may be served in sufficient quantity to be the mainstay of the meal. Ingredients for these soups may be chosen to supply large amounts of proteins, carbohydrates, minerals, and vitamins. Whatever has not been supplied by the particular soup should be added to the menu: scalloped potatoes with a meat-vegetable combination, not with a cream soup; possibly a fruit salad with a cream soup. Since the various kinds of soups vary greatly in nutritive value, the type to use in a particular menu must be given careful consideration.

Stock, from which most soups are made, is the liquid left from cooking meats, poultry, or vegetables. *Consommé* is well-seasoned

Using leftovers in making soup · On the cutting board at the left is the untrimmed meat, which will be returned to the refrigerator. At the right front is the discarded gristle. At the right back is the trimmed meat. In the center is the cut-up meat, ready for browning

Jane and Steven Coons

veal or poultry stock, or a combination of meat and poultry stocks. _Bouillon_ is seasoned beef stock, free of fat and clarified. Brown stock is produced by browning meats before they are boiled. Vegetable stock contains valuable vitamins and minerals but because of its blandness should be added to meat stock, gravies, or cream soups rather than used alone. Though the process of making stock may sound simple, actually the preparation of stock that is clear and tasty requires skill. For this reason many consumers prefer to buy clear soups in cans instead of making their own. Many excellent canned varieties are available.

Cream soups are made from a thin or medium white sauce to which is added a purée of one or more vegetables. According to the taste of the family, vegetable or meat stock may also be used. Among the vegetables most commonly used for cream soups are corn, peas, asparagus, tomatoes, celery, mushrooms, onions, and white potatoes.

Bisques are usually made by combining a thin white sauce with chopped sea food, and often with some of the liquid in which the sea food has been cooked. Lobster bisque and clam bisque are those most frequently served. Occasionally tomato bisque appears on a menu; it is a thinner variety of cream-of-tomato soup.

Chowders are another variation of cream soups. They always contain diced or chopped vegetables or sea food. Bits of browned salt pork and diced white potatoes are ingredients of a true chowder. In some localities tomato juice is added to the chowder or is substituted for the white sauce.

Preparing and Serving Soups

Soup from Leftovers

For the average cook the most valuable soups are those that are built around leftover meats and vegetables and the water in which these foods have been cooked. In days when wood or coal ranges were in use and there was a constant fire in the kitchen, an iron pot was often kept simmering on the back of the range. Into it all desirable leftovers were put. After a time a rich liquid was drained off, seasoned, and bits of meat were added. The product was a nutritious and appetizing soup, an economical main dish. The thrifty cook saves all the water from foods and keeps it tightly covered in the refrigerator. She also uses bones, carcasses of poultry, scraps of meat, and leftover vegetables to contribute to soups. Bones (the large ones should be cracked) and carcasses should be boiled slowly in a large amount of salted water until the marrow and bits of meat separate from them. Meat scraps, browned in fat with a sliced onion and some carrot to give a richer flavor, may be added to the soup kettle.

As the mixture cooks, test it for flavor: undercooked stock is tasteless; overcooked stock is too strong. When the bones separate from the meat, both meat and bones should be removed and the stock strained. If time permits, the stock should be cooled, then chilled in the refrigerator until the fat collects on top so that it can be removed. Stock made in this way will not be clear nor entirely free from fat, but it is an inexpensive base for delicious soup.

Meat-Stock Soup

Occasionally you may wish to make a meat-stock soup without using leftovers.

Great chefs spend days on the preparation of such a dish. The method which follows is a very simple adaptation of their work.

You should have a shinbone of beef on which about a pound of meat remains, or a knuckle of veal with about a pound of the neck. Remove the meat, saw and crack the bones, put them into about two quarts of cold salted water on low heat, and boil very slowly in a covered kettle for 2 hours. Meanwhile cut the meat into small pieces and brown it in fat. Veal should be only slightly browned. Toward the end of the browning, add a sliced onion and three medium-sized carrots diced. A slice or two of turnips diced, a half dozen peppercorns, a bay leaf, celery tops, or parsley improves the flavor. Add the meat and the vegetables to the bones and continue the slow boiling to the end of the 2 hours. Now strain, cool, and chill the stock in the refrigerator. To use, remove the fat, reheat, and season. If diced vegetables are to be added, cook them quickly in a little water in a covered pan to preserve vitamins, flavor, and color. When the vegetables, and perhaps some of the meat, have been added to the soup, it is ready to serve.

Cream Soups

Since most cream soups are made of white sauce and a purée of some vegetable, their quality depends largely upon the skill with which the sauce is made. The basic ingredients of white sauce are flour (which thickens it), fat, and a liquid (usually cream or milk). A table of proportions for thin, medium, and thick white sauce is given on page 423.

The white sauce may be made by three methods: (1) entirely over direct heat, (2) entirely in a double boiler, or (3) by the compromise method. Each method has its advantages and disadvantages. Two steps in all three methods are the same: the milk should be heated before it is added to the fat-flour mixture; the fat should be melted before the flour is added.

When using the *direct-heat method*, melt the fat in a saucepan, over very low heat or in the oven; do not let it brown. Add the

	METHOD	ADVANTAGES	DISADVANTAGES
	COMPARISON OF METHODS FOR MAKING WHITE SAUCE		
1	DIRECT-HEAT	Rich flavor; little time to prepare	Too rapid cooking causes lumpiness; sauce may scorch
2	DOUBLE-BOILER	No scorching; lumping unlikely	Two double boilers required; less-rich flavor, more time required
3	COMPROMISE	Less time than for No. 2; no scorching or lumping Flavor richer than in No. 2	Time greater than for No. 1; double boiler plus top of a second double boiler needed

flour and stir constantly until a smooth paste is obtained. Then add the hot milk gradually, stirring constantly, and let the sauce boil gently for 2 minutes.

For the *double-boiler method* heat the milk in the top of a double boiler. In a second double boiler, melt the fat, add the flour, and stir to a smooth paste. Now add the hot milk, stirring frequently until the sauce thickens. Cook 10 minutes longer over hot water and occasionally stir to prevent lumping.

To use the *compromise method*, heat the milk in one double boiler. In the top of the other, melt the fat over low direct heat, add the flour, and stir to a smooth paste. Now place this pan over hot water. Add the hot milk, proceeding as in the double-boiler method.

Because the thickening of the sauce is not completed until the boiling point is reached, the directions above call for boiling or cooking after thickening begins. Moreover, this boiling or cooking is necessary to prevent the fat from separating from the rest of the sauce and to avoid a raw-starch taste. With proper care all three methods produce successful results. Time and experience should determine the method to be used.

Vegetables for cream soups are cooked and rubbed through a sieve and then added to the hot white sauce. The usual proportions are $\frac{1}{2}$ cup of vegetable purée to 1 cup of liquid sauce. However, you should use very strongly flavored vegetables, such as broccoli, in smaller amounts.

Cream-of-tomato soup has to be prepared in a special way to prevent the acid of the tomatoes from curdling the milk in the white sauce. The safest method is to melt the fat, add the flour, stir to a smooth paste, and cook for a minute or two. Add the tomato purée, stir, and cook until the thickening is completed and the starch cooked. Pour this

thickened sauce into the measured milk, being sure that the milk is cold and very fresh. It is now safe to heat the soup for serving. Never use soda in the tomatoes to prevent curdling; it destroys vitamin C.

Chilled Soups

Soups may be served either hot or cold but never lukewarm. Cold soups are made in exactly the same way as hot soups and then cooled and refrigerated. Chill the bowls in which the soup is to be served as well as the soup. Cold soups are ideal for summer meals. Among the most popular are Vichyssoise (made from leeks, potatoes, and white sauce) and cream of tomato. Consommé and bouillon are excellent served as chilled soups.

SEASONINGS FOR SOUPS

KIND of SOUP	APPROPRIATE SEASONINGS
Meat stock....	Basil or marjoram (last hour of cooking) Chili
Fish chowders	Savory or thyme
Oyster stew...	Mace
Chicken......	Nutmeg, rosemary, or saffron
Vegetable....	Savory or whole spice (pea) Rosemary (spinach) Cloves (borsch, potato) Dry mustard (bean, lentil, cream celery) Basil (tomato bouillon) Chili

Seasonings, Garnishes, and Accompaniments for Soup

The purpose of *seasonings* is to accent the true flavor of the soup. The amount of seasoning to use for each soup depends upon the blandness of the chief ingredient, the strength of the seasoning, and personal taste. It is better to have too little seasoning than too much. When you add seasonings, start with a little and add gradually until the soup suits the taste. Allowing the soup to simmer after the seasoning has been added blends the flavors. Experience will teach you how much seasoning to use and which of the herbs are best with each kind of soup. Do not limit yourself to the few seasonings with which you are already familiar; use new ones. Some favorites are charted on page 157.

Garnishes are added to the soup just before it is served. Among those desirable are slivered almonds or other nuts on cream-of-chicken and cream-of-mushroom soup; chopped chives, parsley, or buttered toasted crumbs on vegetable soups, clear or creamed; chopped olives on chicken-noodle soups; popcorn on tomato soup; croutons on cream soups. Browned onion rings, croutons, paprika, chopped egg, grated cheese, and crumbled bacon are other garnishes which are good with many kinds of soups.

Accompaniments are served with the soup, rather than as a part of the soup. The purpose of accompaniments is to emphasize the flavor of the soup and to add further food value to the meal. Among the favorites are crackers, corn sticks, cheese straws, and melba toast.

Short Cuts to Soups

Concentrated and *dehydrated* soups require very little time for preparation. Bouillon cubes, either beef or chicken, dissolved in hot water and carefully seasoned, will make a pleasant thin soup that can be served as an appetizer. Dehydrated soups are on the market in packaged form. To these, liquid is added and the mixture is cooked according to the directions.

Canned soups of excellent quality are readily available. Condensed soups require the addition of liquid according to directions on the label. To make an especially enriched dish, and for reasons of thrift, milk, meat, cereals, vegetables, stock, or desirable left-over foods may be added. Canned soups may be combined successfully: beef or chicken-noodle with vegetable, cream-of-chicken with cream-of-asparagus, and tomato with clam chowder. To add flavor to casserole dishes, creamed foods, or sauces use beef bouillon, chicken, tomato, or mushroom soup. These quickly prepared soups are a convenience for the woman employed outside the home.

Kinds of Salad and Their Uses

The first "salad bowl," made by mixing greens of the field in a large container, was produced by the ancient Arabians. They warmed olive oil in the sun and used it for a dressing. The Greeks later created new recipes, developed new herbs, and introduced spices. The Romans improved the dressing. A princess of the Medici family of Florence, Italy, powerful in the fifteenth century, introduced salads to the French. Europeans brought the salad bowl to America, where it has been enthusiastically accepted. From the Bohemians, exceptional salad makers, and the Germans, who have

158

used salads for centuries, we have learned secrets of seasoning which have made the salad an even more popular American food.

Salads are as numerous and as varied as the foods from which they are made. They may be as simple as a spoonful of chopped cabbage dressed with oil and vinegar or as elaborate as shrimp in aspic. They may form part of a family luncheon or dinner or appear as refreshments at parties. A salad may be used as an appetizer, a luncheon or supper main dish, an accompaniment to the meat course, a separate course following the meat, or in place of dessert.

Because of the great range of color, shape, and texture in fruits and vegetables, which make up most salads, salad ingredients may be combined into most attractive and appetizing dishes.

Ways of Using Salads

Because of their varied ingredients, salads may contain most of the needed food values. In addition to their nutritive value, they furnish the crisp chewy foods required for healthy teeth and gums and supply bulk in the diet. They may be used in various ways.

At dinner, salads may be served at the beginning of the meal *as an appetizer*. These salads should be tart and light so that they will stimulate the appetite for the rest of the meal.

Salads used *as garnishes or accompaniments* to the meat course may be placed on the plate with the meat course and eaten with it. They should be small, colorful, daintily arranged, and consist of mixed fruits, vegetables, or greens. Stuffed prunes are very commonly used in this way.

A salad that serves *as the main dish* of a luncheon or supper must furnish most of the calories in the meal. Protein-rich salads may be made with meat, fish, sea food, cheese, eggs, nuts, or beans. The protein salads are less fattening than other high-calorie salads, such as potato salad.

A salad may be used *as a substitute for dessert* to add a light finish to a heavy meal. It is often sweet and may consist of a combination of fruits, sometimes molded in a fruit gelatin. Coconut, cream cheese, or whipped cream are often used with the fruit.

Salads may be served *as refreshments* at social occasions accompanied by a hot muffin or cheese straws and a beverage. Fruit salads, tossed vegetable salads, and sea-food combinations are favorites for this kind of use.

Selection of Ingredients

It is most important in selecting salad ingredients to consider how the salad is to be used in the day's menus. If it is to be a main dish, ingredients with a high calorie content must be chosen, such as meat, fish, cheese, or eggs. Certain vegetables, such as celery, tomato, cucumber, and peas, combine well with these to give contrast in color, texture, and flavor. All ingredients should be fresh to ensure that the salad will be delicate and its proteins safe for use.

Greens and Other Vegetables—The markets offer a wide choice of salad greens and vegetables throughout the year. The selection and care of greens and vegetables is discussed in Chapter 18.

Greens for salads should contrast in taste, texture, shape of the leaves, and color. Some appropriate combinations are as follows:

1. Raw spinach and iceberg lettuce
2. Chopped parsley and green cabbage
3. Romaine and watercress

Vegetables and other foods may be com-

Salad bowl · The greens have been washed and crisped. To them shortly will be added slices of radish, green pepper, cucumber, scallions, wedges of tomato, and the dressing. The carrot sticks and radish roses will be served as garnishes

bined for salad in many ways, including the following:

1. Tomatoes, cucumbers, lettuce
2. Potatoes, onions, diced egg, green and red peppers
3. Carrots, celery, raisins
4. Cabbage, pineapple, peanuts
5. Chives, cottage cheese, watercress

Fruits—Variety in flavor and texture are added to the diet by using fruits in salads.

There is a wide choice of fresh, canned, frozen, and dried fruits. If a salad is to be frozen, raw grapes should not be used since they tend to become soft and unappetizing when frozen.

Appetizing combinations of fruits with other foods are as follows:

1. Apples, celery, nuts
2. Pineapple, cottage cheese, pimento
3. Melon balls, mint leaves, oranges
4. Avocados, grapefruit, watercress

160

Preparing and Serving Salads

To save time and work in making salads, put all the ingredients, seasonings, and utensils together in one work center, preferably near the refrigerator.

Some ingredients are marinated before they are added to a salad, that is, they are moistened with French or other thin salad dressing until they become well seasoned. Each kind of food, such as meat or fish or potatoes, should be marinated separately, drained, and combined with the other foods just before the salad is served. Any garlic or onion which may have been added to the dressing must be removed before marinating.

SALAD GARNISHES

Carrot curls · Pare large, crisp carrots with vegetable parer. Shave off lengthwise strips as shown; roll around finger tip; chill on ice

Radish roses · Cut off tails and most leaves; cut as shown; they open up on ice

Flowerets of raw cauliflower and broccoli · Break cauliflower or broccoli into small blossoms; slice if necessary to reduce pieces to dainty proportions

161

Washing and draining salad greens

The greens used in salads must be washed thoroughly, then drained. Excess water will dilute the dressing, and prevent the leaves from becoming coated with the seasonings. After being washed and drained, the greens should be refrigerated.

Foods that do not cut easily with a fork should be cut into pieces convenient for eating. Raw celery and cold potatoes may be diced; raw cabbage, carrots, and lettuce may be shredded; raw carrots may be grated, diced, or sliced.

Canned fruits and vegetables should be drained and chilled thoroughly before they are used in salads. To ensure freedom from harmful microorganisms, nonacid, home-canned vegetables must be boiled for 10 minutes.

If canned meats are flaked before using, the texture of the salad is improved.

The making of attractive salads requires care in planning, in combining the ingredients, and in arranging. For best results, follow the suggestions below:

1. A large bowl, individual plates, or individual salad bowls may be used for serving salads. Chilled bowls or plates should

162

always be used. If a bowl is used, a distinctive flavor may be introduced into meat or vegetable salads by rubbing the bowl with a clove of garlic or a cut onion. Chopped and tossed salads are usually served in a large bowl, the dressing being added to them in the bowl and everyone serving himself. Salads that must be cut for eating should be served on salad plates. Individual servings of molded salad may go to the table turned out into a nest of greens or into orange, cucumber, or tomato shells set on plates.

2. The foods used in salads and salad dressings should be left in the refrigerator until just before using. Only a few salads (potato, wilted lettuce, and other greens) are served without chilling.

3. For attractive servings it is important that you put salad ingredients together neatly and simply, and arrange small to medium-sized portions, suiting the size to the purpose that the salad will serve in the meal. Salads are interesting if they have their ingredients arranged with a center of interest. Apple wedges may radiate from a center of prunes stuffed with cheese. A salad should not extend over the edge of the plate. Salad greens aid in making an attractive serving. They should be eaten with the salad.

4. To prevent salad foods from becoming crushed or bruised, handle them as little as possible. When tossing green salads to distribute the ingredients and to coat them with the dressing, use a few light strokes, preferably made with forks. In overmixing, vitamin C is lost and the salad is less attractive in appearance.

5. Avoid using too much dressing. Dressings are added to salads to moisten and season the foods and to bind them together. An excess is wasteful and decreases the crispness and flavor.

Selecting and Preparing Salad Dressings

There are three basic dressings for salads. *French dressing*, made of an oil, acid, and seasonings, is especially suitable for green salads, and for acid or bland fruit salads. *Mayonnaise* is made of oil, vinegar, egg yolk or whole egg, and seasonings. Commercial mayonnaise is required by law to contain a certain percentage of oil and egg. This rich dressing, though used on all kinds of salads, is most appropriate with meat, fish, egg, and tart-fruit salads. *Cooked dressings* contain milk or water, egg or starch, fat, seasonings, and acid. They usually cost less than mayonnaise and are less rich than either French dressing or mayonnaise. Cooked salad dressings combine well with mild-fruit, vegetable, or gelatin salads. However, they may be used on any salad.

There is a wide choice of ingredients from which to make salad dressings. The fat may be an oil or a liquid animal fat. Olive oil has a rich, distinctive flavor. Peanut oil and vegetable oils are more delicate in flavor and may be less expensive. Of the animal fats, pork drippings, rendered chicken fat, or table fat may be used. Tart fruit juices are sometimes used to acidify dressings, but vinegar more often serves for this purpose. Among a wide selection of vinegars, cider and white-wine vinegars are most used for dressings. Tarragon, malt, and red-wine vinegar have decided flavors appropriate to bland foods. Among the seasonings commonly used are salt, sugar, spices, sauces, such as Tabasco and Worcestershire, and herbs.

Making Salad Dressings

The oils and liquids must be well blended in salad dressings. *French dressing* is the least complicated to make since the ingredients are combined by beating or by shaking together in a tightly covered jar. Since the oil separates quickly from the liquids the dressing ingredients must be shaken together just before using. Interesting variations of basic French dressings are described in the Cookbook, page 398. Ingredients for *mayonnaise* must be combined carefully to prevent them from separating or curdling. If the oil separates from the liquid, beat an egg yolk and add the dressing to the new yolk. Beating 1 tablespoon of either water or vinegar into the dressing may restore its

French dressing · Oil, vinegar, salt, pepper, herbs, and other seasonings are shaken up together in a tightly covered jar. French dressing, carefully prepared according to your favorite recipe, may be kept indefinitely, but it should be vigorously shaken before it is used

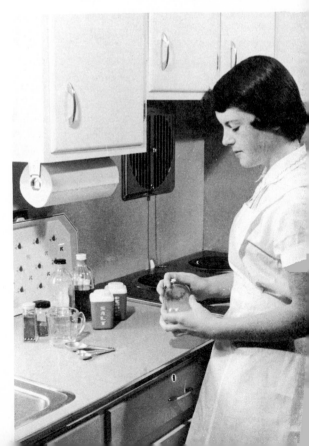

consistency. Mayonnaise should be tart, smooth in texture, and stiff enough to hold shape when spooned out. Variations are to be found in the Cookbook, page 399.

Cooked salad dressings are modified white sauces which include eggs, acid, and seasonings. A white sauce is prepared in a double boiler (see pages 156–157). The acid is then beaten into the eggs and this mixture added to the prepared white sauce in the double boiler. The sauce mixture is then stirred until the egg is completely cooked.

A variety of flavors and food values result from adding other ingredients to the mayonnaise and cooked dressings—for example, whipped cream, fruit juices, grated cheese, chopped vegetables, nuts, pickles, and hard-cooked egg.

Care of Salad Dressing

Oil and fat become rancid when exposed to light, warmth, and air. Keep the jars covered tightly in the refrigerator and wipe them off carefully after each use.

¶ *Understanding:*

1. Which soups would you select for your luncheon meals? Why?

2. What do you gain from using dried-milk solids or soybean flour in soups?

3. What leftover foods are appropriate in soups?

4. What are some of the most attractive garnishes for your soups?

5. What are the advantages of making soups rather than using prepared soups? What are the disadvantages?

6. What quality will you look for in the selection of ingredients for tossed green salads?

7. How will you care for vegetables for salads to preserve their freshness?

8. What are the advantages to the homemaker of serving a salad as a main dish?

¶ *Planning:*

1. Plan a menu to use leftover foods in a rich soup.

2. Find recipes for two kinds of soups to prepare at home. Show what chief food values each soup contributes to the meal.

3. Plan a Saturday meal for your family in which a salad provides the main dish. Compare with the cost of a meal in which a soup provided the main food values.

4. Plan salads to provide the chief mineral and vitamin content in two luncheons. Show what additional food values may be added by the dressing that is chosen.

¶ *Practicing and Evaluating:*

1. Combine ingredients for a tasteful cream-of-tomato soup. Serve with an accompaniment that adds protein values.

2. Prepare a minimum-cost soup as a main dish. How did you keep the cost low?

3. Prepare a soup using leftover meats, vegetables, and cereals. What care was given the leftover foods?

4. Collect the ingredients and utensils needed for a tossed green salad. Combine the ingredients so that they are crisp and flavorful.

5. Prepare a main-dish salad rich in protein values. What foods will combine well with this salad to make a balanced meal?

6. Prepare salads planned for two different meals. What food values did each salad contribute?

¶ *Reading Further:*

Good Salads, Bulletin HE20 (1960). Iowa State University Extension Service, Ames, Iowa.

Salads—Cool, Crisp, and Colorful, Bulletin E908 (1962). Cornell University Extension Service, Ithaca, New York.

Tasty Salads, Bulletin E479 (1960). Oklahoma State University Extension Service, Stillwater, Oklahoma.

Pillsbury Mills

Luncheon desserts

you will learn: The place of desserts
in the diet; How to prepare luncheon desserts: custards,
puddings, cakes and cookies, fruit combinations,
pastries and fillings

Concluding a meal with dessert is not a new practice. In medieval days the cook sent a pudding or custard to his master's table, and on great occasions he would often produce a special dessert, an elaborate confection of sugar, pastry, and spice molded into a statuette or group of figures.

From earliest times, sugar, an important ingredient in desserts, has been known in some form in every country. The word itself comes from Sanskrit, an ancient language of India. It was in India, where sugar cane is a native plant, that sugar was first made. Not until many centuries later, however, did the makers of sugar learn how to refine the raw sugar into the white granulated type most common today.

165

Natural sugar is present, in varying amounts, in many foods, but without additional sugar, the body is not apt to get enough to supply the needed energy. Sweet desserts, therefore, have an important place in the diet.

The Place of Desserts in the Diet

Desserts have come to be thought of not as the climax but rather as a delightful conclusion of satisfying meals. They should be pleasant in taste and texture, attractive in color and arrangement, and of the appropriate temperature, hot or cold, when served. But, though the pleasing appearance and taste of the dessert are important, its place in the nutritional pattern of the meal must also be taken into account.

Suiting the Dessert to the Meal and to the Individual

Although desserts may supply the body less in vitamins and minerals than other dishes of the meal, they do make valuable contributions of carbohydrate, fat, and protein. Their relation to the luncheon, light or heavy, must be planned carefully. A light-calorie menu requires a dessert which is high in fuel value; it needs the supplementary protein and fat found in such desserts as mince pie and chocolate-nut pudding. A high-calorie meal, on the other hand, should be followed by a low-calorie dessert, like a fruit cup or sherbet. Since luncheon is a light meal, the heavy desserts with high calorie value are discussed in this unit. However, luncheon and dinner desserts may be used interchangeably, depending on the food value of the other courses of the meal. (For dinner desserts, see pages 254–260.)

In choosing and serving desserts for any meal, the individuals who are to eat the meal should be considered. Valuable as sugar is as a source of energy, it is harmful

if eaten in excess. People who are leading quiet lives need much less than workers engaged in strenuous activity outdoors. A logger in a lumber camp thrives on beans baked in molasses, griddle cakes with maple sirup, coffee with plenty of sugar, and pies well sweetened. The same amount of sugar would be harmful for a sedentary worker.

In the early years of our country's development, rich desserts were more common because more people did heavy work. The early cookbooks show many more recipes for cakes, pies, sweet puddings, preserves, and jellies than do ours. Today, with machines taking care of a great deal of the strenuous labor that, in pioneer times, was done by hand, people are eating more fruits for their energy supply and fewer rich desserts because their bodies do not need so many calories. Desserts should be suited to the kind of work done by the individuals who are to eat them.

They should also vary, in type and size of serving, with the ages of the individuals. The young children in the family should have simple desserts—fruits, junkets, custards, gelatine, and tapioca puddings. You have learned that adults require fewer calories as they grow older; small dessert servings will fit their food needs. You and your friends use more energy than any other age group; your desserts should, therefore, be satisfying and supplied in larger portions than those for young children or adults. Garnishes of dried fruits, coconut, and simple sauces added to your desserts help to increase the

166

caloric values of your meals. Between-meal energy is best provided for all ages by fruits, milk and fruit drinks, or cookies.

The choice of a light or heavy dessert should be determined somewhat by the season. In cold weather, energy needs are greater—and heavy desserts are appropriate. In hot weather, for both comfort and health, the intake of sugar should be less.

The Importance of Sugar and the Dangers of Its Overuse

Sugar has an important place in every diet. It furnishes an easily available and economical form of energy and aids in the digestion of fats and proteins. Used in moderation, sugar emphasizes the flavor of other foods. Sugar comes from several sources and, though the forms differ slightly, one form may be substituted for another as sweetening. *Glucose*, also called dextrose, is the sweetening agent found in fruits, honey, and vegetables. It is the body's most useful energy fuel—so high in energy value that it is often fed into the veins of persons who are very ill. *Fructose*, found in honey and plant juices, and *lactose*, in milk, are also simple forms of sugar. *Sucrose*, found in sugar cane, sugar beets, and in the sap of maple trees, is the sugar most commonly used in cookery. Adequate sugar should be included in the diet—but it must not crowd out other foods which help to supply energy.

America is the largest consumer of sugar among the nations. The average per person is about ninety-six pounds a year, or over two-thirds of a cup each day. The tremendous amount of money spent annually for candy bars, soft drinks, and soda-fountain confections could be used more wisely for milk, vegetables, fruits, meat, and cereals. A taste for sweets is easily formed and difficult to control. Overuse of sugar is partly respon-

The United Fresh Fruit and Vegetable Association

Fruit desserts can be very attractive

sible for the American tendency toward overweight and also explains much malnutrition.

Since sugar appears in greater quantity in the dessert than in any other part of the meal, it is well to know the effect that rich desserts may have on the health of the family if they are served too frequently. The most obvious effect is overweight in children, teen-agers, and adults. The underweight person may gain some weight by eating rich desserts but have his appetite dulled for foods that he needs more than sweets. Overweight persons may also be malnourished if sugar has supplied as much as a fourth of their calorie needs so they have less appetite for valuable proteins and other nutrients. After a heavy meal, simple desserts will be preferred to sweet fillings and rich pastries. If the menu requires it, your dessert, besides supplying sugar, may furnish the minerals and vitamins found in canned or fresh fruits.

167

Making Custards

Custards, soft or baked, fulfill nutritional needs because of the food values present in their basic ingredients—milk, sugar, and eggs. Both soft and baked custards require skill in preparation. *Soft custard* is what your grandmother called boiled custard, though, since boiling will cause the custard to curdle, it is never really boiled. *Baked custards* are firm in their consistency. They can be varied by the use of flavorings or by serving with butterscotch or caramel sauce and garnishing with fruits or whipped cream.

In making custards precise methods are required:

1. Beat the eggs only enough to break the structure. Overbeating results in a porous baked custard or may produce a foam on the top of a soft custard.

2. Scald the milk; heat to a temperature just below boiling in the top of a double boiler over hot water before combining with the other ingredients. (As you gain experience, you will learn to scald milk over very low direct heat.) Scalding the milk prevents its curdling and shortens the cooking period.

3. For soft custard, add the scalded milk to the egg-and-sugar mixture in a second double boiler or in a pan to be set over simmering water which does not touch the bottom of the pan. Stir the custard constantly. For baked custard, stir the scalded milk gradually into the egg-and-sugar mixture and pour into a baking dish or individual dishes. Set into a pan containing sufficient hot water to cover two-thirds of the baking dish or cups; this prevents the outside of the custard from becoming overdone while heat is penetrating to the center.

4. To secure a velvety-smooth consistency, cook soft or baked custards at a low temperature. Undercooked custard does not thicken when cooled and tastes like raw egg. Overcooked custards curdle, are watery, and lack flavor. Remove a soft custard from

1

MAKING SOFT CUSTARD

The scalded milk has been added to the egg-and-sugar mixture in the double boiler. From this point until the custard is removed from the heat, it must be stirred constantly

The custard now coats the spoon thoroughly and is therefore ready to be taken from the fire

2

Ingredients · Measuring milk into the top of a double boiler to scald it

The hot milk is gradually added to the slightly beaten eggs and sugar

The custard has been poured into individual glass cups and set in a baking pan, into which hot water is being added. Baking in water prevents the outside of the custard from becoming overcooked while the heat is penetrating to the center

BAKED CUSTARD

The Borden Company

Unmolding the custards · The edges are being loosened to let the air in. Then they will be turned out on the serving plates

Custards may be served with fruits, with sauces, with a bit of jelly, or with whipped cream over which a few nuts are sprinkled

the heat when it coats the spoon. There is enough heat within the custard to complete the cooking. When you wish to prevent further cooking, pour the soft custard into a chilled bowl. Baked custard is done when a knife inserted into the center comes out free of custard particles. Remove the dish from the pan of hot water and set it aside to cool before serving.

Junket is a simple milk dessert prepared by a method similar to that for custard. The thickening agent is rennet, an enzyme easily destroyed by high temperatures. Therefore the milk must be warmed but not scalded.

Making Puddings

Puddings make substantial and appetizing desserts. Prepared pudding and pie filling mixes in several flavors may be used. Some instant types need only be mixed with cold milk and allowed to stand; others must be cooked briefly. Crumbs of hard candies, graham crackers, or grapenuts sprinkled over pudding give a pleasant texture contrast.

Starch Puddings

A well-prepared *cornstarch* or *tapioca* pudding should be light and delicately textured, barely holding its shape. There should be no raw-starch flavor.

Starch puddings require essentially the same methods as custards. Since they become pasty upon standing, they should not be cooked too long before serving. The cooking process is as follows:

1. Before adding cornstarch to a liquid mixture, separate the starch grains with a very little cold liquid or with the sugar or cocoa of the recipe. This will prevent lumping.

2. You may cook these puddings first over a low direct heat and then finish cooking them slowly in a double boiler. Keep the water simmering below the bottom of the top pan. Undercooked puddings taste of raw starch and egg.

3. Stir starch puddings constantly while they are over the low direct heat, but only at 5-minute intervals when they are over hot water. Overstirring results in a heavy, pasty pudding. A slotted spoon or a fork is good for stirring because it mixes thoroughly and helps to prevent lumping.

4. If you wish a fluffy pudding, add a beaten egg white.

Steamed Puddings

Steamed puddings, such as *suet* or *plum pudding*, are rich in food values. They should be cooked slowly by steaming. For commercial steamed puddings it is necessary only to reheat them, usually in their cans. These puddings are available in excellent variety and are convenient timesavers. However, the making of steamed puddings is easy if a few simple rules are followed:

1. The ingredients, which usually include flour, liquids, fat, egg, bread crumbs, and seasonings, are combined as in quick breads.

2. Pour the mixture into pans or molds, cover tightly, and place on a rack over hot water in a covered kettle. The use of a pressure cooker shortens the time for steaming.

3. Coffee cans or one or two baking-powder cans will serve nicely as molds. Make sure that covers fit in tight. Remember to fill the molds not more than $\frac{2}{3}$ full.

Cakes are of two general types: butter cakes made with shortening, and sponge cakes made without shortening. Each cake has its characteristic ingredients and methods of mixing and baking. The chiffon cake, using oil as shortening, combines some of the characteristics of each type and uses some of both methods.

Cakes with Shortening

The basic ingredients of cakes made with shortening are sugar, fat, eggs, a liquid, flour, leavening, and seasoning. Fine granulated sugar will help to produce a fine-textured cake, especially in angel cakes. Except in white-cake recipes, brown sugar may replace white sugar, weight for weight (see Food Equivalents, page 351). Sirups or honey may replace part of the sugar in cakes with shortening. Butter, fortified margarine, or hydrogenated lard are among the shortenings that may be used. Shortening and liquid should be at room temperature. Eggs, however, if they are to be separated, should be cold since they are more easily separated when cold. Eggs two or three days old and at room temperature produce the greatest volume when beaten. The use of soft-wheat flours, because of their gluten, results in a more delicately textured cake than the use of hard-wheat flour. Because cake and pastry flours have smaller gluten particles than those in bread flour and produce a tender, fine texture in cakes, many prefer them. All-purpose flour may be substituted for soft-wheat, cake, or pastry flour (see page 351). Other ingredients used in cakes have already been discussed.

There are *three methods of mixing cakes* with shortening: the conventional, the conventional-sponge, and the quick method.

1. In the *conventional method,* mix the fat and flavoring until smooth and light. Add the sugar by tablespoons and beat until fluffy after each addition. If the fat becomes too soft or liquefies, chill the mixing bowl; then proceed with creaming. Either beat the egg until thick and add to the creamed mixture, or add it unbeaten. Then beat the mixture until ingredients are completely combined. Add one-fourth of the flour mixture (salt, baking powder, and flour) to the creamed mixture and stir until the flour is barely blended. Then add one-third of the milk and stir the mixture. Repeat the process of adding the flour mixture and milk until both are used. Alternate additions assure a smooth consistency. The last addition should be flour. The addition of flour first and last prevents the batter from separating.

2. To mix cakes by the *conventional-sponge method,* cream the fat, flavoring, and one-half of the sugar. Add the flour mixture (salt, baking powder, and flour) to the creamed mixture, first one tablespoon of flour, next one tablespoon of milk, then one tablespoon of flour, stirring after each addition. Add one-half of the remaining milk and flour and stir. Now add the last of the milk and flour and stir again. Beat the egg whites until they mound in the bowl; then beat gradually the remaining sugar into the whites until stiffly-pointed peaks form. Fold the egg whites into the batter, using a spatula, and stir a few strokes.

3. For the *quick method* have all ingredients the temperature of a warm room. The fat should be very soft. Put all the ingredients but the sifted flour mixture into a bowl. Beat with a rotary beater for 25 strokes; clean the sides of the bowl with a rubber

CAKES MADE WITH SHORTENING

1. Measuring the fat · The measuring cup has been packed solidly with the fat, then leveled off at the top, and is now being turned into the mixing bowl

2. The sugar is being added gradually to the fat, which has been creamed. The process of creaming the fat continues as the sugar is added

3. The eggs, which have been beaten until they are thick and foamy, are being added gradually to the creamed sugar and fat. After all the sugar has been added, beat three hundred strokes or until the mixture holds its shape

4. One-fourth of the flour, salt, and baking powder mixture is being added to the fat, sugar, and egg mixture, stirring until most of the flour is blended (about 25–30 strokes). Add a third of the milk and stir until blended (about 25 strokes). Repeat until all the flour and milk have been added, then stir approximately 150 strokes

5. The batter is being poured into pans, on the bottom of which a circle of waxed paper has been fitted and greased. Divide the batter evenly and spread it smoothly so that the batter at the edges of the pans will be slightly higher than that in the center

6. One layer of the cake has been turned out on a cake cooler and the waxed paper in the bottom of the pan is being removed gently

1

Iowa State College

2

3

4

5

scraper. Beat for 100 more strokes, cleaning the sides of the bowl two or three times. Sift the flour mixture over the batter. Beat 150 strokes, cleaning the sides of the bowl after 75 strokes.

To make cakes successfully *the pan* must be the right size for the amount of batter. A pan of proper depth supports a cake while rising and protects it while baking. If the pan is too deep, the crust will be too light in color and the batter will not rise to the proper height. When a cake pan is too small, the batter runs over the top and the cake burns around the edges. Since the browning of the crust is affected by the brightness of the pan, shiny metal or glass should be used.

The pans for cakes with shortening must be prepared for the batter. You may fit paper into the bottom of the pans, greasing the paper but not the sides of the pan. For cupcakes, grease the bottom of muffin pans or use individual fluted paper cups in the muffin pans (the paper cups will save pan washing). To ensure a tender cake, push the batter gently from the mixing bowl into the cake pans with a rubber spatula. Spread the batter evenly over the pan and insert a knife in the batter, moving it back and forth to remove large air bubbles, which would affect the texture. A layer-cake pan should be filled from one-half to two-thirds full. When batter is used for cupcakes, fill the pans not more than one-half full. Remove any batter that may have spilled on the tins. Your cake is now ready for the oven.

6

Herbert Lanks, from Black Star

Putting the cake into the oven

The oven must be preheated for about ten minutes before baking cake or cookies. Arrange cake or cookie pans alternately on the oven rack so that there is a space around each pan and a distance of approximately two inches from the sides of the oven. Opening oven doors during the baking process is likely to lessen the volume of cake and cookies and prevent even browning. When done, all cakes should be delicately brown and should shrink slightly from the sides of the pan. As further tests, the cake should spring back when it is touched lightly, and a toothpick or metal cake tester inserted in the center should be free from crumb particles when removed. Overbaking destroys flavor and shrinks a cake. The finished product should be light with a fine texture, have a slightly rounded top, a tender grain, and a sweet well-flavored taste. Cupcakes should be slightly rounded, and evenly

173

browned on top, sides, and bottom. The cake should cool 10 minutes with the pan placed on a cake rack. To transfer cake to rack, loosen the edges with a spatula, place the rack over the pan, and invert. Greased waxed paper should be removed from the surface of cake immediately.

Cakes without Shortening

Sponge and angel cakes are made without shortening or leavening ingredients. They are leavened by the air beaten into the egg whites and by the steam formed in baking. When these cakes are made properly, they are tender and have a delicate flavor and a light texture. Their surface is flat, or just slightly rounded, and lightly browned. The interior is fine-grained and slightly moist. Sponge cakes are similar to angel cakes in volume, flavor, and lightness.

The basic ingredients used in cakes without shortening are eggs, fine granulated sugar, and soft-wheat flour, which is known as cake or pastry flour. Sponge-cake recipes call for whole eggs; angel cakes contain only egg whites. The light texture of both these cakes depends largely on the egg foam. Lemon juice in sponge cakes and cream of tartar in angel cakes stabilize the foam and tenderize the eggs, resulting in a light, tender product.

Sponge and angel cakes should be baked in ungreased pans. A tubular pan supports the delicate batter and spreads the heat more evenly. These cakes should be baked until they are springy to the touch. You may use the test on page 173. After the cake has cooled in an inverted position, its elastic quality makes it easy to remove from the pan.

Chiffon Cakes

Chiffon cakes, made with vegetable oil, have some characteristics of both the cakes with, and those without, shortening. In size and texture they are like angel cakes. The oil imparts a rich taste, aids in giving a tender, moist interior, and improves the keeping qualities of the cake. Chiffon cakes are baked and cooled by the processes described here and on pages 466–467.

Other Cakes

Prepared cake mixes with improved keeping qualities are now available in endless variety. They are easy to use, and the product often compares favorably with homemade cakes in texture and flavor. Directions on the package often suggest interesting variations, and a mix may serve as the basis for carrying out some traditional recipe. Cake batter may be made at home and frozen in the home freezer or the freezer compartment of a refrigerator. All kinds of cakes may be purchased ready-to-eat from the grocery or bakery.

Cake Icings or Frostings, and Fillings

A good icing or filling clings to the cake, remains moist and easy to cut, and helps to preserve the freshness of the cake. Ways of making several kinds of icing and fillings will be found in the Cookbook, pages 473–474.

Mixes for frosting are increasingly popular. By adding cream, fruit juice, coconut, chopped raisins or nuts, one can make a variety of fillings or frostings for desserts.

Before you ice a cake, cool it and brush it free of crumbs. Ice the sides first; then heap the icing in the center of the top and spread it to the edges. With a layer cake, ice the top of the bottom layer first; then place and ice the next layer. When all layers are assembled, ice the sides and finally the top. Icing must be spread quickly and lightly before it begins to harden. The peaks and swirls may be left unsmoothed, as they are decorative. However, some persons prefer to smooth the icing. The less the icing

SPONGE CAKE

1

Egg whites were beaten until foamy, sugar being added gradually. The meringue now stands in stiff peaks

2

Remaining sugar is being added to egg yolks which have been beaten to thick consistency

Flour is now sifted over the yolk mixture. Use a rubber scraper or wooden spoon to fold the flour into the egg-yolk mixture

3

4

Combine yolk-and-flour mixture with meringue, cutting and folding gently

5

After cake batter is poured into ungreased tube pan, run a small spatula or knife around the edges to bring large air bubbles to the top. Spread the batter evenly

Baked in a slow oven (325° F.) fifty minutes, the cake, when cooled and removed from the pan, should be light, with a close, moist texture

6

1   2   3

SEVEN–MINUTE FROSTING

1. Combine all the frosting ingredients in the top of the double boiler. Here strawberries are being added to make a pink frosting. 2. Beat with an electric mixer or rotary beater one minute. Now place the top of the double boiler over boiling water. 3. Do not allow the boiling water to touch the top container. Beat about seven minutes. Remove from water as soon as frosting forms stiff peaks

4. Remove top of double boiler from heat. Add flavoring. 5. Beat frosting in the top of the double boiler or in a mixing bowl for about two minutes, or until it will spread in soft swirls. 6. Spread a very thin layer of frosting on the cooled cake so that crumbs will not be loosened and appear in the finished frosting. Then thickly spread on more frosting. Always ice the sides of a cake first and then finish by icing the top

4   5   6

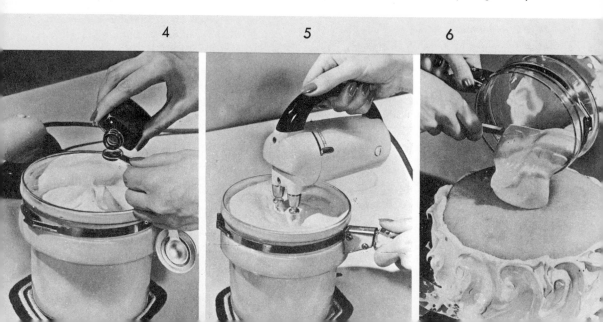

is handled, the better its consistency. Iced cakes can be cut more easily if the knife is first dipped into hot water.

Fillings are cooked like starchy puddings or soft custards, but they are usually sweeter and richer. They are used between layers or in the hollowed-out center of cakes. Sometimes they are used in combination with icing; since both are rich in food values, either alone is adequate. Cool both filling and cake before combining them.

Cookies

Cookies, a variation of cake, contain similar ingredients. The chief differences are in the proportions of the ingredients, the methods of handling the batter or dough, and the time of baking. There are five general types of cookies—though many variations. The classifications are made according to the consistency of the batter.

TYPES OF COOKIES

1. *Bar and sheet cookies* are made of soft batter a bit stiffer than that of cakes. Brownies are typical of these cookies. The batter is baked in shallow pans and then cut into shapes.
2. *Drop cookies* have a slightly firm batter. They are pushed from a spoon onto a cookie sheet. Placing them about two inches apart allows for spread during baking.
3. *Refrigerator cookies* are made of a stiff dough, rich in fat. The dough is shaped into rolls, wrapped in waxed paper, and chilled. Cookies are cut in thin slices from the roll. Doughs made rich with nuts and fruits are a popular variation.
4. *Rolled cookies* are made of stiff dough. They are rolled thin on a lightly floured board and cut into shapes for baking.
5. *Filled cookies* are made by placing such foods as fruits, jelly, and mincemeat between two layers of shaped cookie dough. The edges are pressed together before baking to prevent leakage of the filling.

177

Pillsbury Mills

Drop cookies · Drop by tablespoons on a greased baking sheet. Space them far enough apart to allow for spreading

Refrigerator cookies · Slice a roll of baking dough that has been thoroughly chilled for several hours in the refrigerator about one-eighth-inch thick and place on ungreased cookie sheet

Rolled cookies · A stiff cookie dough is rolled thin on a lightly floured board. The rolled cookies may be cut into any desired shape by using a knife, a pastry wheel, or fancy cookie cutters

In baking cookies, the following directions will be helpful:

1. In greasing baking sheets, follow the recipe directions carefully. Too little grease makes cookies stick; too much causes them to spread.

2. To ensure good circulation of heat, use baking sheets smaller in length and width than the oven.

3. For even baking, place the baking sheet in the middle of the oven. Unless the oven is well regulated, turn the baking sheet around when the baking period is half finished.

4. Be sure the cookies are done before taking them from the oven. Drop cookies are done when they are springy to the touch; bar cookies shrink slightly from the sides of the pan when done.

5. Remove baked cookies immediately from the baking sheet to wire cake racks or other surface to cool.

Storage of Cakes and Cookies

Cakes that contain shortening dry less quickly than those low in fat content. To prevent a cake from becoming dry, store it in a covered container or wrap it in waxed paper or metal foil. Cake remains fresh for several days when wrapped closely in waxed paper and stored in the refrigerator. Because they tend to become too moist, cakes with heavy, moist fillings should not be stored. Iced cakes, if properly stored, can be kept fresh for a few days and may be kept frozen for weeks. Freezing cakes and then storing at 0° F. is an excellent means of preserving freshness. Fruit cakes improve in flavor with freezing. Cookies containing cereal and gelatin should not be frozen. A wrapping of vaporproof cellophane is effective for frozen cakes and cookies.

Because cookies lose their individual textures and flavors easily, only one kind should be stored in each container. Cookies containing nuts, fruits, molasses, chocolate, or milk stay fresh longest. Most cookies are best when used within a week after baking. Batters and doughs for cakes and cookies will keep as long as two weeks in the refrigerator and for months in the home freezer or freezing compartment of the refrigerator.

Making Fruit Combinations

Variations of biscuit dough combined with fruits, called *shortcakes*, are delicious desserts. The shortcake dough has more sugar and shortening than biscuit dough and is cut into larger rounds, which are stacked when baked. Melted table fat may be placed between layers of dough before baking. The layers are then separated and fresh or thawed frozen fruit placed between them. The cake is covered with more fruit, whipped cream, or ice cream.

Baked dessert *dumplings* are made of a sweet biscuit dough. Fruit which holds its shape, such as apples, peaches, or apricots, is prepared as for baking. The dumpling dough is rolled thin and cut into squares. Then the fruit is placed in the center of the squares, the seasonings are added, and the dough is brought up around the fruit to cover it completely. Before baking, all edges should be pinched together to hold the fruit in place. The dumplings should be baked in a shallow pan.

In *cobblers* the fruit juice is thickened with tapioca, white flour, or cornstarch. The fruit and thickened juice are placed in a baking

Better Homes & Gardens (1, 2, 6)
Swans Down Cake Flour (3, 4, 5)

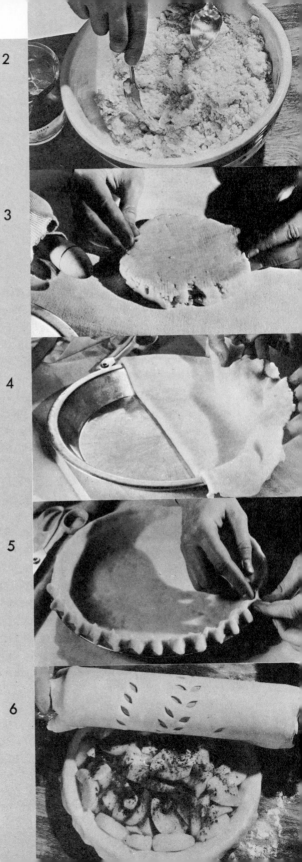

1 **2** **3** **4** **5** **6**

MAKING PASTRY

1. Shortening is being cut into the flour-and-salt mixture with a pastry blender

2. When the pieces are the size of small peas, sprinkle the cold water, a tablespoon at a time, over part of the mixture. Mix gently with a fork. Push the lumps that form to one side of the bowl. Sprinkle the next tablespoon of water over the dry part. Continue until you have used all the water called for in the recipe. Gather the dough together into a ball. Let stand for several minutes

3. Cut a circle of waxed paper one inch larger than your pie pan. Lay it on your pastry cloth or board and flour it lightly. Divide the dough in half and form each half into a ball. Flatten one ball slightly and roll it with a lightly floured rolling pin within the circle of waxed paper. In this way you can tell how much to roll the pastry. Always roll from the center out to the edge

4. Fold the circle of pastry to lift it into the pan, then unfold it

5. In making an open pie, flute the rim by pinching it with your fingers

6. Roll the other half of the pastry in the same way for the top crust, making it a half inch larger than the bottom crust. Trim the bottom pastry even with the edge of the pan. Moisten the edge. To prevent the pie top from tearing, roll it over your rolling pin and unroll it on top of the filling. Fold the top crust under the lower crust. Crimp the edge by pressing the dough between thumb and finger of one hand and the forefinger of the other

dish, covered with sweet biscuit dough, and baked. Or this order may be reversed, the dough being covered with the fruit and baked. This second type of cobbler may also have a top covering of dough if desired.

Fruit rolls are made by rolling out sweet biscuit dough, spreading it with sugar, cinnamon, butter, and thickened fruit sauce that contains finely chopped fruit, and then rolling it up lengthwise. The edges are sealed and the roll is baked. It is then sliced and served hot with hard sauce or cream.

Serve fruit combinations as soon as they are done, because the fruit juices soak into the biscuit pastry in a very few minutes and tend to make it soggy.

Making Pastry and Fillings

Pastry is a dough made of flour, salt, shortening, and liquid. It is used for piecrust, tarts, and shells for serving foods such as creamed chicken or peas. Pastry dough contains more fat and less liquid than biscuit

Lemon meringue pie · Note height and texture of meringue. The filling is barely stiff enough to hold its shape, yet soft enough to form a pleasant contrast to the meringue

dough. Pastry flour (soft-wheat), all-purpose flour, or bread flour (hard-wheat) may be used. Soft-wheat flour tends to give a mealy pastry; hard-wheat flour, or all-purpose flour, gives a flaky pastry. Cooking fats such as lard and hydrogenated fats make the dough tender. Vegetable oil may also be used as shortening for pastry.

Ways to Make Pastry

There are three basic methods for making pastry: the cold-water, hot-water, and oil method. *Cold-water* pastry has layers of thin, tender flakes. Here are directions for combining ingredients for this texture:

1. Sift the salt with the flour. Cut the cold fat into the dry ingredients, with a knife or pastry blender, until the fat particles are the size of small peas and are coated with flour. Light cutting strokes are essential to prevent fat and flour from pressing compactly into a heavy, tough pastry.

2. Sprinkle the cold water by teaspoons over the surface of the flour, and toss the mixture lightly and quickly with a fork until the dough is damp enough to hold together when pressed gently with the fingers. Too much water will make the dough so sticky that it cannot be handled and will produce a tough pastry. Too little water will make a crumbly, heavy pastry. Normally, about

180

three tablespoons of liquid to one cup of flour is correct.

Hot-water pastry is mealy with a granular rather than a flaky texture. Combine ingredients as follows:

1. Pour the boiling water over the fat and beat until creamy.

2. Add the water-fat mixture to the sifted flour and salt. Toss lightly and quickly with a fork.

3. Form the pastry into a ball, wrap in waxed paper, and chill 2 hours or more before rolling.

Oil as a shortening produces a texture between that of a flaky and a mealy product. Milk, commonly used as the liquid in this pastry, adds flavor and is an aid in producing a delicately browned product. The following mixing method is used:

1. Sift the flour and salt together.

2. Combine the oil with the cold liquid.

3. Pour the liquid mixture into the dry ingredients; toss quickly until just blended.

4. Roll between waxed paper.

Ginn, (Frank D. Lucas)

A perfect pie fresh from the oven

Pastry mixes are a convenience to the busy homemaker. The directions on the package should be followed carefully. You may purchase packaged pie combinations which include the pastry and filling. Home-prepared mixes for pastry may be made by combining flour, salt, and shortening. When kept tightly covered and stored in the refrigerator, this product remains fresh for a period of weeks.

Rolling and Shaping Pastry for Pies

To roll pastry for pies, press the pastry dough into a flattened ball and place it on a lightly floured board or pastry cloth or waxed paper. Roll only enough pastry for one crust at a time. With a slightly floured rolling pin roll lightly, with quick short strokes, from the center toward the edges until the pastry is $\frac{1}{8}$ inch in thickness and as nearly circular as possible. Lifting the roller at the edge of the dough prevents the edge from becoming too thin. The rolled dough should be about two inches larger than the pan. If a portion of the dough sticks, it may be lifted and a little more flour used on the rolling surface. However, if too much flour is worked into the dough, the pastry will be tough. Handle pastry as little as possible and do not turn over during rolling. Fold the dough in half. Place it over half of an ungreased piepan, unfolding it and fitting it closely to the pan to exclude air. Or the dough may be rolled

181

around the rolling pin and then carefully rolled off into the pan. Do not stretch the piecrust as you place it in the pan because stretching tends to toughen pastry.

To freeze pastry, divide the dough into portions for single pies before rolling it out. Roll the pastry into circles of desired size. Put the circles on top of each other separated by layers of waxed paper. These flat shapes are convenient for storage in the home freezer.

For a *one-crust* pie, cut the dough evenly about one inch beyond the edge of the pan, using kitchen shears or a knife. Fold this edge under leaving a $\frac{1}{2}$-inch rim that stands up all around the edge of the pan. This edge may be fluted by using the forefinger of one hand and the thumb and forefinger of the other. The dough edges are pressed between the thumb and forefinger and slightly swirled upward while the forefinger of the other hand holds the dough next to the thumb and finger flat on the pan's edge. This process of fluting the edge of the pie is repeated all the way around. The fluted edge is attractive and extends the depth of the pan to hold filling and topping. If the crust is to be baked unfilled, prick small holes in the dough with a fork on the bottom and sides of the pan. Expanded air under the crust will then pass out through the holes, and the crust will keep its shape as it bakes. Or place a smaller pie plate inside the crust while it bakes.

For a *two-crust* pie, the lower crust should not be punched with holes, but the edge of the lower crust should be moistened with cold water before it is filled (this helps to hold the two crusts together when you seal them). After the pie has been filled, cover it with dough that has been rolled in a manner similar to that used for the lower crust. To prevent the pie from boiling over,

trim the lower crust close to the pan's edge; fit the upper crust in place and trim to extend 1 inch beyond the edge of the pan; turn the extended edge of the top crust under the edge of the bottom crust and press firmly against the inside of the pan to seal the edges. The rim of dough may be fluted with the fingers. Or you may form the same type of seal by extending the lower crust 1 inch from the pan's edge, and then turning this lower edge up over the top crust, which has been trimmed to the edge of the pan. A design of slits cut into the center of the upper crust with a knife will allow steam to escape as the filling cooks, and will also add a decorative touch.

A properly baked piecrust will have a light golden color and slightly uneven surface. Its crust will be dry, crisp, and tender.

Pie Fillings

Fruit, cream, and chiffon fillings make pies that are delicious for desserts. In *fruit pies* the filling and crust are generally baked together. The top crust may be made in one piece or in strips of pastry crisscrossed or interwoven across the pie to form rectangular or diamond-shaped openings. The fruit for pies may be cooked or uncooked, fresh fruit, thawed frozen fruit, dried fruit that has been cooked, or fruits canned in a light sirup or water. Fully ripened fruits give the best flavor. In making fruit pies the following suggestions will be helpful:

1. Fruits are prepared according to the particular requirements of the recipe. They may be precooked or partially cooked to shrink them before they are put into pies. This applies especially to apples.

2. The juice of fruits may be thickened with cornstarch, tapioca flour, or white flour. White flour gives an opaque appearance to the thickened juice.

182

3. The flavor of fruit pies is improved by the use of table fat; a few grains of salt also help. Spices, such as cinnamon, allspice, cloves, or nutmeg, when used sparingly, add to the delicacy of apple and pumpkin pie.

4. There are several ways to prevent fruit pies from boiling over in the oven: (1) Follow the recipe exactly, making accurate measurements. (2) Seal in the juices when the upper crust is added to the pie, as described on page 182. (3) Heat the oven to 425° F. before putting the pie into the oven, and place the pie in the center. This high temperature prevents the pie from becoming juice-soaked. After 20 minutes of baking, lower the temperature to 350° F. to allow the filling to cook further without boiling out and to prevent the crust from burning.

In making *cream pies*, a prebaked crust may be used. In some custard pies, the filling may be added to the pastry-lined pan before the pastry is baked. Cream fillings are usually thickened by both egg (the whole egg or the egg yolk) and starch, flour, or cornstarch. In some of these pies, the egg whites are used for a meringue topping. Milk or cream, salt, and flavorings, in addition to starch and egg, are used as ingredients. Among the favorite cream pies are coconut-cream, butterscotch, chocolate, lemon, banana, and custard. In making cream fillings, the procedures are similar to those used for custards.

Meringue for pies is made by beating egg whites and adding sugar. For general directions on how to make meringue, refer to page 480. Special directions for the use of meringue in pies are given below:

1. If flavoring is desired, fold it in gently before adding the meringue to cover the pie. Spread the meringue quickly, starting at the edges. It should touch the crust all the way around to prevent its shrinking away from the edge.

2. Baking meringue-topped pies requires care. The finished meringue should stand in firm, moist, light peaks. Overcooked or undercooked meringues will have a beadlike appearance and become watery. Overcooking also results in a shrunken, dry, tough meringue.

A *chiffon pie* is made by folding a meringue into a thick custard or other cream-pie filling. The mixture is placed in a baked pie shell and cooked for about twenty minutes. Chiffon pies may also have gelatin fillings. The use of gelatin in cookery is discussed in Chapter 19. The most common chiffon pies are chocolate, lemon, butterscotch, and pumpkin.

If you are a creative pie maker, you will find many uses for scraps of piecrust, depending on the ages in your family, the occasions in prospect which require tidbits, and the icebox leftovers or jam-pot possibilities for tasty combinations. Every adult has memories of cinnamon-sugar piecrust squares, apple (or peach or apricot) turn-overs, and patty shells to be filled with creamed peas and chicken. Somewhat newer notions include pastry cheese straws, tiny sausages wrapped to make "pigs in blankets," diamond shapes to be topped with bits of preserved fruit, cheese bits, peanut butter, and other spreads, bacon with relish for canapes or hors d'oeuvres. If invention or materials should run low, pie dough sugared lightly, shaped by a favorite cookie cutter and browned delicately, will please the children as a simple accompaniment to a fruit dessert. By-products of pastry desserts may be quite as interesting as the originals.

¶ Understanding:

1. In meal planning what factors determine dessert choices?

2. Which of the high-calorie desserts provide calcium? riboflavin? vitamin C?

3. If a soft custard curdles, what possible causes would you suspect?

4. How can you tell when a soft custard is done? a baked custard?

5. Why is complete cooking of starch-thickened products necessary? How do you know when they are sufficiently cooked?

6. In what ways does overmixing affect your cakes?

7. How should you mix and handle pastry to ensure a tender product?

8. How will fruit combinations add to your menu?

9. Under what circumstances will you purchase cooky mix? pastry mix?

¶ Planning:

1. Plan an attractive dessert to be served easily for a guest luncheon.

2. Plan a dessert to give texture and color contrast to a dinner menu.

3. Plan a suitable desert to serve for a light luncheon; for a medium luncheon; for a heavy luncheon.

4. Plan two desserts to include milk and eggs. What cookery principles will you observe?

5. Plan two fruit desserts not commonly served in your home. Work with your mother to include them in the week's menus.

6. Bring from home the recipe of a favorite dessert. Plan a meal in which the dessert is appropriate.

7. After reading the labels on prepared cake mixes, plan to bake a cake and time the mixing and baking processes.

¶ Practicing and Evaluating:

1. Make a stirred custard of good texture and flavor. Serve the custard chilled for your family dinner. How was it received?

2. Prepare a cornstarch pudding for a guest luncheon. Garnish to increase the food values. Serve with appropriate cookies.

3. Compare the cost of cookies, cakes, and pies made at home with similar products on the market.

4. Prepare cupcakes by the quick method of mixing, timing the process. How can you improve in technique?

5. Prepare cupcakes from a commercial mix. Compare the time of preparation with that in number 4.

6. Bake cookies and store them to retain their flavor and texture.

7. Prepare a fruit-combination dish. Compare with a pie made of the same fruit.

8. Mix the ingredients for a tender flaky piecrust and bake. Why are piecrusts sometimes tough?

9. Prepare a fruit pie and bake. What did you do to prevent the loss of juice? to prevent a soggy crust?

¶ Reading Further:

Family Fare, Food Management and Recipes. Home and Garden Bulletin 1 (1960). U. S. Department of Agriculture, Washington, D. C.

Refer to standard cook books

Cleveland Public School System

Planning and preparing luncheon

you will learn: The importance of luncheon;
How to plan appropriate luncheons; How to prepare
luncheons efficiently

In most homes there is one light meal a day. Since a plentiful breakfast is necessary, the choice of a light meal lies between luncheon and dinner. Which is chosen depends on factors in the family situation. In some communities dinner, the heaviest meal of the day, is served at noon, and supper, a somewhat lighter meal, is served in the evening.

Urban living generally requires that some members of the family lunch away from home, and therefore dinner is served at night to the reassembled family. In this case, economy and the social needs of the group make it the heavier meal, with luncheon more like a lighter supper. In planning your family's meals, luncheon and supper menus are interchangeable.

185

The Importance of Luncheon

Luncheon is a means of restoring the energy used since breakfast and of providing enough energy to carry on until dinnertime. The last half hour of a busy forenoon usually brings a sharp realization that the body needs refueling. The mind refuses to concentrate and movements are less sure; there are mistakes, which might cause accidents. After a brief time of relaxation and a good lunch, one resumes activity with the same zest that one had earlier after a good breakfast. Since luncheon habits are a factor in vigorous and happy living, a knowledge of foods and a willingness to plan for the best possible luncheons are necessary. Unless this planning is given careful consideration, luncheons will be slighted, and serious results may follow.

Planning Appropriate Luncheons

Because the family is usually separated at midday, luncheon is the most highly individual meal of the day. Each person must recognize his own needs and, with help from the homemaker, plan to supply them. His age, the activities in which he is engaged, and other factors discussed in Chapter 1 should help him to determine the luncheon he should eat. Children and youth, who are growing rapidly, and adults who are doing hard work require a heavy luncheon because their daily food allowance is heavy. Adults doing moderate but fairly active work should eat moderately. Adults doing sedentary work, the aged who are taking life in leisurely fashion, and the overweight should have a light luncheon. A luncheon is classified as light, moderate, or heavy, according to its caloric content. However classified, it should contain dishes of foods from several of the groups in the Daily Food Guide.

A light noon meal requires the eating of a heavy breakfast and a hearty dinner. If a peanut-butter sandwich (made with whole-wheat bread), carrot strips, and milk are to be the noon fare, the breakfast should contain fruit, cereal, and an egg. At dinner liberal servings of meat, vegetables, and perhaps a heavy dessert will be required to fulfill the protein, vitamin, mineral, and energy needs of the day. A light luncheon menu, which can readily be changed to a moderate luncheon, follows:

Making cheese sauce · The white sauce has already been prepared in the double boiler, and the cheese cut from the piece is being grated on a piece of waxed paper. After it is grated, it will be sprinkled into the cream sauce and heated until the cheese has melted

186

Tuna-Fish Salad Sandwich
Mixed Fruit
Milk

A moderate luncheon may offer a main dish, salad, dessert, and a beverage. Such a luncheon is planned for homemakers, teachers, doctors, bankers, students, salespeople, or any others whose activities are moderately strenuous. This meal will probably be followed by only a moderate or moderate-to-heavy dinner. If the breakfast has been sufficient to supply one-third of the daily food needs and a moderate luncheon is eaten, the dinner will be planned to complete the day's food needs. This practice of supplying about one-third of the daily food needs at each meal is an excellent one. The periodic intake of equal amounts of food is conducive to regular eating habits and good digestion, and it ensures sufficient energy to carry out the day's activities. The following menu, suitable for either a moderate luncheon or a light dinner, is adapted from the light-luncheon menu above:

MODERATE-LUNCHEON MENU

Tuna-Fish Salad
Harvard Beets
Whole-Wheat Muffins
Mixed Fruit
Milk

A heavy luncheon satisfies those who prefer to have their heaviest meal at noon because the energy required in the afternoon is greater than that at night when the work of the day is finished. For this reason the heavy luncheon should contain high caloric values, which may be obtained from creamed soups; sandwiches; hot dishes of meat, cheese, and eggs; vegetables; rich breads; and desserts. Protein is a very important food in the heavy luncheon. Since this is the heaviest meal of the day, and may be the only one in which meat is served, the protein dish must be given adequate forethought if it is to provide for the protein needs and keep within the food budget. If a person's habitual food pattern or his energy needs place the heavy meal in the middle of the day, weather may need to be considered in the menu planned. Protein dishes especially appropriate for cold weather are stews, casseroles, chowders, sausages, roasted meats, and fowl. In hot weather jellied meat, fish, or fowl combinations, cold spiced meats, canned meats and fish, deviled eggs, grilled cheese sandwiches, and a salad of kidney beans and cheese are some of the especially desirable and appetizing protein dishes.

The heavy luncheon menu can be formed from a moderate luncheon meal by the addition of a soup, another vegetable, and a heavier dessert. Here is the moderate-luncheon menu altered to become a heavy luncheon:

HEAVY-LUNCHEON MENU

Cream-of-Spinach Soup
Tuna-Fish-and-Noodle Casserole
Harvard Beets
Carrot Strips
Whole-Wheat Muffins   Butter
Mixed Fruit   Sugar Cookies
Milk   Coffee

If luncheons are to be served economically and efficiently at home, they must be planned with the rest of the week's menus and the necessary supplies included in the market order. Also the homemaker may consider the demands they will make on her time and distribute the tasks for her convenience.

Luncheon must be not only nourishing but also attractive. The preservation of food values in preparing luncheons, or any other meals, is of the greatest importance. Carefully follow food-cookery directions to preserve flavor, texture, and color, as well as nutritive substances.

Time-Saving Procedures

In planning the preparation of luncheon, the foods to be served should be divided into two groups: those that must be prepared ahead, and those that are prepared at the time. Foods that require cooking, marinating, chilling, or freezing will fall into the first group. The preparation of foods in this category must be planned carefully if the busy homemaker is to use her time wisely. If these foods are to be served for luncheon, time can be saved by preparing them in advance to be served in different ways at two or more meals. Biscuit mix kept in the refrigerator will, for example, provide good hot breads for several different meals; a gelatin salad or dessert may be served with different garnishes; ham may be sliced, ground for patties, or used in a sandwich spread; potatoes may be steamed to be used mashed for dinner or diced for luncheon salad. (For further suggestions of foods to be chilled or marinated, refer to Chapter 13.) The second type of foods, those which may be prepared quickly, are especially adapted to the luncheon which must be completed within a short lunch period. Scrambled, poached, and soft-cooked eggs may be prepared quickly and are appetizing luncheon dishes. Methods of cooking meat quickly include broiling, frying, and pressure-saucepan cookery. Vegetables as well as meat may be prepared successfully in a pressure saucepan. Some salads may be

combined in a very few minutes if the ingredients have been properly cleaned and chilled ahead of time. Also classified with quickly prepared foods are such canned products as meats, soups, vegetables, and fruits, which may only require heating. Certain frozen products also can be prepared in a few minutes and are a great convenience for a quickly prepared meal.

Your efficiency in preparing luncheon in a limited time, say 20 to 30 minutes, may be increased by dividing the preparation steps. The problem of inadequate food-preparation space may also be solved by doing this. If you are planning a soufflé for lunch, all but the beating of the egg whites may be completed the day before, or directly after breakfast, or at any other time that will permit the cream-sauce mixture to cool before the whites are added. Many recipes can be broken down into the steps of their preparation. Casserole dishes can be prepared early in the morning or the day before, placed in the refrigerator, and removed a short time before their baking should begin. For the quick preparation of luncheons, the planning of meals that can be prepared for cooking or cooked in advance and frozen is one of the greatest efficiency measures.

Making and Using a Work Plan

A work plan may be made which will organize the tasks involved in the preparation of the meal. The first luncheon meals for which work plans are made should be simple. Such a meal might include a fruit juice and a commercially prepared dessert. As experience is gained, foods more difficult to prepare may be introduced, one at a time. A suggested menu to be served by a beginner appears on the next page.

MENU I

(Two-Course Meal for Four)

Baked Beans (canned)
Boston Brown Bread (canned)
Carrot and Celery Strips
Fruit Cup (canned-fruit cocktail, plus bananas)
Milk

Here is a recommended work plan for a beginner to use in the preparation of the above menu:

Jane and Steven Coons

Making chicken salad · The chicken has already been diced and placed in the bowl. The celery is being cut up. After the salad dressing is mixed with the other ingredients, pepper and salt will be added to season the salad to taste

WORK PLAN

After breakfast	Place a can of fruit cocktail in refrigerator to chill.
11:35 A.M.	Make personal preparation (wash hands; put on apron and hair net).
	Assemble bread, beans, carrots, celery, and cooking and serving equipment. (Bread may have been previously heated in can, in which case it will be kept hot until just before the meal is served.)
11:41	Open canned bread and beans; heat beans.
	Slice bread and place on plate.
11:46	Scrape carrots and scrub celery; cut in serving pieces; arrange on plate.
	Place bread, carrots, and celery in refrigerator. Set the table.
11:52	Open fruit cocktail and place in dishes. Add sliced bananas; place in refrigerator.
11:55	Remove bread, carrots, celery, and milk from refrigerator; pour milk.
	Place beans in serving dish.
	Place each on table.
12:00	Serve lunch.

(For information on table setting and serving luncheon meals refer to Chapter 25.)

You may wish to try a luncheon menu requiring more preparation than Menu I. Make your plan for Menu II, allowing 28 to 30 minutes for preparation.

MENU II

(Two-Course Meal for Four)

Grilled Cheese Sandwiches
Coleslaw (cabbage, carrots, raisins, mayonnaise)
Tapioca-Fruit Pudding
Hot Chocolate

Menu III, below, will test your increasing skill in management. For the preparation of

189

this meal, a minimum of 75 minutes will be required.

MENU III

(One-Course Saturday or Sunday Luncheon for Six)

Creamed Dried Beef on Toast
Gelatin Fruit Salad (lime flavored with pears and grapes)
Chocolate Cupcakes
Milk   Coffee

Evaluating Luncheon Preparation

Success in the preparation of luncheon meals depends upon many factors. Have you accomplished the following?

1. Provided about one-third of the daily nutritive requirements

2. Selected foods suitable to the age and occupation of the individuals

3. Planned the menu within the budget; prepared the meal within the allotted time; served an appropriate luncheon for the occasion

4. Achieved contrast, color, and variation of textures and flavors

5. Made a work plan which ensured quick and easy preparation

6. Used correct cooking techniques, producing an appetizing appearance with minimum loss of food values

7. Served the meal promptly to your family

8. Provided an attractive, friendly, restful atmosphere

¶ *Understanding:*

1. Why is the luncheon a necessary daily meal for you and your family?

2. What characteristics does the adequate luncheon possess?

3. How does the planning of a luncheon differ from that of a breakfast?

190

4. What difference in luncheon menus should be made for people of varying ages? for people engaged in various kinds of work?

5. What are the reasons for planning luncheons in relation to the other meals of the day?

¶ *Planning:*

1. Adapt a light luncheon menu so that it is appropriate for individuals engaged in moderate work; in heavy work.

2. Plan a luncheon for a family of two adults, a five-year-old boy, and a fourteen-year-old girl. Check the meal for adequacy in calories.

3. Plan a work schedule for four students cooperating in the preparation of the following menu:

Corned-Beef Hash and Egg Casserole
Tossed Green Salad
Toast Strips
Milk

¶ *Practicing and Evaluating:*

1. Evaluate two luncheon menus for nutritive values, texture, and color qualities. Suggest changes to improve the meals.

2. Assist with the planning and preparation of a light Saturday luncheon to be prepared in 30 minutes. How will you preserve the food values from loss?

3. Plan a Saturday luncheon, one dish to be prepared Friday evening, the remaining food preparation to be dovetailed into your Saturday-morning work.

4. Choose your lunch at school or away from home using the principles of good nutrition which you have learned. Check the meal for vitamin C, iron, and caloric values.

¶ *Reading Further:*

It's Lunch Time, 4–H Circular 162 (1961). University of Missouri Extension Service, Columbia, Missouri.

Time-Saving Meals, Bulletin 293 (1960). Arkansas State University Extension Service, Little Rock, Arkansas.

UNIT FIVE

Dinners

16

Dinner meats

you will learn: The importance of meat in the diet;
The kinds of meat; How to select meats; How to care for
meat in the home; Principles of meat cookery;
How to carve meat

Meat has always been one of man's most important foods, and methods of providing it have kept pace with civilization. In early times man hunted his own meat, killed it himself, and ate it raw or cooked it at once. This means of providing food made life precarious, for frequent failures in hunting might mean starvation. Later, when man learned to preserve his meat through drying and other crude methods, he was less fearful of winter months when prey was scarce. As animals were domesticated, each family still provided its own meat, but they now had a double source —wild game and the home supply—and were still more secure against hunger. As early as the Middle Ages, in Europe, the first group handling of meat was undertaken, and official slaughterhouses were established. The processes of slaughtering, dressing, and preserving, done completely by hand, were, of course, extremely slow. Now, with modern machinery and assembly-line use of labor, it takes less than 45 minutes to kill and dress a steer. Such methods combined with the family facilities of refrigeration and the home freezer for storage have made meat available at any time.

The Importance of Meat in the Diet

Meat is the flesh of any animal as it is used as food, but homemakers limit the term to the flesh of mammals which are raised for food. Poultry, fish and shellfish, and such game as quail and venison are considered as separate classifications. Because meat supplies a large amount of protein, dinner meals, whether at noon or in the evening, are usually planned around a substantial meat dish. Its flavor appeals to most appetites, and the fact that it is a concentrated food with little waste and that it is easily and completely digested makes meat a good basic dinner dish. Though meat is expensive, it can be managed on a limited budget if meat cuts sufficient for several meals are bought at one time, stored properly, and served in a variety of ways. Its cost, when proper thrift has been exercised, is justified by its importance in the diet. (For information on the nutritive values of meat refer to Chapter 1 and to Table IV in the Appendix.)

Kinds of Meat

The consumer must recognize the characteristics of the different kinds of meat in order to be able to tell beef from pork, or veal from lamb.

Beef

The flesh of mature cattle is called beef. It is one of the two meats in greatest demand in the United States, the other being pork. The best beef is firm and has a bright cherry-red color. It should be well marbled with fat and should have a smooth covering of creamy-white fat. Young beef has porous, red bones; older animals have white, flinty bones. The more tender cuts of beef include roasts and steaks from the rib and loin. Less-tender cuts are chuck, brisket, plate, rump, round, and flank.

Veal

Veal is the flesh of calves less than 14 weeks old that usually have been fed on milk. Good veal is light grayish pink in color, fine-grained, and delicately flavored. It has a fairly firm, velvety texture with little fat and no marbling. Veal bones are porous and red.

Meat that is stamped "calf" is from animals older than veal (3 to 10 months) but younger than beef animals. The flesh has a firmer texture, a deeper color, and a more pronounced flavor than veal. All veal and calf cuts are tender. The most common ones are roasts, chops, and cutlets.

Lamb

Lamb is the flesh of young sheep. It is fine-grained and velvety in appearance with an outside covering of clear, white fat. The bones are porous and reddish in color, and the meat is a darker red than beef. The natural paperlike covering on lamb roasts should be left on during cooking. It should, however, be removed from chops.

Pork

193

CUTS OF BEEF

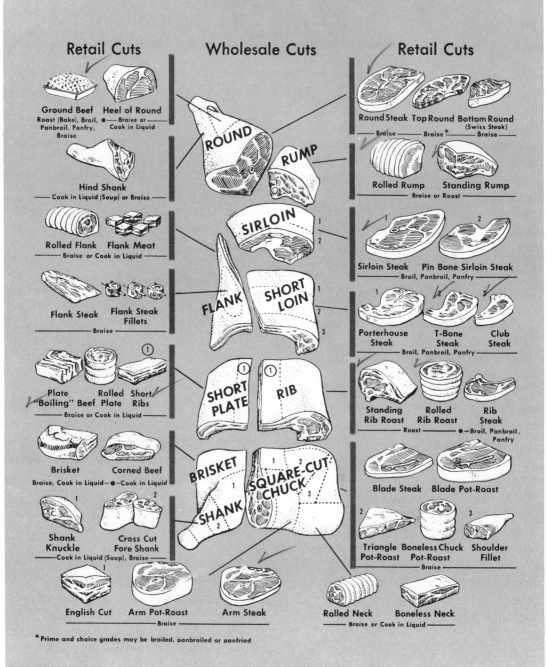

Retail Cuts

Ground Beef
Roast (Bake), Broil, Panbroil, Panfry, Braise

Heel of Round
— Braise or Cook in Liquid —

Hind Shank
— Cook in Liquid (Soup) or Braise —

Rolled Flank   **Flank Meat**
— Braise or Cook in Liquid —

Flank Steak   **Flank Steak Fillets**
— Braise —

Plate "Boiling" Beef   **Rolled Plate**   **Short Ribs**
— Braise or Cook in Liquid —

Brisket   **Corned Beef**
Braise, Cook in Liquid — ● — Cook in Liquid

Shank Knuckle   **Cross Cut Fore Shank**
— Cook in Liquid (Soup), Braise —

English Cut   **Arm Pot-Roast**
— Braise —

Wholesale Cuts

ROUND

RUMP

SIRLOIN

SHORT LOIN

FLANK

SHORT PLATE

RIB

BRISKET

SQUARE-CUT CHUCK

SHANK

Arm Steak

Retail Cuts

Round Steak   Top Round   Bottom Round
(Swiss Steak)
— Braise — — Braise * — — Braise —

Rolled Rump   **Standing Rump**
— Braise or Roast —

Sirloin Steak   **Pin Bone Sirloin Steak**
— Broil, Panbroil, Panfry —

Porterhouse Steak   **T-Bone Steak**   **Club Steak**
— Broil, Panbroil, Panfry —

Standing Rib Roast   **Rolled Rib Roast**   **Rib Steak**
— Roast — ● — Broil, Panbroil, Panfry

Blade Steak   **Blade Pot-Roast**

Triangle Pot-Roast   **Boneless Chuck Pot-Roast**   **Shoulder Fillet**
— Braise —

Rolled Neck   **Boneless Neck**
— Braise or Cook in Liquid —

* Prime and choice grades may be broiled, panbroiled or panfried

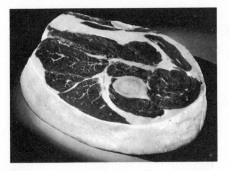

Pot roast

T-bone steak

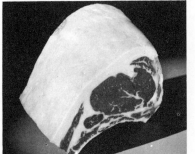

Standing rib roast

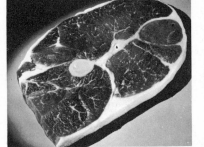

Round steak

Rolled rib roast

Sirloin steak

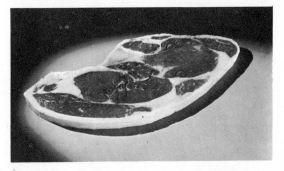

Flank steak

Rolled rump roast

Bottom-round steak

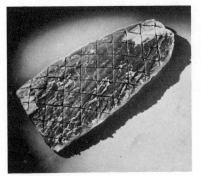

195

CUTS OF VEAL

Retail Cuts   Wholesale Cuts   Retail Cuts

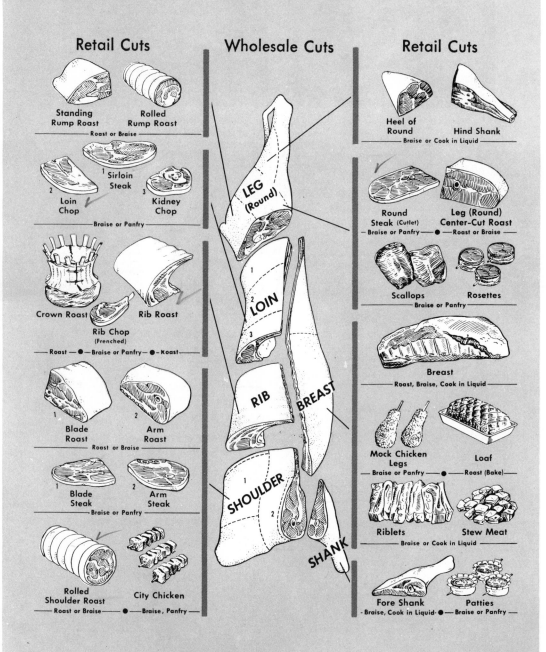

Retail Cuts (left)

Standing Rump Roast   Rolled Rump Roast
— Roast or Braise —

Loin Chop (2)   Sirloin Steak (1)   Kidney Chop (3)
— Braise or Panfry —

Crown Roast   Rib Roast
Rib Chop (Frenched)
— Roast — ● — Braise or Panfry — ● — Roast —

Blade Roast (1)   Arm Roast (2)
— Roast or Braise —

Blade Steak (1)   Arm Steak (2)
— Braise or Panfry —

Rolled Shoulder Roast   City Chicken
— Roast or Braise — ● — Braise, Panfry —

Wholesale Cuts (center)

LEG (Round)

LOIN

RIB   BREAST

SHOULDER

SHANK

Retail Cuts (right)

Heel of Round   Hind Shank
— Braise or Cook in Liquid —

Round Steak (Cutlet)   Leg (Round) Center-Cut Roast
— Braise or Panfry — ● — Roast or Braise —

Scallops   Rosettes
— Braise or Panfry —

Breast
— Roast, Braise, Cook in Liquid —

Mock Chicken Legs   Loaf
— Braise or Panfry — ● — Roast (Bake) —

Riblets   Stew Meat
— Braise or Cook in Liquid —

Fore Shank   Patties
— Braise, Cook in Liquid — ● — Braise or Panfry —

National Live Stock and Meat Board

Breast

Cutlet of round steak

Loin chop

Boneless rump roast

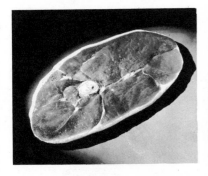

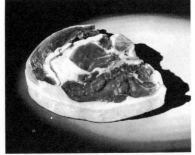

Rib chop

Leg. Shank and arm

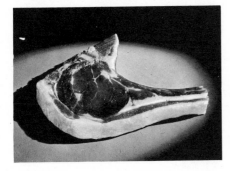

The flesh of older sheep is called mutton. Like mature beef, mutton has a stronger flavor than meat from the younger animals.

Pork

The meat in greatest demand in the United States is pork, the flesh of hogs. Fresh pork is firm, fine-grained, and well marbled with fat. It should be well covered with a layer of fairly firm, white fat. The flesh in young animals is grayish pink; in older animals, a delicate rose. Pork-loin roasts, fresh and cured hams, Boston butts, picnic or shoulder hams, bacon, spareribs, and chops are common retail cuts. Pigs feet are a delicacy and in many markets they are sold pickled. Cured hams are smoked or tenderized or fully cooked.

197

CUTS OF LAMB

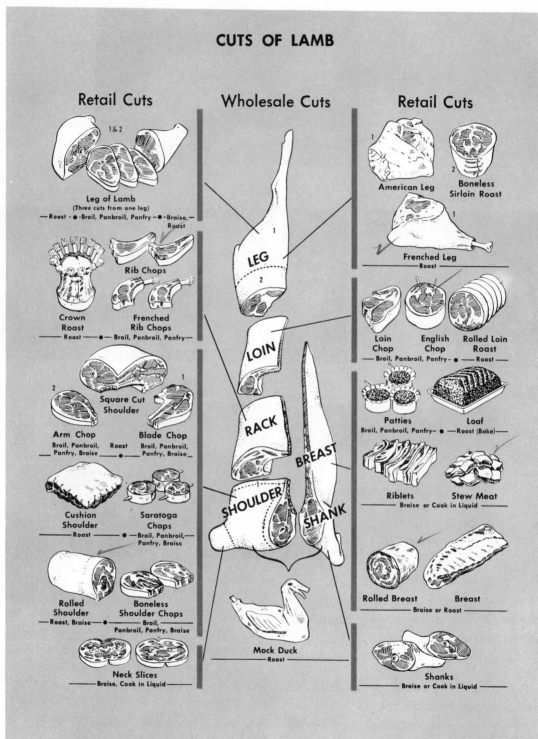

Retail Cuts

Leg of Lamb
(Three cuts from one leg)
— Roast - ● -Broil, Panbroil, Panfry – ● -Braise,—
Roast

1 & 2

Rib Chops

Crown Roast
— Roast - ● — Broil, Panbroil, Panfry —

Frenched Rib Chops

Square Cut Shoulder

Arm Chop
Broil, Panbroil,
Panfry, Braise

Roast ●

Blade Chop
Broil, Panbroil,
Panfry, Braise

1

2

Cushion Shoulder
— Roast —

Saratoga Chops
● — Broil, Panbroil,—
Panfry, Braise

Rolled Shoulder
— Roast, Braise - ●

Boneless Shoulder Chops
— Broil,
Panbroil, Panfry, Braise

Neck Slices
— Braise, Cook in Liquid —

Wholesale Cuts

LEG

1

2

LOIN

RACK

SHOULDER

2

BREAST

SHANK

Mock Duck
— Roast —

Retail Cuts

American Leg

1

Boneless Sirloin Roast

2

Frenched Leg
— Roast —

1

Loin Chop

English Chop

— Broil, Panbroil, Panfry – ●

Rolled Loin Roast
— Roast —

Patties
Broil, Panbroil, Panfry– ●

Loaf
—Roast (Bake)—

Riblets

Stew Meat
— Braise or Cook in Liquid —

Rolled Breast

Breast
— Braise or Roast —

Shanks
— Braise or Cook in Liquid —

Cuts of Meat

In choosing among the cuts of meat in the markets one finds small or larger roasts to suit the size of the family. The range from chopped meats, which can be extended in soups and meat loaf, through the less expensive cuts is usually ample for the shopper on a limited budget.

Normally there are many cuts of beef, veal, lamb, and pork available in markets. In planning menus, in obtaining the best food value, and in budgeting money, it is

Chops (arm and blade)

Loin chops

Rolled shoulder

Leg

Cushion shoulder

Rib chops

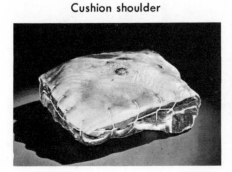

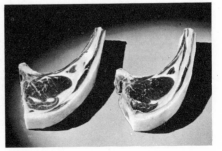

CUTS OF PORK

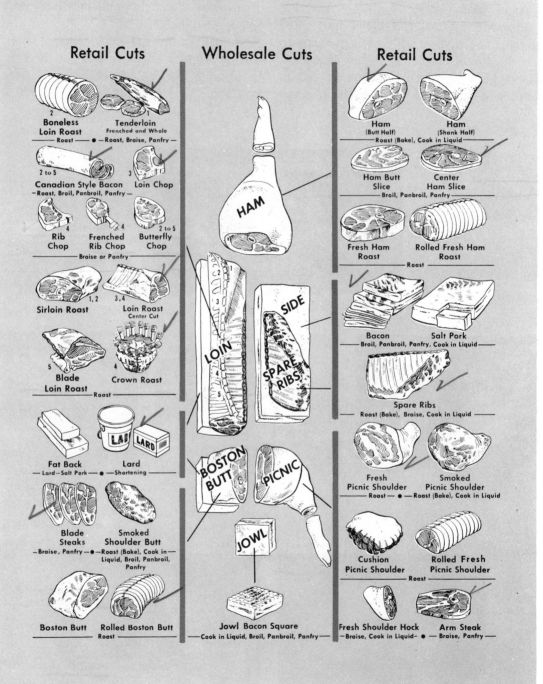

Retail Cuts

Boneless Loin Roast — 2
— Roast —

Tenderloin — 1
Frenched and Whole
— Roast, Braise, Panfry —

Canadian Style Bacon — 2 to 5
— Roast, Broil, Panbroil, Panfry —

Loin Chop — 3

Rib Chop — 4

Frenched Rib Chop — 4

Butterfly Chop — 2 to 5
— Braise or Panfry —

Sirloin Roast — 1, 2

Loin Roast — 3, 4
Center Cut

Blade Loin Roast — 5

Crown Roast — 4
— Roast —

Fat Back
— Lard—Salt Pork —

Lard
— Shortening —

Blade Steaks
— Braise, Panfry —

Smoked Shoulder Butt
— Roast (Bake), Cook in Liquid, Broil, Panbroil, Panfry —

Boston Butt

Rolled Boston Butt
— Roast —

Wholesale Cuts

HAM

LOIN

SIDE

SPARE RIBS

BOSTON BUTT

PICNIC

JOWL

Jowl Bacon Square
— Cook in Liquid, Broil, Panbroil, Panfry —

Retail Cuts

Ham
(Butt Half)

Ham
(Shank Half)
— Roast (Bake), Cook in Liquid —

Ham Butt Slice

Center Ham Slice
— Broil, Panbroil, Panfry —

Fresh Ham Roast

Rolled Fresh Ham Roast
— Roast —

Bacon

Salt Pork
— Broil, Panbroil, Panfry, Cook in Liquid —

Spare Ribs
— Roast (Bake), Braise, Cook in Liquid —

Fresh Picnic Shoulder

Smoked Picnic Shoulder
— Roast — — Roast (Bake), Cook in Liquid —

Cushion Picnic Shoulder

Rolled Fresh Picnic Shoulder
— Roast —

Fresh Shoulder Hock
— Braise, Cook in Liquid —

Arm Steak
— Braise, Panfry —

National Live Stock and Meat Board

Ham, shank and arm

Rib chops

Loin roast

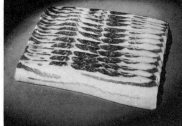

Sliced bacon

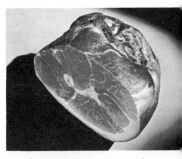

Smoked ham, butt half

Smoked ham. Center slice

Smoked picnic ham

Salt side

Fresh picnic shoulder

advantageous for the consumer to be thoroughly familiar with the variety of meat cuts and the best ways in which to use each. To become familiar with the size and shape of meat cuts learn the location of the cuts in the carcass. The charts and pictures on pages 194–201 will help you to do this.

Qualities of Meat

The quality of meat may be partially judged by its appearance. Fresh, well-cared-for meat looks moist. Because meat absorbs odors easily and spoils quickly, it should be purchased from clean places that have good storage facilities.

Tender meats tend to be firm and fine-grained. The flavor is richer when there is a covering of fat over the carcass and a marbling of it among the muscles. The covering of fat also checks evaporation and spoilage. Meat which has been properly stored will have an even color throughout. Beef and lamb are more tender and develop a better flavor if they are aged or ripened by storing at a temperature just above freezing for 2 or 3 weeks. New commercial processes are said to accomplish the same result in less time. Whatever the method of aging, cuts from the parts of the animal which receive the most exercise are less tender and require longer, slower cooking. They are no less desirable in flavor and food value.

Government Inspection

When shopping for meat, it is wise to look *Know* for the government inspection stamp.

It shows that trained inspectors have examined the animals and found them in good health at the time of slaughter; they also have approved the packing plant as clean. When the wholesale cuts meet the inspector's qualifications, they are stamped with a round purple stamp bearing the words "U. S. Inspected and Passed." This stamp in abbreviated form may also be found burned into smoked meats. The vegetable dye used in the government stamp is harmless.

About three-fourths of the meat and meat products in the United States come from federally inspected meat-packing houses. The Federal Meat Inspection Act does not regulate slaughtering and selling of meat unless it is shipped from one state to another or goes into foreign trade. States and cities generally have local regulations concerning meats, but usually there is no inspection service for the meat slaughtered on farms. This meat will usually be darker in color if the animals have been grass-fed.

Government Grading

United States standards for beef, veal, lamb, and mutton were set up to aid the consumer in determining the quality of meat. Although all grades of any one kind of meat are equal in wholesomeness and food value, they vary in flavor and tenderness. Not all meat is graded; only a few cities require the grade to be marked on carcasses. When carcasses are graded they are priced according to the following classes:

1. The U. S. Prime, or top grade, is a distinctly luxury cut of beef. This grade is tender, marbleized with fat, and is readily cooked by broiling or roasting.

2. U. S. Choice applies only to grain-fed steers and heifers. Usually it is the highest quality of beef sold in markets. Many cuts of Choice meat are excellent for

broiling and roasting. The purchaser should remember that Choice (the highest grade given to mutton) when marked on mutton corresponds only to the grade Good on beef, veal, and lamb.

3. U. S. Good is next to Choice in quality. There is a thinner layer of fat in this grade. It is used for much the same purposes as Choice. U. S. Good is commonly found in retail stores.

4. U. S. Commercial is next below U. S. Good in grade. It is the highest grade given to range-fed (unfattened) cattle. This grade of beef, lamb, veal, and mutton is most suited to moist-heat methods of cooking, such as pot roasts and stews. Fat may be present in a thin layer and it may be slightly yellow.

5. U. S. Utility beef is the lowest grade found in retail markets. It comes from animals of advanced age, and the cuts require long, slow cooking in moist heat. Lamb, veal, and mutton of this grade are rated as U. S. Cull.

6. U. S. Cutter and U. S. Canner are the lowest grades of beef used for food. The meat is wholesome and nutritious, but it is less tender than the better grades.

Pork must meet government inspection standards but is not graded like other meats.

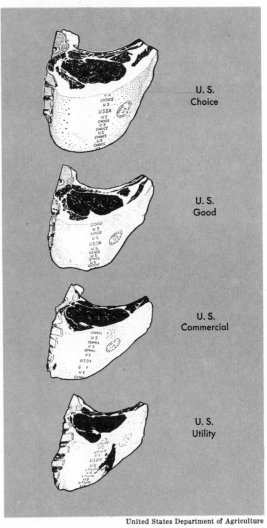

United States Department of Agriculture

Grades of rib roasts

Amounts of Meat to Buy

Whether meat should be bought in quantity depends on prices and on storage facilities. With a home freezer or freezer locker a large purchase, a quarter or even half of a carcass, can be an economy. With only refrigerator storage one may still purchase the meat needed for several days. A half ham purchased on Saturday may be the mainstay for a week or more. It may be baked ham for Sunday; thin slices will be good with breakfast eggs; a thick slice saved for the purpose may be broiled for Wednesday dinner; the ham hock baked with beans is an excellent Saturday supper; scraps from Sunday's baked ham have endless possibilities. A little imagination can make the purchase of half a ham an economy. Less expensive cuts, not always available, may be purchased in quantity if they can be safely kept until used.

Whether buying for a single meal or for several meals, the following figures on stand-

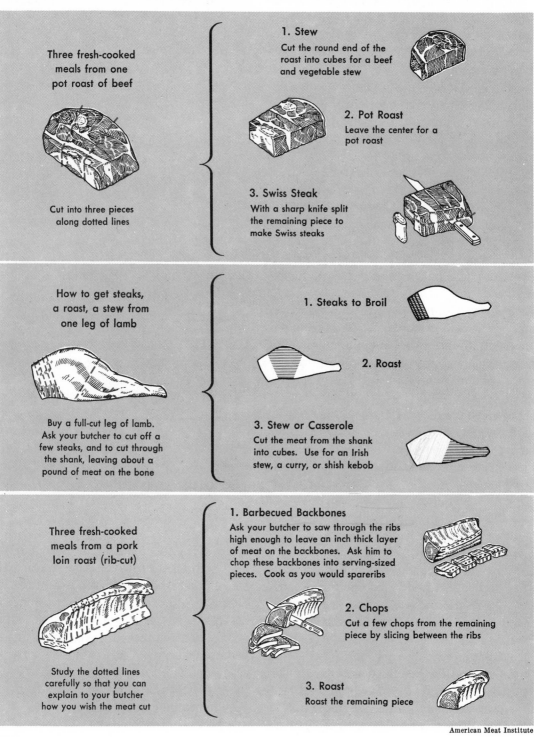

Three fresh-cooked meals from one pot roast of beef

Cut into three pieces along dotted lines

1. Stew
Cut the round end of the roast into cubes for a beef and vegetable stew

2. Pot Roast
Leave the center for a pot roast

3. Swiss Steak
With a sharp knife split the remaining piece to make Swiss steaks

How to get steaks, a roast, a stew from one leg of lamb

Buy a full-cut leg of lamb. Ask your butcher to cut off a few steaks, and to cut through the shank, leaving about a pound of meat on the bone

1. Steaks to Broil

2. Roast

3. Stew or Casserole
Cut the meat from the shank into cubes. Use for an Irish stew, a curry, or shish kebob

Three fresh-cooked meals from a pork loin roast (rib-cut)

Study the dotted lines carefully so that you can explain to your butcher how you wish the meat cut

1. Barbecued Backbones
Ask your butcher to saw through the ribs high enough to leave an inch thick layer of meat on the backbones. Ask him to chop these backbones into serving-sized pieces. Cook as you would spareribs

2. Chops
Cut a few chops from the remaining piece by slicing between the ribs

3. Roast
Roast the remaining piece

American Meat Institute

ard servings will help you estimate the amount of meat to buy. One standard adequate serving may be had from $\frac{1}{4}$ pound of boneless meat, $\frac{1}{3}$ to $\frac{1}{2}$ pound of meat with bone, $\frac{1}{4}$ pound of liver, $\frac{1}{6}$ to $\frac{1}{8}$ pound of prepared sausage, and 1 ounce of dried beef.

The size of the family and the daily requirements of individuals are also factors in the amount of meat purchased. Some persons require more, some less, depending on their age, their activities, and their health. The total amount needed daily is the sum of the individual needs. Price, quality, the food budget, and available storage space also govern one's decision as to the quantity of meat to buy.

Care of Meat in the Home

Fresh Meat

Fresh, raw meat is perishable and should be stored in the coldest part of the refrigerator. A temperature of 33° to 36° F. is desirable. Many refrigerators have meat-storage compartments directly below the freezing compartment. Once the meat is in the kitchen the outer wrapping should be removed immediately; the meat should then be loosely covered and stored in the refrigerator. When meat is stored in this way, only a small amount of surface drying occurs. This method increases its keeping qualities.

In general, larger cuts of meat are less perishable than smaller ones because they have proportionately less surface area. Most beef, lamb, and veal cuts can be stored safely for 3 or 4 days in the refrigerator. Pork should be cooked within 2 days. Ground meats, sausage, and variety meats should be cooked within 24 hours for safety. If variety meats must be bought in advance, it is a good idea to precook them and reheat at serving time. Cooked meats must be kept tightly covered and refrigerated.

Frozen Meat

Frozen meat retains its original quality only when it is stored at 0° F. or lower. Before freezing, the store wrappings should be removed and the meat rewrapped tightly in heavy waxed paper or metal foil to prevent drying. Frozen meat which has been thawed is more perishable than fresh meat. Thaw just enough for the meal since it must not be refrozen. Not all meats require thawing before cooking.

Cured Meat

Like fresh meats, ham and other cured meats should be stored in the refrigerator both before and after cooking. They need not, however, be kept quite as cold as fresh meat: and a dark, cold, dry basement or storeroom may be satisfactory. Proper storage of cured meats is important since the moisture which condenses on them at room temperature lessens their keeping quality.

Preparation of Meat for Cookery

Meat cuts from processing plants are usually ready to cook. When meat is properly handled, it needs no cleaning. Washing meat causes a loss of both flavor and soluble nutrients; instead, it should be wiped with a damp cloth just before cooking.

When wholesale cuts of considerable size are purchased, the tender meat should be separated from the less tender since the cooking methods are different. Bones should be sawed into short lengths and used to add food values and flavor to soup.

205

Meat is cooked to improve the flavor and to make it juicy and tender. Like other protein foods, meat should be cooked at a low temperature to obtain the greatest tenderness and flavor and to prevent undue loss of fat and juices. Thiamine, riboflavin, and niacin, especially, tend to flow out with the juices. Low cooking temperatures give a more uniformly cooked meat with more servings and a more digestible protein. Less spattering and burning of fat result and the drippings are more edible.

Cooking fresh pork until it is well done is especially important because it may contain the trichina parasite, which causes a fatal disease in human beings. This parasite is easily killed by thorough cooking. Weiners,

prepared sausages, and other pork products which might be used without further cooking are required by law to be treated in the processing plant for trichinosis.

All meat contains some natural salt, but most persons add seasonings. Large cuts of meat which are cooked very slowly may have salt added either before, during, or after cooking. Small cuts are usually seasoned after browning.

Herb seasoning adds to, and brings out, meat flavor. Beef is most often seasoned with basil, marjoram, savory, thyme, or rosemary. With pork, thyme, chives, sage, basil, rosemary, or marjoram are used. Lamb is good with mint, savory, rosemary, or dill. For variety in the flavor of veal, season it with tarragon, sage, rosemary, summer savory, thyme, or basil. Other seasonings suitable for meats are onions, parsley, horse-radish, garlic, and sauces such as raisin sauce and those commercially prepared.

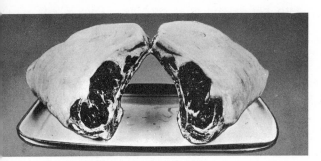

EFFECT OF TEMPERATURE IN ROASTING

Two standing ribs taken from right and left sides of beef carcass and weighed, with same weight

Same ribs after roasting · Left roasted at 450° F. Right roasted at 300° F. Both roasted to internal temperature of 140° F.

National Live Stock and Meat Board

Tender Meat Cuts

The tender cuts of meat can be cooked in their own juices without added moisture. Methods of cooking tender meat include roasting, broiling, and frying. These are known as dry-heat methods.

Roasting—Roasting is done in an oven, in an uncovered pan, with no added water. Roasts should be placed on a rack. They may be wrapped in metal foil to save the juices or melted fat may be spooned over the meat during the cooking. This is called basting and is unnecessary if the meat has been placed in the pan fat side up so that the melting fat will baste the meat as it cooks. If the meat has very little fat, lard pieces may be inserted in slits made in the lean, and

206

another piece of fat placed on top. This process is called larding. Between 300° and 325° F. is a desirable temperature for roasting.

A meat thermometer is the best means of determining when the roast is done. The possible presence of the trichina parasite makes it especially important to check the doneness of fresh pork. The thermometer is inserted to about the center of the cut; no part of it should touch a bone or rest on fat. (See page 429 for temperatures and time for cooking meats.)

Beef roasted to the rare stage has a lightly browned exterior, with uniform rose-red slices and a narrow layer of gray near the edge. There is an abundance of juice. Medium-done beef also should have a lightly browned exterior, but the slices will be light pink, and the gray layer at the outer edge will be deeper. The juice will be lighter in color. Beef cooked to the well-done stage will have a browned exterior. The slices will be grayish brown, there will be less juice, and the juice will be colorless.

Roast veal should have an even reddish-brown exterior color with a grayish-white interior. It should be juicy and tender but firm. Veal is usually cooked to the well-done stage to bring out the most flavor.

Fresh pork, always cooked to the well-done stage, should be a uniform brown with a crisp but not hard crust. The inside will be grayish white with no pink, and the juice will be a delicate brown. Any pinkness in either juice or meat indicates that the meat is not thoroughly cooked. Smoked pork should have a uniform dark golden-brown exterior, well glazed. The interior should be pink, firm, juicy, and tender with a nearly colorless juice.

Hams should be allowed to warm to room temperature before baking. A ham is done

National Live Stock and Meat Board

Measuring distance for inserting meat thermometer in roast · Measure distance to center of largest muscle

when the small bone in the shank end will come out easily and the larger bone in the round end is loose. Precooked hams, of course, require less time for cooking than others.

Roast lamb is plump and juicy with a crisp, golden-brown exterior. The juice should be faintly pink to light brown. The interior will be grayish brown and tender.

Broiling—Broiling meat means cooking by direct heat. Broiling may be done over an open fire or under an open flame or under the heat unit in the broiling compartment of a range. Pan broiling can be done on top of the range in an uncovered frying pan. Excess fat may be saved for seasoning, shortening, or frying. Only small cuts of meat are broiled since large cuts would not cook uniformly.

With automatically controlled oven temperatures *range broiling* is a simple task:

1. Grease the broiler rack with a small amount of fat to prevent sticking—except for such meats as bacon and sausage.

2. Preheat the broiler—except for bacon

and sausage, which are usually placed on a cold rack.

3. Slash the fat edge of the meat at 1-inch intervals. Cutting allows this edge to heat thoroughly and more quickly, preventing its curling.

4. Place the meat on the rack with the top surface 2 to 3 inches from the heat unit, depending on the thickness of the meat and the degree of doneness desired. (Refer to chart on page 429.)

5. Cook until done on one side. To cook on the other side, turn by piercing fat with a fork or by using tongs. Never pierce the meat itself as this causes loss of juices.

6. Cook the meat to the desired degree of doneness. Season and serve hot.

Pan broiling is satisfactory for small cuts of meat cooked uncovered in a hot frying pan, if one removes the fat as the meat cooks. Follow the directions below:

1. Heat the griddle or frying pan to speed the cooking.

2. Lay the meat on the ungreased surface. Drippings from the meat prevent sticking.

3. Keep a moderate cooking temperature. Never allow the fat to smoke.

4. Turn the meat frequently for even cooking.

5. Scrape or pour off excess fat from the griddle or pan as it accumulates.

6. Cook until done but avoid overcooking.

Veal is seldom broiled because it has insufficient fat. *Fresh pork* is never broiled, since broiling may leave the center rare, and so fail to kill the dangerous trichina parasite. *Cured ham* may be broiled for a tender juicy product.

Beef, when properly broiled to the rare stage, will have an even brown exterior with a thin grayish-brown layer just under the surface. The interior will be uniformly rose-red and tender, with red juice. The meat will be puffy and full. Medium-broiled beef has an even brown exterior with no charring of the bone or fat. The grayish-brown layer will be deeper than in rare beef and the in-

Baking ham · Wrap loosely in heavy paper or foil, fat side up, on rack in uncovered roasting pan. Insert meat thermometer in center of thickest part of meat away from bone

Half an hour before ham is done, remove from oven and discard paper. Take off rind, score fat in squares or diamonds. Use pieces of string fastened with toothpicks to make guide lines for scoring

Armour and Company

terior will be light pink. It will have less juice, and the juice will be light in color. The meat will be plump. Well-done beef is brownish gray throughout with very little juice. The juice is yellowish in color and the meat is shrunken in appearance.

Broiled *lamb* should have an evenly browned exterior. The fat will be light golden brown and the interior will be juicy and grayish brown in color with a tinge of pink. It will be tender and puffy. Well-done lamb will have no trace of pink.

Frying—In this process the meat is cooked in a small amount of fat in an uncovered pan on top of the range. The method differs from pan broiling in that the fat is allowed to accumulate.

1. Heat a griddle or frying pan and add a small amount of fat. Greasing the pan is unnecessary in the case of bacon or of ham cooked unfloured.

2. Roll the meat in flour or corn meal if desired. Flouring increases browning and makes a crisp exterior on the meat.

3. Leave accumulated fat on the griddle or in the pan.

4. Cook the meat uncovered at a moderate temperature until done. Drain the meat quickly on absorbent paper. Serve at once.

Variety Meats

Variety meats are tender but their strong flavors require additional steps in preparation. If brains and sweetbreads are soaked in salted water to which vinegar has been added, they will be more firm and less perishable. Remove the membranes and use the brains and sweetbreads in omelets, scrambled eggs, salads, or creamed dishes. They also may be fried in deep fat or pan-fried, or they may be baked.

Liver is tender and needs no precooking.

209

BRAISED LIVER

National Live Stock and Meat Board

Flouring the liver

Browning the liver

Braised liver garnished with crisp bacon and served with baked potatoes and gravy

Cut away the outside membrane, large blood vessels, and tough tissue before cooking. Liver may be fried, baked, broiled, or simmered. Kidneys have a strong flavor and should be soaked in running water. They may be precooked, chopped, and used in stew. Liver and kidneys may also be ground for loaves and patties.

Heart must be cut apart to remove the large veins, gristle, and blood vessels. Tongue must be scrubbed before cooking. Both tongue and heart are simmered in salted water until tender, and cooled in the cooking liquid. The skin and roots of the tongue are then easy to remove. Both meats may be sliced, or used in stews, or ground and used as lean meat in any recipe. They may also be spiced or pickled. Hearts may be stuffed, and either baked or braised.

Less Tender Cuts

Cuts of meat that are less tender may be improved in various ways. Pounding or breaking the tissues, as pounding flour into meat for Swiss steak, is one means of tenderizing meat. Another means is sprinkling over the meat a tenderizing powder, which contains enzymes from the papaya plant. Follow directions on the label for amount of powder and time to wait before cooking the meat. Grinding or cubing is still another method of breaking up the connective tissues.

Less tender cuts of meat must have moisture added for cooking. The steam or liquid of moist heat softens the connective tissues and makes the meat tender.

The moist-heat methods of cooking are braising, stewing, and steaming under pressure. With any one of these methods, some flavor is lost and some nutrients are dissolved into the liquid. Before liquid is added or steam applied, the meat should be browned slowly on all sides to develop flavor. Season-ings should next be added. The use of the drippings for gravy or sauce prevents any loss of flavor and nutrients.

Braising—Water, vegetable juices, meat stock, milk, or cream may be used as liquid. Braising is done either on top of the range or in the oven. The meat is browned in fat and then simmered in a covered dish with a small amount of liquid. Tender meats, such as pork liver or pork chops, may also be braised. Directions for braising follow:

1. Heat a heavy utensil, add fat if the meat is floured, and brown the meat slowly on all sides. Flouring the meat adds to the quality of the brown crust.

2. Add seasonings as desired. With less tender cuts, such as brisket, flank, chuck, and rump, add also a small amount of liquid.

3. Cover the meat tightly to hold in the steam, which softens the tissues. If cooking is done on top of the range, keep the liquid simmering until the meat is tender.

4. Place the meat on a heated platter and keep it warm until served.

5. Use the liquid and juices from the meat for gravy or sauce to accompany the meat.

Pot-Roasting—Pot-roasting meat is a process similar to braising. Meat should be browned first and then placed on a rack in a kettle. A small amount of water is added, and the kettle is covered tightly. The cooking temperature should be low. When vegetables are cooked with the roast, add them just in time to be steamed tender at the same time that the meat is tender and ready to serve. The seasoning of pot roasts should be governed by personal taste. Onions, chives, or herbs add to the flavor.

Stewing—The main difference between braising and stewing is in the amount of liquid used. In stews a greater amount is used, and the meat, cut in small uniform pieces, is served in the liquid.

Pressure Cookery—After the liquid has been added, carefully follow manufacturer's directions for using the cooker. Additional foods (see directions on page 210) may be added during the last minutes. Pressure cookery produces excellent results with a great saving of time.

Frozen Meat

Some frozen meats may be cooked without prethawing. Exceptions are large roasts that will require long cooking and a great deal of fuel, ground meats that must be thawed for shaping or combining with other foods, and cubed meats that must be browned. Any thick piece of meat cooks more uniformly if thawed before cooking. Meat to be broiled will lie flat and cook more evenly if prethawed.

Leave the meat wrapped while thawing. The time required for thawing varies with the shape and weight of the meat, the thickness of the cut, its wrappings, and the room temperature. At room temperature 3 to 5 hours may be required for steaks about an inch thick. Thawing in the storage part of the refrigerator may require from 15 to 20 hours for the same size steak.

When meats are thawed before cooking, the same recipes or cooking methods are used as for fresh meats. If meats such as thin chops, cutlets, steaks, and meat patties are cooked while frozen, allow 8 or 9 minutes longer cooking time for 1-inch-thick pieces. For larger pieces of frozen meat, cooking time must be still longer. The cooking temperature should be low for these pieces in order not to overcook the outside while the inside is thawing. The use of a meat thermometer inserted in the thawed meat aids in cooking to the desired doneness.

Leftover Meats

There are many ways to use leftover meats with other foods in appetizing hot dishes, such as chop suey, browned hash, croquettes, stuffed peppers, meat loaves, and casseroles. Broth may be made by simmering meat bones in water. Meat gravies or drippings can be used in sauces to extend meat flavors and food values. Leftover cooked meats may also be served cold, either sliced or in a salad. Leftover meats sometimes are enjoyed even more than when first cooked.

Carving Meat

Carving is an art which is fun to learn. Knowing the structure of the meat to be carved is an important aid to the carver.

A standard carving set contains three pieces: knife, fork, and steel. For most meats the knife should have a slightly flexible 8-to-9-inch blade, though a knife with a shorter blade is desirable for carving steak. The two-pronged fork should be equipped with a protective guard that should be used at all times. The steel is used to sharpen the knife blade to a good cutting edge. When the carving knife is not in use, wrap the blade in cloth to preserve its cutting edge.

There are many ways in which you can make the carver's task easier. Provide a large platter and sufficient space for the host to carve. Meat is easier to carve when not overcooked. When a roast is permitted to stand for about fifteen minutes between cooking and carving, the meat becomes firmer and easier to cut. A heated platter and plates

Carving a rolled rib roast of beef · A. Insert the fork firmly into the roast on the left side. Slice across the grain parallel to the cut surface, making uniform slices $\frac{1}{8}$ to $\frac{3}{8}$ inch thick. B. As each slice is carved, lift it to the side of the platter or to a hot plate

Carving a standing rib roast of beef · A. The roast is placed on the platter with the smaller cut surface up and the ribs to the carver's left. Insert the fork between the two top ribs. From the outside edge of the roast slice toward the ribs, making the slices from $\frac{1}{8}$ to $\frac{3}{8}$ inch thick. B. With the tip of the knife cut close along the rib to release each slice. C. After each slice is released, lift it on the blade of the knife to the edge of the platter or to a hot plate

National Live Stock and Meat Board

prevent the servings from cooling quickly. The carver may either stand or sit. It is important for the carver to plan the servings so that choice portions will be equally divided among the guests. Planned carving produces neater pieces and makes the meat go farther. All meat is cut across the grain with the exception of steak. Work for rapid carving in order that the meat may be served hot.

Rolled Rib Roast

1. Place this roast with the larger cut surface on the platter.

2. After placing the guard up on the fork, push the prongs firmly into the roast on the left side about two inches from the top.

3. Beginning at the far right side, slice the roast across the grain toward the fork; cut uniform slices about three-eighths of an inch thick.

4. The cord holding the rolled roast together is removed as necessary to carve slices. Using the knife for cutting and the fork for loosening the cord, allow the cord to drop to the platter.

5. As the slices are carved, lift them to a hot serving platter.

Other Rolled Roasts

Shoulder and rump cuts are often boned and rolled at the market. Because of the length of the rolled roast, its carving is easier if it is placed horizontally on the platter. These roasts are sliced in the same manner as rolled rib roasts.

Standing Rib Roast

1. Remove the short ribs and separate the backbone from the ribs to make the carving easier. (Preferably, this is done before roasting.)

2. Lift the fork guard and insert the prongs between the two top ribs. Begin at the out-

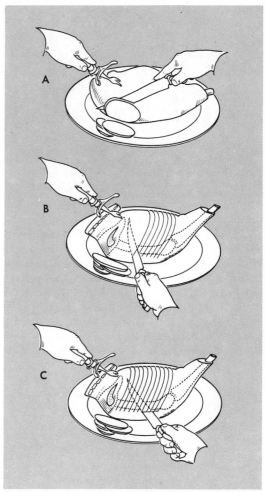

National Live Stock and Meat Board

Carving a leg-of-lamb roast · A. The roast is placed before the carver so that the shank bone is at the right and the thick meat section on the left side. Insert the fork into the large end of the leg. Carve a few slices from the near, thin, side.

B. Turn the roast so that it rests on the surface just cut. The shank bone now points up from the platter. With the fork in the left of the roast, begin at the shank end and slice down to the leg bone, making parallel slices about $\frac{1}{4}$ inch thick. Continue slicing until enough slices have been made or until the aitch bone is reached.

C. With the fork still in place, run the knife along the leg bone, releasing the slices

213

National Live Stock and Meat Board

Carving a porterhouse steak · *A.* The steak is placed on a platter with the backbone to the right and the flank end to the left. Hold the steak with the fork inserted at the left. Cut close around the T-shaped bone and lift it to one side. *B.* With the fork in position, cut across the full width of the steak. *C.* Make wedge-shaped portions, widest at the far side. Each serving should consist of a piece of the tenderloin and a piece of the large muscle. Reserve the flank end for additional servings as needed

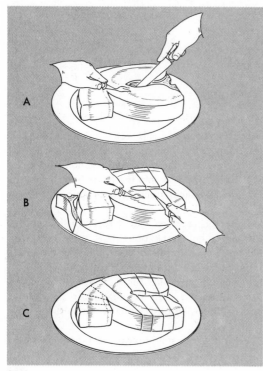

side edge and slice across the grain toward the ribs. The slices should be about $\frac{3}{8}$ of an inch thick.

3. Release each slice by cutting with the knife tip close along the rib.

4. After cutting each slice, lift it on the blade of the knife to the side of the platter or onto another hot platter.

Roast Leg of Lamb

1. Place the leg with the shank bone to the right of the carver.

2. Hold the leg in position with the fork inserted in the large end of the cut. Carve three or four lengthwise pieces from the side nearest the carver.

3. Place the roast so that it rests on the cut surface. The shank bone is to the right pointing up from the platter. Again hold the roast with the fork inserted at the left.

4. Start at the shank end and slice $\frac{3}{8}$-inch pieces to the bone.

5. Slice along the leg bone at the base of the sliced pieces to release them.

Steaks or Center-Cut Ham Slices

1. A board, cut to fit the center section of the platter, protects the cutting edge of the knife as well as the finish of the platter.

2. In carving a steak, hold it with the fork inserted at the left of the cut of meat.

3. Cut close around the bone, then lift it to the side of the platter.

4. Cut straight across the steak and make wedge-shaped portions. This ensures that each serving will have some of the choice meat.

Baked Fresh and Smoked Ham

1. Place the ham fat side up on the platter with the shank end to the carver's right.

2. Insert the fork on the left to hold the ham in position.

Porterhouse steak · The best grade of raw beef should show color and marbling of fat similar to this

Pork loin roast · High-grade pork is a rich pink in color and liberally marbled and coated with fat

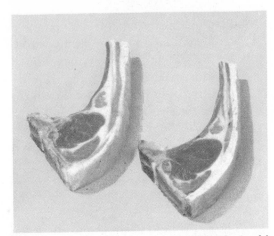

Rib lamb chops · The best grade of lamb should show color similar to this and clean, white fat

Rolled rib roast of beef · This roast has been perfectly cooked, with the result that it has retained its juices; it is evenly browned; and the slices will range from well-done at the outside to medium and rare inside

3. Cut three slices from the side of the ham next to the carver.

4. Place the ham so that it rests on the cut surface. Again hold the ham firmly with the fork at the left and cut a wedge from the shank end to make slicing easier.

5. Cut from $\frac{1}{4}$- to $\frac{1}{2}$-inch slices down from the outer surface to the bone in parallel slices.

6. Release the slices by cutting along the bone toward the fork.

7. For additional slices, turn the ham over and cut from the other side.

As host, the head of the family often finds great pleasure in expertly carving a roast of beef, or a browned capon or turkey. It is a joy, too, to watch his deft movements in handling his tools and in apportioning the appetizing meat, the center of the whole meal. Watching him gives the family a feeling of well-being and anticipation of good food and a pleasant dinner hour.

¶ *Understanding:*

1. Why is meat important in your diet?
2. What qualities will you look for in choosing fresh beef?
3. How does lamb compare with veal and pork in food values?

216

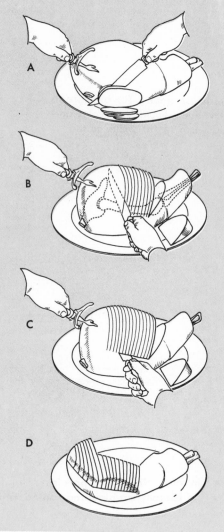

National Live Stock and Meat Board

Carving a baked ham · A. The ham is placed on the platter with the shank end toward the carver's right. From the near side carve off several slices. B. Turn the ham so that it rests on the surface just cut. Hold the ham firmly with the fork at the left. Begin at the shank end and slice down to the leg bone, making parallel slices about $\frac{1}{4}$ inch thick. Continue slicing until enough slices are made or until the hip bone (at the left) is reached. C. With the fork still in place, run the knife along the leg bone, releasing the slices. D. Now turn the ham so that it lies in the original position (see A above). Continue the slicing as indicated

4. List the less-tender cuts of beef and the best methods for cooking them.

5. Sketch a beef carcass and show the location of the cuts which can be cooked successfully by dry heat.

6. How do the tender and less-tender cuts of meat compare in food values?

7. What are the best ways to store meat in the home to preserve its qualities?

8. How does the temperature and length of time for cooking meat affect its doneness?

¶ Planning:

1. Plan a dinner meal to include roast beef. What food values will the beef contribute? Substitute beef liver. What will be gained?

2. Plan a method for cooking beef briskets. How should the cut be served?

3. Plan meats for two home dinners that require a minimum time for preparation.

4. Assist with planning the weekly meat order for your home, keeping within the family budget.

5. Plan a Sunday dinner meat so that leftovers will provide another meal.

6. Plan two luncheon meals illustrating different uses of heart; different uses of kidney.

¶ Practicing and Evaluating:

1. Cook a less-tender steak so that it is appetizing. How much money was saved by not purchasing a more expensive cut?

2. Assist with the preparation of a meat-and-vegetable dish for dinner. What food values for the meal did the dish provide?

3. Thaw frozen meat and assist with its preparation by roasting. Evaluate for tenderness and flavor.

4. Broil a steak in the range to the well-done stage. In what ways will you improve procedures another time?

5. Pan-broil and pan-fry two similar cuts of meat. Compare flavor, appearance, and texture.

6. Carve and serve a steak at home. Evaluate your experience.

7. Assist with carving and serving a rolled roast. How could you improve the performance?

8. Prepare brains for cooking with scrambled eggs as part of a luncheon meal.

9. Pan-fry liver and serve as a main dish for a quickly prepared luncheon.

¶ Reading Further:

BULL, SLEETER, *Meat for the Table*, McGraw-Hill Book Company, Inc., New York.

How to Make Turkey Rolls, Bulletin 70 (1959). University of Missouri Extension Service, Columbia, Missouri.

JENSEN, LLOYD B., *Meat and Meat Foods*, The Ronald Press Company, New York.

Look to Your Skillet Skills, Bulletin 43 (1960). Iowa State University Extension Service, Ames, Iowa.

Meat Manual, National Livestock and Meat Board, Chicago, Ill.

Short Cuts to Hot Meals, Circular 668 (1960). Oregon State College Extension Service, Corvallis, Oregon.

U. S. Grades of Beef, Marketing Bulletin 15 (1960). U. S. Department of Agriculture, Washington, D. C.

G. H. Davis, from F. P. G.

Fish and poultry

you will learn: The importance of fish in
the diet; How to select and care for fish; Principles of
fish cookery; The importance of poultry
in the diet; How to select and care for poultry;
Principles of poultry cookery; How to carve poultry

There was once a time when man either fished or hunted for most of his food. What he brought home—animals, game birds, or fish—depended upon the region in which he lived and the season of the year. In the winter he would procure his food chiefly by hunting, but during the summer months he would explore the streams, rivers, lakes, and oceans for fish. Whatever he caught, he cooked and ate at once. Today, with modern methods of food storage, we are able to eat many kinds of meat and fish throughout the entire year. An understanding of the value of fish and poultry in the diet, as well as of meat, and a knowledge of the varieties available will be helpful in the planning of new, interesting, and valuable menus.

The Importance of Fish in the Diet

Fish, whether fresh, frozen, canned, or cured, when properly cooked, is a palatable and readily digested food. The chief food value is its high-quality *protein*; it is, therefore, an excellent alternate for meat. Fish compares favorably with lean meat in protein content.

Many of the fin fish are low in *fat* values. What fat there is in lean fish is carried in the liver. Among the least fat are bass, perch, flounder, trout, haddock, and cod.

Those that contain the greatest amount of fat are salmon, catfish, mackerel, bluefish, herring, shad, sturgeon, tuna, and red snappers. The additional fat used in fish cookery adds to the total energy value and makes fish comparable to meat in energy content. Among the shellfish low in fat value are oysters, clams, and lobsters. Fish are excellent sources of *minerals*, including iodine and other trace elements. The softened bones of such canned fish as salmon contain a high percentage of calcium. The livers of fish are their most potent sources of *vitamins*. (For the food values of fish see Table IV in the Appendix.)

Selection and Care of Fish

There are two kinds of fish: those with fins, bones, scales or heavy skins, and tapering bodies; and those with shells. Varieties of lean and fat fish with fins number in the thousands. Among the shellfish are oysters and clams, with hinged shells, and lobsters, with crustlike shells.

Fresh Fish

Consumers should be informed as to which fresh fish are available and their best uses. It is also helpful to know the various forms in which fresh fish are sold.

Market Forms of Fish—There are several forms of *fin fish* from which to select. Whole fish keep best but involve more waste. Before being used they must be drawn (have the viscera taken out), and the scales, heads, and fins must be removed. Fish dealers do this without charge. Drawn fish have only the viscera removed. Dressed fish are ready to cook either whole or in pieces.

Fish steaks are cross slices and fillets are lengthwise slices. Fillets, which are usually boneless, may be cut double to include both sides of the fish joined by a narrow strip of flesh. Sometimes the skin is left on fillets.

Shellfish may be marketed alive in the shell. Shrimp may be marketed in the shell without heads. Clams, lobsters, and crabs should be cooked alive to ensure freshness. They may be marketed as whole cooked products. Oysters, scallops, and shrimp are available shucked. Fresh shucked oysters are marketed by liquid measure and packed in waxed or metal containers. They must be refrigerated or surrounded by ice. In some parts of the country oysters are packed according to commercial grades: Extra Large, Large, Medium, Small, and Very Small. Fresh shrimp are sold by the pound in Jumbo, Large, Medium, and Small grades. Lobster and shrimp are also sold as cooked meats. Lobster meat, removed from the cooked lobsters and chilled, and cooked

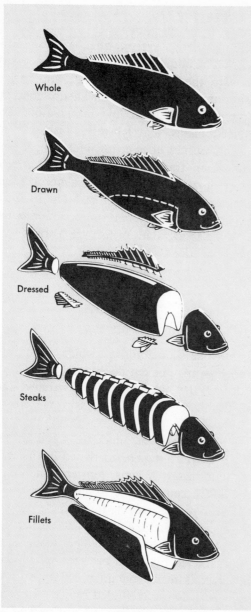

Whole

Drawn

Dressed

Steaks

Fillets

Market forms of fish · The whole, or round, fish appears just as it was caught. The entrails have been removed from the drawn fish. The dressed fish has been scaled and eviscerated. Usually the head, tail, and fins are removed. Fish steaks are cross-section slices of larger-sized dressed fish. Fillets are sides cut lengthwise away from the backbone

shrimp without shells are also sold by the pound.

Characteristics of Good Fresh Fish—The best-quality fin fish have a sheen with scales clinging tightly to the skin, or the skin is firm, as on catfish. The odor of fish must be fresh. Fish with bright, clear, bulging eyes, reddish gills, and no slime are fresh. Good-quality fish have firm flesh which is elastic enough to spring back into place when pressed. The flesh of fish should cling tightly to the bones.

Shellfish must have a fresh, characteristic odor. A clean, bright appearance with natural color also indicates quality in shellfish. Oysters should be plump with a natural creamy color, the liquor should be clear, and they should be free from pieces of shell. There are three types of clams: small clams, medium-sized clams, and large chowder clams. Clamshells tightly closed or shells which close at a touch indicate freshness.

Keeping Fish Fresh—Both fin and shellfish are highly perishable. They are usually frozen for transportation and should be kept frozen until cooked. They need not be thawed before cooking.

Immediate dressing and chilling of fin fish is necessary for their safe use. Always buy fish from markets that provide excellent refrigeration or keep fish embedded in chipped ice. For storage at home, keep fish in the coldest part of the refrigerator. The fish should be kept closely covered or well wrapped in moisture-proof paper because their odor easily penetrates other foods. When fish are to be kept for more than 24 hours, they must be frozen. Cooked fin fish also must be kept in the coldest part of the refrigerator. Even so, it will lose flavor and food value after a day or two. It may be kept for a longer time if it is frozen.

Shellfish must be refrigerated. Freezing

is the only safe means of preserving its quality if it is to be stored for two or three days. Cooked shellfish should be stored in a tight container in the coldest part of the refrigerator.

Frozen Fish

The best-tasting frozen fish are those chilled immediately upon being caught. When properly frozen and stored, they have a taste similar to that of fresh fish. Fish are dressed and wrapped carefully in moisture-proof paper, quickly frozen, and stored at 0° F. or below. Most shellfish is available frozen. It may be purchased ready to cook or ready to eat. Frozen fish keeps satisfactorily for as long as a year. In no instance may any fish be thawed and then refrozen. The purchaser of packaged frozen fish should read the label carefully.

Canned Fish

The main dish for an unplanned company dinner may be easily and quickly prepared from canned fish, such as salmon, tuna, lobster, shrimp, sardines, oysters, and crab. Cans of fish, such as tuna and salmon, vary greatly in price according to their color, the size of the pieces, and the richness of flavor. However, there is little difference in food value. Once a can of fish has been opened, it must be kept thoroughly chilled in the refrigerator.

Dried, Salted, and Smoked Fish

Only lean fish can be processed through drying. Oily fish becomes rancid. Cod is the most commonly dried and salted fish. Fat fish, such as mackerel and herring, may be pickled. Salmon, haddock, and herring are also smoked. Cured fish should be kept in dry, cool storage.

United States Fish and Wildlife Service

Scaling · Lay fish on a table and hold it with one hand firmly by the head. With knife almost vertical, using back of knife, scrape off the scales. Work from tail toward head. Since scales are more easily removed from wet fish, it is advisable to soak the fish in cold water for a few minutes before scaling

Removing head · After the entrails have been removed, cut into the fish behind the gills. If the backbone is large, cut down to it on each side of the fish and snap the backbone by bending it over the-edge of the cutting board

Removing the dorsal fin · Cut the flesh along both sides of the fin, then give a quick pull forward toward the head of the fish. Remove the fin with its bones attached

221

Fin fish · With how many of these fish are you familiar?

Shellfish · How many of these fish can you identify?

Principles of Fish Cookery

Fish is cooked by simple methods. The small amount of connective tissue is softened readily while the protein is coagulated and the flavor is developed. A short cooking period prevents the protein from becoming tough and safeguards the moisture content. Careful handling prevents the fish from breaking into pieces.

Fin Fish

Lean fin fish are improved by moist-heat methods of cooking, that is, by boiling, steaming, poaching, simmering, or baking with sauce. Fat fish are best baked, stuffed, broiled, or fried. Seasonings of salt, pepper, mixed spices, horse-radish, or onions add flavor to fish. Among the sauces suitable for fish are cucumber, hollandaise, tartar, cheese, lemon, and white sauce. Covering the cooked fish with a tasty sauce helps to make it appealing to both the appetite and the eye. Sauces also add flavor and food values.

To *simmer* fish in water, place it on a rack in a kettle, lay it in a frying basket, or tie it

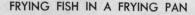

FRYING FISH IN A FRYING PAN

Covering fish with seasoned meal or bread crumbs

What's New in Home Economics

Turning fish when one side is brown

Removing excess fat by placing cooked fish on absorbent paper

Serving fried fish with a garnishing of cole slaw, cucumber, and radishes

in cheesecloth. A little vinegar added to the water helps to coagulate the outer portion of the fish and thus helps to prevent the flesh from breaking apart.

Frying may be done either in shallow fat or in deep fat. The cooking fat should have a high smoking point, that is, it should not quickly decompose and give off fumes when heated. A fat of delicate flavor is best. Either a small whole fish or pieces of serving size may be fried. Deep-fat frying of fish requires a temperature of 375° F. A layer of fish dredged in flour or corn meal is placed in the frying basket and cooked in the fat until golden brown.

Broiling is an excellent method of cooking fish. Small or medium-sized fish may be broiled whole or split without removing bones or tail. Fish fillets and steaks also may be broiled. They are less likely to fall apart if the skin is left on. Broiled fish is done when it flakes easily with a fork. Lift it carefully onto a hot platter and serve immediately.

Baking fish is a simple process. French dressing or melted fat is used to coat the outside or it may be rolled in seasoned bread crumbs and sprinkled with onion juice. Serve baked fish immediately on a hot platter. The fish suitable for baking are bass, pompano, carp, whitefish, halibut, trout, and red snapper. Fish weighing 3 to 5 pounds may be stuffed and baked with or without the head and tail. The seasoned bread stuffing is kept in the fish by sewing the opening of the flesh or by using small metal skewers. If the fish is laid on a piece of foil, it can be turned easily. Fish fillets may also be stuffed and baked.

Shellfish

Shellfish may be cooked by the general methods given for fin fish. It is important

225

International Minerals & Chemical Corporation, and *Forecast*

Broiled swordfish steaks · These steaks were brushed with melted fat before being placed on a greased broiler rack. During the broiling (about eight minutes for each side) they were brushed frequently with melted fat

Broiling brook trout · These trout are being brushed with fat during the process of broiling, so that they will not dry out

International Minerals & Chemical Corporation, and *Forecast*

ROLLED STUFFED FILETS OF FISH

Practical Home Economics

Frozen filets thawed and being spread with a mixture of fat creamed with minced parsley and onion, grated lemon rind, salt, and pepper

The spread filets are being rolled and fastened with a toothpick. They are then placed in a well-greased baking dish. The top of each filet will be dotted with the remaining spread

Baked in a moderate oven for twenty-five minutes, these filets, with the toothpicks removed, have been garnished with lemon wedges and served with fresh peas

not to overcook them. Oysters, for example, will become tough if even slightly over-cooked. Heating them to the desired temperature is all that is necessary. Overcooked shrimp are tough and shrunken, and lobster is stringy as well as tough when cooked too long.

To prepare fresh *shrimp*, wash them in cold water and drop into rapidly boiling salted water. When the water reaches boiling temperature again, lower the heat and simmer. Mixed spices may be used in the water. Remove the shells from the cooked shrimp. Along the outside curvature of each shrimp there is a dark line that should be removed. Shrimp may be served chilled in cocktails and salads. They may also be served hot in combination with other foods in main dishes, or by themselves, French fried, creamed, or in Newburg sauce. Ready-cooked and canned shrimp are used in the same ways.

Oysters may be scalloped, fried, or used in stews. Or they may be served uncooked on the half shell or in cocktails.

Fresh *clams* in the shell are cooked alive by boiling them in water. The heat is then reduced and they are steamed until the shells are partially opened. After removing the meat from the shells, discard the dark body mass. Wash the meat when it is to be fried or used in chowders. Steamed or canned clams may be used in the same manner. Raw clams are used on the half shell as hors d'oeuvres and in cocktails.

Fresh *lobster* must be alive up to the moment of cooking. To boil lobster, plunge it head first into briskly boiling salted water. Cover the kettle and return to boiling; lower the heat, and simmer. Plunge the cooked lobster into cold water, drain, and cool. Place the lobster on its back and cut the entire length of the body. The intestine, running from head to tail, and the sac near the head

226

must be removed. Cooked lobster may be served in the shell. The meat is removed as it is eaten and may be dipped into melted butter. The meat may also be broiled, creamed, used in salads, or combined with other foods in main dishes.

The Importance of Poultry in the Diet

Chicken and turkey have long been the mainstay of special meals—Sunday dinner, Thanksgiving, Christmas. Wild turkeys preceded domesticated ones in the history of our Thanksgivings, and the pioneer hunter could be thankful, too, for wild geese, ducks, pheasant, quail, grouse, partridge, and the prairie chicken, each with its distinctive flavor. Now poultry is as plentiful on the market as meat, and often less expensive.

Poultry is sufficiently useful in the home meal to make it well worth the extra care required in selection and storage and the time consumed in preparation and serving. It furnishes pleasant variety from meat and fish; it contains a high-quality protein and is richest in minerals and vitamins and in fat. The white meat of poultry, because it has a small amount of connective tissue, is more tender than the other meat. It is also low in fat content. Mature poultry has more fat than young poultry at the broiler stage. Because its caloric content is, on the whole, lower than that of meat and because it is bland in flavor and readily digestible, poultry is well suited to many special diets. It is frequently lower in cost than other meat and is completely equivalent as a food.

Selection and Care of Poultry

A bird with a wide body, a broad, full-fleshed breast and short, thick legs is the best choice. The crop should be empty because food in the crop may cause deterioration. Avoid choosing a bruised bird or one with the skin reddened by poor bleeding.

Poultry dealers may use government service that provides health inspection, grading, and labeling.

Market Forms of Poultry

All types of poultry may be marketed in several different forms, from live birds that require complete preparation for cooking to ready-to-cook birds. Birds are seldom bought alive unless they are purchased direct from a farm or a poultry house. When birds have been slaughtered and bled, and have had the feathers removed but the feet and head left on and the entrails left in, they may be called market dressed, fresh dressed, or New York dressed. When dressed poultry has been drawn, the entrails, head, and feet have been removed, and the giblets have been wrapped separately. Some pin feathers and the lungs and oil sac may remain to be removed. Eviscerated, or ready-to-cook, poultry has been cleaned and the head, feet, most of the pinfeathers, and the entrails removed. In many markets completely ready-to-cook poultry, whole or cut in pieces, may be bought wrapped in cellophane. Desired parts of the bird, such as giblets or dark meat, may be purchased packaged or loose. Necks and backs of chickens are inexpensive. Turkey steaks may be purchased. Most of these

This sign, a grade-and-inspection mark, means "graded for quality and inspected and passed as wholesome food"

This grade mark means "graded for quality." It is used only with the inspection mark, which denotes wholesomeness

This inspection mark means "passed as wholesome food but not officially graded for quality"

forms are also marketed as frozen products. Canned poultry, like canned ham, may be a luxury food but convenient on the storage shelf for unplanned meals or special occasions. Cans may vary from large cans containing the whole bird to be carved to smaller cans of pieces useful in salads and in creamed or casserole dishes. Smoked turkey is another luxury favored by some as a special treat.

MARKET CLASSES OF CHICKENS

CLASSES	WEIGHT READY-TO-COOK Pounds
BROILERS or FRYERS	1 to 3½
ROASTERS	2½ to 5
CAPONS	4 to 8
STEWING CHICKEN (hen or fowl)	2¼ to 5

Kinds of Poultry

The commonest kinds of poultry are chickens, turkeys, and ducks. Since, however, geese, guinea hens, and game birds are occasionally found in the markets, it is desirable to understand their qualities also, and how to cook them.

Chicken—Usually the heavier breeds of chicken are chosen for meat. Hens of lighter-weight breeds are usually used for egg production; the young male birds are sold as fryers or broilers. When flocks are culled, older birds are sold for stewing. Young chickens of high quality have a smooth, thin, pliable, light-yellow skin and firm flesh. They are free from bruises and discoloration. The feet are smooth and yellow. Plumpness and flexible breastbones are desirable characteristics. Age is an important factor in choosing chickens because the method of cooking and tenderness depend on the maturity of the bird. Chickens are also classified by ready-to-cook weight.

Broilers have very little fat. Either one-fourth or one-half of a bird is required for each serving. A bird of broiling size may be fried or roasted as well as broiled.

Fryers are easily disjointed for frying.

They have enough fat underneath the skin so that they may also be roasted. From $\frac{3}{4}$ to 1 pound of chicken is generally allowed per serving.

Roasters carry enough meat to be roasted whole. A good layer of fat lies under the skin. They may be fried if covered and steamed during the latter part of the cooking process. Allow from $\frac{1}{2}$ to $\frac{3}{4}$ pound for each serving that you plan to have.

Capons are unsexed males. These birds have excellent flavor and tenderness and yield a high proportion of white meat. Capons are splendid for roasting. A generous half pound provides a single serving.

Stags, young roosters, have coarse skin and developing spurs. They are best stewed or braised. About three-fourths of a pound is required for a serving.

Fowls have a thick, coarse skin with non-

THREE GRADES OF CHICKENS

U.S. Grade A · This is a stewing chicken of A quality. It is well fleshed with a full breast and meaty legs. It has no defects. A good layer of fat is well distributed under the skin. The bird is well picked and free of pin feathers. The skin is without tears or bruises

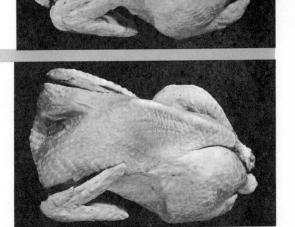

U.S. Grade B · This is a stewing chicken of B quality. It is fairly well fleshed and has a fair covering of fat. It is fairly well picked and there are no pin feathers. It has no deformities or broken bones and no skin tears or bruises. (Minor deformities and minor tears and bruises are allowed in B-quality birds)

U.S. Grade C · This is a stewing chicken of C quality. It falls short of the standards for B quality in being poorly fleshed and poorly covered with fat. It might also have been poorly picked and had minor skin tears or bruises, some deformities, or a broken bone, because these defects are allowed in C-quality poultry

Choice poultry, wild duck, and pheasant are luxury foods

flexible breastbones. Braising and stewing are the best methods to tenderize them. A generous half pound serves one person.

Roosters have coarse, tough meat. They are excellent for soup and also may be stewed. Roosters cost the least per pound. From $\frac{1}{4}$ to $\frac{1}{2}$ pound provides a serving.

Turkeys—Turkeys may be purchased in the size that fits the need. Small, meaty turkeys may come from the Jersey Buff breed or the Beltsville Small White. The turkeys usually chosen by the average family are the Narragansett, Bourbon Red, White Holland, or Black breeds. The largest of all turkeys is the Broad-Breasted Bronze.

The *broiler* class of turkey has been developed for small-family use. It may be

broiled, fried, or roasted. A fourth of a small bird or a disjointed piece of a larger bird makes one serving.

The *hen* turkey, which matures more quickly than the tom, has a better form and more fat at the same weight. They are not tender birds despite their fat. Roasting or baking at a low temperature or steaming with a cover tenderizes the bird. Three-fourths of a pound provides an average serving. The breastbones in hen turkeys under eight months of age are flexible; the meat is tender and the skin is soft, pliable, and smooth. Tom turkeys over ten months of age have coarse skin and hardened breastbones. Mature hen and tom turkeys have developed strong connective tissue, and the skin is likely to be dry and have patchy areas of surface fat. They may be made tender by using the moist heat method (page 210) for a portion of the cooking time.

In some places turkeys are graded by quality: U.S. Grade A and U.S. Grade B.

Ducks, Geese, Guineas, Pigeons—This group of fowl offers a flavor more like that of wild game than do chickens and turkeys. There is a larger proportion of fat in *geese* and *ducks* and their meat is all dark. Young ducks weighing 2 to 4 pounds at 8 to 12 weeks are called *ducklings*. Young geese from 5 months up to 1 year are classed as *goslings*. Good-quality birds have tender meat. Their bills are not completely hardened and their windpipes are easily dented. Ducklings and goslings are most delicious when broiled or oven-roasted. Mature ducks at 3 to 5 pounds and geese at 5 to 7 pounds have less tender meat and may need to be covered for a portion of the cooking time. Their bills, windpipes, and breastbones are hardened. *Guineas* from 5 to 9 months old are comparable to pullets of the same age in plumpness and amount of fat underneath the skin. The meat is dark. They may be roasted whole. *Squabs* are young pigeons weighing from ¾ to 1½ pounds and yielding only one to two servings each. They should be broiled.

Care and Storage

Fresh poultry is highly perishable and must be kept well refrigerated before and after cooking. Uncooked poultry should be stored in the coldest part of the refrigerator loosely covered in waxed paper and should be used within 24 hours. Frozen poultry must be kept at 0° F. or used within 3 days if kept at ordinary refrigerator temperatures. Cooked poultry, gravy, giblets, drippings, and stuffing should be tightly covered and carefully refrigerated as soon as they cool.

Preparation of Poultry for Cooking

Drawn poultry and "ready-to-cook" poultry need further cleaning. Pinfeathers can be pressed out with a knife or drawn with tweezers. Lungs and oil sac should be removed. If leg tendons have not been removed from large chickens and turkeys, this may be done by slitting the shank about two inches below the hock joint and pulling the tendons out. The first joints of the wings of turkeys, geese, and ducks should be removed. They may be added to other foods for soup stock. Hairs are removed by a quick singeing over a low flame. The giblets should be washed. The bird should be scrubbed thoroughly inside and out in lukewarm water with soda, and rinsed with clear water. Packaged poultry should be wiped with a damp cloth.

Frozen poultry, whether whole or in pieces, is best thawed in the refrigerator. Cover poultry loosely with waxed paper. Separate small parts so the air can reach each one. Allow about two days for a large whole bird to thaw or overnight for a small bird, a half, or a quarter. Pieces such as legs, thighs, and wings require from 3 to 9 hours. Cross-cut steaks of poultry require from 6 to 8 hours for thawing. Poultry may be thawed on a rack under cool running water. By this method several hours are required for a large bird. Because of the loss of nutrients, never let the bird soak in water. Small whole birds may be thawed at room temperatures if cooked immediately after thawing. Frozen boneless steaks, because they are extremely perishable, are often cooked without thawing.

For information on the slaughter and preparation of poultry at home refer to bulletins from the agricultural extension service of your state university or write to the United States Department of Agriculture for leaflets and other literature.

Principles of Poultry Cookery

Poultry, like meat, should always be cooked at a low temperature so that it will be tender, retain its juices, and be evenly cooked to the bone. The method used for cooking depends upon the age and condition of the bird. Dry-heat methods—broiling, frying, and open-pan roasting—are suitable for plump, tender birds. For lean or very mature birds, moist-heat methods, such as braising and stewing, are best. Old birds need long, slow cooking in water or steam.

Broiling

Poultry broiling is similar to meat broiling but slower since the irregular shape of the poultry carcass or pieces may require a longer time for thorough cooking. The cooking of chicken may be started in the broiler and finished in the oven. Chickens and turkeys are often broiled whole on a revolving spit, with frequent basting.

Frying

Frying may be done either in shallow fat or deep fat. For both methods the bird is cut into serving-sized pieces. For *shallow-fat frying* heat the fat in a heavy skillet. Use about one-half inch or more of fat. Do not allow the fat to smoke. Put the thickest pieces of chicken in first. Allow plenty of room around each piece. If the pan is crowded and there is not enough room for all the pieces to lie in the fat at one time, the pieces may be browned, a few at a time. Then all the pieces should be replaced in the pan and the cooking continued over low heat or in the oven.

In *deep-fat frying* the fat should be deep enough to immerse the pieces of chicken completely. Lower the chicken into the fat, a few pieces at a time, in a frying basket. Lay the cooked pieces on absorbent paper as they become tender and keep them hot until serving time.

FRYING CHICKEN

Poultry and Egg National Board

1. Coating the pieces of chicken with seasoned flour · A quick and simple method is to put the seasoned flour in a paper bag and, one piece at a time, shake the chicken thoroughly

3. If chicken is tough, after the pieces have been browned, add carefully a small amount of water. Cover to hold in the steam

2. Place the pieces of chicken in hot fat in a heavy frying pan. Turn to brown each piece evenly

4. Testing for doneness · Fried chicken is done when the fork pierces it readily

MARKET CLASSES OF TURKEYS

CLASSES	WEIGHT READY-TO-COOK Pounds
FRIERS or ROASTERS (very young birds)	4 to 8
YOUNG HENS (fully grown birds)	6 to 12
YOUNG TOMS (fully grown birds)	14 to over 20

Roasting

Poultry is roasted whole and usually is stuffed. Stuffings are made with a cereal base, such as bread crumbs or rice. Ducks and geese are sometimes stuffed with sauerkraut, which absorbs some of the fat. Whole carrots, stalks of celery, onions, or apple halves also are used.

Before stuffing the bird, additional seasonings may be rubbed over the inside. Pile the stuffing into the body cavity lightly because it expands as it absorbs the juices of the bird during cooking. Close the opening by lacing with thread or with metal skewers. Stuff the neck opening in the same way and lace shut. The legs are secured by slipping them through slits previously made in the flesh above the body cavity or by tying the legs together. Turkey, chicken, and guinea should be rubbed all over with melted fat. For especially lean birds, lay a strip of bacon or salt pork over the breast. Ducks and geese do not need added fat, but they should be thoroughly seasoned. Poultry may be sprinkled lightly with flour.

A shallow pan is best for roasting; a cover is not required. The larger the bird, the lower the temperature should be. Large birds should be turned frequently since those parts highest in the oven will cook fastest. Start with the breast side down, and turn several times from side to side or with breast up or down. Turn by holding the neck and ends of the legs with paper towels or cloths. Baste after turning. If ducks and geese are excessively fat, prick portions of the skin during cooking to allow some of the fat to drain out. Do not overcook. The bird is done when the meat seems slightly shrunken under the skin, when the joints are flexible, and it feels as if the bones could be easily removed. There should be moderate amounts of meat juice as well as fat in the dripping pan.

BROILING CHICKEN

Poultry and Egg National Board

Brushing chicken with fat before broiling

The broiler pan has been adjusted so that the chicken will be 4 or 5 inches from the heat

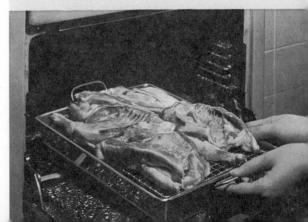

233

ROASTING A CHICKEN

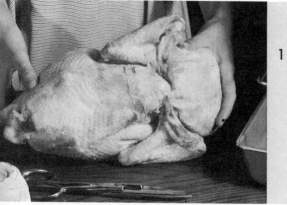

1

Trussing · After stuffing bring the neck skin to the back and fasten securely. Wings are brought to the back with tips across the neck skin. This helps to hold it in place

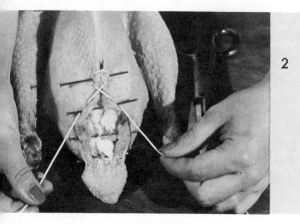

2

Lacing up the stuffed chicken

Pull down skin over ends of legs and tie. Then tie the drumstick ends together and fasten securely to the tail piece

3

Braising

Braising is the most satisfactory way to cook poultry which is not quite tender enough to roast. The method is the same as that for the braising of meat. The pieces are sprinkled with flour to coat them, browned in hot fat, then simmered or baked in a covered pan with or without a small amount of liquid.

Stewing

Birds more than a year old should be cooked slowly in water to soften the tough connective tissues. The meat is juicier if allowed to cool in the broth. The food value and flavor lost into the liquid may be saved by making gravy or sauce to serve with the meat or by using it for soup. Meat from stewed poultry may be used in creamed dishes, meat pies, à-la-king dishes, or in salads.

Using Poultry Leftovers

Poultry provides the most acceptable of all leftovers. Sliced cold, it is as delicious as when hot; diced in salad or creamed, it is an excellent main dish for luncheon; what look like bare bones of the turkey will make tasty soup with rice as an addition. The Cookbook gives recipes under Soups, Salads, Meats, and Casseroles.

The cooked chicken should be a rich, even brown

4

Poultry and Egg National Board

The bird should be placed on its back with the legs toward the carver's right. The first step in carving a bird is to remove one leg (above left). The wing from the same side is removed next

Slice the breast evenly and separate the leg from the thigh

Carving Poultry

Good tools are necessary for expert carving of poultry. The bird should be carved on a heated platter that is large enough to allow for ease of work. The procedure is as follows:

1. Place the bird on its back with the legs pointing either toward you or to your right, if you are right-handed.

Remove the legs first. Insert the fork into the thigh to hold the bird firmly, or grasp the end of the leg bone with the fingers of the left hand. Cut between the leg and the body and through the skin on the back.

Separate the leg of a large chicken or turkey from the thigh by cutting down through the joint.

2. Remove the wings by making a cut about an inch above where the wing joins the body. By cutting at an angle you will hit the joint and can remove the wing. Separate turkey wings at the elbow joint.

3. In carving the breast of turkey or chicken, anchor the bird with a fork placed across the breastbone, and slice the breast down and away from the carcass with a slight sawing motion.

In carving the breast of a goose or duck, after anchoring the bird as above, run the point of the carving knife under the flesh to loosen it from the breastbone. Cut sections across the grain of the meat and at right angles to the breastbone and lift them off the bone with the knife and fork, or cut the breast in long slices with the grain and parallel to the breastbone.

4. Slice the leg of a turkey by holding it upright on the platter and cutting down through it. Turn the leg to get uniform slices.

Slice large turkey thighs by cutting the meat parallel to the bone while holding the thigh firmly on the platter with a fork.

Arrange the carved pieces on a hot platter or serve on dinner plates with dressing.

¶ Understanding:

1. Which forms of fresh fish sold in your markets are best suited to the family budget? How will you determine the freshness of fish? Why is freshness especially important?

2. What are the means of safe storage for fresh and cooked fin fish? for canned fish? for cured fish?

3. By what guides will you select shellfish? How will you store them?

4. What are the precautions to use in freezing fish? How should frozen fish be cared for after delivery from the market?

5. Summarize the nutritive value of fish. Compare with meat in value; in expense.

6. Explain moist and dry methods of cooking fish. How do you know when fish are sufficiently cooked?

7. What kinds of fish are suitable for baking? What kinds of sauce are served with fish? What does a tasty sauce served with cooked fish contribute to the meal?

8. What important food values does poultry furnish in the diet?

9. What characteristics will you look for in choosing high-quality chickens for frying?

10. How do light and dark meat of chicken or turkey compare in cost?

¶ Planning:

1. Investigate types of fresh fin fish available locally and plan two family dinners which include these fish. In one meal use a lean fish and determine its method of cookery and serving. In the other meal use a fish rich in fat.

2. Plan a dinner using scalloped oysters. In what respects will oysters replace roast beef in a meal?

3. Find a menu including a fish dish which might be appropriate for unplanned company dinners. What proportion of the food values of the meal will this dish provide?

4. Include an inexpensive shellfish in a dinner menu. What other foods will be appropriate to complete the food requirements of the meal?

5. Plan to use shrimp in dinner menus in three different main dishes. What food values do the shrimp provide?

6. Find a dinner menu including roast lamb and select a poultry dish to replace the lamb. What other changes will you make in the menu?

7. Plan a special-occasion dinner menu to include a duck or goose. What other foods will you serve to keep the cost of the dinner moderate?

8. Plan means of cooking a chicken that is over a year old. Suggest the step processes to follow.

236

¶ *Practicing and Evaluating:*

1. Cook fish which has not been thawed. Check for flavor and texture.

2. Fry fin fish to be golden brown and tender. Compare with fried scallops for cost.

3. Use lobster meat in the main dish of a dinner. How does it compare in food values and cost with chicken?

4. Assist with the preparation of a chicken to roast. How would you shorten the time in preparing roast chicken again?

5. Help with the preparation of chicken for deep-fat frying. What are the important steps to follow for a tender product?

6. Help to fry a $3\frac{1}{2}$-pound chicken, steaming the product part of the time. In what other ways could the chicken have been satisfactorily cooked?

7. Carve the breast of a bird, keeping the servings hot.

8. Find a poultry-combination recipe for a family of four adults. Estimate the cost. Compare with the cost of an entire serving of poultry for the same family. Do the same, using a fish-combination recipe.

¶ *Reading Further:*

Barbequed Chicken, Bulletin E–862 (1960). Cornell University Extension Service, Ithaca, New York.

Fish and Shellfish (1960). Bureau of Commercial Fisheries, Washington, D. C.

How to Cook Shrimp, Bulletin I–49 (1960). U. S. Department of Agriculture, Washington, D. C.

How to Freeze Fish (1959). University of North Carolina Extension Service, Raleigh, North Carolina.

Outdoor Fish Cookery (1960). Bureau of Commercial Fisheries, Washington, D. C.

Poultry Grading and Inspection, Agriculture Information Bulletin 173 (1961). Agricultural Marketing Service, U. S. Department of Agriculture, Washington, D. C.

Take a Can of Salmon, Bulletin I–49 (1960). U. S. Department of Agriculture, Washington, D. C.

Turkey on the Table the Year Round, Home and Garden Bulletin 45 (1961). U. S. Department of Agriculture, Washington, D. C.

Jane and Steven Coons

Vegetables in the daily diet

you will learn: The values of vegetables in the
diet; How to recognize kinds of vegetables; How to select
and care for vegetables; How to cook vegetables

Many of our now common
vegetables were regarded as oddities when
they first found their way into European
markets. Explorers coming into the Amer-
icas found the Indians eating strange plants,
and they took these new vegetables with
them when they returned to their own
countries.

Until after the voyage of 1492 more than
half of our vegetables were known only to
the American Indians. Of these vegetables,
the most important were, probably, the

various kinds of beans. The Old World had
a bean with a large, broad seed that is still
widely grown, but the explorers found the
Indians growing several unfamiliar varieties.
The Indians were also growing pumpkins,
squashes, and potatoes. All these vegetables
have made significant contributions to the
rich variety of human foods.

Man's eating habits, as far as vegetables
are concerned, have been influenced by
climate. The natives of the polar regions eat
scarcely any vegetables, living almost en-

238

tirely on animal food; the inhabitants of the tropics, on the other hand, live almost entirely on vegetables, practically to the exclusion of meat. In the temperate regions both vegetables and meat are eaten but more vegetables in summer than in winter. In recent years, however, at least in the United States, the transportation and refrigeration problem has been solved to such an extent that more and more regions can enjoy all types of fresh vegetables during the entire year. Today there are about fifty different vegetables in the markets of the United States at all times. With such variety, it is possible, with knowledge and imagination, to plan menus that include many vegetables.

The Values of Vegetables in the Diet

Vegetables are so varied in food value, in flavor and texture, in color and shape, that they are invaluable in planning attractive nutritious menus. They can be used, alone or with other foods, to obtain endless pleasing combinations of flavor, texture, and color. What is more appetizing than a plate of vegetables attractively arranged—the bright orange of carrots or yams, the creamy whiteness of onions, the dark rich green of broccoli, the bright red of tomato, or the vivid touches of pimento? The possibilities are endless. Onions, garlic, and chives give a distinct flavor to dishes made of bland foods. Radishes and celery add crispness to a meal.

For their nutritive values, vegetables are highly important in the daily diet. They contain carbohydrates, some protein, and, most important, a good supply of minerals, vitamins, and cellulose.

The carbohydrate content ranges from less than 3 per cent in lettuce to around 23 per cent in lima beans. Some of the carbohydrate needed in the diet can be supplied through beans, peas, and lentils. Peas contain considerable sugar. Corn and potatoes have much starch. Parsnips, also high in starch, are an alternate for corn and potatoes and should not be classed with green and yellow vegetables. In general, vegetables contain less sugar and more starch than fruits. Younger vegetables are sweeter; their sugars change to starch as they mature.

Vegetables supply little protein in relation to their weight, with the exception of peas and fresh lima beans which have about 6 to 8 per cent protein. There is only a trace of fat in vegetables. This makes them especially useful for balancing fat-rich foods in the diet. The high water content of vegetables is also noteworthy. Many of the succulent ones—tomatoes, celery, lettuce—contain more water than orange juice or milk. Peas and potatoes are about three-fourths water.

We depend on vegetables for several of the important vitamins. Dark-green leaves are rich in both vitamin A and vitamin C, or ascorbic acid. Depth of color is a good index of carotene and hence of vitamin A in green leaves and green vegetables. Spinach, turnip greens, and broccoli, for example, have many times more vitamin A value than pale-green heads of lettuce and cabbage. Deep-yellow sweet potatoes have an exceptionally high value of vitamin A and also contain ascorbic acid. Carrots are a rich source of carotene, which the body changes to vitamin A.

Tomatoes, like the citrus fruits, are important for their contribution of vitamin C. One large vine-ripened tomato contains one-half of a day's requirement of vitamin C. This vitamin also occurs in smaller amounts in many other vegetables, such as cabbage, brussels sprouts, sweet potatoes, white potatoes, and turnips.

The B vitamins occur in a variety of vegetables in different amounts. Lima beans and peas, corn, and dandelion greens have more thiamine than most vegetables. Turnip greens and kale are among the rich sources of riboflavin. Beans and peas are a fair source of niacin.

All vegetables contain minerals of some kind. The dark-green, leafy vegetables are among the best sources of iron and calcium. There is more calcium in outside green leaves of head lettuce and cabbage than in the inner leaves.

Iodine occurs in vegetables only if it is present in the soil in which they are grown. In general, soils rich in minerals produce vegetables valuable for the minerals they contribute to the body. Read pages 10 to 13 again to refresh your memory of other foods that are sources of minerals. Name some of the most important ones.

Kinds of Vegetables

Learning the kinds of vegetables available for home meals, whether they come from a home garden or are purchased at a market, can be as fascinating as it is important. Meals should not be limited to a few common vegetables when different ones are so easily available. If you are to become an expert shopper, you must recognize the many vegetables at the market, have some idea of their cost in relation to their value, and of how they can be used with other foods. Vegetables fall into a few broad classifications. You will already know the more common kinds under each, but you should also become familiar with many others. Using the descriptions on the opposite page, you should identify the vegetables at your market and plan to use them.

Choice and Care of Vegetables

Vegetables may be purchased fresh, frozen, canned, dried, or dehydrated. Your choice, as with fruits, will depend on the quality, cost, use, storage space, and time available for preparation. Judging the quality of vegetables comes with knowledge and practice.

Fresh Vegetables

Though fresh vegetables are available at all times in almost every part of the country, the cost of out-of-season varieties is sometimes prohibitive for moderate- and low-income groups. Locally grown vegetables are less expensive than those that have been shipped in because of the saving on transportation and packing. Growing your own vegetables can result in still greater saving. Freshly picked vegetables, prepared immediately, are richer in food values, flavor, and color, and they retain their texture better than most market vegetables. Vegetables keep best at markets when they are blanketed

U. S. D. A.

Iceberg lettuce has firm heads and a very crisp texture. The inner leaves are bleached white

The butter-head type of lettuce has a soft head and green buttery leaves

Romaine lettuce has stiff, narrow leaves and elongated heads

J. Horace McFarland Co.

U. S. D. A.

Mustard

Escarole and chicory form mats rather than heads

New Zealand spinach

Water cress

Spinach

J. Horace McFarland Co.

241

with pulverized ice, stored in refrigerator bins, or sprayed frequently with ice water. To get fresh products, buy from a dealer who has a rapid turnover of vegetables. Before buying it is a good plan to check the time at which a new supply is brought into the market. Personal shopping aids in securing fresh green vegetables. In some localities it is best to shop two or three times a week to ensure maximum quality in color, taste, and nutritive value.

In judging the quality of fresh vegetables, notice whether they are protected from dust, flies, and handling. Note the color of the vegetable and its condition: is it free from wilt and decay? The degree of maturity is important: vegetables are best just before reaching full maturity. Undersized vegetables may have poor texture and lack flavor; oversized ones are likely to be high in starch content, tough, and fibrous. Vegetables to be cooked whole should be uniform in size — onions to be boiled, potatoes to be baked.

Vegetables may be government-graded and priced accordingly. For some purposes the best grade should be chosen. However, if economy is necessary, a lower grade used in appropriate dishes may furnish the same food elements. Potatoes are marketed by U. S. grade more often than other vegetables. The grades are U. S. Fancy, U. S. Extra No. 1, U. S. No. 1, and U. S. No. 2.

Your freedom in selecting vegetables in a market may be limited in many ways. Some may not be handled, so what can be seen must serve. Others are in boxes, where only the top may be judged, or in bags labeled with weight and price. Purchasing by weight is the method to be preferred, providing one can be sure of quality. In some markets the shopper may select, package, and weigh certain vegetables. Your success in choosing vegetables will depend upon the advantages of the market and your knowledge and experience.

All vegetables, including those packaged in cellophane, should be carefully sorted and thoroughly cleaned after purchasing. Washing vegetables removes dust, spray residue, and soil bacteria. Protecting these foods from bruises and broken skins will greatly lengthen their keeping qualities. Careful preparation of vegetables for storage saves space and time in preparing meals. Since leafly vegetables dry out quickly, they should be stored in a covered container or wrapped in waxed paper or put in a plastic bag, and placed in the refrigerator. Stalk vegetables ending in flower clusters should be placed briefly in salt water, head down, to help clean the clusters before storage. Celery leaves should not be removed as they can be used in a variety of ways. Celery stalks should be stripped from the base. Cutting away the entire base is wasteful and lessens the keeping quality.

Because some vegetables deteriorate rapidly under any storage conditions, they must be used very soon after purchase. Mushrooms and all seed vegetables, because of their protein content, are subject to loss, even under refrigeration. Mushrooms should be cooked at once. The amount should have been planned carefully since leftovers must not be stored. Lima beans, peas, and string beans should not be stored more than a few hours.

Most tubers and root vegetables (white potatoes, onions, turnips, and beets) can be stored in a cool, dry place where air can circulate around them. The best temperature for potato storage is 50° F. Sweet potatoes do not keep well and should be bought in small quantities. Inspecting stored vegetables occasionally is necessary as spoilage bacteria spread rapidly. Any spoiled vege-

Vegetable platter, prettily and
conveniently arranged

table or spoiled portion of a vegetable should be removed at once. Before white potatoes are cooked, all sprouts and green areas must be removed. Storage of tubers and root vegetables over too long a time is wasteful.

Every care must be taken to conserve food values in vegetables until they can be used to nourish the body. A loss that may be even greater than that occurring in cookery results when vegetables are not properly cared for after picking. Whether you have chosen your vegetables in the market or in the garden, they should be stored, if storage is necessary, in the refrigerator at once, or, better still, prepared immediately for cooking or for serving uncooked. The leafy and green vegetables, especially, begin to lose their vitamins, flavor, and texture as soon as they are picked. Refrigeration will slow down the process but not prevent it entirely. Parboiling (briefly cooking in boiling water) stops the ripening action, which changes the sugars to starch, and also helps to preserve the color of green vegetables, such as peas, beans, and broccoli.

Nevertheless, some vitamins are lost. After parboiling, the vegetables are cooled and refrigerated. Cooking is completed just before serving. The care of vegetables as discussed in this chapter will conserve their texture, color, flavor, and food value.

Frozen Vegetables

Vegetables which are quick-frozen are comparable to fresh ones in food value, flavor, color, and texture. Throughout the year, menus may include a variety of frozen vegetables. These are waste-free and ready to cook. Their use saves much time in shopping and in meal preparation. Frozen vegetables are available in 10-, 11-, 12-, and 15-ounce packages.

Quick freezing will not improve the flavor or texture of foods. The quality depends on the growing, handling, and processing of the product. In most commercially frozen vegetables the nutritive elements are preserved to a high degree until they reach the consumers. They should be harvested at the peak of their

243

LEAFY VEGETABLES

KINDS	CHARACTERISTICS
Cabbage	Light- or dark-green varieties; heads loose, cone-shaped; compact and round or flat
Red	Red in color
Chinese	Stalk vegetable; similar to celery in shape, similar to cabbage in taste
Brussels sprouts	1-to-1½-inch, compact, cabbage like heads; bright-green
Collard	Loose cabbagelike head; long, flat leaves
Kale	Large, thick leaf, texture similar to cabbage; darker green
Lettuce	
Iceberg	Firm, crisp, tightly formed heads
Butterhead	Less crisp but greener than iceberg
Romaine	Elongated types with coarse leaves; has a definite flavor
Leaf	Leaves smooth or curly; leaves do not form a head
Endive, or chicory	Curly, raged leaf
French endive	Small, long leaves similar to those of Chinese cabbage
Escarole	Loose head; thin, feathery, green leaves
Watercress	Small plant, dark-green leaves, grows in water
Parsley	Clusters of tiny, feathery, bright-green leaves
Spinach	Broad, dark-green leaf

STALK OR SHOOT VEGETABLES

KINDS	CHARACTERISTICS
Broccoli	Crisp central stalk with tightly clustered bright- or purplish-green buds
Cauliflower	Related to broccoli; has solid clusters of white or creamy flowerettes attached by stems to a short central stalk, giving the appearance of one large head; crisp, green, tight-fitting leaves at the base
Celery	Crisp, slightly ridged stalks growing from a central base and tipped by yellow-green leaves
Pascal	Vivid green color and narrow ribs
Golden Heart	Creamy white
Mushrooms	Creamy-white, firm buttons; young round unopened caps, or more mature open caps; short stems
Swiss chard	Cylindrical plant; thick, tender stalk, yellow-green leaves

FRUIT-AND-SEED VEGETABLES

KINDS	CHARACTERISITCS
Cucumber	Glossy, green skin; elongated shape
Eggplant	Smooth, glossy, egg-shaped plant; dark-purple skin
Snap beans	Bright-green or yellow color; snap readily, few strings
Okra	Small, greenish-white or dark-green pod; crisp
Tomatoes	Firm, smooth, shiny skin; pinkish-red, scarlet, or yellow color

FRUIT-AND-SEED VEGETABLES

KINDS	CHARACTERISTICS
Sweet peppers	
Bell	Glossy, deep-green to bright-red skin; thick walls
Bullnose	Shape varies from short and wide to long and thin
Pumpkin	Bright orange; firm, thick walls. 5 pounds or more
Squash	Similar to pumpkin. Many varieties: acorn, hubbard, zucchini, cymling

SEEDS

KINDS	CHARACTERISTICS
Peas	Bright-green, brittle, well-filled pods; firm, tender, sweet peas
Lentils	Similar to peas; lens-shaped and brownish in color
Lima beans	Small or large; plump well-filled pods; dark green
Soybeans	Green or dried; small, round
Corn	Green husks; golden to dark brown. Silk. Well filled ears; evenly developed kernels, tender and milk-filled

TUBERS

KINDS	CHARACTERISTICS
Potato	
Idaho and russet	Mealy potato; smooth skin with shallow eyes; even shape
Red Triumph	Waxy potato

ROOTS

KINDS	CHARACTERISTICS
Sweet potatoes	Mealy, light-yellow potato; tapering ends
Yams	Similar to sweet potato; moist and sugary
Jerusalem artichokes	Green color, similar to potato; is more fibrous
Beets	Bright, deeply red-colored, bulblike vegetable with crisp green tops
Kohlrabi	Similar to beets in shape and size; greenish white
Carrots	Bright-yellow color; long, firm, crisp, well-shaped roots
Onions	
Bermuda and Spanish	Mild-flavored; flat, large, brittle-skinned
Globe	Yellow, white, or red; strong-flavored
Chives	Slender, hollow cylinders
Leeks	Similar to onions but green in color, milder in flavor; long, broad leaves
Scallions	Thick necks and small bulbs
Shallots	White, underdeveloped bulbs; deep-green tops
Parsnips	Resemble carrots; smooth, firm, creamy in color
Radishes	Round or long; red or white
Rutabaga	Globe-shaped; purple at top; tapering yellowish root
Salsify	Related to chicory; tapering root; fresh branching ends

freshness and food value, the period should be short between harvesting and quick-freezing, and the foods should be stored at temperatures of 0° or below. It is important that frozen foods do not thaw between market and home storage.

Many markets have several brands of quick-frozen vegetables. A new development, also available, is dehydro-frozen vegetables, in which the moisture content has been removed at sub-freezing temperatures. Such vegetables may be stored without refrigeration. When they are rehydrated, they return to their original fresh appearance with taste and texture intact.

Quick-frozen vegetables must be kept solidly frozen until they are used. Freezing, unlike canning, does not destroy the organisms which cause spoilage; it merely inactivates them. Frozen foods may be kept from 1 to 2 weeks in the freezing unit of your refrigerator. A frozen-foods compartment with the temperature kept at 0° F. will keep frozen vegetables a year. Thawed quick-frozen vegetables should not be refrozen because of the loss in food values, flavor, and texture.

Canned and Dried Vegetables

Though fresh vegetables are generally preferred and frozen vegetables are a convenient alternative, both may be too expensive for a large family on a limited budget. The same, or nearly the same, values may be found in canned, dried, or dehydrated vegetables, and all can be included in menus in innumerable ways. The best way to learn about these foods is to study the food-analysis table on pages 511–517 and the well-stocked shelves of any good market. Every kind of vegetable will be represented among the cans, and the contents of different-sized cans will serve from one to six or eight people. Choices

among the dried or dehydrated vegetables may be slightly less but the range is still wide and interesting. Consider the beans alone, from soybeans, lima, and kidney to the various sizes of white navy beans. And think of the excellent dishes for which these can be the basic ingredient. For variety as well as economy you should shop carefully for canned and dried vegetables. A supply of both on your shelves and some knowledge of their possibilities will help you to plan and prepare nutritious meals.

One of the great advantages of canned and dried vegetables is that they are easily stored and will keep for a long time. The best storage space is dark, dry, and cool. High temperatures will, in time, affect the color and flavor of canned foods though not their wholesomeness. Dampness will rust cans and loosen labels. Packages of dried vegetables take a minimum of space. When part of a package has been used, the package should be closed carefully to protect the remainder and returned to the shelf. Whatever the size of the family, as far as storage space allows, these vegetables should be bought in quantity—several cans or packages at a time, or in case lots.

Canned Vegetables—Though canned vegetables have suffered some nutrition losses, they are still rich in food values. The commercial canners place great emphasis on growing carefully selected crops, on quick harvesting when food is at its prime, and on immediate preparation of foods for canning—important factors in saving nutritive values, especially vitamins. The canneries are usually placed close to the fields to ensure vegetables of fresh quality. Home canners also should recognize that canning preserves only quality that is already present, and should, therefore, use only the best.

The leafy green vegetables, such as kale,

FIVE MEMBERS OF THE CABBAGE FAMILY

Cauliflower

Cabbage

Broccoli

Brussels sprouts

Kale

Celery

Mushrooms

spinach, and mustard, lose some flavor, color, texture, and vitamins in the canning process. Canned tomatoes compare favorably with fresh tomatoes in calories, thiamine, and niacine. Canned tomatoes show less iron, vitamin A, and vitamin C than fresh ones, though the eating of larger quantities may help to make up for these losses. Canned tomatoes make important vitamin-A and vitamin-C contributions to the diet.

Other favorites among canned vegetables are peas, lima beans, green beans, corn, beets, and onions, all of which retain most of their original food value. In the canning process, food nutrients dissolve to some extent in water. To save the food nutrients, use the liquid in which the vegetables are packed when you prepare them for a meal.

The canned vegetables that you purchase have been processed in the sealed container in which you buy them. They have been cooked at an accurate temperature for the correct period of time to destroy spoilage organisms. Cans are numbered to indicate their sizes. Those most used for vegetables are the No. 303 can, that serves from three to four, and the slightly larger No. 2 can, that serves from four to five. (No. 303 is also used for soups and fruits; No. 2, for juices and fruits.)

To purchase economically you should note the cost in relation to amount of content. Large cans are probably more economical if they fit your family needs. If you wish to serve four, and $\frac{1}{2}$ cup is a serving, you will purchase a 16-ounce can of peas containing 2 cups. Unless a can of tomato soup is labeled "concentrated," a 16-ounce can will serve only two. If it is a concentrated soup, the addition of an equal amount of water or milk makes it sufficient for four. If your family is two, you may use half the peas in the 16-ounce can and set the remainder in the

refrigerator in their can tightly covered to be used in a day or two.

Descriptive labels on canned food are a real help to the shopper. They carry information required by the Federal Food, Drug, and Cosmetic Act and usually some voluntary information from the producer. The law requires name of product, contents in weight or liquid measure, name and address of producer or distributor, and, for certain foods, a list of all ingredients. The style of pack, size, maturity, seasoning, contents in cups or pieces, number of servings, and recipes are usually given. Grades for canned vegetables are most commonly stated as Fancy, or A; Extra Standard, or B; and Standard, or C. These grades are based upon government inspection and indicate differences in tenderness, uniformity, and color, not differences in wholesomeness, sanitation, or nutritive value. You should read labels for grades and brand to find the quality desired.

Dried Vegetables—Dried or dehydrated vegetables are less expensive than other types, offer great variety, and have advantages in transportation and storing. Though they have lost some of their vitamin-A content and all the vitamin-C content, their caloric value and mineral content are largely preserved. There is no waste in the use of dried vegetables; if $\frac{1}{8}$ cup each of cabbage, carrot, and potato are required for vegetable soup, the remainder can be left in the packages for another time. In addition to serving as a base for soups, dried vegetables may be creamed, buttered, or used in a casserole. Dried vegetables, including the legumes, are rich in minerals and are sources of protein, especially the soybean. You should read the label on the package for useful information. Labels on dried vegetables often carry special directions for using or recipes for combining the product with other foods.

Cooking Vegetables

Fresh Vegetables

The manner in which fresh vegetables are prepared for cooking affects their food value. Though cutting or slicing them thin means faster cooking and affords interesting shapes, the amount of surface exposed to air or cooking water results in great loss of vitamins. Chopped, minced, or shredded vegetables lose vitamin C rapidly because they are cut across the cell. Rather, cut carrots lengthwise and cabbage in wedges.

To conserve the food value of tuber and root vegetables, scrub them and use without peeling. If it is necessary to peel them, make the peelings thin or scrape no more than skin-deep. Peeling removes much of the mineral matter and vitamins. Carrots, cabbage, and turnips may be cut in interesting shapes, chilled quickly, and served; young beets and cauliflower flowerets are delicious eaten raw. You are assured of getting most of their food value when you eat them uncooked.

Vegetables are cooked to soften the cellulose or structural framework, to make them more tender, and to reduce their bulk. Cooking also alters the starches in vegetables, making them available for quick digestion. The flavor of some vegetables is improved through cooking. No matter what method is used in cooking vegetables, care should be taken to conserve food values and to produce an appetizing dish.

Certain principles are especially important in *boiling* vegetables:

1. Put the vegetables into boiling water, using the smallest amount possible. The kind of vegetable being cooked determines the amount of water necessary. With spinach, the water that clings to the leaves after the last rinsing is sufficient. Potatoes may be covered with water to gelatinize the starch quickly, or cooked in a small amount of water in a tightly covered pan. The strong flavor of onions is retained if they are cooked in a small amount of water. For a mild flavor, some people cook onions and other strong-flavored vegetables in an excess of water, but important nutrients are lost in the water. Carrots cooked in too much water have a flat taste because the sugar content upon which their flavor largely depends is lost in the water.

2. After adding the vegetables and salt (usually 1 teaspoon per quart of water), bring the water back to the boil as quickly as possible and cook only until tender. Overcooking, like the use of too much water, results in the loss of flavor, color, texture, and volume, as well as in the loss of nutrients. Carrots, for example, darken in color if overcooked, because the sugar caramelizes. To

Cooking vegetables in a minimum amount of water

United States Department of Agriculture

249

A mixed grill of sweet potatoes, tomatoes, and mushrooms

5. To conserve the sugars, minerals, and vitamins dissolved in the water by cooking, save the liquid in which the vegetable has been cooked and serve it with the vegetable or use it in soups, sauces, gravies, or molded salads.

Vegetables cooked by *steam* are held out of the water by a rack in a tightly covered pan or in a vegetable steamer. A pressure saucepan shortens the cooking time by about three-fourths. The vegetables are cooked under carefully controlled high pressure in a small amount of water. Vitamin retention in this method is high but it is easy to over-cook vegetables. Manufacturer's instructions should be followed closely. Vegetables may be cooked completely by steam in a heavy pan with a tightly fitting lid and a rack to hold the vegetables above the water.

preserve the shape of vegetables that contain a high percentage of water, keep the water boiling at a moderate rate; when the water boils too rapidly, it is likely to break down the structure of the vegetables.

3. To retain food values, especially vitamin C, cover with a tightly fitted lid.

4. To preserve the color of green vegetables, cook them uncovered for the first few minutes. This allows much of the volatile acid to escape with the steam, thus helping to prevent the chlorophyll (the green pigment) from turning olive green. For a rich color in red cabbage, which may turn blue in cooking, add 1 teaspoon of vinegar at the end of the cooking period. The red pigment of both cabbage and beets is brightened by a sour sauce.

250

Baked potatoes · These potatoes have been baked in a hot oven (425° F.) for 40 to 60 minutes. As soon as they came from the oven a crisscross gash was cut in the skin of each and the potato pinched so that some of the soft inside popped up through the opening. A pat of table fat has already been dropped into two of them. Salt and pepper will be added

United States Department of Agriculture

The little liquid left should be served with the vegetable. Butter, fortified margarine, meat drippings, or white sauce especially seasoned, and the addition of garnishes, will season boiled or steamed vegetables. Experimental studies indicate that steamed vegetables, particularly potatoes steamed in their skins, retain a high percentage of their food values.

Naturally tender vegetables may be *pan fried* in a covered skillet with a small amount of table fat. There is a minimum of food loss. The process of *deep-fat frying* is taken up on pages 417 and 421.

Broiling may be used for tomatoes and other tender vegetables. Onions are parboiled before broiling. Vegetables may be broiled with meat for an easy, attractive meal.

Whole vegetables, *baked* at 350° to 375° F. retain maximum food values. Pared vegetables should be baked in a covered casserole. Stuffed vegetables are prepared by combining the scooped-out center of the vegetable with such foods as ground meats, cereals, and seasonings, and replacing in the shell. Among the vegetables to be stuffed are potatoes, onions, peppers, tomatoes, and eggplant. All should have firm, well-shaped shells. Scalloped vegetables or vegetables au gratin are baked with milk or white sauce or meat stock. Vegetables suitable for creaming may be scalloped. The addition of cheese or bread crumbs as a topping makes an au gratin dish. Glazed vegetables, such as carrots, parsnips, and sweet potatoes, are boiled or steamed until almost tender, placed in a baking dish or top-of-range pan with sugar or sirup, and cooked.

Managing meal preparation so that cooked vegetables may be served at once prevents losses in food values. Vegetables shrink when they stand; this is an economic loss,

meaning fewer servings for the money. Tomatoes, because their acid retards loss of vitamin C, are the only vegetables which do not lose appreciable food values by standing after cooking. Cooked fresh vegetables when ready for the table should be whole or in pieces of uniform size which are tender and hold their shape well; they should be attractive in color and seasoned to bring out the natural flavor.

Quick-Frozen Vegetables

Frozen vegetables may be cooked either while still frozen or after thawing. Thawed food should be cooked at once. Throw away (without tasting) any thawed food with a peculiar odor, color, or texture. To break a block of frozen food for uniform cooking, partially thaw it in the package; this protects vitamin C. Corn on the cob should be completely thawed or the cob will still be frozen when the corn is tender.

The cooking time of frozen vegetables

Frozen asparagus · The cooking of frozen vegetables may be started in boiling water without thawing them first

251

varies with the variety and the maturity of the vegetable. They usually cook in about one-half the time of fresh ones. The green soybean is an exception; it requires as long for cooking after freezing as before. Frozen vegetables must not be overcooked. Also important nutrients are lost by improper cooking. (See the chart on page 419 for times for cooking frozen vegetables.)

Canned Vegetables

Commercially canned vegetables have been thoroughly cooked, so need only to be heated. (For the use of home-canned vegetables see Chapter 24.) Do not open canned vegetables until time to use them, for flavor and vitamin C are easily lost. The liquid, about one-third of the contents, should be drained into a saucepan and boiled until $\frac{1}{3}$ to $\frac{1}{2}$ cup remains. Then add the vegetable and heat; do not boil. Season for your family's preferences and serve. If the liquid is not to be included in the dish with the solid vegetable, it should be used elsewhere because of the water-soluble vitamins, minerals, proteins, and carbohydrates that it contains. Combined with milk the liquid can be used for creaming vegetables or in making scalloped dishes.

Canned vegetables are used in buttered, creamed, scalloped, and baked dishes very much as fresh or frozen vegetables. They combine well with meat in casseroles and are often used in a sauce over baked meats. Two or more kinds of vegetables may go well together in a baked dish; cheese, mushrooms, or herbs are tasty additions.

Dried and Dehydrated Vegetables

Legumes, soybeans, beans, peas, and lentils are among the dried vegetables commonly used. Soaking, preferably in soft or softened water, greatly reduces the cooking time. Soaking makes beans lighter in color and less strong in flavor. Gentle boiling in a covered saucepan is best for these vegetables. Since legumes contain a high percentage of protein, slow cooking makes them tender and keeps them whole. Soybeans are richest in protein of all legumes and less expensive than other protein foods. If well seasoned, they are delicious used alone. They may also be added to casseroles or soups, or used to extend meats for patties or meat loaf.

Among the dehydrated vegetables, corn, broccoli, sweet potatoes, and cauliflower require soaking; carrots, celery, cabbage, beets, and potatoes do not. They are marketed in packages with full directions for preparation. Cooked, they should be plump and tender and may be served like fresh vegetables. They are excellent additions to soups and baked dishes. Information on the value of a few dried or dehydrated foods is listed in Table IV of the Appendix, and recipes for their use appear in the Cookbook.

¶ *Understanding:*

1. Why is it necessary to use sufficient vegetables in your diet?

2. Compare the nutritive value of potatoes, green peppers, and peas.

3. What characteristics will you look for in green vegetables?

4. What care would you expect fresh vegetables to have in the market?

5. Why may vegetables lose their flavor and color in cookery? Which of the nutrients in vegetables are easily lost in cooking? Which vegetables have textures easily affected by cooking?

6. Would you use fresh or frozen vegetables for scalloped dishes? for buttered dishes? Why?

7. How will you care for fresh vegetables which do not need refrigeration? How can you

maintain the freshness in green vegetables? in leftover vegetables? in frozen vegetables?

¶ Planning:

1. Plan two days' menus for your family that include a variety of vegetables. How can you encourage your family to eat vegetables?

2. Plan a variety of vegetables for a week's menus, keeping within your budget.

3. Plan to use dehydrated vegetables in a meal. How will they compare in food value with frozen vegetables?

4. With the help of food-value charts, plan a vegetable plate adequate in protein and caloric values.

5. Plan guides to aid in the choice of root vegetables.

6. Make plans to reduce vegetable-preparation time for a dinner meal.

¶ Practicing and Evaluating:

1. Buy two green vegetables. What qualities did you require in each?

2. Assist in making the family weekly market order for root vegetables. How can you practice economy in purchasing?

3. Open cans of two grades of peas, asparagus, and corn. Compare flavors, textures, colors, and amounts of solid content. Determine to what type of dish each is best suited.

4. Prepare a vegetable not commonly used at your home for a luncheon or supper meal. How did you preserve the food values, color, and texture?

5. Cook peas in a pressure saucepan and serve creamed; steam broccoli and serve buttered. Check the products for appearance.

6. Assume responsibility for cooking the vegetables for a dinner. How can you be more economical? How can you simplify your preparation of vegetables?

7. On a market trip study the information given on labels of frozen and canned vegetables and make choices. To what extent did you rely on buying guides?

8. In a luncheon meal use canned vegetables in a cream soup and in a buttered dish. By what guides did you select the vegetables?

9. Prepare potatoes by two methods. Compare the preparation time and the cost.

10. Improve the methods of storing vegetables in your home. Report progress.

11. Compare the flavor and appearance of leftover cooked broccoli stored covered with that stored uncovered for a day in a refrigerator.

¶ Reading Further:

Asparagus Facts and Recipes, Bulletin 332 (1960). University of New Jersey Extension Service, Trenton, New Jersey.

Cooking Frozen Vegetables and Fruits, Cornell Extension Bulletin No. 873, Cornell University, Ithaca, N. Y.

Green Vegetables for Good Eating, Bulletin 41 (1961). U. S. Department of Agriculture, Washington, D. C.

How to Cook Vegetables, Cornell Extension Bulletin No. 883, Cornell University, Ithaca, N. Y.

Potatoes in Popular Ways, Home and Garden Bulletin 55 (1962). U. S. Department of Agriculture, Washington, D. C.

Tips on Selecting Fruits and Vegetables, Marketing Bulletin 13 (1961). U. S. Department of Agriculture, Washington, D. C.

Vegetable Varieties, Bulletin E–443 (1960). University of Oklahoma Extension Service, Stillwater, Oklahoma.

Vegetables: Selection, Care, Cooking, Bulletin 923 (1959). University of Texas Extension Service, Austin, Texas.

Ways to Serve Vegetables, Bulletin 294 (1959). University of Minnesota Extension Service, St. Paul, Minnesota.

Dinner desserts

you will learn: How to select desserts for dinner;
How to use gelatin in desserts; How to make frozen desserts;
How to use fruit in desserts

Some of the desserts popular today have a long history. The French were making ice cream at the time of the American Revolution. Sherbet is much older. After the French Revolution, exiles in many countries set up ice-cream parlors and sold ice cream, cakes, and other French confections. (The French have always been noted for their cookery.) Until the last quarter of the nineteenth century, however, when the

ice-cream freezer was patented, ice cream remained in the holiday-treat class. From then on, it has become more and more popular, until today it is used not only as a party food but as a favorite dessert and even as a between-meal snack.

Gelatin pudding too was formerly a holiday dish. Gelatin, in the early cook books, was called isinglass because it was sold in thin transparent sheets that resembled that substance. It was made in those days from the air bladder of the sturgeon, cod, or other fish. Later, chemists discovered that elements of gelatin could be extracted from animal substances and its use became more common. Eventually it appeared as a powder, unflavored in packets, or sweetened and colored in packages in a wide variety of fruit flavors. Since combining gelatin with liquid is a simple process and many variations are possible, it has become a valuable ingredient of many desserts.

Selecting Dinner Desserts

A light dessert is appropriate with the heaviest meal of the day. A dessert high in calories should be reserved for those dinners that are otherwise low in calories. Plan desserts to provide the food values needed for a well-balanced meal and to furnish contrast to the main meal. A frozen dessert, such as ice cream, an ice, or sherbet, may provide an excellent choice. Molded light desserts and fresh fruits offer variety and make a satisfying dessert for a heavy dinner. Many persons prefer a highly flavored cheese and hard crackers at the end of the meal rather than a sweet dessert.

Gelatin Desserts

Gelatin is the base for all molded desserts. It is used also in molded salads and as a thickener in ice cream, salad dressings, and jellies. Gelatin is a protein food extracted from bones, ligaments, tendons, and cartilage of beef. Though one of the elements of high-quality protein is missing, this may be easily supplied by the use of milk, eggs, or cheese. Since gelatin is combined with large amounts of liquid and other ingredients, the quantity of protein received from a serving is very small. Gelatin is so easily digested that it is a desirable food for invalids or convalescents.

Unflavored gelatin is nearly colorless, tasteless, and odorless. It contains only protein. Flavored gelatin contains also sugar, fruit flavors, and food dyes. Both kinds of gelatin are sold already measured in correct amounts for a pint or quart of liquid. The unflavored product can be purchased in bulk sheets, though homemakers find it inconvenient in this form either to use or to store.

Types of Gelatin Desserts

There are many types of gelatin desserts, the simplest being plain jellies and those to which fruits have been added. Gels are jellies which have been whipped to a frothy stage during the process of hardening. Snows or sponges have beaten egg white folded into them. Spanish creams are made by adding gelatin and beaten egg whites to a stirred custard; Bavarian creams are gelatin mixtures combined with whipped cream. Charlotte russe is thin cream, sugar, and flavorings thickened with gelatin. It may be molded in bowls lined with cake, ladyfingers, or soft cookies. Gelatin desserts are served chilled. Recipes for these desserts are in the Cookbook.

Gelatin Cookery

Gelatin desserts offer many advantages to the cook who likes to experiment. There are directions on the package for the amount of

Making charlotte russe · The mold has been lined with ladyfingers, and the mixture of sugar, egg yolks, gelatin, and milk has been cooked and cooled. When the icy evaporated milk has been beaten to softly rounded peaks, it will be folded into the cool mixture and the whole poured over the ladyfingers

nutritious dessert suitable for your dinner menu. Plan contrasts in color, in flavor, and in texture. You may have original ideas for a garnish or accompaniment. If you use fresh pineapple in the gelatin, the pineapple must be cooked and cooled before using or its enzymes will prevent congealing. Beaten cream or egg white give interesting results when folded into half-congealed gelatin. Two kinds of gelatin whipped separately, then folded together and returned to the refrigerator will produce an interesting dessert.

Results are most satisfactory if foods are added to gelatin after it begins to set. If they are added too soon, they will not remain evenly distributed. Beaten cream or beaten eggs blend best if added as the gelatin begins to congeal. For layer effects, partially fill the mold with part of the gelatin, set it in the refrigerator, and allow it to congeal. Then add a layer of chilled, drained fruits, nuts, or other foods. Next add more gelatin and return the mold to the refrigerator until the new layer congeals. Continue adding fruit and gelatin layers as desired. This dessert must remain in the refrigerator until it is time for it to be served.

If the mold has been greased slightly with vegetable oil, the gelatin will come out easily; if not, it may be dipped into lukewarm water for 5 seconds to release it. Loosening the gelatin around the top with a knife helps it to slide out easily. To get the gelatin out of the mold, invert it on a plate; or turn the plate upside down on the mold, turn over plate and mold together quickly, and lift the mold from the gelatin.

Glass dishes for serving gelatin desserts bring out the beauty of gelatin combinations; garnishes of nuts, coconut, or candied fruits, or a topping of fruit sauce or whipped cream add further attractiveness.

liquid to be used with the gelatin contained, suggestions as to whether hot or cold liquid gives better results, and how it is to be combined with the gelatin. Beyond these directions, which you can easily follow, imagination may be used. In planning a gelatin dessert the first choice to be made is probably the flavor or color of the gelatin—or is that choice determined by leftover fruit juice that is to be used as part of the liquid? Two good colors or two good flavors can be lost in a wrong combination; on the other hand, the right combination may emphasize a desirable flavor. Unflavored gelatin may be the best base if the fruit or juice to be added is definite in color and flavor.

Having chosen the gelatin, you carry out the simple principles of combining gelatin with other foods. Select fruit or nuts or other additions which will make an attractive and

Frozen desserts that may be made at home include ice cream, frappés, ices, sherbets, parfaits, and mousses. *Ice cream* is a cream or custard mixture which is beaten during the freezing process. *Frappés* are sweetened fruit juices frozen to a mush. *Ices* are made of fruit juices to which sugar and water have been added and the mixture frozen. Ice crystals are prevented from forming if gelatin or egg white is included. *Sherbet* is an ice to which beaten egg whites have been added, or in which milk or cream or ice cream are used in place of all or part of the water content. Sherbets have a smooth texture; the addition of gelatin lends further smoothness. New York ice cream contains the same ingredients as plain cream except that enough egg is used to produce a definite yellow color. *Mousses* have a heavy whipped-cream base and are frozen without beating.

Ice Cream

The usual ingredients for commercial ice cream are milk, cream, condensed milk, evaporated milk, or a combination of any of these; sweetening; flavoring; an emulsifier used to produce a velvety texture, and a stabilizer which helps prevent the formation of large ice crystals. An emulsifier, such as eggs, helps to incorporate air into the mixture. The stabilizers most frequently used are gelatin, ice-cream powders, eggs, cornstarch, and flour. Children's party ice creams may be made more attractive by the use of vegetable coloring. Beautiful coloring and texture varieties can often be achieved by the use of fruits and their juices. As an added delight, ice cream may be frozen in molds into interesting shapes.

Plain, or Philadelphia, ice cream is made from cream, sugar, and flavoring. Egg may be added. Among the flavorings to be used are vanilla, maple, banana, chocolate. Plain ice cream serves as a base to which fruits or nuts may be added for a great variety of fruit and nut ice creams. The addition of macaroons and other dried and broken cookies, or of grapenuts, to plain ice cream makes a bisque. Ice creams classified as puddings are plain ice cream containing a mixture of fruits. Their rich color is due to the addition of eggs. The ingredients for ice creams and sherbets in a variety of flavors may be purchased as prepared mixes. With such additions as fruits and nuts a festive ice cream can be produced with little effort.

The most important part of ice-cream making is the freezing. The texture, which should be fine and velvety, depends on proper freezing. Beating keeps the ice crystals small

Making ice cream at home in a typical household freezer

Mead, from United States Department of Agriculture

One of the steps in making ice cream in the home refrigerator · The control in the refrigerator has been set to its coldest position. The ingredients have been combined according to the recipe and poured into the refrigerator trays or molds. The mixture has been frozen to a mush and has now been transferred, one tray at a time, to the bowl in which it is being quickly and thoroughly beaten. In actual practice in your kitchen, you would, of course, remove but one tray at a time, beat the mixture, and return it to the tray and to the refrigerator as quickly as possible

and introduces air. Refrigerator ice cream and freezer ice cream are made by different recipes because the freezing is done in two entirely different ways. Creams frozen in the refrigerator are beaten only once or twice during freezing; freezer ice cream is beaten

constantly. Frozen desserts made in the refrigerator do not freeze well if they are too sweet.

Ice cream made in the refrigerator requires careful following of directions in using the refrigerator. Set the control to the coldest position before starting the ice cream so that the temperature will have time to lower sufficiently. Combine the ingredients according to the recipe, and pour the mixture into refrigerator trays or other molds. Moistening the bottom of the tray on the outside with water speeds the freezing.

When the ice-cream mixture is frozen to a mush, remove it to a chilled mixing bowl and beat it quickly with a rotary beater until smooth. Whipped egg white or cream or gelatin may be added. After beating, the freezing is continued. The whole process takes 2 to 4 hours. Refrigerator ice cream is best when served within 3 hours after freezing.

In making *freezer ice cream* thoroughly clean the can, cover, and dasher of the freezer; scald, and cool before each use. After the ingredients are combined, they must be chilled before they are poured into the can. Because the mixture expands with the cold, the can should never be filled more than three-fourths full.

Ice and rock salt must be packed around the can of the freezer. One part salt to eight parts of ice is best for ice cream; one part salt to four parts of ice is preferred for ices and sherbets. The larger the proportion of salt, the faster the freezing. Slow freezing, however, gives a more velvety product. To prepare the freezer, pack ice tightly around the can until the freezer is one-half full. Then add a layer of salt. Repeat with alternate layers until the freezer is filled, ending with a layer of ice. The freezer crank should be turned slowly for the first 5 minutes to chill the mixture thoroughly. Then the crank should be turned rapidly and regularly until the ice cream freezes, making the crank difficult to turn.

When freezing has been completed, the dasher is removed from the can and the ice cream is pressed down with a spoon. Special care must be taken at this point to avoid getting salt water into the ice cream. The can should be recovered tightly, the brine drained from the freezer, and more ice and salt packed tightly around the can again. The freezer should be wrapped in paper or heavy cloths and allowed to stand for 1 to 2 hours before the ice cream is served. This helps the ice cream to harden completely and to ripen.

Ices, Sherbets, and Frappés

Natural fruit juices and pulp add flavor, food value, and texture to ices and sherbets. In almost any combination of flavors for ices, some lemon juice and some salt improve the flavor. The texture of ices and sherbets is grainy; frappés are slightly rough and icy. All frozen desserts should have a delicate flavor; ices, frappés, and sherbets are more pronounced in flavor than the others.

Fruit Desserts

Fruits are desirable desserts after a heavy meal as they help to complete dietary needs without adding calories. The color, texture, and flavor of fruits make them generally acceptable, and wide range of choices helps to add interest to menus.

Among the many fruits which are appetizing desserts when served alone are grapefruit halves, either fresh or broiled, and orchard fruits, which can be baked, broiled, stewed, or served fresh. Strawberries, raspberries, blueberries, and many other kinds of berries are delicious chilled. Such fruits as pineapple, bananas, and figs may be served alone or in combination with other fruits.

Fruit Combinations

Interestingly flavored and colorful compotes can be made by combining fresh fruits. Green grapes, strawberries, melon balls, and peaches may be held together by a whipped flavored gelatin mixture. Stewed-fruit compote can be made of fresh or dried fruits. Some dried fruits come mixed in the package. Many appetizing combinations can be made of canned fruit, using some of the sirup. Compotes, whether of cooked or fresh fruits, may be further enhanced by grated rind of citrus fruits, by coconut, or nuts. Crystalized fruits may complement the decorative quality, flavor, texture, and food value of the compote. Fruits in salad combinations for dessert (oranges, grapefruit, and grapes; pineapple and banana, and others) may be served with a bland dressing and a garnish of nuts, or possibly with a bright red cherry. Molded dessert salads may be made of vivid, fruit-flavored gelatin and colorful fruit contrasts. Fruit combinations with whipped cream make good frozen desserts.

Fruit Whips

Fruit whips are made from fruit that has been cooked soft, put through a sieve, and combined with egg whites which have been beaten to softly rounded peaks. Prunes, peaches, or apricots may be used. Often the egg yolks are stirred into a custard to serve with the fruit whip. For *uncooked whips* the

Making fruit cup

the fruit pulp, sugar, and salt are heated together until the sugar is dissolved. The hot sirup is then poured slowly over stiffly beaten egg whites while the mixture is beaten constantly. Lemon juice is used as an aid in holding a light texture. The mixture is piled lightly into an ovenproof dish and baked. The baked fruit whip should be served at once, with soft custard or whipped cream. Fruits alone or in combinations, fruits dried, canned, or fresh, served simply or with elaborate additions, may be adjusted to the requirements of any dinner menu. If calories are needed, cheeses and whipped cream in the fruit salads, or eggs in the whips and their accompanying custards will supply them. Simpler fruit servings furnish vitamins and minerals without adding calories. Not only can fruits be made to complete the menu nutritionally, but they can furnish the festive note which any meal needs in a dessert.

egg whites are beaten until foamy, sugar is added, and the fruit pulp is beaten in gradually until the mixture mounds. An uncooked whip should be served immediately since the egg whites do not hold their volume. In *baked fruit whips*, also known as soufflés,

¶ *Understanding:*

1. What determines your choice of desserts for dinners?

2. What techniques will you use when combining gelatin with other foods?

3. What are the characteristics of a good gelatin dessert?

4. What frozen desserts would be appropriate for your family's Sunday dinner? Explain your choices.

5. What are the advantages of freezing ice creams in a hand freezer? in a refrigerator?

6. What qualities are important in homemade ice creams?

7. With what types of meals will you serve fruit desserts?

¶ *Planning:*

1. Plan quickly-prepared desserts to accompany two dinner meals high in caloric value.

Making a fruit soufflé · Sirup and fruit pulp are being mixed with beaten egg whites to which cream of tartar has been added. Notice the egg yolks carefully put aside for refrigeration in a covered container

2. Plan gelatin desserts appropriate for light dinners; for heavy dinners.

3. Plan a menu for your family in which frozen custard is an appropriate dessert; pineapple ice; strawberry mousse.

4. Plan two inexpensive fruit desserts to use with moderately heavy dinners.

5. Plan fruit desserts appropriate for two light dinners.

¶ *Practicing and Evaluating:*

1. Prepare a simple dessert for a heavy meal, keeping cost at a minimum.

2. Prepare a gelatin dessert for dinner. What desirable characteristics will you expect? What are the advantages of serving gelatin desserts?

3. Using a hand freezer or the refrigerator, make ice cream which is fine-textured and firmly frozen. What qualities will you look for when evaluating the finished product?

4 Make ice cream, using condensed or evaporated milk. Compare the cost with that of ice cream made with light cream.

5. Prepare a sherbet moderate in cost. Compare the texture with that of a purchased product.

6. Freeze ice cream and pack it for use several hours later. Evaluate the product for flavor and texture.

¶ *Reading Further:*

Honey in Your Baking, Bulletin 281 (1959). Kansas State University Extension Service, Manhattan, Kansas.

Pies: Pastry, Fillings, Meringue, Bulletin 1027 (1959). Cornell University Extension Service, Ithaca, New York.

Jane and Steven Coons

Planning and preparing dinner

you will learn: The importance of dinner;
How to plan dinners; How to manage
dinner preparation efficiently

Some writers have deplored the fact that, as the evening hours approach, in every block of twenty houses twenty dinners are being cooked by twenty homemakers. This waste of fuel, energy, and money, they say, could be prevented if the twenty families would go to a public dining hall. But there are few restaurants or hotels whose meals, if eaten three times a day, week after week and month after month, do not become intolerably monotonous.

And there are few daily "eaters-out" who will not accept eagerly an invitation for home-cooked food. In addition to the enjoyment that comes from eating well-cooked food, the dinner at home, for which the family gathers, often with friends, can give much pleasure as a social event. The happiness of a family gathered around the dinner table is enough of a reward to most homemakers for the planning and preparation of a delicious meal.

262

The Importance of Dinner

Dinner, the main meal of the day, depends for its size and type on the kinds and amounts of food served in the other meals. If breakfast has been satisfying and nutritious but luncheon has been light, the evening dinner must provide the remainder of the day's food values. A heavy dinner at noon calls for a lighter meal, supper, in the evening. (See Chapter 15.) There are several advantages in serving dinner in the evening. Often this is the one time when all the members of the family are at home and can enjoy each other's company. Most of the heavy work of the day is over, with the result that the family is more relaxed. Evening dinner can be more elaborate in menu and more festive in service than other meals; leisure adds to the enjoyment of the food and to the social situation.

Planning Dinners

All family dinners should emphasize balance in food values and service which is attractive rather than elaborate. A protein dish at dinner is needed to fulfill the daily food allowances. Since this usually is the most expensive dish, the selection of other foods is planned around this protein. These other foods should include one or more vegetables (at least one of which should be leafy and green, or yellow), a salad, and a dessert. Appetizers or a soup may be added. Family dinners usually consist of two or three courses: a meat course with potatoes and one or two vegetables, a dessert course, and occasionally a soup or salad course. Sometimes the salad or one of the vegetables is omitted, depending on family tastes. Dinners may be simple, wholesome, nutritionally adequate and not difficult to prepare. These are everyday family meals. Attractiveness of service will add to the pleasure of the simple meal. On special occasions, as for a birthday or in entertaining guests at Christmas (see page 343), the family may enjoy greater elaborateness of menu and of service. Both the simple and elaborate meal must furnish adequate nutrients.

Nutritional Guides

The Daily Food Guide (page 18), which helped in the planning of breakfasts and luncheons, is equally useful for dinners. In addition, Chapter 1 and Table IV in the Appendix give information on the values of different foods in terms of calories and of the proteins, minerals, and vitamins needed to balance the meal.

Meal Costs as Guides

Since dinner is the heaviest meal of the day, it is usually the most expensive. Keeping this meal within the food budget may be the most challenging task in meal planning.

Minimum-cost meals may include such protein dishes as less-expensive stewed chicken, or less-tender cuts of meat. Through the use of meat tenderizer, seasoned or unseasoned, less expensive cuts may be served always tender. Dried-milk solids used in hot breads, puddings, and some casserole dishes furnish more economical protein than whole milk. Cottage cheese (the least expensive and the lowest in calorie value of the cheeses) and egg dishes made from Grade B or C eggs are true protein alternates for meat.

263

PROTEIN DISH	MINERAL AND VITAMIN VEGETABLE	STARCHY VEGETABLE	BREADS	SALADS
Pork, fresh....	Creamed carrots Buttered broccoli	Mashed potatoes Scalloped corn	Whole-wheat bread Hard roll	Waldorf, Lettuce, and Tomato
Pork, cured... (hams)	Green beans Buttered beets Peas	Sweet potatoes Buttered corn Parsley potatoes	Hot biscuits Corn muffins	Pineapple Cole slaw Tomato and cucumber
Beef.........	Brussels sprouts Buttered peas Baked eggplant	Baked or Scalloped or Oven-browned potatoes	Rye bread Hot rolls	Tossed salad Pear and cheese Banana and nut
Lamb.........	Glazed carrots Asparagus Cauliflower with cheese sauce	Baked or Browned or Parsley potatoes	Blueberry Muffins Caraway-seed rolls	Lettuce with tart dressing Citrus fruit
Veal.........	Broccoli with Curry sauce Brussels sprouts Creamed onions	Potatoes au gratin Hashed brown potatoes	Hot rolls Graham muffins	Tossed greens Waldorf Grape-fruit and avocado
Tongue.......	Creamed spinach Carrots Stewed tomatoes	Diced rutabaga French-fried potatoes	Rye hard rolls	German potato
Chicken and other fowl..	Asparagus with pimento Peas with mushrooms	Corn on the cob Stuffed baked or Mashed potatoes Sweet potatoes with orange slices	Oatmeal bread Hot rolls Biscuits	Tomato aspic Molded fruit
Fish.........	Buttered broccoli Creamed celery	Paprika potatoes Parsley potatoes	Corn sticks Whole-wheat bread	Beet and celery Green bean and pickle
Chili con carne or Baked beans..	Buttered spinach Stuffed celery		Whole-wheat or Rye or Brown bread Corn muffins	Molded fruit Orange and grapefruit
Macaroni and cheese..	Grilled tomatoes Peas and celery		Whole-wheat bread	Greens with garlic dressing Citrus fruit with honey dressing

264

DESSERTS	EXTRAS
Applesauce Chocolate cookies Apple pie	Tomato relish Pickled beets Fruit juice
Blueberry pie Lime sherbet Apricot whip Baked apple	Tomato juice Pickled crab apples Corn relish
Orange sherbet Chocolate pie	Radishes Peach preserves
Mixed fruit cup Cheese and crackers	Mint jelly
Peppermint ice cream Spice cake	Tomato sauce Cranberry juice
Mixed fruit compote Lemon meringue pie	Horse-radish sauce Relish plate
Strawberry shortcake Pineapple sponge Pumpkin pie Mince pie	Cranberry sauce Vegetable juice Tart fruit juice Relish plate
Honeydew melon Lemon pudding	Cucumber sauce Tartar sauce Hush puppies
Orange custard Baked apple Pineapple upside-down cake	Cucumber sticks Carrot sticks
Cherry pie Fruit cookies Lemon ice	Melon pickles Grapefruit juice

There are many extended meat dishes, such as stuffed green peppers, Spanish rice, hamburger roll, and chile con carne, which help to make money go further. The cost of the dinner may also be kept low by using less expensive but hearty vegetables and breads. Two or more vegetables at a meal are not uncommon. However, the mistake should never be made of substituting starchy foods, such as potatoes or turnips, for green or yellow vegetable dishes high in the needed minerals and vitamins. Hot breads add interest and variety to the less expensive dinner, and the use of fortified margarine may result in additional saving.

For a low-cost meal, desserts such as fruit cobblers, bread or rice pudding, loaf cakes, fruit shortcakes, and pies are simple yet filling and nutritious. Often well-ripened fresh fruit can be bought at a good price, or canned fruits can be used in these desserts. Water-packed canned fruits are equally nutritious and cost less than other canned fruit. It is quite possible, even on a restricted budget, to serve desserts which add much to the meal in the minerals and vitamins contained in fruits.

Moderate-cost meals require less restraint in the selection of the meat dish. Chuck roasts, round steaks, chickens, ducks, and chops may be managed on this budget. Meat tenderizer (follow suggestions and directions of the manufacturer) will make it possible to broil the less expensive steaks and chuck roast which has been cut into steaks. The prices of meats may be influenced by their demand in the locality. The weekly menu plans should be flexible enough to capitalize on unexpected reductions in meat prices.

To keep the cost of the meal moderate, the use of seasonal produce is necessary, requiring familiarity with the various

in high-cost meals as compared with lower-cost meals will be:

A more expensive type of protein dish
More expensive types of vegetables
Higher grades of canned products
Foods which are scarce or out-of-season
Specially prepared novelty foods
Elaborate sauces, garnishes, and decorations
More fresh fruit

Food-Combination Guides

The chart on pages 264–265 suggests pleasing combinations of foods for balanced dinners. Current prices will often determine choices within each group.

The Menu

Dinner, since it usually involves more separate dishes than breakfast or luncheon, requires more time and effort in preparation.

Cutting and shredding salt codfish · One piece of the fish is being prepared for creamed codfish. As a first step this slice of dried fish is being cut up

Preparing meat for hash · On the cutting board at the right front are pieces of gristle and fat that have been trimmed from the leftover meat. Just behind the rejected portions are trimmed pieces of meat. One of these pieces is being cut. Each piece will be trimmed of any further gristle or fat. The carefully cut and trimmed small pieces are at the left near the scissors. One of the great differences between delicious hash and an indifferent dish is the care with which the leftover meat is prepared

vegetables and fruits on the market. Interesting garnishes, sauces, and accompaniments can go far in dressing up the moderate-cost dinner.

Higher-cost dinners may include extras which add festivity and charm. Out-of-season fruits in an unusual salad, less common and particularly fine cuts of meat, and more expensive desserts, such as parfaits, are among the possibilities. Even if the budget allows for higher food costs, the nutritive and caloric values of the menu should be identical with those of the low-cost or moderate-cost meal. The chief differences

The first step is to decide on a menu which meets the family's food allowances, tastes, and purse. It must be further checked to make sure that it can be carried out. The dinner must be simple enough for one worker to prepare unless help is available, and it must be checked to make sure that all foods needed are on hand or procurable. The size of the kitchen, the type of range used, and the time-saving equipment available are all factors in the planning of dinners. Items on the dinner menu should be checked with kitchen equipment available for their preparation.

Many housewives use an electric roaster and an oven when two different temperatures are needed at the same time. Ranges equipped with two ovens are available. Some of the individual range ovens are so designed that they can bake two foods at different temperatures at the same time. A home freezer or the freezer compartment in the refrigerator makes possible a variety of quickly prepared and easy-to-serve dishes from frozen foods. Electric mixers, blenders, and grills are great timesavers. With an electric mixer it may be possible to make a cake just before dinner when it would be impossible to do it at that time by hand mixing. Choosing menus with reference to equipment is part of efficiency in planning a dinner. An elaborate menu should be checked for the labor involved, unless family members or outside help can assist in preparation.

Once the menu has been decided, a market list should be made covering supplies not on hand. Recipes for every dish on the menu should be checked carefully for needed supplies. Seasonings, cooking fats, and other items required in small amounts, as well as such items as cream and sugar for coffee, must not be overlooked. Staples as well as special items must all be checked before your market list is complete. The value of preparing menus for several days ahead, as well as the value of well-planned market orders, is discussed in relation to breakfast on page 87.

A SUGGESTED MARKET-ORDER FORM

Do not write in this book

	ITEMS	AMOUNT	PRICE
Dairy products			
Protein dishes			
Cereals and breads			
Fruit			
Vegetables			
Staples and miscellaneous			
Seasonings			
		Total cost	

Managing Dinner Preparation Efficiently

Two workers can make the preparation of dinner more efficient. The homemaker usually takes the responsibility for the main dish and one or two others. She delegates specific tasks to her helper. These may be setting the table, cooking a vegetable, preparing the salad or dessert, and washing the dishes. There should be a clear understanding concerning the division of work. The girl should see that her assistance is valuable only to the extent that she can fit into the plans she and her mother have made.

Using a Work Plan

If a daughter is to assist her mother in preparing dinner, a plan which shows her responsibilities will make their teamwork more efficient. The work plan below for a specific menu is set up as a guide to the assistant worker.

THE MENU

(A Dinner Low in Cost)

Meat Loaf
Scalloped Potatoes*   Buttered Beets
Biscuits and Honey*
Canned-Peach Shortcake*
Milk   Coffee

*Assistant's responsibility

Preparing and Serving Dinner

After reviewing the work plans on pages 88–89 and 189 and the dinner work plan below, note the assistant's responsibilities on the following menus:

MENU I

(A Dinner Moderate in Cost)

Spaghetti and Meat Balls
Green Beans and Onions*
Apple, Celery, and Nut Salad
Whole-Wheat Bread and Butter*
Sponge Cake* with Fruit Sauce
Milk   Coffee

*Assistant's responsibility

MENU II

(A Meal High in Cost)

Consommé
Rib Roast
Browned Potatoes
Frozen Peas with Mushrooms*
Molded Fresh-Fruit Salad*
Ice Cream in Meringue Shell
Milk   Coffee

*Assistant's responsibility

THE WORK PLAN

5:00. Make personal preparations.
5:05. Assemble potatoes, milk, butter. Grease casserole. Heat oven.
5:10. Peel and slice potatoes.
5:18. Place potatoes, flour, milk, and butter in casserole. Put in oven at 350° F.
5:23. Set table. Assemble serving dishes and utensils. Heat plates and utensils on top of oven.
5:30. Assemble flour, fat, sugar, baking powder,

and baking sheets, for biscuits. Turn oven heat control to 400° F.
5:35. Sift dry ingredients; cut in fat; add milk; roll and cut biscuits; place on sheet.
5:50. Place biscuits in oven.
5:51. Pour milk. Put butter and honey on table. Check table.
5:58. Remove potatoes from oven to table.
5:59. Remove biscuits and place on table.
6:00. Serve dinner.

It is sometimes best to prepare certain dinner dishes in advance. The dessert of the first menu and the molded fruit salad of the second can be prepared and placed in the refrigerator when you get home from school.

If you should find yourself responsible for preparing a complete meal with your family arriving just in time to eat it, a baked dinner would be a wise choice because there are few last-minute tasks to perform before you serve it. Plan your menu so that several foods can be prepared ahead and set aside until time for baking. Such care may make the difference between a hurried meal with mistakes and an unhurried successful dinner.

Working according to a definite plan will help you, moreover, to acquire comfortably the skill which enables your mother and other experienced homemakers to prepare and serve meals expertly. You can learn when and how the different menu dishes may be prepared so that the meal is completed when it should be served. You will learn, too, that even the most careful plan does not always work out perfectly. Vegetables may not be tender at the expected moment. The meat thermometer may not register the temperature required for doneness. Your mother learned long ago to allow time for such emergencies as these. Experience in using a well-thought-out work plan, moreover, will give you skill, confidence, and pride in serving a good meal.

Serving Dinner

Dinners should be served in an unhurried, pleasant manner. Promptness is the minimum of courtesy on the part of the diners. Appreciation of the homemaker's efforts and enjoyment of the food are other courtesies expected of those for whom the meal was prepared. Methods of serving and details on table setting and etiquette for dinners are discussed in Chapter 25.

¶ *Understanding:*

1. What determines whether a light or heavy dinner should be served?

2. What guides will you depend upon as aids in dinner planning?

3. What foods will you include in hearty, low-cost dinners?

4. In what way is the planning of meals affected by the type of kitchen equipment to be used? by the assistance available?

5. What foods may be prepared ahead of time without affecting food values or textures of the food?

6. Why is it important to divide tasks among family members in the preparation of a home dinner?

7. How does a work plan help an inexperienced person with meal preparation?

8. In what ways can low-cost meals be made to include adequate nutrients?

¶ *Planning:*

1. Plan a substantial dinner with a moderate-cost protein dish. Evaluate the meal for food values.

2. Plan a three-course dinner menu to be served to four adult guests. Combine the salad and dessert courses and include a hot bread. Estimate the approximate cost of the meal and the preparation time required.

3. Use the Daily Food Guide and the nutrition information from Chapter 1 to evaluate two dinner menus. How can you improve these menus?

4. Make a work plan for your share in preparing a dinner. Review the recipes you will use to make sure your kitchen will supply all ingredients.

5. Using the form on page 267, make a market order for a day's meals.

6. Check your use of preparation time in preparing a dinner meal. How could you have reduced preparation time?

7. Plan simple table decorations for a company meal at home (see page 325).

¶ *Practicing and Evaluating:*

1. Prepare an appropriate, inexpensive main dish for a dinner at home. What values does the dish add to the dinner?

2. For a moderate-cost dinner use canned or frozen foods in two dishes. Compare the cost with that of fresh foods.

3. Assist with the preparation of a salad and a dessert. What precautions did you use to conserve food values?

4. Aid with a dinner that has been planned to be prepared in 25 minutes. How could you have saved in cost with a longer time for preparation?

5. Assist with a dinner for guests by removing the main-course dishes and serving the dessert and beverage. What procedure of correct etiquette did you follow?

6. For a special-occasion family dinner, set the table using a simple centerpiece and appropriate linen, silverware, china, and glassware.

¶ *Reading Further:*

BATJER, MARGARET Q., and ATWATER, MIMI, *Meals for the Modern Family*, Chapter 3. John Wiley and Sons, Inc., New York.

CARSON, B., and RAMEE, N. C., *How You Plan and Prepare Meals*. McGraw-Hill Book Company, Chicago, Illinois.

Family Fare, Home and Garden Bulletin 1 (1960). U. S. Department of Agriculture, Washington, D. C.

Good Meals at Moderate Cost, Bulletin 62 (1961). University of Wisconsin Extension Service, Madison, Wisconsin.

It's Dinner Time, 4–H Bulletin 164 (1961). University of Missouri Extension Service, Columbia, Missouri.

Individual
Food Needs

CHAPTER

21

Ginn. (Frank D. Lucas)

Helping to meet the food needs of children

you will learn: The food needs of children;
How to help children enjoy their food; How to take
responsibility in the care of children

Meeting the food needs of children involves much more than the provision of the correct diet; it involves also the forming of healthful food habits. No matter how carefully the child's meal is planned and prepared, it does him no good unless he eats it—and only partial good unless he enjoys eating it. All too often mealtime becomes associated in the child's mind with unpleasantness and discipline; this may affect his

eating habits unfavorably for years to come. Everything possible should be done not only to provide adequate and appropriate meals for the child but also to encourage his enjoyment of his food, and, while teaching him good food habits, make mealtimes happy times.

The idea of happy learning is a relatively recent one. It was first put forward by the great German educational reformer, Frie-

272

drich Froebel, a little over a hundred years ago. Froebel disapproved of the stern, knuckle-rapping methods generally used in teaching young children. He believed that learning can be fun; that we learn better when we enjoy the learning. To prove his idea he organized a school for small children that he called a *kindergarten*, or child garden. Here, through games and play with blocks and toys, the children learned to use their hands and their minds and to cooperate with their playmates—learned happily. The idea of the kindergarten spread to other countries, including America, where the beginning of school has now become a happy experience for millions of children.

A child's education, however, begins before he goes to school, even before kindergarten. It really begins at birth, and it is important that he learn in these very early days habits and attitudes that will help him as he grows. Home is a kind of prekindergarten, which can make use of Froebel's idea of happy learning. The family—parents and older brothers and sisters—are the child's first teachers. They must take responsibility for the proper growth of his body and his personality through his first years.

Watching the development of a small child's personality is a wonderfully interesting experience. If, understanding his needs and knowing how to satisfy them, you can share in that development, it can be even more of a joy. Whether you are bathing, feeding, or putting the child to bed, it is a real challenge to your intelligence and good management to see if you can secure the response you wish, and the child's willing acceptance of your services may well be a matter of pride. Can you give the baby a properly prepared formula and get satisfaction in his comfort with it? Can you prepare and serve a simple supper to a two-year-old and put him to bed properly afterward? His cooperation will depend on his secure feeling that you love him and are willing and able to take care of his wants. If you understand what his habits should be and patiently help him in forming them, keeping in mind Froebel's idea that happy learning is the best, you will be assisting in his proper development as well as winning his affection and respect. Your ability to handle a variety of situations with younger children will, moreover, give you a responsible place in your home and promote your own growth toward adulthood.

Learning the Food Needs of Children

Whether you have younger brothers or sisters or sometimes assist with the care of children in the neighbors' families, you should be able to help plan and prepare simple meals for children and to guide them in their eating. This work can become one of your most interesting responsibilities.

The First Two Years

Proper food is essential to the development of a strong, healthy baby. Only a doctor

should advise a mother what to feed her baby. He may recommend the mother's milk for the infant's first few months. It is a good source of calcium and phosphorus, of vitamin A, thiamine, riboflavin, valuable proteins, and of an easily digested form of fat. Mother's milk also provides a natural immunity which helps to keep the baby well and to give him a healthy start in life. Cows' milk, modified according to the doctor's directions, makes a satisfactory substitute

273

when necessary. Goats' milk is also some-times used. There are prepared formulas that need only to be supplemented as directed by the doctor. The time at which orange juice, vitamins, and other foods are intro-duced into the diet varies in accordance with the baby's needs.

The foods most commonly added to the milk diet during the first year are strained cereals, egg yolk, strained vegetables and fruits, and scraped meat. As the baby gets his teeth, toward the end of the first year, doctors suggest that finely chopped foods re-place strained foods. Canned baby foods, both strained and chopped, are available. They are ready to heat and serve and are a good source of vitamins and other nutrients. Fresh vegetables may be prepared for the baby by cooking them and putting them through a sieve; for an older child, by chop-ping them. Ripe banana and strained orange or grapefruit juice are the best raw fruits to give during the first year. Strained cereal for babies may be purchased already cooked. It needs only the addition of warm milk. Babies prefer it thin at first but gradually learn to eat it thicker. Enriched cereals should be chosen. Crisp toast or zwieback may be given when the baby starts to chew.

Babies grow more in their first year than at any other time. They should triple their birth weight by the end of the first year. For such rapid growth, the diet must be rich in all the nutrients. Although babies eat only small servings of food at a time, they eat more often than adults and they eat more in proportion to their weight.

After the first year, though the young child's need for food is somewhat less, his diet must be sufficient for his continued growth and must supply energy for his in-creasing activity. At this time it is important to establish life-long habits of sound eating.

274

Overemphasis on a particular food—for ex-ample, milk as the "perfect food"—may lead to nutritional anemia and to refusal of differ-ent foods as they are offered, thus building habits both harmful and objectionable in adults. It is easier to establish good habits from the start than to break bad ones in an older child. Likewise, it is less expensive to build good health than to cure the ills of undernourishment or overnourishment.

From Two to Five

Your mother realizes that she need not continue to prepare separate meals for chil-dren after the days of serving baby food are over. In most cases children can safely graduate from chopped junior foods to family food sometime around their second birthday. A few alternates may be needed, such as a simple fruit dessert instead of pastry. How-ever, the filling for pie, baked in custard cups, may be served to children. Their food should be bland but seasoned sufficiently to make it palatable. Pickles, chili, and other highly seasoned foods should not be given to children. Nor should their appetites be dulled by overrich or sweet foods. Fried foods or fatty meats, such as sausage, are too rich for children. Sweets, such as cookies, cakes, rich crackers, and candies, should be used sparingly. These foods satisfy appetite without supplying sufficient protein, vita-mins, or minerals. If used at all, they should come at the end of the meal. Dried fruits, such as apricots and raisins, are nutritious and may replace rich cookies or candy.

Children should not have stimulating beverages, such as tea, coffee, or carbonated drinks. They can learn to accept cheerfully the fact that some foods are for grownups only, and, on the other hand, the family may benefit by adapting its diet somewhat to the needs of the children. Family meals should be planned to make sure that they are adequate, both in amounts and kinds of foods, for the child's rapid growth.

Daily food allowances for the young child are:

3 to 4 cups of milk
1 serving of meat, liver, poultry, fish, or cheese
1 egg
1 yellow or 1 green vegetable
1 or 2 other servings of cooked or raw vegetables
2 servings of fruit
2 tablespoons of table fat
2 slices of bread (preferably whole-wheat)
1 serving of whole-grain cereal
1 serving of junket, custard, or ice cream

Among the many ways of making sure that the child gets his daily food allowance is the pleasant one of allowing him some choice of foods and respecting his decisions on the amount he wishes. Overemphasis by mothers, nurses, or nutritionists on a particular food—spinach for iron, carrots for vitamin A—may lead to real problems in the child's attitudes and even in his health. Children can gradually learn to enjoy a wide variety of foods which will protect their health and make mealtime a pleasure throughout their lifetime.

If a child will not willingly drink his three or four cups of milk daily, part of it can be included in soup, or in his dessert pudding, junket, or ice cream. If he is overfond of milk, he should be offered other tempting and nutritious foods before he satisfies his hunger with milk.

Helping Children to Enjoy Their Food

Preparing the Child to Eat

It is important that you give children a chance to rest and relax before eating so that they will not be too tired to eat. A new food is best introduced at the beginning of a meal when children are hungry. Don't be discouraged if they take only a taste for the first few times. Serve only one new food at a time, giving them a chance to learn to like it before trying another. Generally foods should not be mixed, for children should like each food for its own taste. Food likes and dislikes should not be discussed before children. They should learn to like all foods.

Make sure the child is comfortably seated with a place to rest his feet, and that it is easy for him to see and reach his food. It is an older person's responsibility to see that children are safe. When a child is old enough to climb into his high chair, give a positive suggestion like, "Hold on with both hands when you climb into your chair." This tells a child much more than, "Watch out! You'll fall." It also gives him confidence. A timid child may have to have his hand held for a few times, but he should be encouraged to do things for himself.

Provide little children with large bibs and let them eat where spilled food can be cleaned up without damage. Easily managed silver, plates with rims, and glasses which do not tip easily are other aids to self-feeding. Don't expect young children to be neat about eating. They have neither the experience nor the muscle coordination of adults. Do not be concerned about their manners when they are very young. They are too busy learning to eat to bother about etiquette. Later they will understand directions given them and will imitate the conduct of others at the table. If your young charges' conduct distresses you, try to be quiet and firm about

Bob Vose, from Black Star

important matters and ignore others. Perhaps
they only need a good example.

Spacing and Time of Meals

Children should be given their heaviest
meal at noon when they are less tired and
will eat heartily. They also need this added
energy for their afternoon activities. About
the same length of time should elapse between
lunch and dinner as between breakfast and
lunch. Many children require a midmorning
and a midafternoon snack to supply them
with needed energy. Such foods as milk,
fresh or dried fruit, plain bread and butter,
or a graham cracker are suitable for snacks.
They should be served at regular times, mid-
way between meals, with the child seated at
a table. There should be no other eating between meals.

Allow a child about twenty-five or thirty
minutes to eat a regular meal. Never try to
hurry him; he may feel the pressure and
even dawdle deliberately. However, if you
see that he is playing, warn him that if he is
through eating, you will untie his bib.
Neither should the youngster be permitted to
gulp his food, scarcely chewing it at all. He
should eat with reasonable speed, neither

hurrying nor dawdling. Though he must
learn to eat well, he is a little individual
whose appetite is not always the same.
Whether or not he has eaten all his food, at
the end of his mealtime take his plate away
with a friendly comment, "I notice you
weren't so hungry today. It's time to get
down from the table now." Do not require
a child to stay at the table until everyone is
through eating. If a healthy child has, for
some reason, eaten lightly, you may expect
him to eat heartily at the next meal. Help
him to understand that you expect him to
eat his food.

Patterns of Eating

Certain patterns of eating can be expected
from children at different ages. After the
first birthday, a child's appetite may be comparatively poor, but he will eat well again by
the time he is three. A four-year-old child
may show definite preferences for certain
foods. By the time the child is six, he will
have a more hearty appetite and will enjoy
trying new foods. A seven-year-old may
dawdle over his food, but by the eighth year
a child will establish his pattern of a normal,
healthy appetite.

Simple Means of Encouraging Eating

A child needs frequent praise for his success in eating. It is a hard process for him to learn. He should be given small helpings and encouraged to ask for seconds. Children become easily discouraged when they are confronted by a plate heaped with food.

Children enjoy meals which are interesting in color and which offer a variety in taste and texture. It is a good plan to include one crisp, one chewy, and one soft food in each meal. Sticky or stringy foods are often rejected by children. A child's food should be served in forms easy for him to handle. For instance, since shredded lettuce is very difficult for him to pick up with his fork or spoon, it is better to leave the lettuce in a leaf which he can pick up with his hands. Instead of using them in salads, raw vegetables may be chopped and put inside bread sandwiches or cut into pieces that can be eaten in the fingers. The rest of his food should be cut into bite sizes so that he can feed himself. A custard or pudding is easy to eat. A surprise, like fruit at the bottom of the custard, may provide additional vitamins and add delight to the meal.

Small children like their food better when they see that it is similar to that served their parents. They enjoy eating with the rest of the family. Toddlers who are able to feed themselves will master acceptable table manners by association with courteous older family members. The child should be allowed to eat with the family unless he plays and tries to attract attention, or unless the family meal is served too late or is inappropriate. There are some children who cannot conform happily to rules of conduct at the family table. The tension is such that no one enjoys the meal. Such children should eat quietly by themselves until they are older. A child who has not formed good eating

Jane and Steven Coons

Making a child comfortable for a meal · Gentle handling, a gay spirit, and a pleasant voice are all assets in preparing a child to look forward to his meals and to enjoy them

habits requires patience and understanding not possible at the family dinner table. He must not play to an audience in his refusal to eat, nor monopolize attention by his antics or his insistence on breaking in on the conversation. Away from these possibilities, he will give in to hunger and eat his meal without fussing or playing.

Rewards for eating are unnecessary. The

277

child should learn to eat as a part of his daily routine. You want him to eat all his carrots because he likes them, not to make you happy. A child who is well and who has learned to enjoy food will eat enough without being threatened or bribed. Food should never be associated with punishment.

You should not say, "You can't have any dessert if you don't eat your potatoes," but rather "I shall serve your dessert when you finish your potatoes." Desserts should never be used as bribes or withheld as a form of punishment; they are the normal conclusion of the child's meal.

Taking Responsibility in Caring for Children

Babies and children have less resistance to bacteria than older persons. Extra care must be taken, therefore, to keep their food and utensils clean. It is important for you to follow your parents' directions for handling food and utensils. Your clothing must be clean, and before handling food your hands must be washed with soap. Washable clothing should be worn if possible. All utensils should be kept sanitary; after being used they should be washed with hot water and a good cleansing agent and rinsed. Bottles for the baby's milk must be sterilized before they are filled, and the nipples must be kept sterile until they enter the baby's mouth. All water given to the baby must be boiled. Every precaution must be taken to protect children against bacteria.

Before a child eats his meal, toilet needs must be attended to and his hands and face washed. A stool in the bathroom will enable him to reach the lavatory, the soap, and his own towel. In his own room a mirror hung low helps him to make a presentable job of combing his hair. Given this independence, he is likely to enjoy getting ready for his meal. If you follow these precautions for yourself as well as for your young charge, you should feel confident, under ordinary circumstances, that his food is adequately protected from harmful bacteria.

Unless it is really necessary, you should

not care for a child when you are ill. If you have a cold or have been exposed to a contagious disease, and must, nevertheless, care for the child, you must protect him in every way possible. Wearing a cloth mask over your mouth and nose will help, and you must take extra care in washing your hands and in handling dishes and foods.

Whether you care for children at home or for another family, you are responsible temporarily for their welfare and happiness. You must know the routines to which they are accustomed and see that they go through them as usual. If this is done, there will be little question of your authority and there will be no problems growing out of their having been left in your care. If your responsibility includes feeding the children, you should know specifically when and where the children are to eat and what foods they are expected to eat, and what foods you are expected to prepare. Knowing where foods and equipment are kept will make your task easier.

Small children naturally love and follow older children. If you are tactful and kind with your small brothers and sisters, they will respond to your suggestions. Try to win them by playing their little games and understanding their wishes. Their trust and cooperation will lighten your work and give you pleasure. With strange children take time to get acquainted. They must feel secure with you before their parents leave them. Being trusted with the care of children puts you in a position to learn many things helpful to you in your family and community. These opportunities are an evidence of the faith placed in you as a responsible person. Gaining a reputation for painstaking, adept care of children offers gainful employment and personal satisfaction to the teen-age student, whose knowledge will be rewarded increasingly in the years ahead.

¶ *Understanding:*

1. Why is it important for you to understand children's food needs?

2. What are the food allowances for the child from two to five?

3. Why should children's meals be served at regular times?

4. How can you help children to enjoy meals?

5. Why do children sometimes refuse to eat?

6. To what extent should independence in eating be encouraged? Why is it important?

7. What is the value of keeping formula, bottles, and nipples sterile?

8. What physical preparations should a child make before eating his meals?

¶ *Planning:*

1. Plan a day's meals for a child one year old; for a child two years old. Check for protein, mineral, and vitamin content.

2. Plan ways of encouraging children to eat a new food.

3. Plan physical facilities for making a child comfortable in his eating.

4. Plan ways in which you will help a child learn habits of cleanliness before eating.

5. What refreshments would you serve for a party of five-year-olds?

¶ *Practicing and Evaluating:*

1. Help with preparing a meal for a family including children. In what ways were the dishes modified for the children?

2. Prepare meats, chopped vegetables, and fruits for children. Serve the foods attractively.

3. Arrange for keeping the young child's mealtimes peaceful and happy.

4. Discuss the outcome of learning good eating habits.

5. Make suggestions for managing a child who refuses to eat a meal.

6. Arrange facilities in a home so that a child can make himself clean for eating his meals.

7. Observe children eating a meal. What foods did they enjoy the most? What were your observations about their food habits?

¶ *Reading Further:*

Baby Sitters Safety Packet, National Safety Council, Chicago, Ill.

BACMEISTER, RHODA W., *Your Children's Manners*, Science Research Associates, Inc. Chicago, Ill.

Eating Problems of Children, The National Association for Mental Health, New York, N. Y.

FLANDERS, JUDY, *Baby-Sitters Handbook*, Science Research Associates, Inc., Chicago, Ill.

Food for Families with School Children, G–13, rev. 1960, Bureau of Human Nutrition and Home Economics, U. S. Department of Agriculture, Washington, D. C.

Food for Families with Young Children, G–5, rev. 1960, Bureau of Human Nutrition and Home Economics, U. S. Department of Agriculture, Washington, D. C.

SMART, MOLLIE STEPHENS, and SMART, RUSSELL COOK, *Living and Learning with Children*, Houghton Mifflin Company, Boston, Mass.

Your Child from One to Six: His Care and Training, Publication 30 (rev. 1945), Children's Bureau, U. S. Department of Labor, Washington, D. C.

Eating to control weight

you will learn: The importance of food to underweights; The value of controlled diets for overweights

In recent years, newspapers, magazines, and television and radio programs have stressed the problem of overweight. Through extensive research, doctors have found that the heart is damaged by use of foods high in fat. Other organs are similarly weakened. Today the greatest problem of preventive medicine is obesity.

Both underweight and overweight should be watched and corrected in growing children. The pudgy baby, sometimes admired as an example of good nutrition, may not be getting a good start in building bone and

muscle tissue. The thin, active five-year-old must have food in the right amounts and combinations if he is safely to continue both growth and activity. The overweight or underweight youth is approaching adulthood with an unnecessary handicap to his physical and social development.

Underweight in children is cause for concern since the body has little reserve upon which to draw for normal growth and activity and with which to resist illness. The thin child's lack of vitality and endurance handicaps him in the classroom and among his playmates; his personality suffers, and unhappiness results. Overweight boys and girls become concerned with their appearance. The condition will not correct itself; it is not likely to be outgrown unless good eating habits are consistently followed. If you need either to gain or to lose, a knowledge of the right diet will enable you to bring yourself to the weight at which you look and feel best. Whatever effort you put forth will be repaid by improved health, restored vitality, and greater attractiveness.

Overweight may come with age and may bring with it a succession of ills which could have been avoided by respecting the body's need for a lighter diet as activity lessened. An overweight older person puts an unnecessary strain on his heart and arteries. He may enjoy eating and, therefore, refuse to modify his diet, but he should realize that a thin person may live longer and more actively. Experiments with animals indicate a longer span of life for those kept thin on a diet low in calories but high in essential nutrients. Since nutrients that are not used up in activity are added to the body as weight, each person must plan his diet in accordance with his need for energy.

The Importance of Food to Underweights

Effects of Undernourishment

Undernourishment is widespread and is found in the homes of the privileged as well as in those of the underprivileged. Such an impoverished condition can become serious, especially in young people. Many girls and boys get accustomed to being underweight. They do not realize that they could look better and feel better merely by eating better meals to increase their weight. People who look as though they suffer from lack of food are seldom attractive. A nervous, restless temperament; a pinched, blue look; and lack of luster in the hair are only a few of the ways in which undernourishment affects the body. In the underweight person, growth slows down and the body becomes less efficient. Fatigue, nervous disturbances, and infections are more likely to occur than when the body is well nourished.

Though underweight may be caused by glandular disturbance or by certain prolonged diseases, it more often results from failure to eat regular, well-balanced meals. Lack of system in some families may be a factor; meals are not planned and no schedule is followed in serving them. Other activities are allowed to interfere so that meals are hastily prepared and hastily eaten in an atmosphere which does not encourage appetite. Having taken little time to enjoy their meal, children and parents are off to the game, the movie, the card party. Such overactivity with too little rest develops tenseness and nervousness and lack of appetite. Worry is another kind of overactivity which may cause loss of weight. Conscientious young people may worry over school grades; others may fret about dates for social affairs or a quarrel with a friend. The persistent worrier may grow alarmingly thin, even become ill. Underweight usually results in irritability, loss of attractiveness, and general unhappiness. Since it is also a very real danger to health, its causes should be determined and measures taken promptly to correct the condition.

Meeting the Needs of Underweights

A doctor should prescribe for underweight cases. He will probably advise that food

281

Pleasant exercise is one of the best ways of controlling weight

should be added gradually in the diet, as a sudden increase might upset the digestion. Outdoor exercise will help to improve the appetite, encouraging a larger intake of food. An increase of from 25 to 50 per cent in calories may be advised. As far as is consistent with a balanced diet, the underweight patient should be served foods which he enjoys and will eat willingly. Well-prepared and attractively served foods will further tempt him. Rich cream soups may be used as a between-meal snack or before retiring.

Consistency in eating is important in building up weight. Every meal must be rein-

forced for caloric value and checked for proper nutrients. If an extra meal a day does not destroy the appetite for the three regular meals, it affords a good means of getting additional calories. A regular high-calorie between-meal snack and also food before retiring are suggested. Meals for the underweight can include foods from Group I on page 284. Liberal use of bacon, butter, cream, and other fatty foods increases the fuel or caloric value of the diet. White sauces on vegetables, cream soups, mayonnaise and other rich dressings on salads are also valuable additions. Milk can be enriched with cream. Daily doses of cod-liver oil or a concentrated preparation supply vitamin D in the diet. The requirement for children and teen-agers is 400 units a day. Egg yolk and liver are good sources of protein, iron, and vitamin A. Since carbohydrates are easily digested and are quickly converted into body fat, they too are suggested for the high-calorie diet. Fatty foods, however, will lessen the appetite and slow up digestion. The desserts offered the underweight should be high in calorie value.

The underweight person must have every encouragement for the right attitude toward his meal. He should be given moderate servings attractively arranged on his plate and should be offered second helpings. Finishing all the food on his plate, however, should not be unduly emphasized.

If you yourself are endeavoring to increase the nourishment in your diet, work with another person who has a similar problem. This plan will help you to be consistent in your eating habits. In planning menus to help correct underweight, you should choose high-calorie foods from Groups I and II listed in the chart, page 284.

Before attempting to control weight through diet, you should determine what weight is desirable for you. Weight-height-age tables (see Appendix) may be consulted, but your individual build, bone structure, and muscle

Jane and Steven Coons

Enjoying cream soup. Starting a hearty meal with a cream soup is a good way to increase nourishment for a person who is underweight

tone must also be considered. Your doctor can determine what your weight should be. Consult him at once if there is persistent loss of weight or if gains seem too rapid. You can cooperate by selecting foods which will help you to reach the weight best for you.

Controlled Diets for Overweights

Your doctor may say that a few pounds over the average weight for you may add to personal attractiveness and provide a reserve of energy to draw upon in emergencies. Physical health is usually better if weight is kept a little above average for a person under thirty, and average or slightly below average

after forty years of age. Since statistics show that the most desirable weight to maintain is that given for one's height and body build at twenty-five, weight tables no longer give figures beyond ages 25–30. A person 25 per cent over the weight recommended for him is considered obese. A tendency to gain

283

weight can be sensibly controlled. Physicians believe that slow, steady reduction of one or two pounds a week is the safest way to reduce. Persistent attention to the proper diet will result in the loss of excess weight in a year.

Causes of Overweight

Extreme overweight is generally the result of eating too much. Lack of activity is both a cause and a result of overweight. Very rarely is overweight due to a disturbance of the function of glands. Children and youth become overweight for a variety of reasons: perhaps a too starchy diet is provided, or possibly ice cream and candy are eaten too frequently. Habits of overeating are often part of a family pattern. Families where "setting a good table" is a tradition

---

HIGH, MODERATE, AND LOW CALORIE FOODS

Group I FOODS HIGH IN CALORIE VALUE

Cream soups
Meats with fat
Meat stuffings
Rich gravies
Dried legumes
Candied dishes
Scalloped dishes
Cereals with cream
Cream cheese
Butter and fortified margarine
Peanut butter
Rich breads
Salad dressings

Fresh fruits with sugar
Fruits canned in heavy sirup
Dried fruits
Jellies, preserves, marmalades
Rich cakes, pies, puddings
Candies
Cocoa and chocolate with
  whipped cream
Sugar and cream
Malted milk, milk shake
Sundaes
Rich sauces

Group II FOODS MODERATE IN CALORIE VALUE

Whole-grain breads
Toasted bread with a minimum of
  butter or fortified margarine
Whole-grain cereals with milk
Lean meats
Potatoes and other root vegetables

Green and yellow vegetables
  lightly seasoned
Fresh or stewed fruits
Plain custards
Plain cakes or cookies
Eggs

Group III FOODS LOW IN CALORIE VALUE

Skim milk, buttermilk
Skim-milk cottage cheese
Thin, clear soups
Lean meats
Poultry, fish
Fresh fruits without sugar

Melons
Watery and fibrous vegetables
Gelatin desserts
Coffee and tea without
  cream and sugar

Sodas and sundaes are delicious between-meal snacks, but they are to be let alone by overweight persons of all ages, and they are also to be denied if they destroy the appetite for the next wholesome meal

often show a decided preference for rich dishes, especially pastries. Their idea of entertainment suitable for friends may be a rich, elaborate meal served in many courses. To them good food is a symbol of social standing and the chief element in hospitality. Their everyday diet is probably generous and the family will have a well-fed look verging on stoutness. The individual in such a family will find that special effort is necessary to break established food habits.

With some people, overeating is a symptom of some emotional problem—boredom, loneliness, discontent, insecurity. Children who feel unwanted may find eating a consolation.

Between-meal sundaes are the cause of many an extra ounce. Marshmallow-nut sundaes add about 400 calories to your total caloric score for the day. To make skipping this dish easier, you may order a glass of milk or lemonade and an apple. Foods high in sugar content and rich in fat from cream and nuts often contribute to a poor complexion.

An appetite for rich foods is the chief reason that overweight people keep eating such foods as sweets and pastries. Eating food which may actually be harmful to health, just because it tastes good, may show a lack of will power. It may also exhibit a lack of knowledge of the calories needed daily.

An additional cause of overeating is the feeling of contentment from a well-filled stomach. This is also a matter of habit. After a short period of adjustment, a smaller meal will prove just as satisfying.

Many overweight men and women claim that although they eat very little they do not lose weight. One test made of a hundred such cases proved that these people lost weight readily when they ate proper foods and in proper amounts. Even though they honestly believed they had been eating very little, they were actually eating more foods rich in fats and sugars than they realized, and they were eating too often during the day.

Meeting the Needs of Overweight

When overweight is caused by eating too much food, the amount of calories consumed daily should be wisely reduced. It is unwise to plan your own reducing diet. Doctors understand the needs of particular cases and can recommend proper changes in the intake of food. In reducing the consumption of food, it is seldom advisable to eat fewer than

1200 calories daily unless so directed by a physician. A more drastic reduction is sometimes carried out under strict supervision of a doctor, usually in a hospital.

In recent years many new "appetite reducing" products have been introduced to the public. There are pills to take, powders to add to liquids, liquids that are fortified with a day's essential nutrients. The liquids are called "liquid diets," containing 900 calories to a quart. It is wise to use these only if a doctor approves. Usually reducing calories in a normal intake of food is preferable. Many companies are putting low-calorie food on the market, such as 2 per cent homogenized milk, artificial sweeteners, low-calorie carbonated beverages, and dietetic jams and jellies. Farmers are encouraged to raise more lean cattle, hogs, and poultry. Sensible cutting down on high-calorie foods is a partial

MODIFICATION OF A RICH MEAL

HIGH-CALORIE MEAL		Modification for a LOW-CALORIE MEAL	
1 serving pot roast and gravy...	375	1 serving pot roast......... (no gravy)	265
¾ cup creamed potatoes........	180	1 boiled potato...........	105
¾ cup buttered corn...........	139	1 cup buttered cabbage...	74
1 serving avocado and grapefruit salad with French dressing...	262	1 serving lettuce salad with French dressing......	74
1 serving ice cream with nuts and chocolate sirup...........	259	¾ cup lemon ice..........	148
1 cup whole milk.............	166	1 cup skim milk..........	87
2 slices bread, white..........	128	1 slice rye bread.........	57
2 squares butter (1 tablespoon)..	100	1 square butter.........	50
Total calories....	**1609**	Total calories....	**860**

solution. However, most overweight people consume more bulk than they need. They enjoy eating and like the satisfied fullness it brings. Group cooperation may help to bolster self-discipline. Diet clubs discuss problems and devise means to help members to control their appetites.

Meals designed to reduce weight should always meet the requirements for protein, minerals, vitamins, bulk, and water. Usually the carbohydrates are curtailed and the amount of fat is reduced, thus forcing the body to use the supply of stored fat. Butter or fortified margarine and the fats found in foods such as milk, eggs, and meat may be used. Fruits and such vegetables as lettuce, tomatoes, cabbage, spinach, cauliflower, and asparagus are desirable for the reducer's menu. The bulk in these foods helps to satisfy hunger and is beneficial in other ways. Regular outdoor exercise, which increases the oxidation of fat and strengthens the muscles, if combined with wise eating, will encourage an attractive figure.

Good eating habits always pay dividends in improved appearance and in increased energy. It is not necessary to be hungry. Three adequate meals a day, planned to eliminate excess amounts of the fattening foods, will maintain health and energy as the pounds disappear. With a little sensible attention, and with no cause to feel sorry for yourself, you can modify a family dinner to reduce the caloric intake.

To develop the habit of reducing the calories in each meal, select a day and begin to adjust to a new pattern of eating. Eat an apple or an orange instead of a rich dessert. Order a lemonade instead of a malted milk. Keep to your determination not to eat rich foods between meals and do not allow one exception; after an exception it is only more difficult to return next day to proper eating.

Learn to satisfy your hunger for ice cream and candy by eating a small serving at the close of some meals. Instead of using the term "reducing diet" in relation to the elimination of calories, it is better to think of a new diet program as an "adjustment to new food habits." Don't be discouraged if you fail to lose weight noticeably at first. It takes time to bring a marked overweight condition back to normal. The accumulated fat cannot disappear overnight; it must be oxidized gradually.

In meeting the needs of the overweight and underweight there is no one combination of foods which can be recommended for everyone. Tastes must be considered and appetite controlled. Each person should know his own needs, keep some record of his progress, and be consistent in following the diet which proves successful for him. Sensible eating practices based on a sound knowledge of nutrition will enable him, in large measure, to control his weight.

¶ *Understanding:*

1. What are the factors that determine individual calorie needs? What is your daily food need in calories?

2. What are the advantages of controlling your body weight?

3. Under what circumstances is it beneficial for persons to weigh a few pounds more than standard weight for them? a few pounds less?

4. Besides calories, what must be considered in meeting the needs of the underweight? In eating high-calorie diets what besides calories must be considered?

5. List the appropriate foods for the daily diet of underweights.

6. Under what conditions is between-meal eating advisable?

7. What foods should seldom be chosen by overweights?

8. What guides can you use as an aid in making a wise choice of foods?

9. What is the correct procedure to follow when one desires to go on a diet?

¶ *Planning:*

1. Plan a day's meals designed to help overcome the effects of undernourishment.

2. Plan menus for several days of sufficient variety to stimulate the appetite of an underweight child.

3. Plan a program of rest and diet to protect the health of an overactive teen-age girl.

4. Plan two one-dish meals to be prepared for an underweight older person who lunches at home alone.

5. Plan a day's meals to minimize the overweight person's desire for between-meal snacks.

6. In a special-occasion luncheon meal, plan substitutions for an overweight guest or member of the family.

7. Plan a method for changing any of your eating habits which you recognize as undesirable for you.

¶ *Practicing and Evaluating:*

1. Check your weight by a chart showing the average weight for your sex, age, and height. Determine the number of calories your day's meals should furnish.

2. Plan a day's menus for yourself that will contain adequate calories; consider both your growth and activity needs.

3. Prepare two vegetables for an underweight child's luncheon, making them tempting in flavor, color, and texture.

4. Prepare a dessert suited to an underweight's luncheon. How did you include additional calories in the dish?

5. Assist in preparing and serving an attractive supper for an underweight older person.

6. Without sacrifice of minerals and vitamins, prepare a low-calorie breakfast for an overweight person.

7. Assist in preparing a luncheon sufficiently high in bulk foods to prevent an overweight person becoming hungry before dinner.

¶ *Reading Further:*

Eat to Control Your Weight, Bulletin 128 (1958). University of North Carolina Extension Service, Raleigh, North Carolina.

Food and Your Weight, Home and Garden Bulletin 74 (1960). U. S. Department of Agriculture, Washington, D. C.

Problems with Figures, Bulletin L–105 (1961). Kansas State University Extension Service, Manhattan, Kansas.

Sensible Weight Control, Bulletin 781 (1961). Oregon State University Extension Service, Corvallis, Oregon.

CHAPTER 23

Feeding the convalescent

you will learn: The importance of following
the doctor's directions; The foods suited to the diet of
convalescents; How to prepare patients for
their meals; How to prepare meals
for patients; How to serve meals to patients

The days of witch doctors and medicine men are past. After centuries of darkness concerning the cause and cure of diseases, some thinking men began to lose faith in the old treatments and to get glimmers of scientific health principles that are still acceptable today. Among these early pioneers in medicine was an Englishman named Nicholas Culpeper, who, in 1665, published an herbal that not only classified herbs but contained a vast collection of knowledge about herbs and vegetables and the way they affect the human system. He became so famous for his knowledge of herbs and their properties that today his name is given to a whole chain of herb and spice shops in London—they are called Culpeper Shops.

Since the day of Nicholas Culpeper, not only has medicine made amazing strides

289

ahead, but doctors and scientists have come to realize the importance of proper diet in relation to health. Doctors now prescribe diets for infants and young children, observing their growth and changing the diet as necessary. Many ailments can be prevented by good nutrition. When illness does occur, though drugs may be prescribed to fight the disease, also the diet is changed to meet the body's needs. Proper attention to diet helps to shorten the course of the disease. For the recovery of the convalescent, one of the most important factors may be the supplying of the right food for restoring and maintaining the strength of his body. Students of nutrition are learning more and more about corrective diets which give the body a chance to help cure itself.

PLANNING MENUS FOR THE SICK

TYPE OF DIET	FOODS INCLUDED
LIQUID	Milk, buttermilk, milk shakes, eggnog, chocolate or malted milk, cocoa, tea, coffee Fruit and vegetable juices, strained Whole-grain cereals, thoroughly cooked and strained thin as an extra food Fat-free broths Cream soups, sieved Ice creams, ices, custards, gelatin, junket Slightly cooked egg in combination with the above foods
SOFT	Everything which is allowed in the liquid diet plus the following: Toast, milk toast, white or whole grain bread Eggs, soft-cooked at low temperature or poached Fruits, cooked and sieved; ripe banana, mashed Vegetables, cooked and sieved (not fried) Cereals, whole-grain, cooked Soft-curd cottage cheese; white meat of fowl; fish; and beef, scraped Custards, puddings, gelatin, junket, plain cakes, cookies
LIGHT, or CONVALESCENT	Everything allowed in the liquid and soft diets plus the following: Chops broiled, and bacon Baked and stewed fruits Baked potato Green vegetables Desserts allowed in the soft diet

In a home where there is illness, members of the family should cooperate in meeting the emergency. Older children should have some knowledge of how to prepare food for the sick in case the homemaker is ill or away. A daughter can help to shorten an illness and make the situation more pleasant for the family if she understands the basic principles of feeding the sick. Illness in the home makes adjustments necessary for every member of the family. Willing cooperation will lighten the burden for all.

The Importance of Following the Doctor's Directions

The importance of following the doctor's orders exactly cannot be overstressed. Never rely on memory regarding a patient's care. Write down every detail and follow it explicitly. Your doctor will appreciate specific questions about the kind of diet which the patient should receive, the amount of food he needs, and the intervals at which he should eat. Also important are special meal-preparation methods which should be used, and sanitary precautions which the helper should observe.

Foods Suited to the Convalescent

Since correct diet is often as necessary as medical care in restoring health after illness, the feeding of the convalescent may be the most important part of his care. Your doctor will outline for you the general type of diet which the sick person should receive and you should know what foods are included in each type. See chart on opposite page.

Planning Menus for the Sick

Some illnesses require more food than a normal diet supplies if the patient is to rebuild his body. Others require less food than normal to give the body organs a rest. After the doctor has prescribed the kind and amount of food, it is necessary that the meals be planned to contain a variety of foods to

Jane and Steven Coons

A typical soft diet

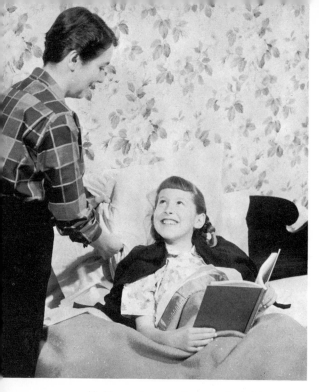

Making a bed patient comfortable

tor; his saying that he doesn't want food or his asking for something not on his diet puts you at a disadvantage before you begin. Study the diet list, and, avoiding disliked foods, plan for proper nutrition and for a variety of tastes, textures, and colors. Vary the food, trying to have some tempting surprise each time. A special effort to interest the convalescent in eating is important.

Foods for the sick should be easy to digest. Since inactivity slows down digestive processes, digestive disturbances may accompany illness. This is not always due to the illness itself but may be traced to nervousness, pain, lack of exercise, or other indirect causes.

The Special Diet

A special diet is one planned by the doctor as a part of the treatment. After operations, acute illnesses, fevers, and body conditions such as irritation of intestines and constipation, special diets may be prescribed. In constipation cases the recommended diet may include bulky food to stimulate intestinal movement, fats or oil to soften the intestinal contents, or smooth, nonirritating food to soothe and rest the intestine. Diarrhea, anemia, and allergies are body disturbances that may be relieved by a special diet. Extreme variations in body weight which may be controlled by food intake are discussed in Chapter 22.

insure a balanced and tempting diet. Since loss of appetite is common in sickness, the menu should be made as acceptable as possible. Sick persons, especially children, should not be forced to eat foods they dislike. Although menus must be built from the prescribed diet list, dishes which the patient likes may be chosen. The patient should not be asked what he prefers since his choice may not be approved by the doc-

Preparing the Patient for Meals

A quiet atmosphere should prevail when a patient is having his meal. As a home nurse you can help accomplish this by your poised manner and low voice. Soft music from the radio or records may add to the patient's pleasure. He should not be disturbed by

discussion of bothersome family problems while he is eating, or by telephone messages, by visitors, or by the intrusion of the family members. Any one of these factors may interfere with the patient's eating all his meal.

His appetite is further encouraged if his

comfort has been attended to before the meal is served. He should not be expected to eat when he is in pain, nor should he be awakened for food. It is better to alter the eating schedule slightly than to inconvenience him or deprive him of needed rest. The patient should have been told ten minutes before the meal is served. While he is attending to his toilet needs, washing his face and hands, and combing his hair, the helper can straighten the bed and pillows and tidy the room. This encourages a desirable frame of mind as well as assuring cleanliness. See that your patient has a sweater or bed jacket near him. A back rest of pillows or a folded blanket may add to his comfort. Sometimes a footrest is helpful. A patient who is rested whose room and person are in order, and who is comfortable and cheerful will enjoy his food more than one who has not been prepared for the meal. Under these conditions diet will make its full contribution to his recovery.

If the patient has no contagious disease and is strong enough, he may enjoy having someone eat with him or talk with him

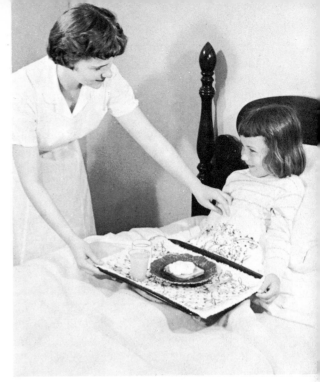

Breakfast for the invalid

while he eats. If the patient must eat in bed, tuck a large napkin or towel under his chin to protect clothing, bed linens, and blankets.

Preparing Meals for the Patient

If you are sharing in the care of a convalescent, you may help with the preparation of the foods prescribed. Cleanliness, previously emphasized for all work with foods, is of special importance. Persons recuperating from illness are more susceptible to bacteria than healthy persons.

Anything which might carry harmful bacteria to them must be carefully protected. The clothes and hands of anyone working with food must be very clean, and all utensils and dishes must be properly handled to prevent contamination of food. The doctor may order the patient's dishes to be sterilized after each meal to protect the family or to make sure that colds or other contagions do not come from the family to the patient. Keeping his dishes completely separated may be recommended. Paper plates, cups, and napkins may be used and should be burned at once after using. Use the same care in cooking and serving food to the convalescent that you would use in preparing food for infants.

Foods to be served to patients must be appropriate to the diet, appetizing, and cooked

293

so as to retain their nutrients. You should understand the relation of diet to the patient's problem. If a patient on a restricted-fat diet is allowed meat, it should be broiled, not fried. Meats may be cooked with either dry or moist heat. Potatoes steamed or baked are advised because they retain their food values better than boiled ones. Eggs should be soft-cooked, poached, scrambled, or used in omelette or soufflé. Cereals are made more digestible by cooking longer than ordinary. Vegetables may be boiled, steamed, or baked. It may be necessary to sieve or strain them.

Additions to vary the flavor of bland foods will often help to encourage a poor appetite. Cheese in small amounts in soufflés, or on spaghetti, or on toast may be used. If fruits are to be cooked, they are best stewed, with skins and seeds removed; some may be baked. On advice of the doctor, fruits properly prepared for convenient handling may be served uncooked.

Since each dish should be prepared with great care, there is no denying that proper feeding of a sick person necessitates extra work. It can be kept at a minimum by using some of the same foods for the family meal. Perhaps less seasoning will be used for the patient than for the family, and his food may be served without rich sauces or garnishes. Fruits, eggs, and vegetables are easy and attractive substitutions for less appropriate items of the family meal.

The home nurse may share some of the pride of the professional nurse in observing the precautions for cleanliness, in following the doctor's orders, in planning and preparing foods, and in giving her patient the best possible surroundings for recovery.

Serving Meals to the Patient

If food is to play its proper part in a patient's recovery, the person responsible for his meals must help him to welcome mealtime. It is important to realize the need for him to forget his illness temporarily. Any surprise or variation will relieve the monotony of his hours in bed. A child may present a special problem, for illness and inactivity are apt to rob him of his appetite.

Prompt serving of the meal will help to prevent impatience on the part of the convalescent. Small servings, as a rule, are more appetizing to a sick person than large ones. The sight of a heaped plate can take away a patient's appetite. Hot foods should be served hot and cold foods cold.

If the patient is being served in bed, meals are managed more easily when arranged on a tray. A tray-table or a tray with legs is convenient if the patient can sit up. If these are not available, an ironing board may be adjusted to the height needed, or a firm pillow may be placed on the patient's lap to hold the tray. If the patient has sufficient strength to get up, serve the food from a table in his room or at the family table.

The tray used for a patient's meals should be large enough to hold all the dishes. A cookie sheet or a breadboard may be used if no tray is available. A paper tray cover and a paper napkin will cut down on laundry. Use attractive dishes which do not tip easily, and arrange them so that the food can be reached conveniently. A single flower or small bouquet or some other special touch gives the tray color. Put a bell on the tray so that the patient can call you.

Serving Liquid Diets

To serve a liquid diet, a tray, a feeding cup, and a glass with a drinking tube are needed. The shape of the drinking tube should permit the patient to take the liquid easily from a comfortable position. Raise the patient's head slightly by slipping your hand and arm under the pillow. Hold the glass or cup with the free hand and permit the patient to guide it to the best position. Persons who are very ill should not be permitted to hold the glass or tube while drinking, nor should a tube be used for the delirious or unconscious patient. A patient in a lying position may drink from a tumbler only a quarter full.

Glass feeding tubes should always be cleaned as soon as used to have them available at all times. Always place the tube below the surface of the liquid to prevent the patient from sucking air. The tip of the tube should be moistened before it is used, to avoid its sticking to the lips, and should be withdrawn from the mouth occasionally during the feeding. Be sure the liquid is not too hot, and give it slowly. Water given after milk is taken will leave the mouth refreshed.

Serving Soft Diets

It is sometimes necessary to feed the patient, but he should be allowed to help, if possible, by managing crackers, toast, or other finger foods. Foods fed to him should be cut into small bites, and different ones offered alternately. Food should be given from the tip of a spoon which is only partially full. Plenty of time should be allowed between mouthfuls. The one who feeds the patient should give the impression of having unlimited time.

Serving Light Diets

Although the light diet served to sick persons may contain a variety of foods, the meal is usually arranged on a tray. The convalescent should feed himself if he is able to handle the utensils. Meats should not be difficult to cut or should be cut in bite-sized pieces before serving. Foods should be drained before serving; this makes eating easier and lessens the possibility of spilling. Bowls, glasses, or cups for liquids should be not more than three-fourths full.

A LIGHT DIET FOR A CONVALESCENT

Breakfast

Apple-Sauce Purée
Ground-Wheat Cereal   Cream
Poached Eggs   Buttered Whole-Wheat Bread
Cocoa

Luncheon

Vegetable Soup   Croutons
Cottage-Cheese Salad
Orange Juice

A milk shake with a bent plastic or paper straw is an easy way for a bed patient to take nourishment

Dinner

Lamb Chop

Baked Potatoes   Buttered Asparagus

Melba Toast

Lemon Gelatin

Milk

Feeding Records

You have already noted that there are several factors which may alter the appetite of the patient. After each meal a brief summary should be made of the amount and kinds of food that the patient has eaten. This survey, along with any signs of nausea or other discomfort, should be noted on the patient's chart. The doctor will need this information and you will find it of value in checking the success of your efforts. It will also help you in making changes to benefit your patient.

¶ *Understanding:*

1. What is the value of following the doctor's directions when you are planning meals for a patient?

2. When a liquid diet is prescribed, what foods can you safely serve? a soft diet? a light diet?

3. Why is the appetizing quality of foods especially to be considered when feeding the sick?

4. How may methods of cookery protect both nutritive and appetizing quality?

5. How should the patient be made ready and comfortable for mealtime? By what means can you encourage the sick to eat?

6. How may meals served in bed be made easily manageable by the patient?

¶ *Planning:*

1. Plan a day's diet for a convalescent for whom the doctor has prescribed soft foods. Which of the foods are appropriate in the family menu?

2. Plan for the use of an improvised tray. Set the tray for a meal, arranging for the comfort of the person.

3. Plan the care of dishes for persons with communicable diseases.

4. Plan the rearrangement of a room in your home for the more convenient serving of meals to a convalescent member of the family.

5. Plan ways to manage time and effort when feeding convalescents.

¶ *Practicing and Evaluating:*

1. Assist with the preparation of an appetizing liquid diet. What makes the meal appropriate?

2. From foods prepared for a family meal select dishes appropriate for a patient's soft diet. Prepare foods to complete the patient's meal.

3. Prepare a light diet for a convalescent. How were the dishes containing milk or eggs cooked for tender products?

4. Using the Daily Food Guide on page 18, check the day's menu on pages 295–296. Is the menu adequate?

¶ *Reading Further:*

GALLAGHER, J. ROSWELL, GOLDBERGER, I. H., and HALLOCK, GRACE T., *Health for Life*, Ginn and Company, Boston, Mass.

Home Care of Sick, Bulletin E–624, New York State College of Agriculture and Home Economics, Ithaca, N. Y.

THOMPSON, ELLA M., and LEBARON, MARGARET, *Simplified Nursing*, J. B. Lippincott Company, Philadelphia, Pa.

WILLIAMS, DOROTHEA, *Building Health*, J. B. Lippincott Company, Philadelphia, Pa.

UNIT SEVEN

Food
Preservation

National Presto Industries

H ome preservation methods

you will learn: How to can foods;
How to prepare foods for freezing; How to make
jellies and preserves; How to
preserve foods by pickling

Preserving food at home is a thrifty practice if fresh fruits and vegetables can be purchased inexpensively during their season, or if home-garden surpluses are utilized. Throughout the year well-balanced and interesting menus may be planned with these foods. You and your mother, viewing the expenditure of time and money, may find yourselves well repaid for the effort of canning, preserving, and freezing fresh foods.

Among the methods of preservation suitable for home use, canning, preserving with sugar, as in jellies and jams, or freezing are the most common. The method must be inexpensive and not too difficult, and the product must have good flavor, color, texture, and food value. If the process is correctly carried out, the product, stored in a cool, dark place where air circulates, should keep well. However, since preserved foods should be used within the year, family needs should be estimated with care. It is better to add to the supply each season than to hold the foods over from one season to the next. The amount of suitable storage space may also, in some homes, be a controlling factor in determining the amount to preserve. The excellence of preserved foods, as well as their economy, depends on correct preservation and storage.

Canning

The methods of canning vary according to the foods and the facilities available and how much one can afford for equipment. Those most often used are the hot-water bath and the pressure-cooker method. The *hot-water bath* is successful for acid foods like fruits, tomatoes, and rhubarb. These foods may be put into the jars or cans either hot or cold. The containers are then completely covered with hot water which is brought to a rolling boil and kept at that temperature long enough to kill harmful bacteria and prevent spoilage.

Nonacid foods, such as asparagus, greens, peas, beans, corn, and meats, must be canned in a *pressure cooker*. The steam pressure raises the temperature higher than other canning methods and ensures the killing of all bacteria. The large pressure canner is most convenient; a pressure saucepan may be used if the pressure can be held at 10 pounds and if the saucepan is tall enough to allow the jars or cans to rest on a rack. Manufacturer's directions must be followed carefully in using any pressure canner or saucepan. Foods should be processed in a pressure saucepan longer than the recommended time for a canner. The pressure-canner method is the best guarantee against spoilage which may occur in canned foods.

The most common *types of spoilage* in canned goods are as follows:

1. *Flat-sour* is a common type of spoilage found in nonacid vegetables which have not been processed properly.

2. *Swell* is a kind of canned-food poisoning in which gas is formed and causes the ends of the can to swell.

3. *Botulism* is a very dangerous type of poisoning caused by microorganisms. Foods of the nonacid variety must be processed by the pressure-cooker method to be safe for use.

Alertness to signs of spoilage when canned food is to be used may prevent food poisoning. Bulging ends on tin cans or a broken seal on a glass jar are indications. Gas bubbles in the liquid or spurting of the liquid as the can is opened show spoilage. A product which has lost its characteristic appearance and has a peculiar odor must not be used. Odors may become more noticeable as the food is heated. Because of the danger of botulism, canned food should never be tasted as a test for spoilage. Do not hesitate to discard food on suspicion of spoilage.

Preparation of Foods for Canning

Canning does not improve the quality of any food. You should not, therefore, attempt to preserve inferior fruits and vegetables which are soft, bruised, or withered. Foods should be canned as soon as possible after coming from the garden or source of supply. Each step from preparing the food through the canning procedure should move quickly.

Ball Brothers Company

CANNING

Inspecting jar tops to make sure there are no nicks or cracks

The tomatoes have been put into a wire basket and are being dipped into boiling water to loosen their skins

The hard core is being removed from the tomato, which will then be skinned and placed in the open jar

Hot juice is being poured over the tomatoes after they are packed in the jar

The jars, filled with tomatoes, have been placed in the boiling-water-bath canner. More water is being added to cover the tops of the jars

1

2

3

4

5

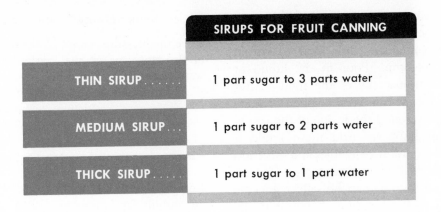

SIRUPS FOR FRUIT CANNING	
THIN SIRUP......	1 part sugar to 3 parts water
MEDIUM SIRUP...	1 part sugar to 2 parts water
THICK SIRUP.....	1 part sugar to 1 part water

Preparation of Fruit—To speed preparation you may skin peaches, apricots, and tomatoes by putting them into a wire basket and plunging them into boiling water for 1 minute, then into cold water. The skins will now slip off quickly and easily. After peeling apples, peaches, and pears drop them into a weak salt solution to prevent browning.

Fruits may be canned without sirup. However, using a sugar sirup improves the flavor, shape, and color. The sirup may be light, medium, or heavy depending on individual taste.

Preparation of Vegetables—Select young, tender, fresh vegetables for canning. After they are cleaned, most vegetables are precooked or blanched to protect the flavor and color. *Scalding* or *blanching* is done by dipping the vegetables, in a wire-mesh basket, into boiling water for not more than 1 minute. *Precooking* differs from scalding in that the food is cooked 5 to 10 minutes. This shrinks the food and makes it possible to pack more into a jar. The liquid used in precooking generally is packed into the jar with the vegetables since it contains some of the food value. Some bacteriologists, however, recommend discarding this water to get rid of spores which are difficult to destroy. It is believed that beans and tomatoes retain more vitamin C when packed raw than when blanched or precooked.

Preparation of Meats—Meats suitable for canning are beef, veal, mutton, lamb, pork, and rabbit. Poultry also may be canned successfully. Only the highest quality of meat, which has been slaughtered and handled under sanitary conditions, should be canned. Meat must be chilled immediately after slaughtering and kept cold until ready to preserve.

A pressure cooker is necessary for the canning of meat since an inner temperature higher than boiling is required. For home preservation, containers of more than quart size cannot be used for meat as they make it impossible to produce a sufficiently high inner temperature.

Containers for Packing Foods

Either tin or glass containers may be used for canning foods. Heat penetrates tin cans fast and they can be plunged into cold water directly from the canner to stop cooking instantly. Glass containers must be free from cracks and chips, and lids should not be dented. The jars and lids must be thoroughly washed and then boiled for 15 minutes before using. Remove only one container at a time; it need not be dried, but to prevent breakage glass should be kept hot while the food is being added.

Fill the containers with food to within 1 inch of the top. Pour in the liquid or sirup until it just covers the food. After filling the jars or cans, run a spoon or knife several times around the inside of the can to displace air bubbles. Add more liquid if necessary. For most vegetables and meat add 1 teaspoon of salt to each quart jar. The salt adds flavor, but it has no effect on the preservation. If tin cans are being used, the lids must be sealed before processing. Seal precooked food right after packing. If the food is not precooked, place the filled cans in a pan of water, heat to drive out the air; seal immediately. When jars are used, screw down the metal cap or collar as tightly as possible, then turn the cap in the opposite direction for $\frac{1}{4}$ inch, leaving the jar partially sealed.

Processing Methods

Processing foods further exhausts the air in the container and destroys microorganisms that cause spoilage.

HOT-WATER-BATH PROCESSING

1. Heat water in the canner. Add the jars or cans of cold packed foods when the water is hot. Hot packed containers can be added when the water is boiling.
2. Add enough boiling water so that the containers are completely covered. Put the cover on the canner.
3. Bring to a rolling, steady boil. Do not start counting time until the water is boiling rapidly. Keep a close check of the time. (Processing times for specific foods are given on pages 495–496.) Add more boiling water during the processing as needed.
4. At the end of the period, remove the jars or cans. Tighten the lids of glass jars if necessary.

302

PRESSURE-COOKER PROCESSING

1. Place the pressure canner on the hottest part of the range, or on the largest unit. Add water according to directions.
2. Place filled and sealed jars in the canner. Check for good circulation around each jar.
3. Place the lid on the canner and clamp it in place.
4. Check to be sure that no steam escapes except at the petcock.
5. Leave the petcock open until steam has come out steadily for 7 minutes.
6. Close the petcock; count processing time from the second the required amount of pressure is indicated on the dial. (Processing times for specific foods are given on pages 495–498.) Adjust heat so that the pressure remains at the desired point.
7. At the end of the period, remove the canner from the heat.
8. Allow the hand on the gauge to return to zero. Open the petcock gradually. Release clamps and remove the lid, tipping the lid away from you.
9. Remove the jars; tighten the lids if necessary. Allow the jars to cool.

Immediately after processing food in tin cans remove the cans from the canner with tongs and plunge them into cold water.

Glass jars may be left in the canner to cool sufficiently for easy handling. Do not lift them by their lids. The food will cool best if the jars are set right side up away from drafts but with space around them for air circulation.

Some liquid may have evaporated, but the jars must not be opened to add more; the keeping quality of the product has not been affected.

To make sure that there is no air in the jar, invert the jar or tap the lid. If air bubbles escape, open the jar and use the food immediately.

Freezing Foods

Freezing keeps the appearance, taste, and food values more like those of fresh foods than any other preserving method. In this process the temperature is kept low enough to inactivate enzymes and microorganisms. Some types of home freezers have special compartments for quick freezing. Others allow for storage only and the quick freezing must be done by a home freezer or locker plant. Overloading a freezer makes it difficult to keep the temperature low enough to preserve frozen products properly. The manufacturer's instructions for each type of home freezer should be followed.

Foods Suitable for Freezing

All high-quality meats, poultry, and sea food can be frozen. Most fruits, except melons, and most vegetables, except lettuce and others with a high water content, can be frozen. One should know which fruits and vegetables make the most satisfactory frozen foods and which are less desirable. State experiment stations are good sources of information on the best vegetables and fruits and on the process for freezing, storing, and using them.

Through research, new information is continuously being made available concerning the successful freezing of foods: their preparation, length of storage, and care after removal from the freezer. You may write to the Bureau of Human Nutrition and Home Economics, United States Department of Agriculture, Washington, D. C., for this information.

Equipment Needed

To prepare food for freezing, nothing is needed beyond regular kitchen equipment except containers, wraps, and labeling supplies. Foods are packaged into containers of

FREEZING STRAWBERRIES

The strawberries are being quickly but gently washed in ice water. Then they will be drained and hulled

Making the freezing sirup · Berries are best when frozen in heavy sirup

The berries are being packed in glass containers. Then the cold sirup is poured into the container to within three-fourths of an inch of the top. Waxed paper is placed on the top of the fruit to keep it immersed in the sirup. Then the cover is screwed on

Corn Products Refining Company and *Forecast*

OPTIMUM STORAGE TIME FOR FROZEN MEAT	
Ground meats with salt.	1 to 3 months
Pork, veal, and fish.....	3 to 4 months
Beef and lamb........	6 to 8 months
Poultry and liquid eggs	6 to 12 months
Fish (cut up or whole)..	3 to 4 months

glass, plastic, light-weight aluminum, or heavily waxed cardboard. Among the wraps used for frozen meat and poultry or cakes and pies are tubular stockinette, heavy metal foil, and heavily waxed paper. Cellophane-lined packages are not suitable for fruits packed in sugar or sirup; heavily waxed-paper boards or glass are satisfactory for either fruits or vegetables. Containers and packages should hold an amount sufficient for a family meal and should be easy to fill and to empty. They should be of convenient sizes and shapes for stacking in the freezer.

Preparing Fruit

Mature fruits should be chosen for freezing and they should be handled carefully. After you have washed, stemmed, peeled, seeded, or pulped the fruit, it may be sweetened either by the dry-sugar method or by the sirup method. In the *dry-sugar method*, sugar should be sprinkled over the fruit while the fruit is lifted carefully with a slotted spoon for even sugaring. The *sirup method* is the same as that for canning. The sirup should be thoroughly cooled before being poured over the fruit.

Preparing Vegetables

The vegetables are cleaned and sorted for size, and inferior ones eliminated. Scalding or blanching is necessary before freezing, just as it is before canning. It may be done by steam or directly by hot water. Blanched vegetables may be cooled by plunging them immediately into ice water or cold running water. They should be drained on absorbent paper toweling or clean dish towels.

Preparing Meat

Meat, poultry, and fish are prepared for freezing exactly as for immediate use. They must be in portions convenient for the family: three or four pounds for roasts, enough slices for broiling, patties between layers of freezing paper. Before it is frozen, all meat should be prepared for cooking. Do not season meat with salt before freezing.

Chickens and turkeys can be stuffed and frozen. If dressing has sage in it, do not store more than 3 months as the sage flavor will permeate the meat. To save space, bones may be removed from meat and poultry before freezing.

Storing Frozen Foods

Frozen foods must be kept at 0° F.; otherwise a peculiar taste may result from chemical changes in the food.

Making Jellies and Preserves

In the process of preserving foods with sugar, heat kills the bacteria and sugar acts as a preservative. The product is stored in sterile, airtight containers.

Foods preserved with sugar, because of the process through which they have gone, do not resemble fresh fruits in texture. In the preparation and cooking of the fruit much

304

mineral and vitamin value is lost, so the food value of sugar-preserved fruits does not compare favorably with that of fresh, canned, or frozen fruits.

However, jellies and preserves are attractive foods having many uses. They are definitely a sweet, and therefore a complement to other foods.

Jellies

Good jelly is tender and translucent, and its molded shape quivers. It retains the flavor and color of the fruit from which it comes. Marmalade, a variation of jelly, contains the fruit pulp and some sliced peel. Jam differs from jelly only in the use of crushed fruit. The fruit is cooked with sugar until the mixture is a thick consistency without preserving the shape of the fruit. Conserves are jams that contain more than one kind of fruit and usually nuts or raisins. Fruit butters are made like jams but are strained and contain less sugar and more spices. To jell properly a fruit must contain sufficient acid and pectin. Fruits are highest in pectin and acid just before they are completely ripe. A combination of part unripe and part ripe fruit is successful for making jelly.

Some fruits (apples, cranberries, currants, gooseberries, grapes, plums, loganberries, and sour blackberries) jell easily. Fruits low in pectin (apricots, cherries, pineapples, strawberries, and pomegranates) can be used in jellies if a commercial pectin is added. Recipes which accompany the pectin should be followed. If fruit is low in acid (as are quinces, pears, and some varieties of apple), lemon juice or citric acid may be used. Both acid and pectin must be added to raspberries and peaches, and to all well-ripened fruit.

Fruits to be used for jelly should be inspected carefully and damaged parts removed.

305

Certo and Sure-Jell

The grapes have been washed and are being stripped from the stem

The grapes have been cooked just enough to start the juice flowing freely. Then they were turned into a cloth bag. The bag is being squeezed gently to extract the juice

The juice and sugar have been cooked together until the jelly stage was reached. The scum has been skimmed off the top and the liquid is now being poured into the jelly glasses

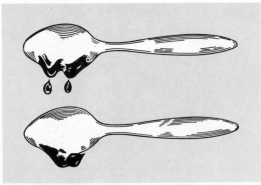

When a spoon dipped in jelly and held horizontally allows drops to fall off, the jelly is not yet ready to be removed from the range.

When, however, the liquid "sheets" rather than forms drops, it is time to remove it from the heat

Stems and blossom ends should be discarded. Skins may be left on unless there are signs of spray residue. The fruit must be washed thoroughly and cut into small uniform pieces. It is not necessary to remove the cores since this part of the fruit is a good source of pectin.

Extracting the Juice—Boil the fruit either in its own juice or in water. Gentle stirring prevents scorching on the bottom of the pan. Overcooking may cause jelly to be cloudy. When the fruit juice starts flowing freely, turn the fruit into a cloth bag and allow the juice to drip into a large bowl. The bag may be squeezed gently to extract the last of the juice. Squeezing may cause cloudiness, so it is wise to strain the juice again through a clean bag. If the particular fruit is high in both pectin and acid, the juice may be extracted from the pulp a second time. The bag of pulp is turned back into the kettle after the first extraction, barely covered with water, and reboiled. Repeat the extraction process. To prevent grape juice from becoming gritty, let it stand overnight so the crystals will settle, or combine it with apple juice.

306

Making the Jelly Mixture—Juice and sugar should be measured accurately in amounts stated in the jelly recipe. Stir the jelly mixture until the sugar dissolves. Boil the mixture rapidly until the jelly stage is reached. When it stops flowing in a stream from the side of a tilted wooden spoon and divides into two distinct drops that run together and leave the edge of the spoon in one large sheet, the jelly is sufficiently cooked. Overcooking destroys color, gives an undesirable flavor, and affects the texture.

Filling and Sealing the Glasses—Jelly glasses should be washed and boiled, then drained and placed on a tray. Remove the scum from the sirup and pour the liquid into the glasses, leaving $\frac{1}{4}$ inch at the top. To seal the glasses, melt paraffin in a pan and pour it over the jelly. If the jelly is hot when you add the paraffin, you will need a second layer when the jelly has cooled to ensure a seal. Some prefer to cool the jelly, protected by sterile tin lids, before adding paraffin. To make a complete seal, the final step in both methods is to rotate the glass before the paraffin hardens. Label the glasses with the name of the jelly and the date.

Preserves

A fruit preserve is made of whole small fruits or pieces of large fruits cooked in a thick sirup. They are translucent, hold their shape, and are packed in the sirup or jellied juice. Among the fruits which hold their shape in preserving are cherries, peaches, pears, plums, and quinces. Special care is needed to keep the shape of berries and small yellow tomatoes. Fruits should be picked and preserved when they are ripe but still firm. Firm fruits may be skinned and then cooked in a thick sirup. The juices are quickly extracted, diluting the sirup. Thin-skinned and very tender fruits are cooked in

Food preservation is an art as well as a science

a thick sirup to prevent loss of shape. Sometimes thin-skinned fruits are allowed to stand overnight in sugar before cooking. This draws out the juice and makes the fruit shrunken but more firm. No liquid need be added as the juice is sufficient for the sirup. If the fruit begins to look shriveled while the preserves are cooking, a little water may be added to the sirup. Preserves are cooked until the fruit is translucent and the sirup is very thick. Sterilized containers are filled three-fourths full with fruit and the sirup is poured over to fill them. Seal while hot, as for jelly or canned fruit.

Storing Jelly and Preserves

A cool, dry place which has good air circulation is desirable. Do not try to keep these products over a year, since color, flavor, and texture deteriorate over such a long period of time.

Home-preserved foods offer definite advantages to offset the labor. Time spent in preserving foods often saves shopping time later. Perhaps most important of all is the family's pride and pleasure in well-stocked shelves, capable of supplying daily needs and equal to the most exacting demands of hospitality.

Preservation by Pickling

Some garden and orchard products may be best utilized by making them into pickles. Green tomatoes, beans, cucumbers, peppers, onions, cauliflower, some fruits, and cabbage are commonly used for pickles and relishes. Cabbage when fermented is known as sauerkraut.

Pickles and relishes are important to the meal. They are eaten for flavor and for their crisp spiciness that stimulates appetite for other wholesome but less flavorful foods. Meat loaf, hash, poultry, and vegetables are among the foods that may be enjoyed more when accompanied by pickles. The flavor of pickles and relishes comes chiefly from spices and herbs carefully selected and well blended to suit a given product. Pickles have both mineral and vitamin value in the diet.

The pickling process applies to any food that is preserved in brine or vinegar, either

Sweet pepper relish · The chopped peppers and onions have been cooked in vinegar and water with sugar and drained. They are now being spooned boiling hot into glass jars

with or without bacterial fermentation. To make good pickles, the products must be fresh, sound, and of proper maturity and must be given the required time to cure and then time to develop flavor. You may make either quick-process pickles from fresh products or salt-stock pickles from products first cured in salt solution or brine for six weeks or longer. Through the brine cure the tissues of vegetables and fruits are better prepared to absorb the vinegar and seasonings. Pickles that have been brined are considered finer in flavor, more crisp in texture, more attractive in color and general appearance and have better keeping qualities than have quick-process pickles.

Pickles may be made sour, in which the flavor of vinegar predominates, or sweet, in which the sweetness is more prominent. Sufficient mustard may be added to pickles to give a desired mustard flavor or in dill or tarragon pickles the flavor is modified by the respective herbs. Spiced pickles may be made from peaches, crab apples, pears, and cherries. Ketchup, chili sauce, chutney, relish, and chowchow are other different forms of pickles.

For cooking pickles, use porcelain-lined, glass, or enameled utensils. If proper preparation methods are followed, the salts and acids and seasonings will produce the desired flavor and firmness in pickles.

¶ Understanding:

1. When is home preservation of food an economical practice?

2. What home-preservation methods are best for meats? for nonacid vegetables? Why?

3. What characteristics should you look for when choosing fruit for preservation? vegetables? meat, poultry, and fish?

4. What factors govern the choice of containers for foods to be canned? to be frozen?

5. For what reasons are foods precooked before preservation? blanched?

6. Under what conditions can fruits low in pectin and acid be used in making jelly?

7. What is a satisfactory test for doneness of jelly? What is the effect of overcooking?

8. Why are pickles and relishes important to meals?

¶ Planning:

1. Plan a means of keeping an up-to-date accounting of canned, frozen, and other preserved foods in home storage.

2. Plan the steps to follow in canning tomatoes, using the boiling-water bath.

3. Plan the preparation of strawberries, peas, and meat patties for quick freezing.

4. Plan to use locally grown fruits in the making of jelly. Which fruits should be combined with others for a firm jelly? Which need a commercial pectin added?

5. Outline the steps of the process for making plum jelly.

6. Plan a variety of preserved foods to meet the needs of a family of four.

7. Plan for several kinds of pickles and relishes to be used in your family meals.

¶ Practicing and Evaluating.

1. Fill food containers with fruits or vegetables for processing and adjust the lids. What precautions did you follow?

2. Assist with the canning of a nonacid food. What did you consider when choosing the processing method?

3. Work with another in preparing a fruit, a vegetable, and a meat to be frozen in a home freezer or by a commercial freezer plant. Discuss the means of packaging.

4. Prepare a sirup for canning peaches. Assist in packing the jar and sealing. In what ways did you consider the experience valuable?

5. Remove jars or cans from a pressure cooker, test for a good seal, and store the food for future use.

6. Help someone prepare a stuffed chicken to be frozen. For how long a period may it be kept frozen?

7. Prepare fish to be frozen. How should they be wrapped to retain their moisture?

8. Taste a fruit preserved with sugar. How does it compare with the fresh fruit in flavor and texture? in keeping qualities?

9. Assist with making preserves, using a thick sugar sirup. What fruits may be successfully used? How may doneness be tested?

10. Compare the flavor and texture of pickles that have been brined and then made by the quick pickling process.

¶ *Reading Further:*

BROBECK, FLORENCE R., *Old-Time Pickling and Spicing Recipes*, M. Barrows & Company, New York, N. Y.

Foods from the Freezer, Pre-cooked and Prepared, Bulletin No. 692, New York State College of Agriculture, Ithaca, N. Y.

4–H Members Learn to Can Fruits and Tomatoes, Bulletin 4–H1030 (1961). University of Kentucky Extension Service, Lexington, Kentucky.

Home Canning of Fruits and Vegetables, Home and Garden Bulletin 8 (1961). U. S. Department of Agriculture, Washington, D. C.

Home Care of Purchased Frozen Foods, Home and Garden Bulletin 69 (1960). U. S. Department of Agriculture, Washington, D. C.

Home Freezing, Bulletin 501 (1961). University of Arkansas Extension Service, Little Rock, Arkansas.

Home Freezing of Fruits and Vegetables, Home and Garden Bulletin 10 (1961). U. S. Department of Agriculture, Washington, D. C.

Home Freezing of Poultry, Home and Garden Bulletin 70 (1960). U. S. Department of Agriculture, Washington, D. C.

SIMPSON, JEAN J., and TAYLOR, DEMETRIA M., *The Frozen Food Cook Book*, Simon and Schuster, Inc., New York, N. Y.

Storing Perishable Foods in the Home, Home and Garden Bulletin 78 (1961). U. S. Department of Agriculture, Washington, D. C.

UNIT EIGHT

Good Manners and Entertaining

R. Day, from F. P. G.

Table setting, service, and etiquette

you will learn: How to set a table properly;
The various types of table service; How to select table
appointments; How to decorate a table
attractively and appropriately; How to appreciate
and use table etiquette

Your enjoyment of a meal depends on the attractiveness of the table, the proficiency of the service, and the observance of accepted principles of etiquette, as much as on the quality of the food. In addition to learning to prepare delicious foods, you will wish to understand social requirements, both for hostess and for guest. The ability to dine without embarrassment in a friend's well-appointed house, or to serve correctly with ease and poise at an attractively set table of your own, are skills of lifelong value. Whatever the practices of your immediate community, you should know the basic principles for correct table setting, for service, and for your own behavior. It is well to remember that very often special local preferences for a certain form of table setting or for a variation in service comes to seem, locally, the only correct usage. Most Southerners would be quite unwilling to serve a formal dinner without hot bread and butter, though according to generally accepted usage butter is not part of a formal-dinner menu. In some localities a bread-and-butter plate is placed above and to the right of the knife rather than in the more usual position, above and to the left of the forks.

Your problem as a guest is to conform to the customs of your hostess no matter what they are. As a hostess you should know the customs generally recognized throughout the country as correct as well as those of your community. Learning to set a table correctly is a good way to begin.

Table Setting

You already know in general how a table should be set for any meal. A certain pattern of arrangement of china, silver, and glass has come to be considered correct because it is practical. A properly set table has appropriate linens (see pages 321–322) and provides the necessary equipment arranged in a convenient and attractive manner.

Laying Individual Covers

The space for each person, including the silver, glassware, china, and napkin, is called the cover. In setting your table you should allow from 20 to 24 inches for each person and mark the center of the space with a plate placed 1 inch from the edge of the table.

Whatever the degree of formality, the covers are laid in the same way.

At the left of each place the forks are laid tines up, with the handles toward the edge of the table. If a dessert is to be pie or anything else to be eaten with a fork, the dessert fork is the one laid nearest the plate. If salad is to be served as a separate course, a salad fork is laid to the left of the dessert fork. The fork for a meat course is laid to the left of the salad or dessert fork. The napkin is usually placed to the left of the forks.

At the right of the place setting and nearest the plate, the meat knife is laid with the cutting edge toward the plate. Spoons are laid to the right of the knife. If soup is

A place setting for luncheon or dinner when a beverage is served with the meal · Notice the position of the bread-and-butter plate and the salad plate. This type of setting is especially desirable for families without servants

served, a soup spoon is laid to the extreme right of the meat knife. Some hostesses use both a dessert fork and a dessert spoon for such dishes as soufflés or ice cream with cake.

All flat silver is laid 1 inch from the edge of the table. The placing of the bread-and-butter plate and the plate for a salad to be eaten with the main course is shown in the picture on page 318. The bread-and-butter knife may be laid across the plate either parallel to the edge of the table or at right angles to it.

Butter or margarine and a roll or slice of bread are put in place just before the family is summoned. The glass for water is placed above the meat knife. Slightly to its right stands any other glass, such as one for milk. Both water and milk should be poured just before the first course is placed on the table.

Arranging Additional Equipment

We are accustomed to somewhat typical patterns in breakfast, luncheon, and dinner menus. For serving the foods of these menus certain equipment is needed.

For *breakfast* a hot beverage (coffee or cocoa) is served by the hostess. It is placed at the right of her cover, with the handle of the pot parallel to her silver. Cups and saucers are placed above her cover, singly or stacked two together. Cream and sugar should be placed to the right of the cups. Fruit is served on a small plate placed on each individual breakfast plate. If uncooked cereal is served, it is placed above the breakfast plate. A dish of marmalade or jelly should have a spoon placed beside it, parallel to silver at the covers. A saltcellar and pepper pot, if they are needed for the breakfast, should be placed between each two persons. A tray of additional breadstuff may be placed on the table. A pitcher of water may stand on a side table or buffet.

Luncheon and *dinner* menus require more equipment than breakfasts. Salad plates are placed as part of the cover, at the left of the napkin. Space should be left above the host's cover for the platter of meat. A carving fork is at the left; the knife and knife rest are at the right. Placement of vegetable dishes or gravy boat will depend on how the

314

A dinner cover · Table appointments, correctly chosen and arranged, although inexpensive, may be as beautiful and harmonious as this dinner cover

food is to be served. A gravy ladle and spoons for serving vegetables should be placed beside the dish or at the right of the person who is to use them. Pickles or a relish should have a pickle fork or a spoon laid beside them. For convenience, extra bread, water, and other foods may be on the table as they are for breakfast.

When you have finished setting the table, look it over carefully. Make sure the necessary pieces of silver are correctly laid at each place. Review the menu to check the service items. Your next duty is to find out whether coffee is being served and to set the tray, fill the cream pitcher, measure coffee and water into the coffee maker and place it where you or another person can start it at the proper time.

Types of Table Service

Three recognized forms of table service which you should understand are the less formal service without servants, American service, and European service. In these servantless days the first is most important.

Service without Servants

Those who believe that the pleasure of eating together is heightened by courteous table manners and lively talk sometimes regret that, without a waitress, some member of the family must occasionally leave the table to take food and plates away or to bring in food and fresh plates for a new course. However, many families who enjoy gay conversation with their meals have found a certain freedom in being by themselves. They can linger at the table enjoying conversation without feeling inconsiderate since no servant is kept from completing her work. Each family in managing its table service must devise some plan of cooperation for the necessary tasks. A definite assignment of duties will prevent discussion as to who shall do what. If each member understands and accepts his responsibility, each task can be

315

Filling the water glass just before calling the family to dinner

Your father's holding of the chair for your mother (she sits down in it from the left), and your brother's seating of his sister give a gracious air to the beginning of the meal. If your table has been properly set, the meat dish is at your father's place, and a stack of hot plates is before him. Probably the vegetable dishes are also at his place because serving all the food at one time lessens the complications of passing hot dishes. This system is especially efficient if a hot beverage, to be served by your mother, accompanies the meal. Some families vary this routine by having the daughter serve one vegetable and the son the other; still others pass the vegetable dishes from one person to another.

Another set of duties, which might well fall to the son, consists in keeping water glasses filled and passing bread as needed. When the meat course is over, he may clear the table, removing the meat dish, then the vegetable dishes, and finally the dinner plates and bread-and-butter plates. He removes plates—his mother's first, his own last—by taking a dinner plate in one hand and a bread-and-butter plate in the other. Plates may be placed quietly, one on the other, on the buffet, serving table, or in the kitchen, but should not be stacked at the table. If there is no separate salad course, the saltcellar and pepper pot are removed after the plates. For practice in correct usage a small tray may be used on which the saltcellars and pepper pots are placed. At this point the table should be brushed free of crumbs. Then the plates for dessert are brought in. If the mother is to serve the dessert, the dessert plates are placed before her and the dessert brought in. If dessert portions are ready in the kitchen, perhaps chilling in the refrigerator, they may be brought in two at a time, the mother being served first. If coffee is to be served with

performed satisfactorily. In some families such duties are performed in rotation, one week by one member, the next by another. The main responsibility of preparing the meal usually falls upon the mother. A good rule is that the person who has cooked the dinner does not leave the table until the end of the meal. On Saturday night or Sunday night, when a daughter or a son may have been the cook, the rule remains a good one. In dividing the tasks, the daughter may take over the duties of setting the table. She may place a pat of butter and a roll or piece of bread on each bread-and-butter plate, and bring the food for the first course to the table. If salad is served with the dinner course, she may place it on the table too. It is your mother's privilege to invite the family to the table.

When the family comes into the dining room, certain courtesies may be observed.

dessert, it is poured by the mother. The daughter, who started the coffee just before she placed the salad on the table, brings the coffee. If the family prefers coffee served in the living room after dessert, the daughter will have set the coffee tray when she set the table. After helping to carry the dessert dishes to the kitchen, she will take the pitcher of cream from the refrigerator, fill the coffeepot, and carry the tray to the living room and place it before her mother.

Each family must solve for itself the problem of who does the dishes. This duty usually will be performed by young people. Those families who do not possess an electric dishwasher can develop their own time-saving methods. Efficiency here, as in so many household tasks, gives pleasure and provides more time for leisure.

There are three fine advantages to the scheme outlined here. The first is that no one person is overburdened, not even the hostess; the second, that no serious interruption to fun and eating occurs; and the third, that in homes where this or a similar plan is followed daily, the most impressive guest causes no change of operation and creates no confusion.

American Service

This service is much like the one you have just studied except that it is carried on with the help of a waitress. She stands beside the host and, as he carves and serves, she takes each plate to the person he indicates. She sees that glasses are kept filled, passes bread, jelly, or relishes, clears each course, and brings the new one. When the family leaves the table, if coffee is served in the living room, she brings the coffee tray to the mistress of the house and sets it on a table before her. Those who wish to learn how very formal this type of service may become are referred to standard works on etiquette.

Many American families put the food on the table in serving dishes just after everyone is seated. Each person serves himself when the food is passed to him

Ginn, (Frank D. Lucas)

A table correctly set for luncheon · Neatness of arrangement and sparkling appointments are highlighted in this inviting luncheon table

European Service

You may attend a formal dinner served in a hotel for a special occasion, such as the wedding of a sister or friend. Your high-school banquet will be formal. Such dinners have menus including several courses. They are usually served in hotels, restaurants, or clubs, or in those houses equipped to entertain on a lavish scale. A dinner of this extreme formality requires an elaborate table setting, the correct seating of guests (the most important woman at the host's right, the most important man at the right of the hostess), and correct service at the table. Several waiters or waitresses are necessary.

The menu to be served in this formal fashion determines the table appointments, the laying of the cover, and the service of the dinner.

A formal dinner always has a soup course, always fish or sea food, always hot meat with vegetables as main course, a salad, a dessert, little cakes (petits fours), and demitasse.

A FORMAL-DINNER MENU

Grapefruit in Shell

Bouillon

Broiled Fish

Roast Turkey

Potatoes Rissole   Cranberry Mold

Head-Lettuce Salad   Roquefort Dressing

Pineapple Torte

Petits Fours   Cheese and Crackers

Mints   Almonds

Demitasse

If a damask cloth is used, the table is covered with a soft, thick, cotton or felt silence cloth or a silence board. A lace cloth or one

318

A table correctly set for a festive but not rigidly formal dinner

with open embroidery or lace inserts is used on a bare table. In the exact center is a centerpiece, simple or elaborate, usually flowers. Candlesticks or candelabra, if used, are arranged halfway between the centerpiece and the place settings of the host and hostess. Symmetrically placed between the candlesticks are dishes of decorative candies, cakes, or small fruits. If place mats and runners or doilies are used instead of a cloth, they should be spaced evenly with their edges parallel to the edge of the table.

Each cover is laid with extreme care. A service plate marks the position of each person. On this plate the napkin is laid. From the time the table is set until it is cleared for dessert no place is left without a plate. Flat silver is laid in the usual way (see the picture above), except that there may be additional pieces. At the left of each plate is the salad fork, then the meat fork, and last the fish fork. The salad knife is to the right of the plate. If no salad knife is necessary, the knife nearest the plate is the meat knife, and next, the fish knife, the edge of each toward the plate. (Not more than three forks and knives are placed on the table before the meal, though others may be put on the table during dinner.) Next to the fish knife is the soup spoon, then the oyster fork or grapefruit spoon.

The first course, whether fruit or fish cocktail, is served on its individual plate, which is set on the service plate. In the course serving soup, the soup plate is also set on the service plate. When the soup is removed, the service plate is replaced by the one for fish. Even if the fish is to come in ready served on individual plates, there must be a clean plate put down first. It is taken away

319

when the fish on its plate is put in place. This rule is inflexible, and without three or four waiters it can delay a dinner seriously. In this type of service no food, except candy or nuts (which are decorative), is ever put on the table. Meats are carved in the kitchen and passed to the guests. For a large formal dinner, since one platter of the meat or one dish of a vegetable would be inadequate, several must be used. As one dish generally serves no more than six persons, more than one waiter is required to pass several dishes at the same time for prompt service. All foods, including accompaniments, are served by the waiter from the left. Second helpings are never offered at a formal dinner. Plates may be removed from either left or right. With several courses to be served in this fashion, carrying the formal dinner through

to coffee in the drawing room involves much detailed knowledge. Complete discussion of correct procedure may be found in any standard book of etiquette.

Though formal dinners with European service may seem complicated, as a guest you need have no serious misgivings. You have learned correct behavior in more simple situations, and assisting with the serving of meals at home has given you poise. A gracious manner in response to service, and alert watchfulness of your more experienced elders will see you through. After all, the number of courses in a meal, or the number of servants required, is of little importance. The success of the occasion depends on each guest's contribution to the general conversation and his quiet, courteous enjoyment of gracious hospitality.

Table Appointments

Among the prized possessions of many households are the linens, silver, glassware, and china with which an attractive table may be set. Heirloom table appointments of much beauty are treasured for generations and used proudly; new "patterns" are selected with the idea that they will be passed

on to children and grandchildren. Certain patterns have become famous for their beauty, which increases with time and use.

Knowing the conventions which surround table setting is important to gracious living. Whether one uses grandmother's linens and silver or modern appointments of one's own

Fostoria Glass Company

Table set for dinner for the first course of fruit cocktail

Space-saving table · This space-saving setting is pleasing in informal balance and simplicity

choosing, the principles are the same. The table must present a neat, orderly appearance and must sparkle with cleanliness. All appointments should be spaced so that there will be no crowding and arranged to give an effect of order and balance. Tables are set according to the type of service, formal or informal, and the specific foods to be served. Formality is increased by choosing the silver, glassware, and china which can be arranged best against one's finest table linen. The table setting should be checked critically for completeness and for beauty of appearance.

Linens

In selecting linens, try to see them as a practical and appropriate background for other table appointments. Important considerations are cost, durability, and ease in laundering.

For an attractive table, the cloth, doilies, or place mats should harmonize with other appointments. A plain cloth or mats are good with patterned china; undecorated china may gain distinction against a cloth or mat of interesting design and color.

Tables set for informal breakfasts, luncheons, or dinners may be attractive in a wide variety of ways. There are no restrictions except good taste in combining color, line, and texture. The new plastics, synthetics, paper, cork, straw, reeds, and oilcloth are practical because of their moderate cost and ease in care. They are all available in attractive colors and designs. While cottons and linens require more care, they are often lovely enough to offset this disadvantage.

Place mats are from 16 to 18 inches in length and from 12 to 14 inches in width. Their compact and uniform groupings add to the attractiveness of a table. Among the informal cloths, the new lintless cottons, ranging from the gay checks, plaids, and florals to the more dignified laces, are all within the modest budget. New weaves and fibers, such as metallic threads, add interest.

321

Breakfast or bridge cloths are 36 inches square or 45 by 64 inches; luncheon cloths, 50 or 54 inches square or 54 by 60 or 72 inches; dinner cloths, 54 by 72 or 90 inches. The length of the table determines the size of the cloth to be used. A dinner cloth should hang over the ends of the table from 8 to 10 inches and on the sides from 6 to 8 inches. A 3-yard cloth provides cover space for six to eight persons. In these days such cloths are used chiefly on festive occasions.

Napkins vary in size from 8 to 27 inches square with the party, or tea, napkin the smallest and the dinner napkin the largest. Finer cloths come with matching napkins, the number depending on the size of the cloth. Bridge sets come with four napkins; luncheon sets, with four or six. In color, napkins may match or contrast with the cloth or mats. Napkins are sometimes bought separately. Paper napkins may be used for breakfast and luncheon family meals. Table linens must be perfectly clean and laid with precision. The silence cloth or felt mats should fit the table exactly. Tiles or cloth-covered pads should be placed under hot dishes which might mar a bare table. Many table surfaces, however, resist marring.

Silverware

Table silver includes flatware, such as knives, forks, spoons, and butter spreaders; and hollow ware, such as pitchers, platters, bowls, and tea and coffee services. Silver pieces may be sterling, plated, or stainless steel.

A table carefully set for a family dinner promotes ease and pleasure in dining

Corning Glass Works

The amount of silverware needed in a household depends on the size of the family and on the entertaining done. Place settings of six pieces in the required number are adequate for most needs. Fewer settings will often do since some pieces are appropriate for more than one purpose: luncheon forks may be used as salad forks; dessert spoons will serve for soup or cereal; and luncheon knives and forks are acceptable for all occasions except the strictly formal dinner. Stainless steel offers variety in informal table setting; some patterns have attractive colored plastic or bone handles.

Flatware may be purchased by the piece, by the place setting, or by the set. Place settings at a stated price may be best for sterling even though one may wish additional teaspoons, butter knife, gravy ladle, and other pieces. Stainless-steel flatware may be purchased in sets or by the piece. Plated ware is usually sold in sets. Because of its long life and constant use, silver should be carefully chosen for beauty and practicality. Whether the pattern is to be ornate or simple depends upon taste, which dictates also the choice of linens, glassware, and china. Artistically good patterns remain acceptable always; one does not tire of them, and they will always contribute to the beauty of a well-set table. However, beauty in flatware is not enough. Knives, forks, and spoons should be tested in the hand for balance and proportion. Try a place setting with other table appointments to observe the effect. Observe the pieces in proportion to themselves and in relation to each other. Do you like the degree of simplicity or ornateness? Do you like the bright finish or would a more mellow tone give longer satisfaction? If you choose well, your flatware will give pleasure each time you set the table and will grow more beautiful with use and care.

Glassware

The many handsome varieties available make the selection of glassware an interesting venture. Tumblers are desirable for everyday use; goblets suggest more formality. Sets of six or eight are a usual requirement; if you entertain on a larger scale, you will need more. The following pieces of glassware are most useful:

GLASSWARE	
PIECES	APPROXIMATE CAPACITY (ounces)
Water glasses or goblets......	9
Glasses for iced beverages....	12
Glasses for juices............	5
Additional sherbet and other glasses according to need...	5

You may find glass plates which match your tumblers and are an excellent size for a salad main dish for a luncheon. Often there are odd glass pieces of attractive design which can be used for pickles, jam, or other accompaniments; there may be charming, individual salts and peppers. The possibilities in inexpensive glass are equal to most needs and to quite exacting taste.

China, Earthenware, and Pottery

The dishes from which one eats daily should be selected for quality and for beauty of design and color. There is more lasting satisfaction in the softer tones and less ornate patterns. Much of the attractive china in our shops is made in England or in America. Among the most beautiful wares are English Royal Doulton, Spode, Minton, and Wedgewood; and American Syracuse, Lennox, and

323

Castleton. Haviland, first made in France, is now produced in America. Though these are the most famous makes of china, there are many other distinctive types. They are less expensive and patterns range from traditional ones to the modern shapes and designs which harmonize with modern furnishings. In the more informal living of many families earthenware or pottery are often preferred. Exotic Italian and Mexican pottery is especially effective against simple, contrasting backgrounds.

California has developed beautiful pottery, as have several other states. American pottery, deeply glazed and durable, is really semivitreous ware or earthenware. It is a general favorite as an accessory set for informal serving. The simple structural design and rich colors of pottery make for very effective table settings. Whatever best suits one's budget and taste, it will be possible to choose colors, shapes, and patterns that will give lasting pleasure.

American dinnerware is of three general types: vitrified china (or porcelain ware), semivitreous ware (or earthenware), and pottery. Of all the wares, china is the most delicate. The vitrifying process through which it goes in glazing makes china nonporous and nonabsorbent all the way through, giving it a fine, fragile, translucent quality. Famous makers of china are proud of their art in devising lovely shapes and patterns, and also of their craft in producing them. Such china is very expensive. Many families that can afford this china prefer, for everyday use, less expensive kinds which can be easily replaced.

Earthenware is made differently from china. Although about the same mixture of minerals is used, the clay is molded into thicker shapes and fired at lower temperatures. Earthenware is durable and will stand hard wear. A deep glaze conceals the pores and adds to its attractiveness.

Pottery is made from coarsely-sieved clays. The dishes are opaque and somewhat porous because they are fired at a lower heat even than earthenware. Pottery is often gay in color and decoration.

Modern living, with breakfast in the kitchen, summer luncheon on the porch, picnics, barbecues, and clambakes, encourages the use of paper or plastic dishes. Inexpensive, light, and durable, these wares can be had in colors from pastel to vivid and in great variety of design. Plastic dishes are practical for very young children. Paper and plastic are appropriate, however, only for very informal serving.

China should be chosen to harmonize with the home furnishings. If the tone of one's home furnishings is modern, china that is modern in design should be chosen. Chinaware may be purchased by the piece, in place settings, or in sets. Made-up sets of china that are complete with place settings for six, eight, or twelve persons are more economical. An open-stock pattern permits you to replace pieces. In diameter the dinner plate is 9 to 10 inches; the luncheon plate, 8 to 9 inches; the dessert or bridge plate, 7 to 8 inches; the salad plate, 7 inches; and the bread-and-butter plate, 6 inches. A place setting includes a dinner and a luncheon plate, a salad plate, a bread-and-butter plate, a cup and saucer, and perhaps a soup plate or cup and a small vegetable dish. Additional dishes are platters for meat, bowls for vegetables, a sugar bowl and cream pitcher, and perhaps a gravy boat. Pitchers should always be tested to make sure that they pour properly. Handles on cups, sugar bowls, and pitchers should be easy to grasp. Every piece should be examined to make sure that it is perfect. Decide whether or

324

not the shapes are easy to clean—inacessible crevices can be very annoying. It is safer to choose a basic set of pottery, earthenware, or china that you have seen displayed as a table setting, for the total effect may be quite different from that of single pieces. Such a display may reveal overornamentation, too vivid color, or poor proportion that were not noticeable in the separate pieces. Comparison of various sets so displayed will make a wise choice easier and surer.

While a basic set of the same pattern is desirable, not all the china need match. Pitchers of different pattern and material can make an attractive contrast; they may be had of pottery, china, glass, copperware, brass, pewter, and silver, in many shapes and color. Streamlined coffee makers and oven dishes set in gleaming chromium may be brought from the kitchen to add beauty to the table. Salad may be served in wooden bowls or on Mexican-glass plates. Dessert plates are often different from those of the main meal. A beautiful china tea or coffee service may be found whose colors blend well with those of the basic set or add a note of contrast to it.

Those who like unique small pieces in pottery, china, or glass will choose interesting dishes for relishes, nuts, candies, and other accompaniments. Choosing "occasional china" requires special skill, a visual memory of lines and colors in the basic set, and an imagination which sees the new piece placed in relation to others for harmony or contrast.

Table Decoration

Table decorations add much beauty and interest to a well-set table. Centerpieces of candles and flowers or fruit make a center of interest for the table design, bringing out color and line in other appointments. Arranged with artistry, centerpieces may have great beauty in themselves. Your family is probably already accustomed to centerpieces for guest tables, but have you tried them for everyday. A breakfast table is more attractive for a few simple flowers, a green plant in a copper urn, or just a useful Lazy Susan as a centerpiece. A colorful bowl of fruit is also attractive. Any family meal, in kitchen or dinette, on the porch or in the dining room, will acquire a new interest from your efforts at decoration and you will enjoy the pleased surprise of your family. A wide variety of materials may be easily secured at little or no cost and can be combined effectively; graceful branches, dried grasses and weeds, bright-colored berries, odd shapes in seed pods, cones, gourds, and even in vegetables. Most of these are best against backgrounds of simple wood, pottery, or copper. If you have an attractive tray, bowl, or vase, think what can be done with color contrasts and interesting effects with shape and line. Vary your centerpiece, planning it to harmonize with the season, the meal, and table appointments. Taking complete charge of table setting, including decoration, will give you interesting experience and great pleasure.

For special occasions, some decorations are probably traditional in your home; others can develop in delightful accidental fashion. You may enjoy decorating the Thanksgiving, Christmas, or Easter table as you have known it since childhood; or you may prefer to look about for something different. Place your mother's poinsettia on her new round hammered aluminum tray; try your red-skirted choirboy figurines around the rim with sprigs of evergreen between them—and you have an excellent, colorful centerpiece for the Christmas dinner table. Every holiday season has its characteristic colors and symbols. Work with what you have—and that includes your imagination. Your mother will welcome your ideas and you will be sharing in homemaking.

Formal teas, receptions, wedding breakfasts, banquets, and all formal dinners derive part of their tone from the beauty and dignity of the table decorations. There are a few conventions that must be observed, such as the severe simplicity of the white place cards, but beyond these there is ample opportunity for variety in table appointments and decorations. If trays are used, they are of silver, pewter, aluminum, or chrome. Containers for flowers are of china, crystal, or metal. The flowers should be selected with great care for their lightness of fragrance and beauty of color and form. They may be arranged for interesting variety in heights and shapes and for beautiful contrasts of color. Candles for very formal tables are usually white or ivory, though for formal teas delicately tinted candles may be used in harmony with flowers and other appointments. Deeper-toned colors are in keeping with the more vivid decorations of tables for Christmas, Easter, St. Patrick's Day, the Fourth of July, and Thanksgiving. Different degrees of formality are achieved through the depth of color tones in table appointments and decorations, the more delicate tones suggesting more formal occasions.

To achieve satisfactory table decoration certain practical considerations should be met:

1. Decorations should be simple and economical. Seasonal material should be used: garden flowers, wheat or barley stalks, bittersweet, holly—according to the time of year.

2. Flowers with heavy fragrance should be avoided as pronounced fragrance detracts from food aroma. Some guests are annoyed by pollen-laden flowers.

3. Decorations should be arranged to take up less than one-third of the table.

4. Table centerpieces should be low (not more than 10 inches above the table) so that they will not obstruct the guests' view. (Check by sitting down at the table.) Buffet arrangements may be taller.

5. Candles must be tall enough for the flame to be above eye level, 14 to 16 inches depending on the holder. If no other light is used, one candle to each person will be needed. Candles should be chilled before using.

6. Table decorations should not be top-heavy or unsteady.

7. The container for flowers must be functional: it should hold enough water to be firm and steady, have a wide mouth, and be of correct size and shape. Flower holders of glass, clay, or heavy wire add stability to the arrangement.

8. A casserole or chafing dish, a birthday or wedding cake, or special desserts, decorative in themselves, may serve as a centerpiece.

Observing the principles of balance, proportion, and rhythm will enable you to achieve the desired decorative effect. With practice your artistic sense will become more dependable and you will work with more confidence, knowing that the results will be appropriate. Refer to art books and current literature for suggestions on flower arrangement and the use of figurines or other ceramic pieces in table decoration. The careful setting of the table with a touch of decoration should be a practice of everyday. A more elaborately appointed table adds to the pleasure and festivity of special occasions.

326

Table Etiquette

Our table customs, which have been in existence for a long time, are common-sense ways of doing things. They also add ease and grace to eating. Knowing correct conduct at the table gives poise; not knowing causes insecurity and embarrassment. The practice of correct conduct at all meals will establish habits which will enable you fully to enjoy party refreshments, school banquets, and similar social occasions.

Everyone should come to the table on time and appropriately dressed. Hands should be clean and hair arranged. Many people ask a blessing before eating, after which there should be a brief pause before the meal begins. If a blessing is asked aloud, a few seconds should elapse before conversation is opened. During the meal pleasant conversation should be carried on.

No one should begin eating until all have been served and the hostess begins to eat. In informal meals everyone at the table shares the responsibility of serving the others. Persons should be asked to help themselves to jelly and other accompaniments, and to pass them. They may politely ask that food be passed to them. No person should help himself first unless requested to do so. It is poor taste for anyone to make himself conspicuous while eating: food should be chewed slowly, with the lips closed; eagerness to talk should be curbed when there is food in the mouth. Scattering crumbs or bits of food is an untidy habit; neatness in eating is expected of everyone. Comments on food at the table are out of order; there should be no mention of disliked foods. Your appreciation of food is shown by your enjoyment of it; hostesses prefer a simple thank-you to overpraise.

Usually no one should leave the table until the hostess rises to indicate that the meal is ended; very young children should, however, be permitted to leave. As all rise, a gentleman may assist a lady by pulling her chair out of the way. On taking leave of your hostess, you might say, "This has been so very pleasant; thank you for inviting me."

All young people welcome opportunities to learn and practice socially-correct procedures. There are accepted practices to be mastered if one is to appear well mannered at the table. Let us follow through a meal and observe the suggestions for handling situations which may arise.

Being Seated

Seating oneself at the dining table is easy if the chairs are directly in front of the cover and the chair seat is even with the edge of the table. It should not be necessary to pull the chair back or make adjustments. To avoid confusion, everyone sits down from the left and arises from the right side of the chair. You should sit back in the chair, erect but at ease, with elbows off the table. When the hands are not being used, they should be kept in the lap. The feet should rest comfortably on the floor.

The hostess sits at the head of the table. If another is helping to serve, the hostess will probably want to sit where she can direct the service. The host sits opposite the hostess. For convenience, the hostess' helper usually sits on her left. For informal meals guests are seated where they will be most comfortable. Formal seating is governed by strict rules, which may be found in standard books of etiquette. Frequent reference to these will assure confidence and poise.

Correct use of knife and fork in cutting · Notice the position of the two forefingers

Correct use of the fork in eating cake

Correct use of the spoon in eating soup · Notice that the spoon is pushed away from the person toward the back of the soup plate

Using the Table Napkin

The napkin serves to protect clothing. It is used sparingly to blot the lips during a meal. Using a napkin correctly shows good taste. A guest waits for the hostess to unfold her napkin. A napkin that is to be used again by a family member is folded in the lap at the end of the meal and laid on the table, preferably to the left. A napkin used by a guest is laid on the table unfolded.

Using Silverware

In cutting meat the knife is held in the right hand with the thumb and the last three fingers on the handle. It is steadied with the forefinger on the back of the blade near the handle. Handle the fork like the knife. It is held in the left hand, braced by the forefinger well down on the handle with the tines kept down. Only one bite of meat should be cut at a time. For carrying the food to the mouth, the knife is laid across the plate and the fork transferred to the right hand. (Europeans keep the fork in the left hand, but transferring it to the right is the accepted American way.) Food is carried to the mouth with a fork or spoon. Each should be held in very much the same way that a pencil is held but at a different angle. In all situations where either a fork or a spoon would do, the fork is the better choice. Unless a butter knife is on the bread-and-butter plate, the dinner knife is used for buttering bread, a small piece at a time. The knife is always placed on the plate when not in use; it is never left leaning against a plate with the handle resting on the table. Spoons are never left in cups. Used silverware should not be laid on the tablecloth. When the meal is finished, place the knife and fork parallel across the plate, the knife on the upper side with the blade turned toward you and the fork in the middle of the

328

plate, tines turned up. Silverware should not be handled except as a tool for eating.

When You Are Serving

When it is necessary to leave the table to serve, place your napkin, partially folded, at the left of the cover, excuse yourself, and rise from the right of your chair. It is more convenient for the server to use the left hand in presenting a dish from the left of the guest. The right hand is used in filling glasses or cups which are on the right side of the guest. Carry the dish in such a way that your fingers do not extend over the rim. Approach the person to be served from the left, holding the serving dish low and close enough to be reached easily. A glass or cup should remain in its place on the table as it is refilled. A small napkin carried in the left hand may be used to catch drops of water from the pitcher. The server should never reach across a guest.

When everyone has finished a course, the dishes for that course should be removed. Platters and serving dishes are taken away first. Beginning with the hostess, or guest of honor, main-course dishes are removed from the left side with the left hand. Other covers are removed around the table beginning at the right of the hostess. If the hostess removes the dishes, she begins at her right and leaves her own until the last. One cover, including bread-and-butter plates, should be removed at a time. A tray may be used to remove saltcellars, pepper pots, relish dishes, and other small items. Only the glass, cup and saucer, and dessert silver should be left after the main course and salad course are cleared.

When You Are Served

Give yourself moderate helpings. Place accompaniments for meat on the dinner plate and eat them with a dinner fork. Butter, relishes, jellies, and marmalades go on the bread-and-butter plates. If these plates have not been provided, such foods may be placed on the side of the dinner plate. Individual nut cups are used occasionally, or nuts may be put on the salad plate and eaten at any time during the meal.

Olives, radishes, and celery are served in small pieces, taken and eaten with the fingers. Fingers may be used for other firm foods, such as shoestring potatoes, potato chips, and bread. If a serving utensil is provided on the dish, it should be used. Take crackers for soup with your fingers and place them either on the plate that holds the soup bowl or on the bread-and-butter plate. Crackers are eaten with the fingers; break large ones

Serving from the left

Jane and Steven Coons

329

in two, but it is unnecessary to break wafer-sized crackers.

In eating soup from a soup plate, dip the spoon away from you. Lift the spoon to the mouth rather than meet it halfway. When you have finished, return the soup spoon to the service plate or leave it on the soup plate.

Canapes or hors d'oeuvres served in the living room are considered finger foods; those served at the table are eaten with a fork. Raw oysters or clams are dipped into sauce with an oyster fork. If small bones of fish get into the mouth, they may be removed with the thumb and forefinger and placed on the plate. After a lobster shell has been cracked, it is held with the left hand and the meat removed with a fork. Chicken, spareribs, and other meats with bone should be eaten with a fork except on picnics, when they may be eaten by holding the bone in one hand. To eat corn on the cob, butter a small portion at a time and lift the corn to the mouth with one hand. Soft vegetables served in side dishes should be eaten with a spoon. Baked potatoes are eaten from the shell and the shell may be eaten if desired. French-fried potatoes should be transferred to the plate with a spoon and eaten with a fork.

Artichoke leaves are picked off one at a time with the fingers and dipped into an accompanying sauce; the edible part is then stripped off with the teeth. The remainder of the leaf is left on the side of the plate. The soft heart should be eaten with a fork. Head-lettuce salad may be cut with a knife.

Teaspoons served with a beverage are used for stirring and tasting. As soon as you have used the spoon, remove it from the cup and lay it on the saucer. If tongs are not provided for loaf sugar, use the fingers.

Bread should not be dipped into a beverage. It is permissible to put a small piece of

bread in the gravy on your plate. It is then eaten with a fork exactly like a piece of meat.

If both ice cream and cake are served on the same plate, eat both with a fork. Eat sundaes with a spoon, placing it on the service dish when finished. Frozen desserts should be eaten without dallying in the eating process. Tea cakes and cookies containing more than two or three bites should be broken in half. Pie should be eaten with a fork from tip to back including all the crust. Spoons used to eat desserts served in stemmed ware or in low dishes should be laid on the service plate.

A finger bowl may be brought in on a doily on the dessert plate with the dessert silver also on the plate. Each person places the doily and the finger bowl just behind the dessert plate and moves a spoon to the right of his plate and a fork to the left. For formal occasions finger bowls are brought in on a plate at the end of the meal as if they were another course. The tips of the fingers are dipped into the bowl, one hand at a time, and wiped on the napkin in the lap. When rich foods have been eaten, the lips may be touched by a moistened finger and blotted with the napkin.

When You Eat Out

Eating in a public place, such as a cafeteria, tearoom, restaurant, or hotel, in the dining car of a train, or in an airplane is an art requiring basic good manners and certain additional knowledge and skill. It is an adventure with many possibilities. You may not be able to eat Chinese food with chopsticks (though you probably will try) but you should be able to manage an infinite variety of foods, whether French, Spanish, German, Italian, Scandinavian, Mexican, or American. Your interest will grow as you eat foods unfamiliar to you and learn their names and something of the parts of the world from which they come.

Choosing Places to Eat—A host or hostess may plan a luncheon or dinner at a restaurant or hotel selected for its special food, service, or entertainment. Tables may be reserved and food ordered in advance for bridal breakfasts, birthday parties, and other occasions. Some restaurants cater to large private parties. Others have built up reputations for special types of service, such as Sunday buffets, afternoon teas, smörgåsbords, and many others. Unique foods are also a basis for choice. Different sections of America have their characteristic foods: the South, its fried chicken and spoon breads; New England, its clam chowder, brown bread and baked beans; the Southwest, its Mexican food, and Virginia, its baked hams. Any large American city will have restaurants featuring foods typical of several countries. A restaurant of high quality will serve fine food, prepared and served in immaculate surroundings. A reputable establishment will also offer expert management, furnish good entertainment, and cater to an orderly and appreciative clientele.

Conduct in Restaurants—At large parties gentlemen check their hats and coats; ladies may check their wraps or wear them into the dining room. If a husband and wife are host and hostess, the wife designates the seats for guests. The conduct is the same as for any formal meal. Couples or small groups wait at the entrance to be shown their table by the head waiter or waitress. The lady precedes the gentleman to the table and is seated by the head waiter or by her escort. She slips her wrap from her shoulders to the back of her chair, with the help of the waiter or her escort. She keeps her purse in her lap.

The lady indicates her choice of foods, and her escort orders for both. She should choose neither the least nor the most expensive foods, considering both her escort's pride and his purse. If he suggests a particular food she may accept graciously. Ordering à la carte (selecting each dish separately) is more expensive than table d'hôte ordering. The table d'hôte dinner is limited in some selections but is a complete meal for a stated price. A plate lunch, the least expensive of all, includes a beverage, but if salad or dessert is desired, they are ordered à la carte.

In the lull between ordering and the arrival of the food, look about and enjoy the atmosphere of the place, the decoration, the entertainment, and the people. An appreciative comment will interest your escort and start conversation. The waiter will bring the food, arrange it conveniently, and inquire about further needs. From here on through the meal, good manners, as described previously, will give you poise and please your escort. Keep the conversation lively but not loud. Boisterousness in public places is crude and the attention gained will be critical not only of you but of your home and family. Eat slowly but do not dawdle. If some special food has pleased you, express your appreciation to your escort. When the meal is finished, your escort will take care of the check, leave a tip for the waiter, and help you with your wrap. You will precede him to the door, which he or the head waiter will hold open for you.

Restaurant dining, either more or less formal, may be enjoyed with other couples or with a group of girls. The general conduct is the same, varying somewhat if you are a guest or a hostess, or going "Dutch treat." As hostess, you have the same responsibility for your guests as at home but must depend upon the cooperation of the waiter. Courtesy is important here, and unobtrusiveness should be practiced in making requests and settling practical details. Your conduct with your guests may be gay and informal, but the group should remember the rights of the other diners. Hilarity permissible in the home is undesirable in a public place where others are also seeking enjoyment. If you are at all alert, expressions on the faces of other customers will warn you if your fun is being carried too far. Don't risk humiliation; keep the tone of the party within the bounds of politeness. Knowing what not to do and what to do will, with experience, give you ease and assurance in your conduct outside your home.

¶ *Understanding:*

1. What are the characteristics of servantless, European, and American table service?

2. What factors determine how your table should be set?

3. What standard do you expect of a well-set table?

4. Diagram the correct arrangement of a cover when a knife is not needed; when a hot beverage is served; when both a bread-and-butter plate and a salad plate are used.

5. What guiding principles should you observe in choosing silver? glassware? china? linen?

6. When you are being served at the table, how should you ask for a second helping? How should you accept jelly? olives?

7. How should you leave the table when serving the dessert? when you have finished eating?

8. What table decorations are appropriate for breakfast?

¶ *Planning:*

1. Choose a type of table service appropriate for Sunday dinner at home. How should your table be set?

2. Visit a store where table linens are displayed and select a cloth of appropriate quality

and design for a breakfast table; for a luncheon table; for a dinner table.

3. Plan for the care of silver in your home. Present advantages of your plan.

4. Plan glassware for use with pottery; with porcelain; with Early American furnishings.

5. Plan the setting of a table for dinner so that no one need leave the table to serve: (*a*) with a host and hostess serving some of the foods; (*b*) with all of the food being served from the kitchen.

¶ *Practicing and Evaluating:*

1. Set a table for a specific type of meal service. Check for correct placement of appointments.

2. Select pictures of linen, silver, glassware, and china to harmonize in design and color. To what type of home furnishings are they best suited?

3. Demonstrate the setting of a table for a breakfast menu. Make the necessary changes for a luncheon menu; for a dinner menu.

4. Collect pictures of table-setting arrangements for luncheons. Score them for placement of appointments.

5. Follow accepted table-etiquette practices at your dining table. How was eating simplified? How was it made more enjoyable?

6. Assist with the serving of meals to a guest in your home. What practices in table etiquette did you observe?

7. Show how a table should be set for a formal luncheon where fruit, soup, meat, salad, and dessert are to be served.

¶ *Reading Further:*

ALLEN, BETTY, and BRIGGS, MITCHELL PIRIE, *Mind Your Manners.* J. B. Lippincott Company, New York.

HAUPT, ENID A., *The Seventeen Book of Etiquette and Entertaining*, David McKay Company, Inc., New York.

HERTZ, BARBARA VALENTINE, *Where Are Your Manners?* Science Research Associates, Inc., Chicago.

L. Willinger–Shostal

Entertaining

you will learn: How to be a gracious hostess;
How to entertain at home; How to entertain and how to act
when entertained at school

The purpose of entertaining is to provide a good time for your guests. Only if the hostess enjoys the party will the guests enjoy it. To ensure success, plan only such entertaining as will cause you no worry about expenses and no doubt about your ability to carry it through to completion successfully. Simple entertaining is usually more enjoyable for both hostess and guests than more elaborate forms. Often you will have to depend on the casual help of friends among your guests or perhaps on that of your younger sister. Only if it is understood that you will return the favor when your sister entertains her friends, will you be able to recruit this help more than once.

333

When you do your first entertaining, you will be grateful for all the years during which your parents have insisted that good manners are to be used everyday. By now the rules of common courtesy are so thoroughly a part of your habits that they are you, and no special ones need be practiced. The most successful hostess is the one who has the most consideration for her guests. She sees that each is having a good time, and draws into conversation anyone who seems not at the moment engaged. A simple question is all that is needed: "Jane, I don't believe Sarah has heard about your trip to Oakland," or "Bob, can't you tell us why we're not going to play Morristown this year?"

A happy hostess does not worry when some trifling thing goes wrong; she corrects it herself quietly or asks one of her assistant hostesses to manage it. Suppose a guest spills chocolate or salad. Your first concern is to spare her feelings and to prevent attention from centering upon the mishap. Smile reassuringly and say, "Let me get you a fresh plate and napkin," or possibly, if the disaster has soiled her clothing, "Let me help you get rid of this spot." Then take the guest to another room and give what help you can. Do not bewail the accident or say that it was your fault. You realize her embarrassment and know that the quickest way to overcome it is to say little and act as if it was unimportant. Returning to the other guests quickly, keep a watchful eye for her return and make sure that she is drawn again into the fun.

Entertaining at Home

Buffet Parties

Buffet parties offer a pleasant informal way to entertain. They are convenient for entertaining a number of guests at a Saturday- or Sunday-night supper get-together. A buffet supper may precede a theater party or follow a football game or skiing, skating, or swimming. Invitations may be given by telephone or informal note. Whether written or oral, invitations for informal parties have no set form; in fact, they are better for originality. Whatever their form, they should include the time, place, and type of entertainment. If your party is a large formal one, consult a standard book of etiquette for invitation forms. Practically all the work for buffet parties can be completed before the first guest arrives. As a youthful hostess, you will have the advantage of your mother's help in preparation, but you should assume as much as possible of the work. With your mother you can decide on the menu. A buffet can be very elaborate, but you will have a better time if yours is made simple enough not to tire you and your mother and yet festive enough to give a party feeling. Your guests must be made as comfortable as possible while they eat, sitting or standing, in the living room. You will add to their comfort if you provide small tables. These should be placed so that they fit in with the furnishings in the room. The coffee table in front of the divan will care for several guests. Card tables covered with luncheon cloths, while not so conducive to group conversation, are better than the risk of accidents while eating.

Planning the Menu—The foods you serve at a buffet party must be easy to eat in the

334

fingers or with fork or spoon. You and your friends will enjoy one hot, hearty food. Hot chili con carne, an inexpensive and satisfying dish, may be served with rounds of brown bread spread with butter. Sandwiches should be cut small to please the girls, but there should be enough of them to satisfy masculine appetites.

A casserole or creamed dish of diced chicken with mushrooms, peas, and potatoes makes a delicious and substantial hot dish. With it serve tiny hot biscuits, split, buttered, and put together. Canned tuna fish or crab meat, creamed or in casserole, is appropriate, but because some people do not care for fish, this choice will probably necessitate a second hot dish, perhaps the hot chili con carne. Bread-and-butter sandwiches will supplement both dishes equally well. If you wish to include a substantial cold dish, hard-boiled eggs with a sharply flavored stuffing will satisfy most tastes. A vegetable salad may be included in the menu. Dessert may be pie, any easy-to-eat pudding, or cut-up fruit. For beverages you might serve a milk shake or, in cold weather, hot chocolate.

Setting the Buffet Table—When you have decided on the menu and learned how many guests to expect, you can plan how to arrange the table. Unless the dining room is very large, it may be well to remove all the chairs and push the table against a wall. When it is not convenient to move the table, you simply arrange the dishes so that they are accessible, some from one side, some from the other. Often the buffet table may be left uncovered, or a bright cover may be used. Many attractive centerpieces can be arranged. Seasonal flowers, fruits, candles, or holiday scenes are attractive. You may wish to emphasize the occasion for which the buffet is planned. Ribbons of school colors, football arrangements, or pennants make decorative centerpieces.

If you are serving a hot beverage, place the equipment on a tray at one end of the table or on a side table. Heavier foods, such as soup or a casserole, are placed at the other end of the table. Beside each main dish you will need a stack of plates and napkins with the proper silverware. The silverware is arranged in neat rows. Vegetables, salads, and relishes are placed near the center of the table. The dessert may be served from the buffet table or passed to the guests from trays.

Approximately five minutes before the guests arrive, you place the food and beverages on the table. The main dish may be served in a chafing dish or a casserole warmed by candles or canned-heat burners; light the warming candles or turn on the electric hot plates and go to greet your guests.

Acting as Hostess—In small houses, there is considerable advantage if not all guests arrive at the same time. After perhaps a third of your guests are present, you suggest that they come into the dining room. "Won't you help yourselves?" may be sufficient invitation when they reach the buffet. If you have some friends who are shy, you may help them select foods. Sometimes other groups become so delighted in their conversation that they block the way of late comers. It is then your duty as a hostess to ask them, "Won't you take your plates into the living room?" You may wish to show a guest a good place to set his plate. If this is the first buffet party your crowd has attended, many will need your tactful guidance. You should occasionally go into the dining room, both to keep the guests circulating and to find out whether more food or beverages should be brought in. A sister or a friend may help out in such matters. When guests have finished one course, they may bring their plates back

A buffet dinner · In this arrangement, used for an Easter party, part of a ham was sliced carefully and the slices replaced to look as if the ham had not been cut. You can use any other ideas that seem desirable in adapting your plans to a Hallowe'en, Christmas, or Valentine party

to the dining room. There should be a table or some other surface on which these dishes may be placed. After dessert has been eaten, china, glassware, and silver may be brought to the dining room by the guests or collected by the assistant hostess, and removed to the kitchen. As hostess you make it easy and pleasant for each guest to enjoy your hospitality and to have fun with other guests. You may be surprised to find that many of your friends will follow your lead, providing enjoyable buffet parties.

Teas

Teas or coffees are gracious ways to show hospitality to friends. Teas may be formal or informal occasions. When a large number of guests is to be entertained, a club or hotel may afford the needed space as well as provide the refreshments. Tea time is from three to five o'clock any afternoon. Coffee time is in the morning or evening. Coffees are like teas except that usually they are less formal.

Tea Foods—Tea foods must be dainty, attractive, and readily eaten with the fingers. The beverages need not always be tea. Cocoa, frappé of carbonated water and sherbet, fruit punch, and iced or hot coffee are appropriate. There are endless varieties of attractive and economical tea sandwiches that you can make. The many kinds of possible breads, fillings, and garnishes are discussed in Chapter 12. Tea cakes and cookies lend further variety to the tea menu. You will enjoy collecting recipes and preparing interesting combinations for desired flavors and color effects. Different kinds of sweets add interest to tea tables. Sometimes candies are placed around the room in small dishes. Many persons prefer candies that are home-made. It may be economical to shell and salt nuts yourself if there is sufficient time (see the Cookbook for recipes).

Tea foods should not require forks or spreaders. The foods should be served in small portions since the purpose of the tea is social and the refreshments are not meant to take the place of a meal. However, if men or boys are invited to the tea, a substantial food should be served. Men prefer nut-bread sandwiches or hot biscuits with ham rather than tiny rounds of bread with a thin tomato slice and a bit of mayonnaise.

Arranging the Tea Table—Arranging a tea table attractively is fun for the hostess. Spotless linen, gleaming china, bright silver, tall candles, and flowers make a tea table dainty and beautiful. A variety of white or pastel cloths are suitable — lace, embroidered organdy or organdy with lace insets, syn-thetic fibers with metallic threads or satin weaves, and damask. Special table acces-sories are not necessary if articles on hand are used to advantage. A growing plant can be as pretty on a tea table as cut flowers. Autumn leaves make effective decoration. Further suggestions are made in the section on table decorating (pages 325–326). Resourceful-ness, with knowledge of how to use color and line, will provide effective arrangements.

A tray for the tea service is placed at one end of the table, directly in front of the person who has been asked to pour. A second bever-age calls for another tray. It is placed at the end of the table opposite the tea tray. The tea tray may be of silver, chrome, aluminum, or lacquered tin. Before the guests arrive the tray should be set completely, usually with-out a tray cloth, except for the boiling water. If the tea is brewed in the kitchen, it is brought in as needed. Sometimes the hot-water kettle for the tray has a spirit lamp placed beneath it to keep the water hot. The kettle may be of silver, chrome, copper, or glass. The teapot usually is of china or silver, as are the cream-and-sugar set. The plate for lemon may match or contrast. A spoon or sugar tongs are needed for the sugar. A fork, preferably one designed for the purpose, should be placed on or beside the plate of lemon slices.

F. P. G.

Sandwich makings · A tray set like this permits guests to please their own tastes. You can carry out the idea with fewer spreads and a smaller number of other choices

Hamburgers, potato chips, with
tiny onions, strips of carrot, and
cucumber are served with grape-
juice and ginger ale in buffet
style

Iowa State College

A buffet table arranged for a larger group, with one hot dish

Towle Silversmiths

H. Armstrong Roberts

Two essentials of a good party for a mixed crowd are shown here: (1) delicious food, served in an attractive way; and (2) something fun to do, such as table tennis—with snacks at intervals

Major Morris Photo and Cambridge, Mass. YWCA

Cups, tea plates, teaspoons, and napkins are placed on or near the tea tray. If napkins are placed between the plates as they are stacked, the napkin will be lifted off with the plate. Or the napkins may be arranged on the table to be picked up by the guests. When the tea plates are placed on the table, one is picked up by each guest and taken to the person who is pouring; she places the filled cup on the tea plate and adds a spoon. The guest then helps herself to the other foods, which have been attractively arranged on the table.

How to Conduct Oneself at Teas—A well-planned tea can be a very pleasant form of entertainment for a large number of guests.

The person chosen to pour should be a poised individual who knows many of the guests. It is considered an honor to be asked to pour at a tea table. The one to pour sits at the end of the table where the tea tray is arranged. She sits erect, yet at ease, and waits for guests to come to be served. If sugar, cream, and lemon are placed before her, she adds whichever is indicated by the guest. If these items are placed on the main part of the table, she asks the guests to help themselves.

The hostess and honored guests stand near the door or together in a place easily accessible to guests as they arrive. After greeting the hostess and honored guests, the guests greet friends, introduce themselves

An autumn tea · Maple spice squares with frosting appear on the tray at the left. Chocolate whirls, French cake drops, and cheese pastries fill the tray on the right

Better Homes & Gardens

Rolled-up sandwiches as well as checkerboard sandwiches are garnished with rhubarb curls. A glass of iced fruit juice completes the refreshments for a simple tea party

to others, and converse in small groups. Guests wait until they are invited by the hostess or one of her helpers to be served at the tea table. Then they go to the room or table where the refreshments are being served.

A less formal tea for a small group may be served in the living room by placing the tea tray on a low table or tea cart in front of the hostess. The best height for the table is 5 or 6 inches above the hostess's knees. If there are few guests she may make the tea at the table, in which case the teapot, a kettle of hot water, and tea containers should be placed on the tray. A cream-and-sugar set with spoon or tongs and a plate of lemon with a fork are also needed. The spoons, cups, saucers, tea plates, and napkins may be placed on the tray or on the table within reach of the hostess.

If there are boys or men among the guests, each carries the served tea plates from the hostess for his partner and himself, or he and his partner may go to the hostess's table together. Women guests without escorts come by themselves or in friendly groups of two or three to the table to be served. As a matter of convenience, the hostess usually places the cup on a tea plate rather than on a saucer so that there will be room for sandwiches and cookies, and guests will have only one plate to manage. Girls may be asked to assist the hostess by passing sandwiches or cookies for second helpings.

Special Luncheons, Suppers, and Dinners

Serving a meal at home is a gracious way to entertain friends. *A formal luncheon*, to be socially correct, should be served in European style, though European service is becoming increasingly rare. Except that the guests are usually all women, and the food of a lighter variety, there is no difference between a formal luncheon and a formal dinner. (For European service, see pages 318–320.) Among the appropriate menus for a formal luncheon, the one on the following page is typical.

341

Fruit Cup
Cream-of-Asparagus Soup   Crackers
Broiled Chicken
Peas with Mushrooms
Rolls   Butter
Molded-Heart Perfection Salad
Raspberry Sherbet   Coconut Wafers
Heart Mints   Nuts
Coffee

Informal luncheons are far more common than formal ones. The following foods may be omitted at an informal luncheon: soup, crackers, salad, mints, and nuts. Larger servings of the other foods may be provided. The informal luncheon may be given with American service or without servants (see pages 315–317).

Late supper may be served informally after the theater, a game, skating, or other outings. Foods should be simple and plentiful. Planning ahead, plus wise marketing, will enable you to have food on hand for impromptu parties. Supper guests often enjoy helping with food preparation. The kitchen should be left orderly for efficient preparation of the next meal.

You will enjoy serving one of the following menus the next time you entertain a group with late supper. All recipes are to be found in the Cookbook.

Cream Cheese on Potato Chips
Stuffed Rolls
Celery   Radishes   Pickles
Root-Beer Float
———

A table set and arranged for afternoon tea

Quickie Steak Sandwiches
Tossed Green Salad
Caramel Custard   Cookies
Lime Cooler

———

Spaghetti and Meat Balls
Lettuce-and-Tomato Salad
Brown Bread   Butter   Jam
Milk

Eating outdoors at a picnic is fun

One of the most delightful ways of recognizing a special day—whether it be Easter, Thanksgiving, Christmas, an anniversary, or a birthday—is to serve a *dinner* to your family and friends. An informal dinner offers wide variety in the number of courses and appropriate foods, and should be easy to plan, prepare, and serve. (See Chapter 20 for dinner planning and preparation and Chapter 25 for the serving of dinners. A menu for a formal dinner, the setting of the table and serving of the meal are also discussed in Chapter 25.)

In planning dinners for special days in your family you will want to include some of the family's favorite dishes. A menu that may be appropriate for your father's birthday dinner is given here:

Fruit Cup with Mint
Standing Rib Roast
Brown Gravy
Baked Stuffed Potatoes
Lyonnaise Green Beans
Tossed Salad with Roquefort Dressing
Parker House Rolls   Butter or Margarine
Birthday Cake
Chocolate Parfait
Salted Nuts   Mints
Coffee

You will want the family dinners to be occasions for fun. Festive table decorations will add to the gaiety of the meals. Lively conversation centered around topics of mutual interest further adds to the enjoyment of the day.

Other Forms of Entertainment

Potluck suppers, where each guest contributes a dish, can be great successes if the menu is planned ahead of time for variety and balance. The hostess usually provides the beverage. Buffet service is enjoyable and convenient for a potluck supper. Guests may be asked to serve and to help in putting the kitchen in order afterwards.

Parties with games or other activities such as music or dancing should have light refreshments. The hostess's responsibility includes making the guest list and planning for the entertainment. A counter where refreshments are served may provide a frozen dessert or an assortment of cold drinks. There may be buffet service or guests may be seated at small tables and served.

Half the success of entertaining at a barbecue depends on setting an attractive table outdoors. Here the various foods are arranged with an eye to color balance and to the convenience of guests in serving themselves

Spice Cakes	Popcorn Balls
with	Fruit Punch
Iced Cider	Hard Candies
——	——
Doughnuts	Strawberry Ice
Hot Cocoa	Tea Cakes

Parties for children should be simple in refreshments and entertainment. Foods should not be overrich. Plain ice cream and cookies may be served in fancy shapes attractive to children.

Picnics can be held at any season, even on a winter day. It is wise to plan them for a time when the highways are free from heavy traffic and picnic grounds are the least crowded. Picnic meals include breakfast as well as luncheon and supper. Menus may consist of foods packed ready to eat or ready to prepare at the scene. (The section on packing lunches, pages 125–127, will be helpful.) Picnics, like any other meal, should be well planned. There will be more time for hikes, swims, bicycling, or whatever entertainment is available if all food details have been taken care of ahead of time. Much of the fun of a picnic comes from getting food and utensils ready and from cooking and eating in the open. The menu and utensils should be checked before leaving home to be sure that nothing has been forgotten. Picnic aids are long-handled forks and spoons, kettles soaped on the bottom for easy soot removal, pot holders, plenty of matches, and, if held soon after a rain, perhaps some paper and dry kindling. Colorful, partitioned plastic dishes or waterproof, disposable paper plates add to the enjoyment.

Many families plan barbecues as a kind of informal entertainment. They enjoy outdoor cooking just as much as eating the food. The whole family may help with the preparation of the food, each member according to his skills. The place of cooking may be a permanent barbecue pit, or it may be a folding, portable charcoal grill. The food for a barbecue is planned around the meat to be prepared over a charcoal or wood fire. Suitable varieties of meat for barbecue include frankfurters, hamburgers, broilers, liver, ribs, and steaks. Whole chickens or large pieces of meat may be barbecued. A good barbecue menu for your friends may consist of chilled tomato juice, grilled lamb chops, roasted corn on the cob, a green salad, cookies, and a beverage. The addition of celery hearts, carrot strips, or roasted bananas split open and sprinkled with cinnamon and sugar makes a more elaborate outdoor meal. In many families the men enjoy barbecuing meats and other specialities.

Entertainment at School

There are many opportunities for school entertainment: class and club parties, after-the-game dances, student-council receptions, Christmas parties, junior-senior banquets, athletic luncheons, and other special occasions.

Careful management can make your school parties delightful occasions. If the affair is to move smoothly and gaily, refreshments and entertainment should be planned in advance. The refreshments will depend on the type of party and the season of year. Favorite dishes of the group should be recognized. The pattern for school entertainment should follow general procedures socially accepted for any gathering.

Simple refreshments add gaiety
to a school party.

Receptions

Receptions may honor guests, introduce a bride or distinguished persons, celebrate anniversaries, or mark any important event. In adult society, a club or hotel is usually used for a reception unless the house is large enough to hold a crowd.

A school group may use a reception to honor guests, such as an assembly speaker, or as a means of entertaining classes. Behavior previously suggested for large teas should be followed at such a reception.

If there is a receiving line, appointed assistants direct the guests about wraps before they go down the line. The hostess, who is first in line, presents each guest to the guest of honor, who stands at her right. The honored guest makes the presentation to the next in line. In any receiving line, except at a wedding reception, each guest shakes hands with each person in the line and acknowledges an introduction with "How do you do." No guest should delay the line by chatting. If it is necessary for a couple to introduce themselves, the boy introduces himself first and then the girl with him. If there is no receiving line, the hostesses at a reception greet guests at the door.

Guests at a reception move from group to group meeting new persons and conversing pleasantly. Since localities vary somewhat in social practices, you may wish to consult an authority on etiquette for information.

When serving refreshments, follow the procedures given for a large tea (pages 336–341). Here is a suggested menu for a reception. This menu may be modified according to your facilities and budget.

A RECEPTION MENU

Miniature Cream Puffs with
"Chickenette" Filling
Fruit Balls   Petits Fours
Spiced Nuts
Colored Mints
Coffee   Cocoa

Other School Entertainments

Open House is similar to a tea or reception in that food is served and there may be a receiving line. For a school dance, refreshments are usually very simple, consisting, often, of a fruit punch, or sherbet, and fancy crackers.

Whether you are a guest or the hostess in any social situation, you have two resources—your habits of good behavior, learned at home, and your understanding, gained from study of the special requirements of the particular occasion. Every tea, reception, and dance will add to your social poise and to your pleasure.

¶ *Understanding:*

1. What are the values from learning accepted entertainment etiquette?
2. What factors determine the menu and means of serving when entertaining?
3. For what reasons is buffet service desirable?
4. How do the foods served for tea differ from those for buffets?
5. What are the characteristics of an appropriately set tea table for a large group? for a small group at home?
6. How should you conduct yourself when you are a guest at a tea?
7. How does a formal luncheon differ from an informal luncheon?
8. When are kitchen parties appropriate? What makes such a party entertaining?
9. Describe an enjoyable picnic; a barbecue.

¶ *Planning:*

1. Plan a Sunday buffet supper for your family. What determines the choice of buffet foods?
2. What refreshments will you serve a small group of friends entertained informally in the living room? in the kitchen?
3. Plan food for a tea at school to honor your mothers. How will you arrange the table?
4. Plan a menu for an informal luncheon.
5. Plan a potluck dinner; include the responsibilities for food and serving.
6. Plan a menu for a supper party so that there will be a minimum of cleaning up.
7. Plan the refreshments for a dance; for a children's party.
8. Assist in planning hostess responsibilities for a reception or an open house at school.
9. Plan a reception to honor the faculty.

¶ *Practicing and Evaluating:*

1. Prepare a dish for an informal buffet. What characteristics make the dish appropriate?
2. Assist with the preparation and serving of the food for an informal buffet lunch for parents at school. Why is buffet service suitable?
3. Assist with arranging a tea table when tea is to be brewed at the table and a second beverage is to be served.
4. Help make a variety of appetizing tea sandwiches. Arrange them attractively.
5. Assist your mother with serving a barbecue.
6. Cooperate with members of a club in planning and serving a potluck meal. What are the advantages of this type of entertainment?
7. Serve as an assistant hostess, introducing guests, at a tea. What did you learn?

¶ *Reading Further:*

Outdoor Cookery for the Family, Bulletin 293 (1960). University of Minnesota Extension Service, St. Paul, Minnesota.
Teas, Parties, Buffets, Bulletin 6 (1963). Iowa State University Extension Service, Ames, Iowa.

UNIT NINE

The Cookbook

Introduction

In order to prepare appetizing and healthful meals, any home manager or cook needs reliable recipes and an understanding of the principles of cooking. The recipes in this book have been thoroughly tested to ensure their accuracy. They are organized in steps which are easy to follow. Once the correct procedure for any process has been established, it is followed in every recipe requiring that process. The practices of good management are stressed. Whenever possible, the same beater, measuring cup, or saucepan is used throughout the preparation of a given dish.

The recipes, especially those for making cakes and pastry, provide for varying both the proportions of ingredients and the methods of mixing. The principles upon which such variations in proportion and methods are based have been developed in the study of food preparation in earlier units.

The recipes are grouped under the usual headings, such as fruit, quick breads, or cakes.

After you have chosen a dish to prepare (with the approval of your teacher or mother), find the recipe you need by consulting the index. Read the recipe several times to understand what you must do to follow it exactly. Then assemble the ingredients and the necessary measuring and mixing equipment. Be careful to select utensils that are suited to the amount of food the recipe will produce.

After you have assembled the ingredients and equipment, grease baking dishes, pans, and baking sheets, unless the recipe states otherwise. Dip molds to be used for making a gelatin dish in cold water. Heat the oven 10 or 15 minutes before you need it for baking and set the controls for the temperature given in the recipe. If you are going to fry in deep fat, place the shortening that you will need in the kettle or frying pan.

TEMPERATURES FOR BAKING

250°–325°	Slow
325°–400°	Moderate
400°–450°	Hot
450°–500°	Very hot

The principles of cookery which have been developed in earlier units provide the background for the step-by-step process in the recipes. All ingredients are listed in the order of their use.

Table fat means butter or fortified margarine.

All-purpose flour is intended except where cake flour is specified.

Ingredients in recipes should be at room temperature before they are combined unless otherwise stated in the recipe. The extent to which suggested seasonings, garnishes, and accompaniments are used will be determined by the preferences of the family and by the food budget.

Standard equipment should be used for all measuring—measuring cups that hold 16 tablespoonfuls, tablespoons that hold 3 teaspoonfuls.

Your kitchen, either at school or at home, may not be supplied with the exact ingredients named in the recipe. Substitutions can be made, often with little or no difference in results. The following table will be useful in making such substitutions.

MEASURES AND ABBREVIATIONS

1 tablespoon (T.).. 3 teaspoons (t.)	1 pint (pt.)........ 2 cups
1 cup (c.).........16 tablespoons	1 quart (qt.)....... 2 pints
½ cup........... 8 tablespoons	1 gallon (gal.).... 4 quarts
¼ cup.......... 4 tablespoons	1 pound (lb.)......16 ounces (oz.)

1 sq. (1 oz.) chocolate	3 to 4 T. cocoa and ½ T. fat
3 to 4 T. cocoa	1 sq. (1 oz.) chocolate and omit ½ T. fat
1 c. fresh sweet milk in batters with baking powder	1 c. sour milk or buttermilk with ½ t. soda for leavening. Omit 4 t. tartrate or 2 t. double-action baking powder
1 qt. sweet milk	¾ c. powdered milk and 1 qt. water
1 c. sweet milk	3 to 4 T. powdered milk and 1 c. water
1 c. sour milk	1 c. sweet milk and 1 T. vinegar or lemon juice
1 c. sweet milk	½ c. evaporated milk and ½ c. water
1 c. whole milk	1 c. skim milk and 2 T. fat
1 c. sifted all-purpose flour	1 c. cake flour and 2 T. flour or 1 c. rice flour or 1 c. rye flour or ½ c. whole-wheat flour and ½ c. all-purpose flour or ½ c. corn meal and ½ c. all-purpose flour or ½ c. bran and ½ c. all-purpose flour or ¼ c. soybean flour and ¾ c. all-purpose flour
⅞ c. all-purpose flour	1 c. cake flour and 2 T. cornstarch
1 T. cornstarch	2 T. flour
1 t. SAS-phosphate baking powder	1½ t. phosphate baking powder for ½ c. milk or 2 t. tartrate baking powder for ½ c. milk or ½ t. baking soda and 1 c. sour milk or ½ t. baking soda and 1 T. vinegar or lemon juice used with 1 c. sweet milk or ¼ t. baking soda and ½ to 1 c. molasses for ½ c. milk or ¼ t. baking soda and 2 T. cream of tartar for ½ c. milk
1 c. honey	¾ c. sugar and ¼ c. liquid
1½ T. quick-cooking tapioca	3 T. regular tapioca (cooked 1 hour)
1 c. coffee cream (20%)	3 T. butter and ⅞ c. milk
1 c. heavy cream (40%)	⅓ c. butter and ¾ c. milk
⅞ c. fat, lard, or oil	1 c. butter
1 c. nut meats	⅓ c. butter
1 egg	½ t. baking powder
1 egg	2 egg yolks in custards and such mixtures, 2 egg yolks and 1 T. water in cookies

351

MEASURING ONE CUP OF FLOUR

Sifting

Spooning flour into cup

Leveling off flour with knife

MEASURING ONE TABLESPOON OF FLOUR

Spoon heaped with flour

Leveling off flour with knife

Dividing tablespoon of flour in two
lengthwise with knife

Teaspoon heaped

Leveling baking powder with knife

MEASURING SHORTENING

Measuring one-quarter cup

Measuring one-third cup

Measuring one-half cup

MEASURING LIQUID

Measuring one cupful

Measuring one teaspoonful

353

Fruits

Orange or Grapefruit Halves

1. Wash and cut fruit crosswise into halves.
2. Cut out center of fruit if desired, using kitchen shears or sharp knife. Remove seeds.
3. Insert knife at center and cut between the pulp and the membrane of the section toward the rind, around the section, and back to center.
4. Permit persons who desire sugared fruit to add the sugar when served.
5. Notch or scallop the edge of the fruit rind, or garnish with sweetened cherries or berries for a decorative effect.

Orange and Grapefruit Sections

1. Wash fruit and cut a thin slice from the stem end with a sharp knife. Pare the fruit round and round like an apple, or after removing the slice from the end, make six cuts down through the peel and strip the peel from the fruit.
2. Cut between the pulp and membrane as described in Orange or Grapefruit Halves, step 3, and lift out each whole section.

Pineapple in Shell

1. Scrub fruit with a brush.
2. Cut pineapple lengthwise into quarters, including the top. Cut down through the meat of each quarter lengthwise and crosswise several times, making bite-sized pieces.
3. Sprinkle fruit with confectioners' sugar. Arrange two orange sections and a sprig of mint in the center of each quarter for a festive serving.

Sliced Pineapple

1. Wash and cut off ends of fruit; cut into $\frac{3}{8}$- to $\frac{1}{2}$-inch slices and pare.
2. Remove eyes of pineapple with a pointed knife. Cut core from center of slice. Chill before serving.
3. Cut slices into bite-sized pieces to be eaten with toothpicks as a snack food.
   Serve pineapple for breakfast, or as a dessert, sprinkled with confectioners' sugar, or serve with dressing in salads.

354

Melons

1. Wash melons and cut lengthwise or crosswise with a sharp knife. Remove the seeds and any membranes to which they cling.
2. Cut into pieces convenient for eating or storage. Chill, covering closely to protect other foods from their odor.
3. Serve melon in its rind or use the meat in fruit cups or salads. You can cut it into balls with a ball cutter or a teaspoon.

Cooked Fruits

1. Wash, peel (if desired), quarter, core or stone orchard fruits.
2. Allow one medium apple, peach, or pear for each serving of fruit sauce or cooked fruit served whole.
3. Force unpeeled fruit through a sieve before sweetening or adding seasonings.
4. Cook berries on low heat until soft before adding sugar. Thicken with flour, cornstarch, or tapioca.

Applesauce   *6 servings*

6 medium apples
$\frac{5}{8}$ to $\frac{3}{4}$ c. water
6 to 8 T. sugar
   or 1 to 2 T. for sweet apples

1. Prepare apples for cooking (step 1, Cooked Fruits, above).
2. Add water to apples in saucepan and cover; cook for 20 minutes or until tender.
3. Add sugar and beat apples until blended or leave whole. Serve hot or chilled.

VARIATIONS: Use recipe for *Applesauce*.

Strained Sauce . . . . .
Use unpeeled apples.
Force apples through sieve.
Add sugar.
Serve with pork or fowl.

Flavored Sauce

$\frac{1}{2}$ t. cinnamon
   or
1 t. lemon juice
   or
1 stick peppermint candy, crushed

Add to sweetened apples.

Add to sweetened apples.

Add to sweetened apples.

Glazed Apples   *4 servings*

4 large apples
$\frac{1}{2}$ c. sugar
$\frac{1}{2}$ t. cinnamon
$\frac{1}{2}$ c. water

1. Core whole, unpared apples; slit peel around middle of each apple.
2. Mix sugar and cinnamon together; fill centers of apples.
3. Put apples in saucepan; add water and cover. Cook for 25 minutes or until tender, turning or spooning liquid over them once.
4. Remove cover during last minute of cooking.

Cinnamon-Candy Apples

6 servings

6 medium apples
  or 12 whole crab apples
1 c. sugar
2 T. lemon juice
  or 1 T. vinegar and 1 T. water
1 c. water
½ c. red cinnamon candies

1. Pare, quarter, and core apples, or pare and core crab apples.
2. Mix sugar, lemon juice, water, and candies in saucepan. Cook for 5 minutes to form a sirup.
3. Add apples to sirup; cook until transparent and tender.

Fried Apples

6 servings

6 medium apples
2 T. drippings
  or table fat
½ to ¾ c. brown sugar

1. Core or quarter unpared apples and cut lengthwise in ¼-inch slices.
2. Heat fat in frying pan and add apples; cover and cook slowly 6 to 8 minutes.
3. Add sugar to apples and cook until transparent and tender, lifting and turning occasionally with a broad spatula or pancake turner.
Serve with bacon or sausage.

Baked Apples

4 servings

4 large apples
4 to 6 T. sugar
2 T. table fat
½ t. cinnamon

Sirup

¼ c. sugar
¼ c. water
2 T. orange juice
  or 2 t. lemon juice

1. Core whole, unpared apples; slit peel around middle of each apple.
2. Put apples in 6 to 8-inch baking dish and fill centers with sugar, fat, and cinnamon.

3. Boil sugar, water, and orange juice together in saucepan for ½ minute to make sirup.
4. Pour sirup over tops of apples and cover dish.
5. Bake apples at 350° F. for 30 minutes or until tender. Spoon sirup over apples twice while cooking.

VARIATION: Use recipe for *Baked Apples.*

¼ c. raisins
¼ c. coconut
Omit cinnamon.

Add raisins and coconut to sugar for apple centers.

Baked Canned Peaches

6 servings

Peach juice
6 peach halves
2 T. granulated sugar
2 T. brown sugar
1 T. lemon juice
½ c. coconut
  or ¼ c. nuts

1. Drain juice from peaches into saucepan.
2. Add sugars and lemon juice to peach juice; boil 3 minutes.
3. Place peach halves in a 6-inch baking dish; pour peach-juice mixture over them.
   Bake at 350° F. for 15 minutes.
4. Sprinkle coconut on peaches during last 3 minutes of baking.

VARIATION: Use recipe for *Baked Peaches.*

Apricot *or* pear halves substituted
  for peach halves

Stewed Dried Fruits

4 to 5 servings

Apricots

½ lb. dried apricots
Hot water to cover fruit
3 to 4 T. sugar

1. Wash apricots, add water; soak for 60 minutes in saucepan.
2. Cook apricots covered, in same water, slowly for 25 to 30 minutes or until tender.
3. Add sugar to fruit before removing from heat.
   (Omit soaking for any tenderized dried fruit; follow directions for cooking on package. Cook dried fruit in a pressure saucepan by following manufacturer's directions.)

Prunes

½ lb. prunes
Hot water to cover fruit
2 slices lemon
2 T. sugar

1. Wash prunes, add water; soak for 60 minutes in saucepan.
2. Cook prunes covered, in same water, slowly for 45 to 60 minutes or until tender.
3. Add lemon and sugar to fruit before removing from heat.

Apples

½ lb. dried apples
2½ c. water
¼ c. sugar
⅛ t. salt

1. Remove particles of core.
2. Rinse apples; put in saucepan and add water. Cook for 40 minutes or until tender.
3. Add sugar and salt to apples before removing from heat. Serve hot or chilled.

Banana Fritters

6 servings

1¼ c. sifted flour
½ t. salt
2 t. baking powder
2 T. sugar
1 egg
½ c. milk
2 t. melted table fat
Shortening for deep-fat frying
3 large bananas, peeled
3 T. sifted confectioners' sugar

1. Sift 1 c. flour, salt, baking powder, and sugar together.
2. Beat egg until thick; add milk and fat, stirring.
3. Add egg mixture gradually to flour mixture, stirring; beat batter 25 to 30 strokes.
4. Use enough shortening to fill a deep heavy pan ½ to ⅔ full when melted; heat to 370° F.
5. Cut each banana into five or six pieces. Roll pieces in remaining ¼ c. flour; dip into the batter.
6. Cook a few pieces at a time for 3 to 4 minutes, turning once. Drain on absorbent paper.
7. Roll each fritter in confectioners' sugar.

VARIATIONS: Use recipe for *Banana Fritters*.

Apple Fritters

4 medium apples, tart
Add another 2 T. sugar.

Slice pared, cored apples into ¼-inch rings.

Pineapple Fritters

6 slices pineapple, drained

Peach Fritters

2½ c. peaches, diced
Omit ¼ c. flour used for rolling fruit.

Stir peaches into batter. Drop by teaspoonfuls into hot fat.

OTHER FRUIT RECIPES

For additional ideas on serving fruit refer to pages 482–488.

Purdey, from U. S. D. A.

Baked apple

358

Beverages

Hot Tea

6 servings

1⅓ T. tea leaves
  or 3 to 4 tea bags
4 c. water, boiling

1. Put tea leaves in glass, china, or enamel container. (Tie tea loosely in cheese cloth or put in tea ball or leave loose.)
2. Add boiling water to tea; cover tightly and steep 3 to 5 minutes.
3. Rinse teapot with boiling water.
4. Strain tea from leaves into teapot or cups (or remove the tea bags) when of desired strength.
   Serve with sugar, cream, lemon, as preferred.

VARIATION: Use recipe for *Hot Tea.*

Iced Tea

2 T. tea leaves
  or 3 tea bags
Ice
Mint leaves
  or lemon slices

Pour strained hot tea over ice in glasses. (*Caution:* A metal spoon in glass prevents breakage.)
Or cool tea, covered, to room temperature and pour over ice in glasses.

Percolated Coffee

4 servings

4 c. cold water
½ c. medium-grind coffee

1. Rinse percolator with boiling water.
2. Put water in lower part and coffee in upper part of percolator; close.
3. Place over medium heat until percolation begins.
4. Reduce heat to allow gentle percolation for 8 to 10 minutes.

359

Drip Coffee

4 to 5 servings

½ c. coffee, drip-grind
4 c. water, boiling

1. Rinse coffeepot with boiling water.
2. Put coffee in filter part. Pour boiling water into upper part; close.
3. Remove upper and filter parts when dripping ceases; cover. Serve at once.

Vacuum-Method Coffee

4 to 5 servings

½ c. coffee, drip-grind
4 c. water

1. Rinse coffeepot with boiling water.
2. Put water into lower bowl of coffee maker.
3. Adjust filter in upper bowl. Add coffee.
4. Fit upper bowl into the lower bowl. Place on heat.
5. Stir coffee when all but 2 or 3 T. of water has risen into upper bowl.
6. Reduce heat; turn off current if nonautomatic electric maker. Cook slowly (brew) 4 minutes; remove from heat.

Steeped Coffee

4 to 5 servings

1 T. egg white
¼ c. cold water
½ c. coffee, all-purpose grind
4 c. water, boiling
¼ c. cold water

1. Rinse coffeepot with boiling water.
2. Beat egg white slightly and add ¼ c. water and coffee; put in pot.
3. Add 4 c. boiling water to coffee and slowly bring to boiling point.
4. Reduce heat and brew 4 to 5 minutes.
5. Remove from heat; add ¼ c. cold water to settle grounds. Set aside 3 minutes in warm place.
Serve immediately, pouring gently for clear coffee.

Café au Lait

4 to 6 servings

2 c. brewed coffee
2 c. milk

1. Brew coffee by any method.
2. Scald milk in top of double boiler over hot water or over low direct heat.
3. Add hot coffee to milk; stir.
Serve immediately.

Demitasse

(After-Dinner Coffee)

2 servings

3 to 4 T. coffee
1 c. water

1. Brew coffee by any method.
2. Serve black (without cream), with or without sugar.

360

Iced Coffee

3 to 4 T. coffee
1 c. water

1. Brew coffee by any method.
2. Pour hot coffee over ice in glasses. (*Caution:* A metal spoon in glass prevents breakage.) Or cool coffee to room temperature and pour over ice in glasses.

Quantity Coffee

45 servings

2 gal. water, boiling
1 lb. coffee, all-purpose grind

1. Pour water into coffeepot and bring to boiling point.
2. Place coffee in muslin bag large enough to hold twice the amount. Tie bag securely.
3. Put bag into boiling water, cover, and reduce heat.
4. Brew coffee 6 to 10 minutes; lift bag up and down several times.
5. Remove bag. Serve.

Hot Spiced Cider

6 servings

1 t. whole cloves
4 small cinnamon sticks
6 whole allspice
2 qt. cider

1. Tie spices in cloth bag, add to cider in saucepan, and boil for 3 minutes.
2. Cool cider mixture; remove bag.
3. Heat spiced cider to boiling point. Serve.

Cocoa

4 servings

3 T. sugar
3 to 4 T. cocoa
$\frac{1}{8}$ t. salt
$\frac{1}{2}$ c. hot water
4 c. milk

1. Mix sugar, cocoa, and salt in top of double boiler.
2. Add water to cocoa mixture; boil for 3 minutes, stirring.
3. Add milk to cocoa mixture; place over hot water, cover. Heat to serving temperature.

VARIATIONS: Use recipe for *Cocoa*.

Iced Cocoa

4 c. cocoa

Chill cocoa for 30 minutes.
Beat well.
Pour over ice.

Hot Chocolate

2 sq. chocolate substituted for cocoa
$\frac{1}{2}$ t. vanilla
$\frac{1}{4}$ c. whipped cream

Cut chocolate into fine pieces.
Add to milk and blend.
Add vanilla.
Garnish with whipped cream.

Chilled Tomato Beverage

6 servings

3½ c. fresh tomatoes
  or 1 can (No. 2½) tomatoes
1 c. chopped celery
¼ c. chopped green pepper
1 T. chopped onion
1 t. salt
½ bay leaf
½ t. horse-radish

1. Mix tomatoes, celery, pepper, onion, and seasonings in a saucepan; cook until vegetables are tender.
2. Force tomato mixture through a purée sieve.
3. Chill tomato beverage before serving.

Serve with accompaniments such as nuts, pretzels, crackers, popcorn, and pumpkin seeds.

Beverage Ice Cubes

Vegetable Beverage

Watercress *or* parsley sprig
Radish *or* carrot rings
Cucumber *or* green pepper, chopped
  herb leaf

1. Fill ice-cube trays ½ full of water; freeze.
2. Place in each section of the tray ingredient desired.
3. Add remaining water to tray; freeze.

Fruit Beverage

Cherry *or* berry
Orange *or* lemon wedge *or* pineapple
  chunk
Mint leaf
Food color added to water

Lemonade

4 servings

1 c. sugar
1 c. water
⅜ to ½ c. lemon juice
4 c. water
Mint leaves or sprigs

1. Combine sugar and water in saucepan; boil for 1 minute to make sirup. Cool.
2. Mix lemon juice, sirup, and water in a pitcher.
3. Pour lemon mixture over ice in tall glasses.
4. Garnish with mint leaves.

Fruit Punch

24 punch-cup servings

2 c. sugar
1 c. water
1 qt. grape juice
1½ c. orange juice (6 large oranges)
1¼ c. lemon juice (6 large lemons)
2 c. crushed pineapple
1 qt. cold water
1 pt. chilled carbonated water
½ pt. tea if desired

1. Mix sugar and water in saucepan; stir until sugar dissolves.
2. Boil the sugar mixture slowly for 5 minutes to make sirup. Cool.
3. Add fruit juices and pineapple (tea if used) to sirup. Chill.
4. Add cold water and carbonated water to punch; serve in punch bowl with block of ice or ice cubes. (Ice blocks may be frozen in refrigerator tray.)

362

Orange-Juice Cocktail

8 to 10 servings

3 c. orange juice
3 T. lemon juice
¼ c. sugar
2 c. carbonated water, chilled in
   bottle

1. Mix fruit juices and sugar together. Pour into refrigerator tray and freeze to mush consistency.
2. Fill chilled glasses ½ full of frozen mixture and add chilled carbonated water. Serve immediately.

Serve cocktail for first course of luncheon or dinner or as refreshment.

VARIATIONS: Use recipe for *Orange-Juice Cocktail.*

1 c. jellied cranberry sauce
2 c. orange juice substituted for 3 c.
2 T. lemon juice substituted for 3 T.

Crush sauce with rotary beater; add fruit-juice mixture.

Banana Milk Shake

4 servings

2 large bananas
5 c. cold milk
¼ c. whipped cream
   or vanilla ice cream
1 T. finely chopped nuts *or* candied
   fruit

1. Mash banana in mixing bowl with fork; add milk, stirring until blended.
2. Pour banana mixture into tall, chilled glasses.
3. Garnish and serve.

VARIATIONS: Use recipe for *Banana Milk Shake* omitting banana.

Strawberry Shake

1½ c. strawberries, sweetened, crushed

Chocolate Shake

¾ c. chocolate sirup (p. 427)

Maple Shake

¾ c. maple sirup
   or brown-sugar sirup (p. 427)

Eggnog

4 servings

4 eggs
¼ c. sugar
⅛ t. salt
4 c. milk
1 t. vanilla
⅛ t. nutmeg

1. Beat eggs in bowl; add sugar and salt, stirring until blended.
2. Add milk and vanilla to egg mixture, stirring.
3. Pour into glasses, sprinkle with nutmeg.

Cereals

Four-Way Cereal Cookery

Cereal Cooked in Double Boiler

Water, salted and boiling
Cereal

1. Add cereal slowly to boiling water in top of double boiler on direct heat, stirring.
2. Boil for 5 minutes, stirring two or three times. Place over boiling water and cover.
3. Cook according to directions in Cereal Cookery Chart (p. 365).
4. Allow water in lower pan barely to touch bottom of top pan.

Cereal Cooked in Pressure Saucepan

Water, salted and boiling
Cereal

1. Add cereal slowly to boiling water in saucepan, stirring.
2. Cover pan, adjust control; follow manufacturer's directions exactly.

(*Caution:* Be sure pressure is normal before removing lid.)

Cereal Cooked in Saucepan

Water, salted and boiling
Cereal

1. Stir cereal into boiling water.
2. Cook the required minutes, stirring three or four times.

Cereal Cooked in Range Well

Water, salted and boiling
Cereal

1. Add cereal slowly to boiling water, stirring gently. Boil 5 minutes, stirring two or three times.
2. Cover range well and cook below boiling point. (Follow manufacturer's directions for use of range.)

364

CEREAL COOKERY CHART

CEREAL	QUANTITY	WATER	SALT	TIME OF COOKING (minutes): SAUCEPAN, DIRECT-HEAT BOILING	PRESSURE SAUCEPAN	DOUBLE BOILER	SERVINGS
Corn meal	¾ c.	3¾ c.	1¼ t.	20–30	5	30–45	4
Granular wheat cereal Regular	½ c.	3 c.	½ t.	Until it thickens, then 15	5	30	4
Partially cooked	½ c.	3 c.	½ t.	Until it thickens, then 5	Until it boils	15	4
Hominy grits	1 c.	5 c., over direct heat 4 c., in double boiler	1 t.	25–30	5	45	6
Oats Regular	1½ c.	3 c.	¾ t.	5–10, covered; set aside 5	2	15	4
Partially cooked	1½ c.	3 c.	¾ t.	2½–5, covered; set aside 5	2	10	4
Granular whole wheat Regular	¾ c.	3–3¼ c.	1 t.	5	5	30	4
Partially cooked	1 c.	3–3¼ c.	1 t.	3		6	4
Rice Regular	1 c.	8 c.	2 t.	20	5	30–35	6–8
Partially cooked	1⅓ c.	1¾ c.	½ t.	2–5; set aside 10			4–5
Macaroni or spaghetti or noodles	1¼ c., broken* or shell	6 c.	2 t.	12–15			4–5

** An 8-oz. pkg. of macaroni or spaghetti = 5 to 5½ c., broken.*

Cereal Gruel

1 serving

1 T. barley flour
  or rice flour
  or oatmeal
  or corn meal
2 T. cold water
½ c. water, boiling
½ c. hot water
  or milk
⅛ t. salt

1. Mix flour or meal with 2 T. cold water in top of double boiler.
2. Add gradually ½ c. boiling water, stirring; cook 2 to 3 minutes over direct heat, stirring constantly.
3. Place pan over boiling water.
4. Add ½ c. hot liquid and salt to gruel, stirring; cook 60 minutes.

Fried Corn-Meal Mush

3 to 4 servings

2 to 3 T. shortening
6 to 8 slices leftover corn-meal mush,
  ¼- to ½-inch thick
2 to 3 T. flour

1. Heat shortening in frying pan.
2. Turn slices of mush in flour to coat outsides.
3. Cook slices in shortening until golden brown, turning once with pancake turner. Serve hot.
   May be served with sirup, jelly, or table fat.

VARIATION: Use recipe for *Fried Corn-Meal Mush.*

Finely ground cooked cereal substituted for corn-meal mush

Curried Rice

4 servings

1½ T. table fat
2 t. finely chopped onion
1½ to 2 t. curry powder
⅔ c. rice
2 c. water, boiling
1 t. salt
⅛ t. pepper

1. Heat fat in large saucepan.
2. Add onion and curry powder; cook until onion is golden, stirring one or two times.
3. Add rice to onion mixture, stirring. Add water and seasonings.
4. Boil rice mixture rapidly for 5 minutes, reduce to low heat and cook for 45 minutes or until tender. Add hot water as needed.
   Serve with lamb or veal.

French-Fried Noodles or Spaghetti

4 servings

3 c. water, boiling
2 t. salt
1¼ c. noodles
Shortening

1. Cook noodles or spaghetti in boiling salted water for 8 minutes.
2. Put noodles in sieve; rinse with cold water and drain.
3. Heat to 390° F. shortening to fill a deep pan ½ to ⅔ full.
4. Fry a few noodles or spaghetti pieces at a time until crisp. Separate them with fork. Drain on absorbent paper.

Serve with creamed tuna fish or chow mein, or crisp and salty as accompaniment to salads.

Baked Noodle Ring

4 servings

4 c. water, boiling
1 t. salt
1 package (4 oz.) or 2 c. dry noodles
3 eggs
⅓ c. finger-broken cracker crumbs
2½ T. melted table fat
1¼ c. milk
¼ c. grated cheese

1. Cook noodles in boiling, salted water in saucepan for 10 minutes.
2. Drain noodles in sieve; rinse in cold water, and put in bowl.
3. Beat eggs until mixed; add crumbs, fat, milk, and cheese.
4. Add egg mixture to noodles; stir gently, and pour into ring.
5. Set ring in pan and add hot water to cover ⅔ the depth of ring. Bake noodles at 350° F. for 45 minutes or until light brown.
6. Fill noodle ring with creamed tuna or asparagus.

Baked Hominy Grits

4 servings

1 c. milk
2 T. melted table fat
2 c. cold boiled grits
2 eggs
1 t. salt
⅛ t. pepper

1. Mix milk, fat, and grits together in bowl.
2. Beat eggs until mixed, add seasonings, and pour into milk mixture, stirring.
3. Pour combined mixture into baking dish; bake at 350° F. for 25 minutes or until firm and light brown.

Eggs

Soft-Cooked Eggs

4 servings

Cold-Water Method

4 eggs, room temperature
1 qt. water

1. Add cold water to eggs in 1½-qt. saucepan.
2. Place saucepan on heat; bring water to boiling point.
3. Turn off heat; cover. Let eggs remain in hot water 3 minutes for soft-cooked eggs, 5 minutes for medium-cooked eggs.

Hot-Water Method

4 eggs, room temperature
1 qt. water, boiling

1. Add boiling water to eggs in 1½-qt. saucepan and cover.
2. Let eggs remain in hot water 4 minutes for soft-cooked eggs, 6 minutes for medium-cooked eggs.

Hard-Cooked Eggs

4 servings

4 eggs, room temperature
1 qt. water

1. Add cold water to eggs in 1½-qt. saucepan. Cover.
2. Place pan on heat; bring water to boiling point.
3. Reduce heat and cook eggs below boiling point (simmer) 15 minutes.
4. Put eggs immediately into cold water.

Fried Eggs

4 servings

2 T. table fat
  or drippings
4 eggs
Salt
Pepper

1. Heat fat in frying pan on low heat.
2. Break eggs one at a time into small plate; slip into hot fat.
3. Cook eggs slowly 3 minutes for soft-fried eggs; 4 to 4½ minutes for hard-fried eggs. Turn eggs with pancake turner if desired. (To steam eggs, add 2 t. boiling water to frying pan the last ½ minute and cover.)
4. Sprinkle with salt and pepper.

Poached Eggs

4 servings

2 c. water, boiling
1 t. salt
⅛ t. pepper
1½ t. vinegar
4 eggs

1. Grease bottom of heavy skillet and place on low heat. Add boiling water, seasonings, and vinegar.
2. Break eggs, one at a time, into small plate; slip each egg into water toward edge of skillet.
3. Cover skillet; cook eggs 3 minutes for soft-poached, 5 minutes for medium-poached.
4. Lift each egg from water with slotted spoon. Sprinkle with salt and pepper.
Serve on toast.

Baked Eggs

4 servings

4 eggs
½ t. salt
Pepper to taste
¼ c. milk
1½ t. table fat
1 t. onion juice

1. Put each egg into a greased individual custard cup. Sprinkle with seasonings.
2. Add equal portions of milk, fat, and onion juice to each egg.
3. Set cups in pan; add hot water to cover ⅔ of cup.
4. Bake eggs at 325° F. for 20 to 25 minutes or until firm. Serve in cups or on toast or heated plate with cheese or mushroom sauce.

VARIATIONS: Use recipe for *Baked Eggs*.

Broiled Eggs

–1– . . . . . .

Put eggs in shallow baking dish; cook on low heat 1 minute or just until edges turn white.
Broil eggs 4 inches from heat unit for 2 to 4 minutes.
Serve from dish.

Broiled Eggs (Cont'd)

–2–

4 strips bacon substituted for table fat	Cook bacon in frying pan on low heat; remove when barely beginning to crisp.
2 T. bread crumbs	Circle inside of each custard cup with strip of bacon.
2 T. grated cheese	Slip an egg into each cup; season and sprinkle with equal portions of crumbs and cheese.
	Broil 4 inches from heat 2 to 4 minutes.

–3–

½ c. cooked spinach, chopped	Use spinach to line bottom and sides of custard cups.
¼ c. medium white sauce	Slip an egg into each cup; season.
Omit milk.	Add 1 T. white sauce to each.
	Broil 4 inches from heat 2 to 4 minutes.

Scrambled Eggs   4 servings

1 to 1½ T. table fat, shortening, *or* pork drippings	1. Heat fat in heavy skillet on low heat.
4 to 5 eggs	2. Beat eggs until mixed; add milk and seasonings, stirring.
¼ c. milk	3. Pour egg mixture into skillet. Cook slowly lifting cooked portion with spatula and turning gently until mixture is firm not dry.
½ t. salt	
Pepper to taste	Serve eggs on heated platter.

VARIATIONS: Use recipe for *Scrambled Eggs*.

Luncheon Eggs

–1–

Omit table fat.	Cut bacon into small squares; cook in ungreased skillet on low heat to golden brown.
3 strips bacon	
3 T. finely chopped stuffed olives	Add egg mixture and olives to bacon.
Parsley sprigs	Serve with parsley.

–2–

3 T. chopped, cooked ham *or* dried beef	Cook meat in skillet until golden brown.
1 T. chopped chives	Add chives and herb with meat to egg mixture.
⅛ t. of basil or thyme	

–3–

½ c. grated sharp cheese	Add to egg mixture.
2 t. finely chopped onion	

–4–

1 to 1½ T. table fat	Heat fat in heavy skillet on low heat.
4 to 5 eggs	Break eggs one at a time in small plate; put in bowl.
½ t. salt	Put eggs in fat without beating. Cook until whites solidify.
⅛ t. pepper	Add salt and pepper.
	Stir with a spoon until firm not dry.
	When finished, both white and yellow should show.

Plain Omelet

2 servings

1½ T. table fat
3 eggs
3 T. milk
⅜ t. salt
Pepper to taste

1. Heat fat in skillet over low heat.
2. Beat eggs until mixed; add milk and seasonings; beat well.
3. Pour egg mixture into skillet and cook slowly.
4. Lift mixture lightly with spatula from bottom of skillet to let uncooked mixture flow underneath.
5. Crease omelet through center when set; fold over with a spatula, and roll from the skillet to a heated platter. Serve immediately.

VARIATIONS: Use recipe for *Plain Omelet*.

Jelly Omelet

2 to 3 T. tart jelly

Spread jelly on top of omelet before folding.

Cheese or Nut Omelet

2 T. grated Parmesan cheese
or chopped toasted nuts

Sprinkle cheese or nuts on top of omelet before folding.

Fluffy Omelet

4 servings

3 T. table fat
½ t. salt
¼ t. cream of tartar
4 eggs, separated
4 T. milk
Pepper to taste

1. Heat fat in large skillet on low heat.
2. Add salt and cream of tartar to egg whites and beat to form stiffly pointed peaks.
3. Beat egg yolks (with same beater) until thick.
4. Add milk and pepper to egg yolks, stirring until blended.
5. Pour yolks over whites; fold in gently.
6. Pour egg mixture into skillet. Cook for 5 minutes on top of range, moving skillet gently several times.
7. Bake at 350° F. for 10 to 12 minutes, or until gloss disappears and omelet is light brown.
8. Remove from skillet using method for plain omelet. Serve with cheese or tomato sauce, if desired (pp. 423, 424).

VARIATIONS: Use recipe for *Fluffy Omelet*.

–1–
1 can (2½ oz.) mushrooms, chopped

Fold mushrooms into egg mixture before cooking.

–2–
1 c. medium white sauce
¾ c. diced chicken
or flaked tuna fish

Combine sauce and meat and heat to serving temperature. Pour on omelet before serving.

–3–
1 c. medium white sauce
½ can (No. 2) asparagus spears

Drain, season, heat, and arrange spears on omelet.

1 Pour beaten yolks over beaten whites. Fold in with spatula until well blended

MAKING A FLUFFY OMELET

4 Loosen omelet with spatula

2 After cooking over low heat until the omelet is just set (five to ten minutes), lift carefully around edges to test color of bottom. It should be a delicate golden brown. Then place in oven at 350° F.

The omelet is done when the spatula comes out clean

5 Make shallow cut with spatula, then fold

Slide omelet to platter

3

6

Scalloped Eggs

4 servings

6 hard-cooked eggs
2 c. medium white sauce
$\frac{1}{2}$ c. bread crumbs
1 T. table fat

1. Cut eggs in quarters and arrange in baking dish.
2. Add sauce to eggs; cover with crumbs and dot with fat.
3. Bake eggs at 350° F. until crumbs are light brown.

Eggs Creole

6 servings

2 T. table fat
$\frac{1}{4}$ c. chopped onion
$\frac{1}{4}$ c. chopped green pepper
$2\frac{1}{2}$ c. tomatoes
2 c. water
1 c. washed uncooked rice
$\frac{3}{4}$ t. salt
6 eggs
$\frac{1}{4}$ t. salt
Pepper to taste

1. Heat fat in baking dish fitted with cover.
2. Add onion and green pepper; cook slowly until onion is golden.
3. Add tomatoes and water to onion mixture; bring to boiling point.
4. Add rice and $\frac{3}{4}$ t. salt to tomato mixture; cook slowly for 25 to 30 minutes or until rice is tender. (Add more water if needed.)
5. Break eggs, one at a time, into a plate. Slip into the baking dish. Season with $\frac{1}{4}$ t. salt, and pepper.
6. Cover dish and simmer 3 minutes for soft-poach, 5 minutes for medium-poach.
Serve in baking dish.

Deviled Eggs

4 servings

4 hard-cooked eggs
$\frac{1}{2}$ t. salt
$\frac{1}{8}$ t. pepper
$\frac{1}{4}$ t. dry mustard
2 to 3 T. cooked salad dressing
 or mayonnaise
Paprika

1. Cut eggs in halves lengthwise. Remove yolks to dish and mash with fork.
2. Add seasonings and dressing to yolks; mix until blended.
3. Refill egg whites with yolk mixture. Sprinkle tops with paprika.

VARIATIONS: Use recipe for *Deviled Eggs*.

–1–

2 T. finely chopped parsley
 or chopped chives
 or chopped celery leaves

Combine chopped vegetable with yolk mixture.

–2–

$\frac{1}{2}$ t. prepared mustard
Few grains of cayenne pepper
2 T. finely chopped tongue
1 to $1\frac{1}{3}$ T. vinegar

Combine meat and seasonings with yolk mixture.

372

Toast and Quick Breads

TOAST

Choose bread for toasting that is a day or more old. It may be cut from $\frac{1}{4}$- to $\frac{1}{2}$-inch thick. Rapid toasting results in a crisp surface and soft interior. Toast made in the oven heated to 300° or 325° F. is crisp and dry.

Plain Broiled Toast   4 servings

4 bread slices
2 to $2\frac{1}{2}$ T. table fat

1. Put bread slices on baking sheet; spread slices with table fat.
2. Broil 4 inches from heat unit 1 to 2 minutes. Serve at once.

Plain Toast   4 servings

4 bread slices
$2\frac{1}{2}$ T. melted table fat

1. Put bread slices or strips on baking sheet. Bake at 325° F. until light brown, turning once.
2. Spread toast with table fat.

VARIATIONS: Use recipe for *Plain Toast.*

Melba Toast

Day-old bread sliced $\frac{1}{8}$-inch thick
Omit table fat.

Put bread slices on a baking sheet.
Bake at 325° F. until crisp and golden brown, turning once.

Cinnamon Toast

1 t. cinnamon
$\frac{1}{4}$ c. sugar

Brush fat on bread.
Mix cinnamon and sugar and sprinkle over bread.
Broil 4 inches from heat unit for 1 to 2 minutes.

373

Orange Toast

¼ c. orange juice
2 t. grated orange rind
¼ c. sugar

Mix juice, rind, and sugar in saucepan; simmer for 2 minutes.
Brush fat and orange mixture on toast.
Broil 4 inches from heat unit 1 to 2 minutes.

Cheese Toast

¼ c. grated sharp cheese
Few grains of cayenne pepper

Sprinkle toasted bread with cheese and pepper.
Broil toast 4 inches from heat unit for ½ to 1 minute.

Milk Toast

2 c. milk
1½ T. table fat substituted for 2½ T.
⅛ t. salt

Scald milk in top of double boiler over hot water. Add fat and seasoning to milk; pour over toast.

French Toast

4 servings

2 eggs
¼ t. salt
½ to ⅔ c. milk
3 T. table fat
   or shortening
4 day-old bread slices

1. Beat eggs until mixed; add salt and milk.
2. Heat fat in frying pan.
3. Dip each bread slice into egg mixture and fry until golden brown, turning once.

Croutons

1¼ cups

¼ c. melted table fat
1½ c. bread cubes
Paprika

1. Put cubes on baking sheet; brush with fat and sprinkle with paprika.
2. Bake cubes at 325° F., stirring gently one or two times, until light brown on all sides.

Use to garnish cream soups or to top vegetable dishes and au gratin casseroles.

VARIATIONS: Use recipe for *Croutons.*

Cheese Croutons

½ c. grated cheese

Add cheese to fat, stirring until cheese melts.

Garlic Croutons

½ garlic clove

Add garlic to fat. Cook for 1 to 2 minutes and remove.

French Croutons

Add ½ c. melted table fat

Cook cubes in skillet, stirring gently with fork.

374

Coconut Sticks

5 to 6 servings

3 bread slices
$\frac{1}{2}$ c. condensed milk
$\frac{3}{4}$ c. coconut

1. Trim crusts from bread; cut each slice into three or four strips.
2. Grease baking sheet lightly.
3. Spread each bread strip with milk; sprinkle with coconut.
4. Broil 4 inches from heat unit until light brown, turning once.

QUICK BREADS

Popovers

4 to 5 servings

1 c. sifted flour
$\frac{1}{4}$ t. salt
3 eggs
1 c. milk
1 T. melted table fat
or shortening

1. Sift flour and salt together in large bowl.
2. Beat eggs until thick and add milk and fat. Stir.
3. Place dot of table fat in each popover cup; heat in oven until very hot.
4. Make a well in flour mixture, pour in egg mixture, and beat with rotary beater until smooth.
5. Pour batter into sizzling pans, filling $\frac{1}{3}$ full.
6. Bake at 425° F. for 20 minutes. Reduce heat to 325° F. and continue baking for 15 minutes or until firm. Turn off heat; leave popovers in oven 10 minutes or until crisp.

BAKING QUICK BREADS

FOOD	TEMPERATURES (degrees Fahr.)	TIME (minutes)
Biscuits	425–450	12–15
Popovers	425–450 for 20 min., then 325 for 15 min.	35
Muffins	400–425	20–25
Coffee cake	375	25
Corn bread	400–425	22–30

Sweet-Milk Griddle Cakes

4 to 5 servings

1⅓ c. sifted flour
3 t. baking powder
2 T. sugar
½ t. salt
1 egg
¾ c. milk
3 T. melted table fat
  or shortening

1. Sift flour, baking powder, sugar, and salt together in bowl.
2. Beat egg until thick; add milk and fat, stirring.
3. Heat griddle slowly.
4. Make a well in flour mixture; pour in egg mixture, stirring quickly until flour mixture is well moistened.
5. When a drop of water on the griddle rolls around, pour batter on hot griddle, making 3- to 4-inch cakes. (About ¼ c. batter for each cake.)
6. Cook cakes until bubbles begin to burst on top; turn with a pancake turner and cook about ½ minute.

Serve, or stack cakes on baking sheet placed in oven at 300° F.

VARIATIONS: Use recipe for *Sweet-Milk Griddle Cakes.*

Pineapple Griddle Cakes

½ c. pineapple, crushed, drained

Add fruit to batter just before baking.

Nut Griddle Cakes

¼ c. nuts, chopped

Add nuts to batter just before baking.

Sour-Milk Griddle Cakes

4 to 5 servings

1¼ c. sifted flour
½ t. baking soda
1 t. baking powder
2 T. sugar
½ t. salt
1 egg
1 c. sour milk
2 T. melted table fat
  or shortening

Follow steps in recipe for Sweet-Milk Griddle Cakes.

376

Plain Waffles

1½ c. sifted flour
2 t. baking powder
½ t. salt
2 eggs, separated
1 c. milk
6 T. melted table fat

1. Sift flour, baking powder, and salt together in large bowl.
2. Heat waffle iron. Beat whites to form softly rounded peaks.
3. Beat yolks until thick; add milk and fat; blend with rotary beater.
4. Make a well in flour mixture; pour in yolk mixture, stirring quickly until flour mixture is just moistened.
5. Fold whites into batter using eight to ten light strokes.
6. Pour about ⅓ c. batter into center of iron or 1 T. in center of each compartment.
7. Bake waffles until crisp and golden brown.
   Serve with melted table fat and hot sirup or honey *or* with orange sauce (p. 426).

VARIATIONS: Use recipe for *Plain Waffles*.

Cheese Waffles

¾ to 1 c. cheese, grated

For each variation, fold the ingredients into waffle batter.

Apple Waffles

1 c. apple, finely diced

Coconut Waffles

½ to ¾ c. coconut, shredded

Nut Waffles

½ to ¾ c. nuts, chopped

Pineapple Waffles

½ to ¾ c. pineapple, crushed

Chocolate Waffles

1½ sq. unsweetened chocolate, melted
1 T. sugar

Gingerbread Waffles

6 servings

2 c. sifted flour
$\frac{3}{4}$ t. baking soda
$\frac{1}{2}$ t. salt
2 t. ginger
2 eggs, separated
1 c. molasses
$\frac{1}{2}$ c. buttermilk
$\frac{1}{2}$ c. melted shortening

1. Sift flour, baking soda, salt, and ginger together.
2. Beat whites with rotary beater to form softly rounded peaks.
3. Beat yolks until thick and add molasses, buttermilk, and shortening; blend with rotary beater.
4. Make a well in flour mixture, add yolk mixture, and stir quickly until flour mixture is just moistened.
5. Heat waffle iron.
6. Fold whites into batter (using beater as spoon). Use 8 to 10 light strokes.
7. Bake waffles slightly more slowly, and 1 to 2 minutes longer, than plain waffles.

Serve with applesauce and bacon *or* cream cheese and candied ginger *or* whipped cream flavored with molasses.

Muffins

12 muffins

2 c. sifted flour
3 t. baking powder
$\frac{3}{4}$ t. salt
2 T. sugar
1 egg
1 c. milk
$\frac{1}{4}$ c. melted shortening
   or table fat

1. Light oven and set at 425° F. Place dot of fat in each muffin cup, melt fat in oven and remove.
2. Sift flour, baking powder, salt, and sugar together twice in large bowl.
3. Beat egg until thick; add milk and shortening; blend with rotary beater.
4. Make a well in flour mixture and add egg mixture all at once; stir quickly until flour mixture is just moistened.
5. Push batter into muffin pans or cups quickly (p. 56).
6. Bake muffins for 20 minutes or until light brown.

VARIATIONS: Use recipe for *Muffins*.

Rich Blueberry Muffins

1 c. fresh blueberries drained and 4 T. sugar *or* 1 c. frozen blueberries drained and 2 T. sugar

Add to dry ingredients.

Bran Muffins

$\frac{1}{2}$ c. bran or bran flour substituted for $\frac{1}{2}$ c. white flour

Set muffins aside for 5 minutes before baking.

Soybean Muffins

2 T. soybean flour substituted for 2 T. white flour

Orange Muffins

$\frac{1}{2}$ c. orange juice substituted for $\frac{1}{2}$ c. milk
1 t. grated orange rind

Add juice and rind to egg mixture.

378

Bacon Muffins

¼ c. bacon fat substituted for fat in recipe
3 slices finely chopped cooked bacon

Add fat and bacon with egg mixture to flour mixture.

Corn Bread

6 servings

1 c. corn meal
1 c. sifted flour
3 t. baking powder
1 t. salt
1 T. sugar
2 eggs
1¼ c. milk
3 T. melted shortening

1. Sift meal, flour, baking powder, salt, and sugar together in large bowl.
2. Beat eggs until thick; add milk and shortening, stirring until blended.
3. Heat a 9-inch square or round pan or molds.
4. Make a well in meal mixture; add egg mixture, stirring quickly until mixed.
5. Pour batter into molds, filling ⅔ full. Bake at 425° F. for 20 to 22 minutes.

Virginia Spoon Corn Bread

6 servings

¾ c. meal, water-ground
2 t. baking powder
2 t. sugar
½ t. baking soda
1 t. salt
1 c. buttermilk
1 c. milk
2 T. melted table fat

1. Mix meal, baking powder, sugar, baking soda, and salt together in large bowl.
2. Add buttermilk, milk, and fat to meal mixture, stirring quickly until meal is well moistened.
3. Heat a square 7- to 9-inch baking pan; pour in batter.
4. Bake bread at 425° F. for 25 minutes or until firm.

Boston Brown Bread

2 small loaves

⅔ c. sifted white flour
1 t. salt
1½ t. baking powder
¼ t. baking soda
⅔ c. whole-wheat flour
⅔ c. corn meal
⅔ c. chopped seedless raisins
1 c. milk
½ c. dark molasses
3 T. melted table fat

1. Grease two coffee cans fitted with covers.
2. Sift white flour, salt, baking powder, and baking soda together.
3. Mix whole-wheat flour, meal, and raisins with flour mixture.
4. Add milk, molasses, and fat to flour mixture, and stir quickly until flour mixture is just moistened.
5. Pour batter into cans, filling ⅔ full, and cover. Set cans in roaster; add hot water to cover ⅓ height of cans.
6. Bake bread at 275° F. for 2 hours; remove cans from water; open and dry in oven at 275° F. for 20 minutes.
7. Remove bread from cans.

Nut Bread

15 to 20 $\frac{1}{4}$-inch slices

2 c. sifted flour
$\frac{1}{3}$ c. sugar
1 T. baking powder
$\frac{1}{2}$ t. salt
$\frac{1}{2}$ c. broken nuts
1 egg
1 c. milk
  or fruit juice
3 T. melted table fat

1. Sift flour, sugar, baking powder, and salt together twice in large bowl; add nuts.
2. Add egg to milk and fat, beating well with rotary beater.
3. Add egg mixture to flour mixture, stirring quickly until flour mixture is just moistened.
4. Push batter into 8$\frac{1}{2}$-inch loaf pan; set aside 25 minutes before baking.
5. Bake bread at 400° F. for 45 minutes. (To prevent a cracked top, cover with inverted loaf pan for first 15 minutes.)

Orange-Nut Bread

18 to 20 $\frac{1}{4}$-inch slices

2 c. sifted flour
1 c. sugar
1 t. baking powder
$\frac{1}{2}$ t. baking soda
$\frac{1}{4}$ t. salt
$\frac{1}{2}$ c. broken nuts
1 orange
Water, boiling
1 c. raisins
  or dates
1 egg
2 T. melted table fat

1. Sift flour, sugar, baking powder, baking soda, and salt together twice in large bowl; add nuts.
2. Squeeze juice from orange into liquid cup measure; add boiling water to make 1 c. (Insert metal spoon in glass cup to prevent breakage.)
3. Remove membrane from orange rind and grind rind with raisins. Add to orange juice and water.
4. Beat egg until thick; add fat and orange-juice mixture, and blend with rotary beater.
5. Add egg-and-orange-juice mixture to flour mixture, stirring quickly until flour mixture is just moistened.
6. Push batter into 8$\frac{1}{2}$-inch loaf pan; bake at 350° F. for 60 minutes.

Quick Coffee Cake

6 servings

1 c. sifted flour
2 t. baking powder
$\frac{1}{2}$ t. salt
$\frac{1}{2}$ t. cinnamon
1 egg
$\frac{1}{2}$ c. sugar
$\frac{1}{2}$ c. milk
1 T. grated orange rind
2 T. melted table fat
  or shortening

1. Sift flour, baking powder, salt, and cinnamon together twice in large bowl.
2. Beat egg until thick; add sugar, milk, fat, and rind, and blend with rotary beater.
3. Add egg mixture to flour mixture, and stir quickly until flour mixture is just moistened.
4. Push batter into 8- to 9-inch square cake pan. Bake at 375° F. for 25 minutes.
Add topping.

Topping

1 T. melted table fat
$\frac{1}{4}$ c. brown sugar
2 T. grated orange rind
$\frac{1}{2}$ c. broken nuts

Mix fat, sugar, rind, and nuts together and spread over hot coffee cake.

Baking-Powder Biscuits

12 to 14 biscuits

2 c. sifted flour
4 t. baking powder
1 t. salt
4 T. shortening
⅔ c. milk

1. Sift flour, baking powder, and salt together in large bowl.
2. Cut shortening into flour mixture with two knives or a pastry blender until mixture looks like rice grains.
3. Add milk to flour mixture; stir quickly with a fork just enough to make a soft dough.
4. Put dough on lightly floured board and knead six to eight times, forming a ball.
5. Roll dough ¼-inch thick for crusty biscuits and ½-inch thick for soft biscuits. Cut with floured cutter.
6. Place biscuits on baking sheet. Bake at 425° to 450° F. for 12 to 15 minutes.

VARIATIONS: Use recipe for *Baking-Powder Biscuits.*

Sour-Milk Biscuits

¼ t. baking soda substituted for 1 t. baking powder
Sour milk *or* buttermilk substituted for sweet milk

Drop Biscuits

⅓ c. additional milk

Drop dough by tablespoons on baking sheet.

Cheese Biscuits

½ c. grated cheese, sharp

Add cheese to sifted flour mixture.

Bacon Biscuits

½ c. cooked bits of bacon, drained

Add bacon to sifted flour mixture.

Pigs-in-Blanket

12 wieners
or frankfurters

Roll each wiener in a strip of rolled dough; let tips show.

Scones

2 T. sugar
½ c. milk substituted for ⅔ c. milk
1 egg
3 T. milk
3 T. sugar

Add sugar to flour mixture.
Beat egg until thick and add with milk.
Divide dough into three balls; roll each ¼-inch thick in shape of circle. Cut each circle into four pie-shaped wedges.
Place on greased baking sheet; brush wedges with milk and sprinkle with 3 T. sugar.

381

Doughnuts

2 dozen

4 c. sifted flour
4 t. baking powder
1 t. salt
4 T. table fat
$\frac{1}{4}$ t. cinnamon
$\frac{1}{4}$ t. nutmeg
$\frac{1}{8}$ t. mace
1 c. sugar
2 eggs
1 c. milk
Shortening for deep-fat frying

1. Sift flour, baking powder, and salt together.
2. Blend fat and spices in large bowl. Add sugar, $\frac{1}{4}$ c. at a time, creaming after each addition until fluffy (p. 171).
3. Beat eggs until thick; add to sugar mixture, blending.
4. Add flour mixture alternately with milk, in three additions, to sugar mixture, stirring after each addition until blended.
5. Chill dough for 5 minutes.
6. Use enough shortening to fill a deep, heavy pan $\frac{1}{2}$ to $\frac{2}{3}$ full when melted; heat to 370° F.
7. Put dough on lightly floured board and shape into ball. Roll dough $\frac{1}{3}$-inch thick; cut with floured cutter.
8. Lift doughnuts with wide spatula; place three or four at a time in hot fat.
9. Cook doughnuts to golden brown, turning once. Drain on absorbent paper.

VARIATIONS: Use recipe for *Doughnuts.*

Drop Doughnuts

$3\frac{1}{2}$ c. flour substituted for 4 c.

Drop dough by teaspoonfuls into hot fat.

Chocolate Doughnuts

$3\frac{3}{4}$ c. flour substituted for 4 c.
Omit nutmeg and mace.
$\frac{3}{8}$ c. cocoa
1 t. vanilla

Add cocoa to flour mixture.
Add vanilla to milk.

Orange Doughnuts

Omit nutmeg and cinnamon.
1 T. grated orange rind
$\frac{1}{2}$ c. orange juice substituted for $\frac{1}{2}$ c. milk

Add orange rind to flour mixture.

Sugared Doughnuts

$\frac{1}{2}$ c. sugar

Place two drained doughnuts at a time in paper bag with sugar.
Shake gently until coated.

Glazed Doughnuts

$\frac{1}{3}$ c. boiling water
1 c. confectioners' sugar

Add water gradually to sugar; mix well.
Dip drained doughnuts into glaze.

Gingerbread

2 c. sifted flour
$\frac{1}{2}$ t. baking soda
$\frac{1}{2}$ c. sugar
$\frac{1}{4}$ t. salt
1 t. cinnamon
1 t. ginger
$\frac{1}{2}$ c. water
$\frac{1}{2}$ c. molasses
$\frac{1}{2}$ c. fat
2 eggs
$\frac{1}{2}$ c. evaporated milk, chilled icy cold
$\frac{1}{4}$ c. apple butter

1. Sift flour, baking soda, sugar, salt, and spices together.
2. Heat water to boiling point; remove from heat; add molasses and fat, and blend.
3. Beat eggs until thick; add molasses mixture, stirring until blended.
4. Add egg mixture to flour mixture; beat 300 strokes.
5. Pour batter into a square 8- to 9-inch cake pan and bake at 350° F. for 30 to 40 minutes.
6. Beat milk in chilled bowl, fold in apple butter; serve on top of cake when cool.

Buckwheat Bread

2 c. buckwheat flour or whole-wheat flour
1 t. soda
1 t. salt
2 c. sour milk or buttermilk

1. Sift flour, soda, and salt together.
2. Make a well in flour mixture and add milk, stirring quickly until flour mixture is just moistened.
3. Push batter into a greased $8\frac{1}{2}$-inch loaf pan.
4. Bake at 350° F. for 30 minutes.
   Serve with table fat and maple sirup. Leftover bread may be used, toasted.

Cheese Straws

1 c. grated cheese
1 c. soft bread crumbs
$\frac{2}{3}$ c. sifted flour
$\frac{1}{2}$ t. salt
$\frac{1}{8}$ t. white pepper
Few grains of cayenne pepper
2 T. melted table fat
1 T. milk

1. Mix cheese, crumbs, flour, seasonings, and fat together.
2. Add milk to cheese mixture, stirring until blended.
3. Place dough on lightly floured board and roll $\frac{1}{4}$-inch thick; cut into $\frac{1}{2}$ by 4-inch strips and place on baking sheet.
4. Bake straws at 375° F. for 10 to 12 minutes or until light brown.

Pastry Cheese Straws

1 recipe for pie pastry (p. 476)
$\frac{3}{4}$ c. grated cheese
$\frac{1}{8}$ t. white pepper
Paprika

1. Place pastry on lightly floured board and roll $\frac{1}{4}$-inch thick. Sprinkle with $\frac{1}{4}$ c. cheese. Dust with pepper and paprika.
2. Fold pastry in halves; pinch edges together; roll again. Repeat this process two more times.
3. Cut pastry into $\frac{1}{2}$-inch strips; place on baking sheet.
4. Bake cheese straws at 425° F. for 10 to 12 minutes.

Soups

Chicken Stock

2 qt. cold water
4 to 5 lb. stewing chicken,
    cut into pieces
$\frac{1}{3}$ c. diced carrots
$\frac{1}{3}$ c. chopped celery
1 sprig parsley, finely chopped
1 medium onion, sliced
2 t. salt
2 peppercorns
$\frac{1}{2}$ bay leaf

To clear stock:

1 egg white
$\frac{1}{2}$ c. cold water

Chicken-Rice Soup

4 c. chicken stock
$\frac{1}{2}$ c. washed rice
$\frac{3}{8}$ c. milk
   or light cream

1 to 1$\frac{1}{2}$ quarts

1. Add 3 qt. water to chicken in kettle. Add vegetables and seasonings and cook, covered, on low heat for 3 hours.
2. Remove chicken; strain stock through sieve. Cool stock to room temperature; then chill until fat hardens.
3. Remove fat from stock with spoon. Store stock, tightly covered in refrigerator.

1. Heat stock in saucepan.
2. Beat egg white until foamy and add to stock. Stir until mixture boils; boil 3 to 4 minutes.
3. Remove stock from heat. Pour cold water over top of liquid; let settle. Strain stock through two thicknesses of cheesecloth.

4 servings

1. Heat stock in saucepan to boiling point. Add rice; cook for 25 minutes or until tender.
2. Heat milk over hot water, or very slowly in saucepan over low heat, to serving temperature. Add milk to stock mixture.

384

Chicken-Noodle Soup

4 servings

4 c. chicken stock
1 c. noodles
½ c. thin cream

1. Heat stock in saucepan; add noodles and cream.
2. Cook stock mixture for 20 minutes or until noodles are tender.

Consommé

6 servings

1 lb. lean beef
1 lb. veal
2 T. shortening
2 T. chopped onion
1 T. chopped celery and carrot
2 peppercorns
1 clove
½ t. thyme, savory, *or* marjoram
1½ qt. water
1 T. chopped parsley

1. Cut meats into small pieces. Saw or crack bones.
2. Heat shortening in frying pan; add beef and cook to light brown, stirring three or four times. Add veal and onion to beef and cook until onion is golden.
3. Add browned meats, vegetables, bones, and seasonings to water in large kettle. Simmer for 3 to 4 hours.
4. Remove meats and bones. Cool stock to room temperature; then chill until fat hardens on top.
5. Remove fat with spoon and strain stock through several thicknesses of cheesecloth. Reheat stock and garnish with parsley.

To clear stock:

1 egg white
½ c. cold water

Note step process in clearing Chicken Stock, p. 384.

VARIATION: Use recipe for *Consommé*.

Jellied Consommé

1 qt. jellied consommé
Chopped pimento, chives, *or* parsley

Beat slightly with fork.
Serve in bouillon cups; garnish with pimento.

Cream-of-Tomato Soup

6 servings

3 T. table fat
3 T. flour
3½ c. fresh tomatoes
  or 1 can (No. 2½)
2 T. chopped onion
1 t. brown sugar
1 t. salt
⅛ t. basil
3 c. milk, scalded
Rye croutons

1. Melt fat in saucepan, add flour, stir to a smooth paste. Set aside.
2. Wash and dice fresh tomatoes; add onion, sugar, salt, basil, and cook 20 minutes. (Cook canned tomatoes 10 minutes.)
3. Force tomatoes through sieve into saucepan.
4. Add the tomato puree to melted fat mixture, stir, and cook until thickened.
5. Pour tomato mixture into the scalded milk. Heat slowly to serving temperature.
6. Prepare croutons (p. 374), using rye bread.

Cream-of-Potato Soup
4 servings

2 to 3 T. table fat
2 T. flour
2 c. milk
$\frac{1}{2}$ t. salt
2 c. diced raw potatoes
$\frac{1}{2}$ t. salt
$\frac{1}{8}$ t. celery salt
$\frac{1}{8}$ t. onion salt
$\frac{3}{4}$ c. water, boiling
$\frac{1}{8}$ t. mace, if desired

1. Prepare thin white sauce (p. 423), using fat, flour, milk, and salt.
2. Add potatoes and seasonings, except mace, to water in saucepan. Cook, covered, for 10 to 12 minutes or until tender.
3. Drain potatoes and save liquid.
4. Force potatoes through sieve if preferred.
5. Combine white sauce and potatoes with liquid and add mace if desired. Heat to serving temperature.
   Serve with croutons, bread sticks, or crackers.

VARIATIONS: Use recipe for *Cream-of-Potato Soup.*

Cream-of-Celery Soup

2 c. finely diced celery substituted for potatoes
2 T. grated sharp cheese

Do not sieve celery.
Sprinkle cheese on soup before serving.

Cream-of-Corn Soup

1 T. flour substituted for 2 T.
1 can (No. $2\frac{1}{2}$) cream-style corn substituted for potatoes
Omit $\frac{3}{4}$ c. water, $\frac{1}{2}$ t. salt, and spices

Cream-of-Onion Soup

3 to 4 medium onions, sliced, substituted for potatoes
Omit spices.
$\frac{1}{8}$ t. marjoram *or* savory, if desired

Cream-of-Spinach Soup

2 c. finely chopped cooked spinach substituted for potatoes
Omit $\frac{1}{2}$ c. water and spices.
$\frac{1}{8}$ t. rosemary *or* tarragon

386

Bean Soup
4 servings

1 c. dried white beans
4 c. water, boiling
$\frac{2}{3}$ c. diced salt pork
1 onion, chopped
3 stalks celery, chopped
1 t. salt
Few grains of cayenne pepper
5 c. water
1 frankfurter, thinly sliced

1. Wash beans and sort for quality. Pour into 4 c. boiling water; remove from heat and soak covered for 4 to 5 hours.
2. Cook salt pork in large frying pan until light brown. Add onion and continue cooking until onion is golden, stirring once or twice.
3. Add beans (drained), celery, seasonings, and 5 c. water to pork and onion; boil 30 minutes; then simmer covered for $1\frac{1}{2}$ hours. Add additional water if desired.
4. Add frankfurter slices.

VARIATION: Use recipe for *Bean Soup*.

Purée of Bean Soup

$\frac{1}{8}$ t. savory, if desired

Force cooked bean mixture through purée sieve.
Add savory, if desired, with seasonings.

Pea Soup with Ham
4 servings

$\frac{1}{2}$ lb. dried peas
4 c. water, boiling
Ham hock
2 T. chopped onion
2 t. flour
$1\frac{1}{2}$ T. cold water
$\frac{1}{4}$ c. finely cut ham from hock

1. Wash peas and sort for quality. Pour into 4 c. boiling water, remove from heat, and soak covered for 4 to 5 hours.
2. Wash and scrape ham hock; put in large kettle and add water to cover.
3. Simmer ham, covered, slowly for 2 hours or until tender; if salty, change water once or twice during cooking.
4. Cool ham in its liquid.
5. Remove fat from liquid.
6. Remove ham from liquid and chop fine enough of it to make $\frac{1}{4}$ c.
7. Dilute stock with 1 to $1\frac{1}{2}$ c. water.
8. Add peas and onion to stock; boil for 30 minutes; then simmer covered for $1\frac{1}{2}$ hours.
9. Remove peas and onion from stock; force through a sieve.
10. Add the purée to stock and bring to boil.
11. Mix flour with $1\frac{1}{2}$ T. water and add to stock, stirring. Add finely chopped ham to stock; boil for 2 minutes, stirring constantly.

Pepper Pot

6 servings

1 large soup bone, cracked or sawed (beef or veal)
Water
1½ t. salt
1 bay leaf
1 small-pod red pepper
⅛ t. pepper
1 T. meat drippings
2 T. chopped onion
2 T. chopped green pepper
2 medium potatoes, diced
2 medium carrots, diced
2 stalks celery, diced
1 T. finely chopped parsley

1. Put bone in well cooker of range or in large kettle; cover with water and add seasonings.
2. Simmer bone and seasonings, covered, for 3 hours or until meat separates from bone.
3. Strain stock into large saucepan; cool to room temperature, and then chill until fat hardens.
4. Remove fat from stock with spoon.
5. Heat drippings in frying pan; add onion and pepper, and cook until onion is golden, stirring once or twice.
6. Heat stock and add vegetables; boil, covered for 15 minutes or until vegetables are tender.
7. Add onion mixture to stock mixture. Heat to serving temperature; garnish with parsley.

Vegetable Soup

5 to 6 servings

1½ qt. meat stock
2 t. salt
2 to 3 peppercorns
¾ c. finely diced carrots
¾ c. finely diced turnips
  or celery
1 c. finely diced potatoes
2 c. tomato pulp and juice
¾ c. chopped cabbage
¼ c. cut green beans   .
¼ c. chopped onion

1. Heat meat stock in large kettle and add seasonings.
2. Add vegetables to stock.
3. Boil stock mixture, covered, for 15 minutes or until vegetables are tender.
4. Simmer soup 5 to 10 minutes.

Sea-Food Chowder

4 servings

¼ c. finely cut bacon
  or salt pork
¼ c. finely cut onion
2 cans (7 oz. each) clams, lobster, *or* other sea food
2 c. cooked diced potatoes
2 c. milk
1 t. salt
⅛ t. pepper

1. Cook bacon in large frying pan for 1 to 2 minutes. Add onion; cook until golden, stirring two or three times.
2. Drain sea food in sieve; save the liquid.
3. Add sea-food liquid and potatoes to bacon mixture; cook covered until potatoes are thoroughly heated.
4. Mince sea food with a knife and add with milk and seasonings to bacon mixture. Heat slowly to serving temperature.

388

VARIATIONS: Use recipe for *Sea-Food Chowder.*

Fresh-Fish Chowder

1 lb. fish, substituted for canned sea food

1 c. hot fish stock substituted for sea-food liquid

Wrap fish in cheesecloth; cook in boiling, salted water (pp. 224–225).
Drain fish, save stock. Use 1 c. stock.
Remove fishbones and flake meat with fork.

Corn Chowder

1 T. finely cut onion substituted for ¼ c.

1 c. milk
   or water substituted for sea-food liquid

½ c. chopped celery and
½ c. chopped carrot substituted for potatoes

1 can (No. 1) corn, cream style, substituted for sea food

Shrimp Bisque

6 servings

¾ lb. cooked shrimp
¼ c. table fat
2 T. chopped onion
2 T. chopped celery
2 T. flour
¼ c. water
1 qt. milk
1 t. salt
¼ t. paprika
⅛ t. pepper

1. Prepare shrimp (p. 226) and put through food chopper.
2. Heat fat in large frying pan. Add onion and celery and cook until onion is golden, stirring once or twice.
3. Mix flour with water; add to onion-celery mixture, stirring.
4. Add milk and seasonings to onion-celery mixture; cook on low heat until slightly thickened, stirring two or three times.
5. Add shrimp to onion-celery mixture; heat to serving temperature.

VARIATION: Use recipe for *Shrimp Bisque.*

Clam Bisque

1 can (No. 1) clams, finely cut,
   or 2 c. fresh clams, chopped, substituted for ¾ lb. shrimp

1 T. finely cut parsley

Add parsley just before serving.

Oyster Stew

4 servings

1 pt. oysters with liquid
2½ c. milk
¼ c. table fat
1 t. salt
¼ t. pepper

1. Inspect oysters for bits of shell.
2. Scald milk in top of double boiler over hot water or over very low heat.
3. Heat fat in saucepan; add oysters, liquid, and seasonings. Cook until edges of oysters begin to curl.
4. Combine milk with oysters. Heat to serving temperature.

Vichyssoise

4 servings

(Potato-Leek Soup)

4 chicken bouillon cubes
3 c. water, boiling
4 leeks *or* 2 onions
¼ c. table fat
4 medium potatoes, diced
⅛ t. pepper
⅛ t. celery salt
1 c. thin cream
1 to 2 T. chopped parsley

1. Dissolve bouillon cubes in water.
2. Wash and slice leeks or onions.
3. Heat fat in frying pan. Add leeks or onions and cook 3 to 5 minutes or until golden, stirring two or three times.
4. Add potatoes, bouillon, and seasonings to leeks or onions; simmer 20 to 25 minutes.
5. Force potato mixture through sieve into bowl; add cream, stirring. Chill.
   Garnish and serve.

Borsch

6 servings

2 T. table fat
2 medium onions, sliced
3 stalks celery, diced
4 medium beets, cooked, chopped
Water in which beets were cooked, strained
2 c. consommé (p. 385) *or* use canned consommé
¼ c. shredded cabbage
1 t. salt
⅛ t. pepper
⅜ to ½ c. sour cream

1. Heat fat in frying pan; add onion and celery; cook until onion is golden brown, stirring two or three times.
2. Add beets, beet water, consommé, cabbage, and seasonings to onion and celery; boil, covered, 3 to 5 minutes.
3. Add cream just before heating to serving temperature.

Wilted-Leaf Lettuce Salad

6 servings

$\frac{1}{4}$ c. pork drippings
1 T. chopped onion
$\frac{1}{2}$ t. salt
$\frac{1}{2}$ t. sugar
1 hard-cooked egg, diced
1 medium head lettuce, broken into
    pieces
$\frac{1}{4}$ c. vinegar (Replace 1 T. with water
    if strong.)

1. Heat drippings in small frying pan; add onion and cook until golden, stirring two or three times. (If preferred add onion uncooked to lettuce.)
2. Add seasonings and egg to lettuce.
3. Add vinegar to drippings and heat to rolling boil.
4. Pour dripping mixture over lettuce mixture; toss lightly together.

VARIATION: Use recipe for *Wilted-Leaf Lettuce Salad.*

Lettuce with French Dressing

$\frac{1}{4}$ c. French dressing substituted for
    drippings and vinegar
$\frac{1}{4}$ t. salt and sugar substituted for
    $\frac{1}{2}$ t.

Omit cooking of onion. Add onion with salt, sugar, and egg to lettuce.
Add dressing just before serving; toss lightly.

Head-Lettuce Salad

4 servings

1 small head lettuce, broken into
    pieces
$\frac{1}{4}$ c. thinly sliced scallion
    or 2 T. finely chopped onion
5 bacon slices, diced
$\frac{1}{4}$ c. vinegar
2 t. fresh herbs
1 t. dry mustard
$1\frac{1}{2}$ t. sugar
$\frac{1}{4}$ t. salt
$\frac{1}{8}$ t. pepper
$\frac{1}{8}$ t. garlic salt, if desired
$\frac{1}{4}$ c. bacon drippings
2 hard-cooked eggs, chopped

1. Combine lettuce and scallion in salad bowl.
2. Cook bacon in frying pan over low heat until crisp, stirring with a fork. Remove bacon and drain on absorbent paper. Set drippings aside.
3. Add bacon bits to lettuce mixture.
4. Add vinegar and seasonings to drippings. Heat to boiling; pour over lettuce.
5. Sprinkle lettuce mixture with hard-cooked eggs.

VARIATION: Use recipe for *Head-Lettuce Salad.*

Chinese-Cabbage Salad

1 small head substituted for lettuce
Thousand Island Dressing (p. 399)
    substituted for all seasonings
    and eggs

Slice cabbage thinly.
Add dressing and serve.

Spinach Salad Bowl

6 servings

1 garlic clove, quartered
½ c. French dressing (p. 398)
8 slices bacon
1 lb. (8 c.) crisp young spinach
3 hard-cooked eggs, chopped

1. Add garlic to French dressing; cover and chill 2 hours.
2. Cook bacon in frying pan over low heat until crisp, turning once. Drain on absorbent paper.
3. Prepare spinach leaves and tear into bite-sized pieces in salad bowl.
4. Crumble bacon into bits and add to spinach; sprinkle eggs on top.
5. Remove garlic from French dressing and pour dressing over salad, tossing lightly.

Cole Slaw

4 servings

2 c. shredded cabbage
¼ c. thin cream
1 T. vinegar
½ t. salt
⅛ t. celery salt
A few drops of onion juice
⅛ t. dry mustard

1. Prepare cabbage just before using.
2. Shake together cream, vinegar, and seasonings in covered jar.
3. Add dressing to cabbage just before serving, tossing lightly.

Green Salad

6 servings

1 medium head of lettuce
¼ lb. uncooked spinach
⅛ lb. chicory
1 bunch watercress
2 scallions, minced
¼ c. French dressing (p. 398)
Garlic clove

1. Remove wilted leaves from greens, wash well, drain, and chill ½ hour.
2. Dry greens by wrapping in towel.
3. Tear greens into manageable pieces.
4. Rub salad bowl with cut clove of garlic, letting tiny shreds remain in bowl.
5. Add greens to bowl and toss lightly with French dressing (pp. 161–164), using a fork in each hand.

A tossed garden salad

Chef Salad

4 servings

1 garlic bud
1 small head lettuce
$\frac{1}{4}$ cucumber, thinly sliced
3 radishes, sliced
1 stalk celery, diced
$\frac{1}{4}$ t. salt
$\frac{1}{4}$ c. French salad dressing (p. 398)
1 tomato, cut into quarters

1. Rub salad bowl with garlic bud.
2. Cut or tear lettuce into bite-sized pieces.
3. Add cucumber, radishes, and celery to lettuce.
4. Add salt and dressing just before serving salad, tossing lightly. Add tomato and serve.

VARIATIONS: Use recipe for *Chef Salad*.

–1–

$\frac{1}{2}$ c. diced cold meat
  or chicken

Toss meat with vegetables just before adding dressing.

–2–

3 T. crumbled Roquefort cheese

Add cheese before tossing.

Vegetable Mold

6 servings

2 T. gelatin
6 T. cold water
2 c. water, boiling
$\frac{1}{2}$ t. salt
2 T. lemon juice
$\frac{1}{2}$ c. diced celery
$\frac{1}{2}$ c. shredded cabbage
$\frac{1}{2}$ c. grated carrot

1. Mix gelatin with water; set aside 5 minutes.
2. Add softened gelatin to boiling water, stirring.
3. Add salt and lemon juice to gelatin mixture. Chill until almost set.
4. Add vegetables to gelatin mixture, stirring lightly. Pour into molds; chill until set.

VARIATIONS: Use recipe for *Vegetable Mold*.

Perfection Salad

1 c. water, boiling, substituted for 2 c.
$\frac{1}{4}$ c. sugar
$\frac{1}{4}$ c. vinegar
2 pimentos, chopped
$\frac{1}{2}$ c. diced celery added

Add sugar and vinegar with lemon juice and salt to gelatin mixture.
Combine pimentos with vegetables.

Jellied Tomato Salad

Omit 2 c. water, boiling.
2 c. tomato juice
  or one can (No. 2) tomatoes, substituted for cabbage and carrot
1 T. finely chopped onion
$\frac{1}{2}$ t. sugar
$\frac{1}{2}$ small bay leaf
$\frac{1}{2}$ c. chopped cucumber
$\frac{1}{2}$ c. diced celery

Cook tomato juice (or tomatoes), onion, sugar, and bay leaf together 10 minutes.
Force tomatoes through sieve and add boiling water to make $1\frac{3}{4}$ c. mixture.
Add softened gelatin to hot tomato mixture, stirring. Chill.
Add cucumber and celery when gelatin begins to set.

Stuffed-Tomato Salad

6 servings

6 medium chilled tomatoes
$\frac{1}{2}$ c. chopped cucumber
$\frac{1}{2}$ c. chopped celery
1 T. chopped onion
1 T. chopped green pepper
2 hard-cooked eggs, chopped
2 T. cooked salad dressing (p. 400)
   or mayonnaise (p. 399)
1 t. salt
$\frac{1}{8}$ t. pepper
Salad greens
6 T. cottage cheese
   or 2 T. grated Parmesan cheese

1. Wash tomatoes; remove stem ends. Slice off top and scoop out center, leaving shell about $\frac{1}{4}$-inch thick. Turn tomatoes upside down on plate to drain.
2. Dice tomato pulp and add vegetables and eggs.
3. Add salad dressing and seasonings to tomato mixture, tossing together.
4. Pile salad mixture lightly into tomato shells placed on salad greens.
5. Top each serving with cheese.

Cart-Wheel Salad

6 servings

3 medium green peppers
1 c. cream pimento cheese
6 or 8 olives, chopped
$\frac{1}{4}$ c. chopped nuts
Lettuce
$\frac{1}{4}$ c. French dressing (p. 398)

1. Wash peppers, remove stem, and scoop out seeds.
2. Mix cheese, olives, and nuts together.
3. Stuff peppers with cheese mixture; chill.
4. Slice stuffed peppers into thin sections; serve on lettuce with French dressing.

Salad Supreme

6 servings

2 c. cooked macaroni
1 c. chopped celery
6 T. chopped sweet pickle
6 T. chopped green pepper
3 T. chopped pimento
1 c. diced sharp cheese
$\frac{1}{2}$ c. cooked peas
$\frac{1}{2}$ c. cooked salad dressing (p. 400)
Lettuce

1. Cook 1 c. broken macaroni according to directions in the Cereal Cookery Chart on page 365.
2. Drain. Chill macaroni for 2 or more hours.
3. Add celery, pickles, green pepper, and pimento to macaroni, tossing lightly.
4. Add cheese and peas to macaroni mixture. Add salad dressing, tossing lightly.
5. Chill thoroughly; serve on lettuce.

VARIATIONS: Use recipe for *Salad Supreme.*

–1–

Omit $\frac{1}{2}$ c. chopped celery.
Add $\frac{1}{2}$ c. diced cucumber
   or 4 chopped hard-cooked eggs.

–2–

Omit 1 c. chopped celery and
   $\frac{1}{2}$ c. sharp cheese.
Add 1 c. chopped frankfurters.

Potato Salad

2 c. diced, cooked potatoes
2 t. chopped onion
1 hard-cooked egg, diced
1 t. salt
A few celery seeds
$\frac{1}{8}$ t. dry mustard
3 T. mayonnaise (p. 399)
  or cooked salad dressing (p. 400)
Salad greens
2 T. chopped pimento

1. Combine potatoes, onion, egg, seasonings, and mayonnaise by tossing lightly.
2. Chill.
3. Arrange salad on greens; garnish with pimento.

Hot Potato Salad

4 to 5 servings

4 medium potatoes
2 T. finely chopped onion
2 T. finely chopped green pepper
  or carrot
2 hard-cooked eggs, chopped
3 slices bacon, diced
3 T. vinegar
$\frac{3}{4}$ t. salt
$\frac{1}{8}$ t. pepper

1. Scrub potatoes and cook in skins; drain and peel.
2. Break potatoes apart with fork. Add onion, green pepper, and eggs; toss together lightly.
3. Cook bacon in frying pan until crisp, stirring occasionally with a fork. Remove bacon; drain on absorbent paper. Set drippings aside.
4. Sprinkle bacon bits into potato mixture.
5. Add vinegar and seasonings to drippings; heat to rolling boil and pour over potato mixture, lifting gently with a fork. Serve hot.

Kidney-Bean Salad

6 servings

2 c. canned kidney beans
$\frac{1}{3}$ c. chopped sweet pickles
2 hard-cooked eggs, chopped
$\frac{1}{2}$ c. diced celery
1 t. salt
3 T. mayonnaise (p. 399)

1. Drain kidney beans in a sieve.
2. Add pickles, eggs, celery, and salt to beans in a large bowl; toss together lightly. Chill.
3. Add mayonnaise to bean mixture, tossing together.

Chicken Salad

4 to 5 servings

1 c. diced, cooked chicken
1 c. diced apple
3 T. lemon juice
$\frac{1}{2}$ c. chopped ripe olives
$\frac{1}{2}$ c. diced celery
3 T mayonnaise (p. 399)
  or cooked salad dressing (p. 400)

1. Combine chicken and apple; sprinkle with lemon juice and toss together.
2. Mix olives and celery with mayonnaise and add to chicken-and-apple mixture. Toss lightly.

Salmon Salad

4 servings

1½ c. salmon
1 c. diced celery
1 hard-cooked egg, chopped
2 t. chopped pickle
½ t. salt
3 T. cooked salad dressing (p. 400)
Salad greens

1. Remove bones from salmon and flake meat with fork.
2. Add celery, egg, pickle, and salt to salmon. Add dressing and toss mixture lightly.
3. Chill salmon mixture, tightly covered. Serve on greens.

VARIATIONS: Use recipe for *Salmon Salad*.

Savory Salmon Salad

3 T. chopped apple
⅛ t. rosemary
⅛ t. savory
Omit pickle.

Add apple and herbs to salmon mixture before adding dressing.

Tuna Salad

1½ c. tuna fish substituted for salmon

Drain oil from tuna fish.

Waldorf Salad

6 servings

4 medium apples
¾ c. chopped celery
⅜ to ½ c. coarsely chopped nuts
2 to 3 T. mayonnaise (p. 399)
   or fruit salad dressing (p. 400)
⅛ t. salt
Salad greens

1. Wash, core, and dice apples.
2. Add celery, nuts, mayonnaise, and salt to apple, tossing lightly.
   Serve on salad greens.

Cranberry Salad

6 servings

2 T. gelatin
6 T. cold water
4 c. cranberries
2 oranges
2 c. sugar
½ c. water, boiling
1 c. broken nuts
1 c. diced celery

1. Mix gelatin with cold water; set aside 5 minutes.
2. Put washed cranberries and washed whole oranges through food chopper into saucepan.
3. Add sugar and water to cranberry mixture and boil for 2 minutes.
4. Add softened gelatin to cranberry mixture, stirring. Cool cranberry mixture to room temperature.
5. Add nuts and celery. Pour into molds. Chill.

396

Fruit Chef Salad

1 medium head lettuce
  or romaine
1 c. cottage cheese
1 c. diced pineapple, fresh *or* canned
1 apple, unpared, diced
¼ c. raisins
¼ c. broken nuts
3 to 4 T. French dressing (p. 398)

1. Break lettuce into bite-sized pieces.
2. Add cheese, fruits, and nuts to lettuce.
3. Add dressing just before serving; toss lightly.

Cinnamon-Apple Salad

6 servings

1 recipe Cinnamon-Candy Apples,
  chilled (p. 356)
Lettuce

1. Place each apple on lettuce leaves.
2. Fill the centers of apples with one of the suggested fillings below.
3. Top each apple with mayonnaise.

Fillings

¼ c. chopped raisins
3 T. chopped coconut

¼ c. grated cheese
3 T. chopped nuts

4 T. chopped dates
3 T. crushed pineapple

3 T. mayonnaise (p. 399)
  or cooked salad dressing (p. 400)

Frozen Fruit Salad

6 servings

1 T. table fat
1 T. flour
1 egg
1 c. fruit juice
1 T. sugar
1 c. heavy cream
  or evaporated milk, chilled icy cold
1 c. crushed pineapple
1 c. cherries
  or grapes (seedless)
1 c. diced apricots
  or peaches
Salad greens
Mayonnaise (p. 399)
  or cooked salad dressing (p. 400)

1. Melt fat in saucepan; add flour; stir until blended. Set aside.
2. Beat egg until thick; add fruit juice and sugar, stirring.
3. Add egg mixture to the fat and flour, stirring. Return to heat and cook until thickened. Chill.
4. Beat cream and fold into chilled egg mixture. Fold in fruits.
5. Freeze egg mixture (p. 258) in refrigerator tray or molds. Serve salad on greens; top with dressing.

Salad Dressings

✓

French Dressing

1 c. vegetable oil
    or olive oil
¼ c. vinegar
1½ t. salt
⅛ t. pepper
¼ t. paprika
¾ t. sugar
1 T. lemon juice
1½ t. Worcestershire sauce
2 garlic cloves

1½ cups

1. Shake oil, vinegar, and seasonings together in covered jar. Remove garlic.
2. Store dressing, tightly covered, in refrigerator. Shake vigorously just before adding to salad.

VARIATIONS: Use recipe for *French Dressing.*

Horse-radish Dressing No. 1

2 T. red tomato catchup
¼ c. prepared horse-radish

Blend with dressing.

Cheese Dressing

½ c. crumbled Roquefort
    or Blue cheese

Add to dressing.

Thousand Island French Dressing

2 T. red tomato catchup
1 hard-cooked egg, finely chopped
1 T. finely chopped olives
¼ t. rosemary

Add to dressing.

398

Mayonnaise

2 cups

1 to 2 t. sugar
1 t. salt
½ t. dry mustard
Few grains of cayenne pepper
¼ t. white peppercorns, freshly
    ground
2 egg yolks
2 T. vinegar
2 c. vegetable oil

1. Add seasonings to yolks, beating until mixed.
2. Add vinegar to yolk mixture, beating until thick.
3. Add oil, a few teaspoons at a time, to yolk mixture, beating after each addition until blended.
4. Store dressing, tightly covered, in refrigerator.

VARIATIONS: Use recipe for *Mayonnaise.*

Russian Dressing

1 c. chili sauce
½ c. olive oil
1 T. chopped capers
1 green pepper, finely chopped
1 T. paprika
1 T. onion juice
1 t. Worcestershire sauce

Add ingredients to mayonnaise, blending.

Horse-radish Dressing No. 2

¼ c. prepared horse-radish

Add ingredient to mayonnaise, blending.

Serve with meats, sea foods, or avocado.

Thousand Island Dressing

2 hard-cooked eggs, chopped
2 T. chopped pimento
1 T. chopped stuffed olives

Combine with Russian Dressing recipe above.

Making mayonnaise dressing

Cooked Salad Dressing

$1\frac{1}{4}$ cups

1½ T. sugar
¾ t. salt
½ t. dry mustard
Few grains of cayenne pepper
2 to 3 t. flour
2 T. melted table fat
3 egg yolks
   or 2 eggs
¾ c. milk
   or water
¼ c. vinegar

1. Mix sugar, seasonings, and flour together in saucepan; add fat and blend.
2. Beat yolks until thick and add milk, stirring.
3. Combine yolk mixture with sugar mixture. Cook, stirring, until mixture begins to thicken. Cool. Add vinegar and reheat, continuing to cook and stir until thickened.
4. Store dressing, tightly covered, in refrigerator.

VARIATION: Use recipe for *Cooked Salad Dressing.*

2 t. chopped pickle
⅛ t. paprika
⅛ t. majoram

Add ingredients to dressing.
Serve on bean or meat salad.

Condensed-Milk Dressing

$2\frac{1}{4}$ cups

2 eggs
¾ c. vinegar and 2 to 3 T. water
1 can condensed milk
½ t. prepared mustard

1. Beat eggs until thick.
2. Add 1 T. vinegar-water mixture to eggs, beating; then add 1 to 2 T. milk, beating.
3. Repeat additions of vinegar and milk, beating after each.
4. Add mustard to dressing, blending.
   Store, tightly covered, in refrigerator.
   Serve on tomato, chopped cabbage, or fruit salad.

Fruit Salad Dressing

$2\frac{1}{2}$ cups

½ c. pineapple juice
½ c. orange juice
2 T. lemon juice
3 eggs
½ c. sugar
⅛ t. salt
1 c. heavy cream
   or evaporated milk, chilled icy cold, whipped

1. Mix fruit juices together.
2. Beat eggs until mixed in top of double boiler; add sugar, salt, and juices.
3. Cook egg mixture over hot water or over very low heat until thickened, stirring. Chill.
4. Fold whipped cream into mixture.
   Serve immediately on fruit salad.

VARIATION: Use recipe for *Fruit-Salad Dressing.*

¼ c. finely chopped nuts
2 t. finely chopped candied cherries

Blend ingredients with dressing.

Spreads and Sandwiches

Fruit-Filled Spread

½ c. chopped dates
⅜ c. cooked, mashed apricots
¼ c. chopped nuts
1 egg
¼ c. sugar
¾ c. apple juice

1½ cups

1. Put fruits and nuts into bowl.
2. Beat egg until thick in saucepan; add sugar and juice.
3. Cook egg mixture over low heat until thickened, stirring constantly. Cool to room temperature.
4. Combine egg mixture with fruits and nuts.
5. Refrigerate in covered container.

Chopped-Liver Spread

½ lb. liver
¾ c. water
2 small onions
3 hard-cooked eggs
1 t. salt
⅛ t. pepper
3 T. melted table fat
Salad greens

2 cups

1. Simmer liver in water until tender; drain by laying in sieve.
2. Chop liver, onions, and eggs or put through food grinder using fine blade.
3. Add seasonings and fat to liver mixture, stirring to a thick paste. Pack into mold; chill until firm.
4. Turn liver mixture on chilled platter; garnish with greens.

Sharp-Flavored Spread

½ can condensed tomato soup
½ c. water
1 to 2 T. finely chopped onion
2½ c. grated American cheese
2 eggs, separated
½ t. salt
½ t. Worcestershire sauce
½ t. paprika
¼ t. white pepper
½ t. dry mustard

1¾ cups

1. Combine soup and water in frying pan; add onion and simmer for 10 minutes.
2. Add cheese to soup mixture, stirring constantly until cheese melts.
3. Beat yolks with seasonings until thick, and add to cheese mixture, stir; cook over low heat.
4. Beat egg whites to form softly rounded peaks; fold into cheese mixture with eight to ten strokes.
5. Heat to serving temperature.

Clam Appetizer Dip

$1\frac{1}{4}$ cups

$\frac{1}{2}$ garlic clove
1 package (8 oz.) cream cheese
2 t. lemon juice
$1\frac{1}{2}$ t. Worcestershire sauce
$\frac{1}{2}$ t. salt
$\frac{1}{8}$ t. pepper
$\frac{1}{2}$ c. cooked, chopped clams
$\frac{1}{4}$ c. clam liquid
Potato chips *or* crackers

1. Rub bowl with garlic.
2. Put cheese in bowl; gradually add lemon juice, seasonings, clams, and broth, stirring until blended. Chill. Serve with potato chips or crackers to be dipped into clam mixture.

Cheese Spread

$2\frac{1}{8}$ cups

2 c. cottage cheese
3 T. cream
1 t. chopped parsley
6 finely chopped stuffed olives
1 t. finely chopped onion
$\frac{1}{8}$ t. celery salt
Few grains of cayenne pepper
Crackers

1. Combine cheese and cream in bowl.
2. Add parsley, olives, onion, and seasonings to cheese mixture, blending. Serve cheese in a bowl on a tray; surround with crackers.

Peanut-Butter Special Spread

2 cups

1 c. peanut butter
1 c. finely chopped raisins
Salt to taste
2 T. orange juice

Combine peanut butter, raisins, salt, and orange juice.

Frankfurter Spread

1 cup

$\frac{3}{4}$ c. ground, cooked frankfurters
$\frac{1}{4}$ c. finely chopped nuts
2 T. chopped pickle
2 T. chopped parsley *or* celery
$\frac{1}{2}$ T. prepared mustard
$2\frac{1}{2}$ T. cooked salad dressing

Combine frankfurters, nuts, pickle, parsley, mustard, and salad dressing.

402

Meat Spread

1½ cups

2 chicken bouillon cubes
2 T. water, boiling
¾ c. ground, cooked pork, neckbone
　　meat
¼ c. finely chopped celery
¼ c. finely chopped sweet pickle
¼ c. chopped peanuts
¼ t. salt
⅛ t. pepper
⅛ t. savory, if desired
4 T. mayonnaise (p. 399)

1. Dissolve bouillon cube in water.
2. Combine pork, celery, pickle, peanuts, seasonings, and mayonnaise with bouillon mixture.

Bacon Spread

1¼ cups

½ c. cooked, crumbled bacon
3 hard-cooked eggs, chopped
2 T. finely chopped pickle
⅛ t. prepared horse-radish
½ t. salt
1 T. French dressing (p. 398)
1 T. mayonnaise (p. 399)

Combine bacon, eggs, pickle, seasonings, and dressings.

Baked-Bean Spread

1¼ cups

1 c. baked beans
¼ to ½ c. cooked, crumbled bacon
2½ T. chopped sweet pickle
½ t. salt
⅛ t. dry mustard
3 to 4 T. mayonnaise (p. 399)
　　or cooked salad dressing (p. 400)

1. Mash baked beans with fork.
2. Add bacon, pickle, seasonings, and dressing to beans; mix lightly.

Grilled Cheese Sandwiches

3 servings

2 T. mayonnaise (p. 399)
1 t. mustard
3 slices cheese
6 slices bread
2 to 3 T. melted table fat

1. Combine mayonnaise and mustard.
2. Lay cheese on three slices of bread; spread with mustard mixture.
3. Cover cheese with remaining bread slices. Brush each side with melted fat.
4. Brown on both sides on grill or broil 3 inches from heat unit, 1 to 2 minutes for each side. Cut sandwiches diagonally.

Garlic Buttered Potato Chips

1 garlic clove
3 T. table fat
1 medium bag potato chips

1. Simmer garlic clove and table fat in saucepan for 3 minutes; remove garlic.
2. Scatter potato chips on baking sheet; brush with the hot fat, and cover with paper towels.
3. Bake potato chips at 350° F. for 5 minutes.

Stuffed Rolls

6 servings

1 can (7 oz.) tuna fish
$\frac{1}{4}$ t. grated onion
$\frac{1}{4}$ c. finely chopped celery
$\frac{1}{8}$ t. salt
3 to $3\frac{1}{2}$ T. mayonnaise (p. 399)
6 oblong rolls

1. Flake tuna fish with fork. Add onion, celery, salt, and mayonnaise to tuna fish and toss lightly.
2. Split rolls lengthwise through middle without cutting clear through.
3. Fill rolls with tuna-fish stuffing.

Party Buns

6 servings

6 hamburger buns
$\frac{3}{4}$ c. deviled ham
3 eggs, soft scrambled
$\frac{1}{4}$ c. grated Cheddar cheese

1. Split hamburger buns; toast both cut sides in broiler, 3 inches from heat unit, for 1 minute.
2. Spread buns with ham, cover with eggs and then with cheese.
3. Broil 1 minute or until cheese melts.

U.S.D.A.

A dainty way to serve
a club sandwich

Cheeseburgers

6 servings

1 t. salt
⅛ t. pepper
1 lb. hamburger
6 slices cheese
6 buns

1. Season hamburger and shape into flat cakes; broil 3 inches below heat unit for 10 to 15 minutes or until golden brown, turning once.
2. Remove hamburger from broiler; lay each cake on an open bun; top with cheese slice and return to broiler for 1 minute. Serve immediately.

Chicken-Salad Sandwiches

1¼ cups

⅔ c. chopped, cooked chicken
¼ c. chopped celery
⅛ t. salt
2 T. chopped pickle
3 T. mayonnaise (p. 399)
6 bread slices
3 T. melted table fat
2 to 3 T. chopped green pepper, pimento, hard-cooked egg, *or* olives

1. Combine chicken, celery, salt, pickle, and mayonnaise.
2. Cut bread slices into desired shapes; brush with fat.
3. Spread bread with chicken salad. Garnish.

Cream-Cheese, Jelly-Nut Sandwiches

4 servings

1 package (3 oz.) cream cheese
¼ c. chopped nuts
6 whole-wheat bread slices
6 T. jelly, jam, *or* preserves
3 T. table fat

1. Soften cheese at room temperature for 20 minutes.
2. Combine cheese and nuts.
3. Trim crusts from bread. Spread one slice with cheese mixture, second with jelly, and third with table fat.
4. Stack the three bread slices together; cut into quarters diagonally.

Cornucopias

6 to 7 servings

1 recipe of pie pastry (p. 476; also pp. 180–182)

Filling

1 can (7 oz.) flaked tuna fish
2 T. finely chopped green pepper *or* finely chopped celery
1 hard-cooked egg, chopped
¼ t. salt
3 T. mayonnaise (p. 399)

1. Roll pastry on lightly floured board; cut into 3-inch squares.
2. Roll squares into cornucopias and secure with toothpicks. (Place clothespin or a roll of foil in the center of each to prevent collapse.)
3. Place cornucopias on baking sheet. Bake at 425° F. for 8 to 10 minutes or until light brown.
4. Combine tuna fish, pepper, egg, salt, and mayonnaise.
5. Fill baked shells with tuna-fish mixture.

Serve immediately as accompaniment for green salad or for tomato soup.

Ribbon Sandwiches

10 to 12 servings

½ loaf unsliced white bread
½ loaf unsliced whole-wheat bread

Filling

¾ c. soft-curd cottage cheese
2 T. finely chopped green pepper
1 T. finely chopped onion
2 T. chopped pimento
⅛ t. thyme, if desired
⅛ t. celery salt, if desired
¾ c. softened table fat

1. Trim all crusts from loaves of bread.
2. Beat cottage cheese until creamy.
3. Combine cheese, pepper, onion, pimento, and seasonings with fat.
4. Spread top of white loaf with filling; then cut a thin lengthwise slice from top of loaf.
5. Spread top of loaf again with filling; cut a second slice lengthwise (same thickness as before) and continue until as many slices as desired are prepared.
6. Repeat same procedure as in steps 1, 4, and 5 with whole-wheat bread.
7. Place white and whole-wheat bread slices together in alternate layers with filling between, using three, four, or five layers depending upon thickness of slices. Use white bread for top and bottom.
8. Press layers together lightly, wrap in waxed paper, and chill.
   Slice across the layers to make sandwiches.

VARIATIONS: Use recipe for *Ribbon Sandwiches*.

Checkerboard Loaf

Proceed as for ribbon sandwiches, using only four layers. All slices must be uniform in thickness.
Cut loaf of ribbon sandwiches into ½-inch slices.
Using 4 of these slices, spread 3 with filling.
Place first slice so that strips run from front to back of table or cutting board. Lay second slice on first so that strips run at right angles to those of first slice. The third slice should be placed like the first, and the fourth like the second.
Press stack lightly together. Make similar stacks of remaining slices. Wrap each stack in waxed paper and chill thoroughly.
Cut into slices ½-inch thick and serve.

Rolled Sandwiches

Bread slices ¼-inch thick

Spread slices with cheese spread and roll in straight roll. Wrap each roll in waxed paper; cover with damp towel.

Jane and Steven Coons

Ingredients assembled for filling

Half of white bread loaf trimmed on all sides
with spread ready to use

Both white and brown slices have been spread with the sandwich mixture. The brown and white slices have been placed, one after the other, in a stack. This is seen in the right front of the picture. Each stack of alternating slices is then cut in slices about $\frac{1}{2}$ inch thick. Notice the top slice at the right rear. Using four of these slices, place the first slice with the strips running from back to front of the table. The second slice should be placed so that the strips will run at right angles to the first slice. The strips of the third slice run in the same direction as the strips of the first slice, and the strips of the fourth slice run in the same direction as the strips of the second slice. When the four slices have been stacked carefully together and pressed firmly, they in turn should be sliced about $\frac{1}{2}$ inch thick. See center back of picture. Checkerboard sandwiches are then placed on a plate as shown at the left

These checkerboard sandwiches must be handled gently and they should not be piled one on top of the other. The garnish will depend upon the flavor of the spread

Canapes

Bread squares, sticks, rounds, *or* crackers of various kinds

Spreads of caviar, horse-radish, sardines, anchovies, well-seasoned chopped meats, hard-cooked eggs, cheese, vegetables, *or* fruits combined with dressings *or* sauces

Seasonings of garlic, onion juice, chopped mint leaves, parsley, *or* chives

1. Trim, cut, and toast bread, or use crackers.
2. Prepare seasoned spreads.
3. Top each piece of bread and each cracker with spread.
4. Garnish canapes; cover loosely and keep chilled. Serve as soon as possible.

Garnish with pearl onions, olive or pimento or vegetable slices, grated cheese, parsley or watercress sprigs, bacon or hard-cooked-egg bits.

Hors d' Oeuvres

–1–

Stuffed olives, halved; pearl onions; dill pickles cored and stuffed with cheese, sliced crosswise

–2–

Nut halves put together with cheese or anchovy filling; cream-cheese balls rolled in chopped nuts; cheese cubes

–3–

Dried-beef slices spread with horse-radish and rolled; browned cocktail sausages; cubed luncheon meats and pickles

–4–

Fresh shrimp; oysters; anchovies curled around capers

–5–

Pineapple chunks rolled in softened cream cheese and chopped mint leaves; prunes stuffed with cheese and chopped nuts

–6–

Celery sticks; carrot curls; radish roses

1. Place chilled food bits on toothpicks or arrange foods on platter.
2. Arrange picks in an hors d'oeuvre holder or stick picks into a shiny apple, grapefruit, red cabbage, or cantaloupe. Serve hors d'oeuvres as soon as possible.

408

Cheese

Bacon-and-Cheese Toast

6 servings

1 egg
3 T. milk
½ t. baking powder
1 c. grated cheese
6 bread slices
6 bacon slices, broiled

1. Beat egg until thick and combine with milk, baking powder, and cheese.
2. Spread cheese mixture on bread. Broil 3 inches from heat unit for 1 to 2 minutes. Top with bacon slices.

Cheese and Rice

4 servings

1⅓ c. quick-cooking rice
5 bacon slices, cooked, crumbled
2 hard-cooked eggs, diced
2 c. grated cheese
½ c. milk, scalded
½ t. salt
Few grains of cayenne pepper

1. Prepare quick-cooking rice, following directions on package.
2. Add bacon and eggs to rice.
3. Melt cheese in top of double boiler over hot water.
4. Add milk and seasonings gradually to cheese, stirring until blended.
5. Place rice mixture on platter and top with cheese mixture.

Macaroni, or Spaghetti, and Cheese

6 servings

1 package (8 oz.) broken macaroni, *or* spaghetti
3 T. table fat
3 T. flour
2 c. milk
¼ t. salt
⅛ t. pepper
2 c. grated cheese
½ c. dry bread crumbs
1 T. table fat

1. Cook macaroni (spaghetti) until tender, following Cereal Cookery Chart, p. 365; drain in sieve.
2. Prepare medium white sauce of fat, flour, milk, and seasonings (p. 423; also pp. 156–157). Add ⅔ c. cheese; stir until melted.
3. Put macaroni, or spaghetti, in a 1½ to 2-quart baking dish and add cheese sauce.
4. Sprinkle remaining 1⅓ c. cheese over macaroni, or spaghetti, and add crumbs. Dot with fat.
5. Set dish in pan containing hot water to cover ⅔ of dish. Bake at 350° F. for 15 to 20 minutes.

VARIATIONS: Use recipe for *Macaroni, or Spaghetti, and Cheese.*

Tomato Macaroni

1½ c. cooked tomatoes substituted for white sauce
Omit the cheese from the recipe.

Sieve tomatoes and add to macaroni before topping with crumbs.

409

Cheese Casserole

8 slices day-old bread
1 pkg. cheese slices (8 oz.)
3 eggs
$\frac{1}{4}$ t. salt
$\frac{1}{8}$ t. pepper
2 c. milk
$\frac{1}{2}$ t. dry mustard
$\frac{1}{4}$ t. Worcestershire sauce

1. Cut bread in half, diagonally. Using eight halves, arrange as pinwheel in shallow 9-inch baking dish.
2. Cover bread with layer of cheese slices. Arrange remaining bread on cheese.
3. Add eggs and seasonings to milk; beat with rotary beater until blended.
4. Pour egg mixture over bread and cheese.
5. Set dish in pan containing hot water to cover $\frac{2}{3}$ of dish. Bake at 325° F. for 25 minutes. Serve at once.

Cheese Loaf

6 servings

1 T. gelatin
$\frac{1}{2}$ c. cold water
1 t. salt
$\frac{3}{4}$ c. hot water
1 c. grated cheese
1 T. lemon juice
1 t. grated onion
$\frac{3}{4}$ c. broken, cooked macaroni
$\frac{1}{2}$ c. salad dressing
$\frac{1}{2}$ c. diced celery
1 T. chopped pimento
2 T. chopped parsley

1. Cook macaroni according to Cereal Cookery Chart, page 365. Drain in sieve.
2. Mix gelatin with cold water; set aside 5 minutes.
3. Dissolve gelatin and salt in hot water.
4. Stir cheese, lemon juice, and onion into gelatin. Chill until mixture begins to set.
5. Add macaroni, salad dressing, celery, pimento, and parsley to chilled gelatin mixture, stirring gently. Pour into molds. Chill.

Cheese Soufflé

4 servings

$\frac{1}{2}$ c. thick white sauce (p. 423)
$\frac{1}{8}$ t. salt
Few grains of cayenne pepper
3 eggs, separated
$\frac{1}{2}$ c. grated cheese

1. Combine white sauce and seasonings.
2. Beat yolks until thick with rotary egg beater. Add to white sauce, beating with same beater.
3. Add cheese to white-sauce mixture, beating with same beater until cheese is melted.
4. Beat whites with cleaned beater to form softly rounded peaks.
5. Fold whites into white-sauce mixture.
6. Pour into a deep, 6- to 8-inch baking dish greased only on bottom. Set in pan containing hot water to cover $\frac{2}{3}$ of dish.
7. Bake soufflé at 350° F. for 30 to 45 minutes. Don't open oven during baking. Serve at once.

VARIATIONS: Use recipe for *Cheese Soufflé.*

Cheese-and-Ham Soufflé

$\frac{1}{2}$ c. ground, cooked ham

Add ham with cheese.

410

Cheese-and-Tomato Soufflé

½ c. strained tomato juice substituted for milk in white sauce

Pour into custard cups for individual servings; bake 20 to 25 minutes.

Welsh Rarebit

4 servings

¾ c. medium white sauce (p. 423)
1 c. grated Cheddar cheese
½ t. salt
½ t. dry mustard
⅛ t. paprika
Few grains of cayenne pepper
Toast *or* crackers

1. Combine white sauce, cheese, and seasonings. Heat to serving temperature.
2. Pour sauce over toast or crackers. Serve at once.

VARIATION: Use recipe for *Welsh Rarebit.*

4 thick tomato slices
4 bacon slices cooked until crisp

Place tomato slice on each slice of toast; top with sauce and bacon slice.

Spanish Rarebit

6 servings

2 T. table fat
2 T. chopped green pepper
2 c. grated cheese
1 egg
2½ c. (No. 2 can) whole-kernel corn
½ c. canned tomatoes
½ c. soft bread crumbs
½ t. salt
⅛ t. chili powder
6 toast slices
6 bacon slices, cooked until crisp

1. Heat fat in top of double boiler. Add pepper and cook until tender, stirring frequently.
2. Add cheese to pepper. Set pan over hot water and stir until cheese melts.
3. Add egg to corn, mixing. Combine with cheese mixture.
4. Add tomatoes, crumbs, and seasonings to cheese mixture, stirring. Heat to serving temperature.
   Serve rarebit on toast. Top with bacon slice.

Cheese Fondue

4 servings

1¼ c. milk
3 eggs, separated
½ c. grated cheese
2 T. melted table fat
1 t. salt
⅛ t. pepper
Few grains of cayenne pepper
1 c. soft bread crumbs

1. Scald milk in top of double boiler over hot water.
2. Beat yolks until thick with rotary egg beater. Add gradually to milk, beating with same beater.
3. Add cheese, fat, and seasonings to milk mixture, beating with same beater until cheese melts.
4. Add crumbs to milk mixture.
5. Beat whites, with cleaned or different beater, to form softly rounded peaks.
6. Fold whites into milk mixture. Pour into deep, 6- to 8-inch baking dish greased only on bottom; set in pan containing hot water to cover ⅔ of dish.
7. Bake fondue at 325° F. for 30 to 35 minutes.
   Serve at once.

411

Goldenrod Beans

6 servings

1½ lb. whole green beans
1½ T. table fat
2 T. flour
½ t. salt
⅛ t. pepper
½ c. evaporated milk
  or whole milk
3 hard-cooked eggs, separated
2 T. mayonnaise (p. 399)

1. Prepare and cook beans according to Vegetable Cooking Chart, page 413. Save liquid.
2. Melt fat; blend in flour and seasonings. Add ½ c. bean liquid to flour mixture; cook until thickened, stirring. Continue to cook for 2 minutes, stirring.
3. Chop egg whites; add with milk to beans. Heat to serving temperature.
4. Force yolks through sieve.
5. Add mayonnaise to flour mixture, stirring. Pour over beans and sprinkle with yolks.

Carrots with Orange Sauce

4 to 5 servings

4 T. sugar
1 T. flour
1 c. water, boiling
¼ c. orange juice
1 T. grated orange rind
1 T. table fat
6 medium carrots, cooked and cut in desired shapes

1. Mix sugar and flour in saucepan. Add boiling water, stirring, and cook until clear. Cook for 1 minute longer, stirring.
2. Add orange juice, rind, and fat to sugar mixture. Add carrots; heat to serving temperature.

VARIATION: Use recipe for *Carrots with Orange Sauce.*

Omit orange juice and rind.

Simmer until glazed, turning once.

Mashed Potatoes

4 servings

4 or 5 medium potatoes, pared
Water to cover
1 t. salt
⅓ c. milk
2 T. table fat
⅛ t. white pepper

1. Cook potatoes, covered, in boiling salted water for 20 to 25 minutes.
2. Drain off excess water; place pan in larger container of hot water.
3. Beat potatoes with fork or masher until fluffy.
4. Heat milk over very low heat and add gradually to potatoes, beating. Add fat and pepper; beat until fluffy.

VARIATION: Use recipe for *Mashed Potatoes.*

Mashed Sweet Potatoes

4 or 5 sweet potatoes substituted for
  white potatoes
Omit pepper.

VEGETABLE COOKING CHART

VEGETABLE	PREPARATION	METHOD OF COOKING	APPROXIMATE COOKING TIME (minutes)	SEASONINGS AND SERVING VARIATIONS
ASPARAGUS	Scrub with brush, remove scales, cut or tie in bundles, cook with tips up.	Cover and cook in boiling, salted water. Cook lower part of stalk 5 minutes before adding tips.	15–20	Table fat White sauce Hollandaise sauce On toast with cheese sauce
		Steam.	15–30	
BEANS **Green or wax**	Wash, remove ends and strings, cut crosswise or lengthwise or leave whole.	Cover and cook in boiling, salted water.	20–30	Table fat and savory or paprika White sauce Pork drippings
		Steam.	25–30	
Lima, fresh	Shell.	Cover and cook in boiling, salted water.	20–30	Table fat White sauce Tomato sauce
Lima or navy, dried	Wash, soak overnight in water 4 times amount of beans. (Allow ¼ c. per serving.)	Cover and cook in water used for soaking. Add salt when half cooked.	2–2½ hr.	Table fat Ham or bacon White sauce, marjoram or basil Tomato sauce
BEETS, whole	Cut off tops leaving 2 inches on beets. Scrub; cook in skin.	Cover and cook in boiling, salted water. Skin when tender.	Young 35 Old 50–60	Table fat Sweet-sour sauce Pickling sauce
	Pare; cut in pieces.	Cover and cook in boiling, salted water.	15–20	
BROCCOLI	Remove tough parts. Split heavy stems. Wash in running water. Stand inverted 30 minutes in salted water. Leave whole, tie in bundle, or cut in pieces.	Cover and cook in boiling, salted water. Cook stalks 5 minutes before adding flowerets.	20–25	Table fat Hollandaise sauce Cheese sauce White sauce Horse-radish sauce
		Steam.	25–30	
BRUSSELS SPROUTS	Remove outer leaves; leave whole. Wash. Stand 30 minutes in salted water.	Cover and cook in boiling, salted water.	10–15	Table fat White sauce
		Steam.	20–25	
CABBAGE	Remove outer leaves. Quarter or shred.	Cover and cook in boiling, salted water.	7–8	Table fat White sauce Cheese sauce Ham or bacon drippings
		Steam.	15	

VEGETABLE COOKING CHART

VEGETABLE	PREPARATION	METHOD OF COOKING	APPROXIMATE COOKING TIME (minutes)	SEASONINGS AND SERVING VARIATIONS
CARROTS	Wash, scrape, or pare. Leave whole or cut in pieces.	Cover and cook in boiling, salted water.	Young, sliced 15–20 Matured, sliced 25–35	Table fat White sauce
		Steam.	20–25	
CAULIFLOWER	Remove leaves and woody base. Wash. Stand inverted 30 minutes in salted water.	Cover and cook in boiling, salted water	Whole 10–12 Divided in flowerets 8–10	Table fat Cheese sauce, paprika White sauce, rosemary
CELERY	Wash; scrub with brush. Cut stalks in 3-inch lengths.	Cover and cook in boiling, salted water.	10–20	Table fat White sauce
		Steam.	25–30	
CHARD, SWISS	Wash. Separate stalks from leaves.	Cover and cook in boiling, salted water 15 minutes. Add leaves. Complete cooking.	25–30	Ham or bacon drippings Lemon juice or vinegar Table fat
		Steam.	18–20	
CORN **On the cob**	Remove husks. Brush to remove silks. Cut away any inedible portion.	Cover and cook in boiling, salted water.	6–12	Table fat
		Steam.	10–12	
Cut off the cob	Cut corn from cob.	Cover and cook in boiling, salted water.	6–7	Table fat White sauce Green or red pimento
GREENS **Mustard** **Kale**	Remove heavy stems. Wash by dipping up and down in fresh waters. Lift leaves from each water.	Cover and cook in boiling, salted water.	20–25	Table fat Ham or bacon drippings
Spinach	Prepare as mustard greens.	Cook covered in water clinging to leaves.	5–6	Table fat Ham or bacon drippings Vinegar or lemon White sauce

VEGETABLE COOKING CHART

VEGETABLE	PREPARATION	METHOD OF COOKING	APPROXIMATE COOKING TIME (minutes)	SEASONINGS AND SERVING VARIATIONS
KOHLRABI	Wash. Pare. Cut in pieces.	Cover and cook in boiling, salted water.	25–30	Table fat White sauce
		Steam.	15–20	
OKRA	Wash. Cut off stem ends. Slice or leave whole.	Cover and cook in boiling, salted water.	Young pods 15–20	Table fat Meat drippings Tomato sauce
		Steam.	20	
ONIONS	Remove peelings under water. Leave whole, quarter, or slice.	Cover and cook in boiling, salted water.	20	White sauce Table fat
		Steam.	15	
PEAS **Green**	Shell. Wash in sieve.	Cover and cook in boiling, salted water.	10–20	Table fat White sauce, white pepper
		Steam.	25–30	
Black-eyed	Shell and wash.	Cover and cook in boiling, salted water.	35–40	Table fat Ham or bacon drippings White sauce
Split or dried	Wash; soak overnight in four times as much water as peas. (Allow $\frac{1}{4}$ c. per serving.)	Cover and cook in water used for soaking. Add salt after first 30 minutes of cooking.	$1\frac{3}{4}$–2 hr.	Table fat, marjoram White sauce Meat drippings
POTATOES **White and sweet**	Scrub. Pare. Cut in pieces, or leave whole unpeeled.	Cover and cook in boiling, salted water.	20–35	Table fat, parsley White sauce, paprika
		Steam.	25–30	
SQUASH **Summer**	Wash. Pare. Cut in pieces.	Cover and cook in boiling, salted water.	15–20	Table fat White sauce, paprika
		Steam.	10–15	
TOMATOES	Remove skin after heating in boiling water or over flame.	Cover and cook without addition of water.	12–15	Table fat, sugar White sauce, $\frac{1}{4}$ t. onion salt
PARSNIPS TURNIPS SALSIFY RUTABAGA	Wash. Pare. Cut in pieces.	Cover and cook in boiling, salted water.	20–30	Table fat Meat drippings White sauce, paprika

415

VEGETABLE	ADDED INGREDIENTS	COOKERY
White Potatoes 6 SERVINGS 6 medium	1/4 c. vegetable oil or softened table fat 1/2 t. salt Dash of paprika 1/4 to 3/8 c. table fat	1. Scrub and dry potatoes; brush with fat. 2. Put potatoes in pan; bake at 425° F. for 40 to 60 minutes. 3. Cut a crisscross gash on top of each potato; sprinkle with seasonings; dot with fat.
Stuffed white potatoes 4 SERVINGS 2 medium	1/2 t. salt Dash of pepper 2 T. table fat 2 to 3 T. milk, heated 1 egg Dash of paprika 1/4 c. grated cheese	1. Cut baked potatoes in halves lengthwise; scoop out pulp and mash. 2. Add seasonings, fat, and milk to pulp. 3. Beat egg until foamy; add to pulp mixture; beat until fluffy. 4. Pile pulp mixture lightly into skins; sprinkle with paprika and cheese. 5. Bake at 350° F. for 5 to 7 minutes.
Sweet Potatoes or yams 4 SERVINGS 4 medium	2 T. vegetable oil or softened table fat 1/4 c. table fat	1. Prepare and bake, using Baked Potato recipe. (Yams cook in about half the time required for white potatoes.)
Stuffed sweet potatoes 4 SERVINGS 2 large	1/4 c. thin cream or pineapple juice 2 T. brown sugar 2 T. table fat	1. Cut baked potato in halves lengthwise; mash pulp with fork but do not remove. 2. Mix cream and brown sugar together; add to potatoes, mixing lightly with a fork. 3. Dot potatoes with fat; broil 4 inches from heat unit for 2 to 3 minutes.

VEGETABLE	ADDED INGREDIENTS	COOKERY
Eggplant 6 SERVINGS 1 medium, pared and cut in 1-inch sticks	½ t. salt 1 recipe French-Fry Batter (see below) Shortening	1. Add enough shortening to fill a deep pan ½ to ⅔ full when melted; heat to 330° F. 2. Dip eggplant sticks into French-fry batter. 3. Cook a few pieces at a time for 3 to 4 minutes, or until lightly browned, turning once. Drain on absorbent paper.
Onions 6 SERVINGS 6 medium, cut in rings	½ t. salt 1 recipe French-Fry Batter (see below) Shortening	1. Sprinkle salt on onion rings and dip into French-fry batter. 2. Add enough shortening to fill a deep pan ½ to ⅔ full when melted; heat to 365° F. 3. Cook onion rings until lightly brown, turning one or two times. Drain on absorbent paper.
	French-Fry Batter ⅝ c. sifted flour ½ t. salt ½ t. dry mustard 1 egg ¼ c. milk	1. Sift flour, salt, and mustard together. 2. Beat egg well and add milk; stirring. Add milk mixture to flour mixture, stirring until blended.
White Potatoes 6 SERVINGS 6 medium	Shortening or vegetable oil ¾ t. salt	1. Wash and pare potatoes; cut into strips ⅜- to ½- inch thick. 2. Wrap potatoes in towel to dry. 3. Add enough shortening to fill a deep pan ½ to ⅔ full when melted; heat to 375° F. 4. Cover bottom of frying basket with potatoes, lower into hot shortening; lift basket above fat one to two times while cooking. 5. Cook potatoes for 3 to 5 minutes or until tender. Drain on absorbent paper. Add salt and serve.

PAN-FRIED VEGETABLES

VEGETABLE	ADDED INGREDIENTS	COOKERY
Eggplant 4-6 SERVINGS 1 medium, peeled	1 egg 2 T. milk ¾ c. bread crumbs 3 T. shortening ½ t. salt	1. Cut eggplant crosswise into ⅜-inch slices. 2. Beat egg slightly; add milk; blend. 3. Dip slices into egg mixture, turn in crumbs; let dry 5 minutes. 4. Heat shortening in frying pan; add slices; cook to golden brown, turning once.
Mushrooms 3-4 SERVINGS ⅓ lb.	1½ T. table fat ¼ t. salt Dash of pepper	1. Scrub mushrooms with soft brush; pare away spots; cut thin slice from stem and discard; slice mushrooms ¼-inch thick. 2. Heat fat in frying pan; add mushrooms; cover. 3. Cook mushrooms for 6 to 10 minutes, stirring three or four times; sprinkle with seasonings. 4. Serve with steak, hamburger, or French-style green beans.
Okra 5-6 SERVINGS 1 lb. medium pods, sliced and cooked	1 egg ½ c. corn meal or fine bread crumbs 2 to 3 T. shortening ½ t. salt	1. Beat egg until mixed. 2. Dip okra slices into egg; roll in corn meal. 3. Heat shortening in frying pan; add okra; cook until lightly browned, turning with spatula three or four times.
Potatoes 4 SERVINGS 4 medium, peeled	3 to 4 T. drippings or shortening ½ t. salt ¼ t. celery salt Dash of pepper Dash of paprika 1 T. water	1. Pare and slice potatoes; dry with towel. 2. Heat drippings in frying pan; add potatoes. 3. Cook potatoes until lightly browned, turning and lifting gently with spatula three or four times. 4. Add seasonings and water to potatoes; cover and steam for 2 to 3 minutes.
Potatoes, hashed brown 4 SERVINGS 3 c. cooked, diced potatoes	3 T. flour 1 t. finely cut onion or chives ¼ c. thin cream or evaporated milk 1 t. salt ¼ t. celery salt Dash of pepper 3 T. shortening	1. Add flour, onion, cream, and seasonings to potatoes. 2. Heat shortening in skillet. 3. Pack potato mixture firmly in pan. Cook on low heat for 20 minutes. 4. Fold ½ of potato mixture over like an omelet; remove to platter.
Tomatoes, green 4-5 SERVINGS 6 medium	2 T. flour 1 T. sugar ⅛ t. nutmeg ½ t. salt Dash of pepper ¼ c. vegetable oil or melted shortening ¼ c. shortening	1. Wash, stem, and cut tomatoes into ¾-inch slices. 2. Sift flour, sugar, and seasonings together. 3. Dip tomatoes into oil; roll in flour mixture; let dry 5 minutes. 4. Repeat process. 5. Heat shortening in frying pan; cook tomatoes until lightly browned, turning once.

TIMETABLE FOR COOKING FROZEN VEGETABLES*

(Use ½ c. lightly salted water for each pint of vegetables.
For lima beans it is necessary to use 1 c. water;
for corn on the cob use sufficient water to cover.)

VEGETABLE	TIME TO ALLOW AFTER WATER RETURNS TO BOIL (minutes)	VEGETABLE	TIME TO ALLOW AFTER WATER RETURNS TO BOIL (minutes)
Asparagus	5–10	Corn	
		Whole-kernel	3–5
Beans, lima		On the cob	3–4
Large	15–20	Kale	8–12
Baby	6–10		
		Mustard greens	8–15
Beans, snap, Green, or wax, 1-inch pieces	12–18	Peas, green	5–10
Broccoli	5–8	Spinach	4–6
Brussels sprouts	4–9	Squash, summer	10–12
Cauliflower	5–8	Turnip greens	15–20

*Bureau of Human Nutrition and Home Economics, United States Department
of Agriculture, Home and Garden Bulletin No. 10, p. 44.

Scalloped Potatoes

6 servings

4½ c. thinly sliced, pared white potatoes
½ c. thinly sliced onion *or* grated cheese
1½ t. salt
⅛ t. pepper
1½ c. medium white sauce

1. Place ⅓ of potatoes and onions *or* cheese in a deep, 6- to 8-inch baking dish.
2. Add seasonings to sauce, and pour on potato mixture ⅓ of white sauce.
3. Repeat with another ⅓ of potato mixture and sauce.
4. Add remaining potato mixture and sauce.
5. Bake at 350° F. covered for 45 minutes. Uncover; bake 15 minutes or longer until tender.

Scalloped Onions

6 servings

4 c. thinly sliced onions
3 T. table fat
½ t. salt
⅛ t. pepper
¾ c. thick white sauce
¼ c. soft bread crumbs
3 T. grated cheese
⅛ t. paprika

1. Wash and peel onions; slice ¼-inch thick.
2. Heat fat in saucepan; add onions, cover, and cook until golden, stirring two or three times.
3. Place onions in shallow, 6- to 8-inch baking dish; add seasonings and white sauce.
4. Sprinkle top with crumbs, cheese, and paprika. Bake at 375° F. for 20 minutes.

419

Scalloped Tomatoes

4 servings

2 c. sliced fresh
  or canned tomatoes
2 T. finely chopped onion
1 T. finely chopped green pepper
½ t. salt
1 to 2 t. sugar
¾ c. soft bread crumbs
2 T. table fat
¼ c. grated cheese

1. Combine tomatoes, onion, green pepper, and seasonings.
2. Place alternate layers of tomato mixture and crumbs in 6- to 8-inch baking dish, ending with crumbs on top.
3. Dot crumbs with fat; bake tomatoes at 365° F. for 25 minutes.
4. Add cheese to top last 10 minutes of baking.

Okra Creole

4 servings

3 T. bacon fat
¼ c. chopped onion
1 small green pepper, chopped
15 to 18 okra pods, sliced
¾ c. chopped tomatoes
1 c. cut corn, canned
1 t. salt
⅛ t. pepper

1. Heat fat in frying pan; add onion and pepper, and cook until onion is golden, stirring two or three times.
2. Add okra to onion mixture; cook 5 minutes, stirring occasionally.
3. Add vegetables to onion mixture; cover and simmer for 15 to 20 minutes.

Corn Fritters

5 to 6 servings

1 c. sifted flour
¾ t. salt
1 t. baking powder
2 eggs
¼ c. milk
1½ c. canned *or* fresh corn, drained
2 t. melted table fat
  or shortening
Shortening for deep-fat frying
If fritters are to be pan-fried, add
  another ¼ c. flour.

1. Sift flour, salt, and baking powder together.
2. Beat eggs until thick, add milk and shortening; blend with rotary beater. Add corn and mix.
3. Make a well in flour mixture and add egg mixture all at once; stir quickly until flour mixture is just moistened.
4. Put enough fat in frying kettle to fill ½ to ⅔ full when melted. Heat to 360° F.
5. Place wire basket in frying kettle.
6. Drop batter by tablespoons into hot shortening; cook for 4 to 5 minutes, turning once.

Corn Pudding

4 servings

1 can (No. 2) corn (cream style) *or*
  1½ c. fresh corn
2 T. flour
1 t. salt
1 c. milk
2 eggs
2 T. table fat, melted
¼ c. bread *or* cracker crumbs

1. If fresh corn is used, split rows of kernels on cob with knife and scrape out contents.
2. Mix corn, flour, salt, and milk together. Beat eggs until thick; add to corn mixture. Pour into a 6- to 8-inch baking dish.
3. Mix fat and crumbs together and sprinkle over corn mixture. Bake at 350° F. for 25 minutes or until firm.

Crisco

FRENCH FRYING

Equipment for French frying · Notice sturdiness of frying kettle and position of thermometer. The handle of the frying kettle must be placed so that it cannot by any chance be hit and the kettle overturned

Notice position of thermometer and of frying basket as potatoes are lowered into the hot fat. The potatoes already fried are lying loosely on absorbent paper in the basket. The same procedure is used in frying fritters

Stuffed Tomatoes

6 servings

1 c. fresh peas
$1\frac{1}{2}$ c. diced celery
$\frac{1}{2}$ t. salt
$\frac{1}{8}$ t. pepper
$\frac{3}{4}$ c. water
6 medium tomatoes
$\frac{1}{2}$ t. salt
$\frac{1}{2}$ c. fine bread crumbs
2 T. table fat

1. Boil peas, celery, and seasonings in water for 20 minutes; drain.
2. Scoop out tomatoes and salt the insides of shells.
3. Stuff tomato shells with vegetable mixture.
4. Place stuffed tomatoes in 6- to 8-inch baking dish; add crumbs to top and dot with fat.
5. Bake tomatoes at 375° F. for 25 minutes.

Stuffed Celery

4 servings

$\frac{1}{2}$ to $\frac{5}{8}$ c. cottage cheese
$\frac{1}{4}$ t. salt
2 t. finely chopped green pepper
  or parsley
$1\frac{1}{2}$ T. mayonnaise (p. 399)
8 to 10 stalks of celery
Paprika

1. Mix cheese, seasonings, except paprika, and mayonnaise together.
2. Cut celery stalks into 3- to 4-inch lengths.
3. Fill grooves of stalks with cheese mixture.
4. Sprinkle with paprika.

421

Baked Eggplant

6 servings

1 large eggplant
1 medium onion, sliced
1 c. water, boiling
1 t. salt
2 eggs
$\frac{1}{8}$ t. pepper
$\frac{1}{2}$ c. coarse cracker crumbs
2 T. table fat

1. Cut eggplant in half; scoop out pulp, saving shells.
2. Cook pulp and onion, covered, in boiling, salted water until tender.
3. Beat eggs until mixed; add slowly to cooked pulp, stirring with fork.
4. Add pepper and half of crumbs to pulp mixture.
5. Put pulp mixture in shells; add remaining crumbs. Dot with fat; bake in a shallow, 8- to 10-inch baking dish at 350° F. for 20 to 25 minutes.

Vegetable Soufflé

6 servings

2 c. canned corn, cream style
  (*or* use any leftover or freshly prepared vegetable)
1 c. thick white sauce
3 eggs, separated
$\frac{1}{4}$ c. melted table fat
$\frac{1}{2}$ t. salt
$\frac{1}{8}$ t. nutmeg
$\frac{1}{8}$ t. pepper
3 T. bread crumbs
2 t. table fat

1. Mash corn; combine with white sauce.
2. Beat yolks until thick. Add fat and corn mixture, stirring.
3. Add salt to egg whites; beat to form softly rounded peaks. Fold into corn mixture.
4. Pour corn mixture into a 6- to 8-inch baking dish; sprinkle with crumbs and dot with fat. Set in pan containing hot water to cover $\frac{2}{3}$ of dish.
5. Bake soufflé at 350° F. for 30 to 35 minutes; serve immediately.

Sauces and Sirups

MAKING WHITE SAUCE

1. Measure and melt the fat in the top of a double boiler. 2. Add the flour gradually, stirring carefully. 3. Add the milk gradually, stirring thoroughly. 4. The finished sauce should be smooth and free of lumps

1   2   3   4

National Dairy Council

CONSISTENCY	FAT	FLOUR	SALT	MILK	USE
Thin	1 T.	1 T.	¼ t.	1 c.	Cream soups
Medium	1½–2 T.	2 T.	¼ t.	1 c.	Scalloped dishes Creamed vegetables
Thick	2–3 T.	3 T.	¼ t.	1 c.	Casseroles
Very thick	3 T.–¼ c.	¼ c.	¼ t.	1 c.	Croquettes Souffles

White Sauces

1. Heat fat in shallow saucepan on low heat.
2. Add flour and salt to fat and stir until well blended.
3. Remove mixture from heat; add $\frac{1}{3}$ of heated milk, blending well. (See Chapter 13, pp. 156–157, for the three methods of making white sauce.)
4. Return milk mixture to heat. As thickening begins, add another $\frac{1}{3}$ of the liquid, blending well; add remaining liquid, stirring. (In cooking small quantities, remove from heat to add second portion of liquid.)
5. Heat milk mixture to boiling, stirring, and cook for 1 to 2 minutes.

VARIATIONS: Use recipe for *Medium White Sauce.*

Cheese Sauce

1 c. grated cheese	Add to white sauce that has been cooled 3 to 4 minutes, beating with rotary egg beater.

Egg Sauce

2 hard-cooked eggs, chopped 2 t. finely chopped pimento Few grains of cayenne pepper	Add to white sauce. Heat to serving temperature.

Mushroom Sauce

1½ T. table fat ¾ c. canned mushrooms *or* ½ lb. fresh, sliced 1 t. finely chopped onion	Heat fat in frying pan. Add mushrooms and onion, cook until onion is golden, stirring two or three times. Add to white sauce. Heat to serving temperature.

423

Tomato Sauce
2 cups

½ garlic clove
1 T. table fat
1 T. chopped onion
1 T. flour
1 c. tomato pulp
1 c. water
½ t. salt
⅛ t. pepper
⅛ t. celery salt
⅛ t. orégano or chili powder
1 T. finely chopped parsley

1. Rub frying pan with garlic. Heat fat; add onion, and cook until golden, stirring two or three times. Set aside.
2. Mix flour into the fat and onion; add tomato pulp, water, seasonings, and parsley, blending.
3. Cook tomato mixture until thickened, stirring constantly. Served with meat balls and spaghetti.

✓ Barbecue Sauce
2¼ cups

1 T. shortening
¼ c. chopped onion
1 c. red catchup
½ c. water
2 T. sifted brown sugar
½ t. salt
⅛ t. pepper
⅛ t. cayenne pepper
2 T. vinegar
2 T. Worcestershire sauce
  or 1 to 2 drops Tabasco sauce
1½ t. prepared mustard
¼ c. lemon juice
½ c. chopped celery

1. Heat fat in frying pan. Add onion and cook until golden, stirring two or three times.
2. Mix catchup, water, seasonings, and celery; add to onion.
3. Cover pan and simmer onion mixture for 15 to 20 minutes, stirring three or four times.

Sea-Food Cocktail Sauce
1 cup

1 to 2 T. grated horse-radish
3 T. lemon juice
¼ t. celery salt
¼ t. salt
⅛ t. pepper
1 c. red tomato catchup

1. Add horse-radish, lemon juice, and seasonings to catchup; mix.
2. Store sauce in tightly covered jar. Chill.

Tartar Sauce
2½ cups

2 medium dill pickles, ground
1 medium onion, chopped
¼ c. finely chopped parsley
2 c. mayonnaise (p. 399)

1. Mix pickle, onion, and parsley together.
2. Blend mayonnaise into pickle mixture.
3. Store sauce in tightly covered jar in refrigerator.

424

Horse-radish Sauce $\frac{5}{8}$ *cup*

$\frac{1}{4}$ c. grated horse-radish
$1\frac{1}{2}$ T. vinegar
$\frac{1}{2}$ t. salt
Few grains of cayenne pepper
$\frac{1}{2}$ c. whipping cream
   or evaporated milk, chilled icy cold

1. Mix horse-radish, vinegar, and seasonings together.
2. Beat cream. Fold horse-radish mixture into cream. Serve at once with tongue, steak, or roast beef.

VARIATION: Use recipe for *Horse-radish Sauce*.

Cucumber Sauce

1 medium cucumber, peeled and finely chopped, substituted for horse-radish
Paprika substituted for cayenne pepper

Hollandaise Sauce $\frac{5}{8}$ *cup*

2 T. lemon juice
2 egg yolks
$\frac{1}{2}$ c. table fat
$\frac{1}{4}$ t. salt
Few grains of cayenne pepper

1. Add lemon juice to egg yolks in top of double boiler. Cut table fat into three pieces; add one piece to yolk mixture.
2. Cook yolk mixture over hot water, stirring constantly until fat melts and sauce thickens.
3. Add second piece of fat, stirring until melted and the sauce further thickens. Add third piece of fat and stir mixture until as thick as mayonnaise. Remove from heat.
4. Add seasonings and beat sauce until glossy. (Beat in 2 T. boiling water if curdled.)
5. Reheat over boiling water if necessary.

Sweet-Sour Sauce *1 cup*

2 T. table fat
2 T. flour
$\frac{1}{2}$ t. salt
Pepper to taste
2 T. sugar
2 T. vinegar
1 c. hot vegetable liquid, meat stock,
   or hot bouillon

1. Heat fat in frying pan; add flour and brown, stirring.
2. Add seasonings and liquid to frying pan. Cook 3 minutes, stirring constantly.

Vanilla Sauce

1 cup

3 T. table fat
1 t. vanilla
¾ c. sifted confectioners' sugar
3 egg yolks
  or 2 eggs
½ c. water, boiling

1. Heat fat in top of double boiler.
2. Add vanilla to fat and gradually add sugar, stirring. Set aside.
3. Beat eggs until thick; add to fat mixture, stirring.
4. Add boiling water to fat mixture, stirring. Cook over hot water until thickened.

Hard Sauce

⅝ cup

¼ c. table fat
½ t. vanilla
¾ c. sifted confectioners' sugar
2 t. hot water

1. Blend fat and vanilla. Add sugar gradually, creaming until fluffy.
2. Add hot water, a few drops at a time, to creamed mixture, stirring. Chill.

Caramel Sauce

⅔ cup

1 c. sugar
½ c. water, boiling
2 T. cream

1. Caramelize sugar by melting in heavy skillet. Add water slowly, stirring constantly.
2. Cook sugar mixture until sugar dissolves.
3. Remove skillet from heat; add cream, stirring.

Lemon Sauce

1 cup

1 T. cornstarch
½ c. sugar
⅛ t. salt
¾ c. water, boiling
1 T. table fat
1 T. finely grated lemon rind
¼ c. lemon juice

1. Mix cornstarch, sugar, and salt in saucepan.
2. Add boiling water to cornstarch mixture, stirring. Cook until mixture thickens, stirring.
3. Add fat, rind, and lemon juice to cornstarch mixture; blend.

Orange Sauce

2 cups

½ c. sugar
2 T. flour
¼ c. milk
2 egg yolks
¼ c. orange juice
2 t. grated orange rind
1 c. evaporated milk, chilled icy cold,
  or whipping cream

1. Mix sugar and flour in top of double boiler. Add milk.
2. Beat yolks until thick; add to sugar mixture.
3. Place pan over hot water; cook sugar mixture until thickened, stirring. Cool.
4. Add orange juice and rind to sugar mixture.
5. Beat cream to form softly rounded peaks. Fold into sugar mixture.
Serve with Sunshine Cake (p. 467).

426

VARIATION: Use recipe for *Orange Sauce*.

Chocolate Sauce

$\frac{1}{4}$ c. chocolate sirup substituted for
    orange juice and rind
1 t. vanilla

Raisin Sauce

$1\frac{1}{2}$ *cups*

$\frac{1}{2}$ c. brown sugar
1 T. cornstarch
$\frac{1}{4}$ t. salt
$\frac{3}{4}$ c. cold water
$\frac{1}{4}$ c. orange juice
3 T. lemon juice
$\frac{1}{2}$ c. raisins
1 T. table fat

1. Mix sugar, cornstarch, and salt together in saucepan. Add water and heat to boiling point, stirring constantly.
2. Add fruit juices, raisins, and fat to sugar mixture; simmer for 5 minutes.

Sweet Spice Sauce

$\frac{3}{4}$ *cup*

$\frac{3}{4}$ c. brown sugar
1 T. cornstarch
$\frac{1}{4}$ c. vinegar
$\frac{1}{2}$ c. meat stock
$\frac{1}{2}$ c. raisins
4 whole cloves
2 slices lemon

1. Mix sugar and cornstarch in saucepan; add vinegar, stock, raisins, and cloves.
2. Simmer sugar mixture for 10 minutes. Add lemon slices to sugar mixture; simmer for 2 more minutes. May be served on tongue or ham.

Cranberry Sauce

$2\frac{1}{2}$ *cups*

4 c. cranberries
1 c. water, boiling
2 c. sugar

1. Sort cranberries for quality; wash.
2. Cook in water for 10 minutes or until skins burst.
3. Remove from heat; force through a sieve.
4. Return purée to saucepan. Add sugar and boil for 5 minutes. Pour into molds.

Brown-Sugar Sirup

$1\frac{5}{8}$ *cups*

$1\frac{1}{2}$ c. brown sugar
2 c. water, boiling

1. Add sugar to water and boil for 5 minutes.
2. Store sirup, covered, in refrigerator.

Chocolate Sirup

$1\frac{1}{4}$ *cups*

$\frac{1}{4}$ c. cocoa
$\frac{3}{4}$ c. sugar
$\frac{1}{8}$ t. salt
$\frac{1}{2}$ c. water
1 t. vanilla

1. Mix cocoa, sugar, salt, and water in saucepan; boil for 3 to 4 minutes.
2. Remove sirup from heat; add vanilla. Store, covered, in refrigerator.

Meats

Creamed Dried Beef in Toast Cups

4 servings

4 slices soft bread
2 T. melted table fat
½ c. broken bits dried beef
1½ c. medium white sauce (p. 423)
   (Omit salt.)
1 T. chopped parsley

1. Trim crusts from bread; press each slice into a muffin cup.
2. Brush fat over each toast cup. Bake at 350° F. for 15 minutes or until golden brown.
3. Add beef to white sauce; heat to serving temperature.
4. Put beef mixture into toast cups. Garnish with parsley.

"Quickie" Steaks

4 servings

½ lb. ground beef
1 T. chopped onion
2 t. flour
¼ c. evaporated milk
¼ t. salt
⅛ t. pepper
⅛ t. savory, if desired
4 slices bread
2 T. softened table fat
1 T. mustard
2 T. shortening

1. Mix beef, onion, flour, milk, and seasonings together.
2. Toast bread slices on one side. Spread untoasted side to the edges with table fat, mustard, and beef mixture.
3. Heat shortening in frying pan. Place bread with meat side down in frying pan; cook 5 minutes or until beef is golden brown.

Chili con Carne

4 servings

2 T. table fat
1 lb. ground beef
½ c. diced onion
¼ c. diced green pepper
½ to 1 garlic clove, finely cut (if desired)
½ c. water
2 c. cooked tomatoes
   or 1 c. tomato purée and 1 c. water
2 c. cooked kidney beans
½ to 1 t. chili powder
1 to 1¼ t. salt
1 t. orégano

1. Heat fat in frying pan; add beef and cook until light brown. Add onion, pepper, and garlic; cook 2 to 3 minutes, stirring occasionally.
2. Add ½ c. water, tomatoes, beans, and seasonings to beef mixture; cover and simmer for 45 minutes.

TEMPERATURE AND TIME FOR COOKING MEATS*

METHOD		CUT	TEMPERA-TURE (degrees Fahr.)	COOKING TIME	MEAT THERMOMETER (degrees Fahr.)
ROASTING	BEEF	Standing Rib (5–8 lbs.)			
		Rare	300	2½ hr.	140
		Medium	300	3½ hr.	160
		Well-done	300	4 hr.	170
		Rolled Rib (6–8 lbs.)			
		Rare	300	3½–4 hr.	140
		Medium	300	4½–5 hr.	160
		Well-done	300	5½–6½ hr.	170
		Rump (5–7 lbs.)	300	4 hr.	
	LAMB	Leg or shoulder (6–8 lbs.	300	3¾–4 hr.	180
	PORK	(fresh)			
		Center loin	350	35–40 min. per pound	185
		Picnic, shoulder	350	30–35 min. per pound	185
	PORK	(smoked): Ham†			
		Whole (10–16 lbs.)	300	18–20 min. per pound	160–170
		Half	300	25–30 min. per pound	160–170
	VEAL	Loin shoulder, and boned and rolled	300	30–35 min. per pound	170
BROILING*	BEEF	Steaks, porterhouse			
		Rare (1 inch)		10–12 min.	140
		Medium (1 inch)		14–16 min.	160
		Rare (2 inches)		20–25 min.	140
		Medium (2 inches)		30–35 min.	160
		Well-done (2 inches)		40–45 min.	170
	LAMB	Chops, loin		12–14 min.	
	PORK	(smoked)			
		Ham Slice (1 inch)		16–20 min.	
		Ham Slice (1 inch tenderized)		10–15 min.	
		Bacon		4–5 min.	
BRAISING	BEEF	Roast, chuck (3–5 lbs.)	Low heat	3½–4 hr.	
		Steak, round (2 lbs.)	Low heat	1½–2 hr.	
	PORK	(fresh)			
		Chops (¾ to 1½ inches)	Low heat	50–60 min.	
		Shoulder steaks	Low heat	35–40 min.	
	VEAL	Chops and cutlets (½–¾ inch)	Low heat	45–60 min.	

*Set oven regulator for broiling. Place meat 3 inches below heat unit.

†Some hams on the market require a shorter cooking period because of the method of processing.

Soybean Chili

1 c. dry soybeans
3 c. water, boiling
6 c. water
2 T. table fat
  or shortening
1 lb. ground beef
  or pork
2 T. chopped onion
2 c. tomato purée
1 t. salt
1 T. chili powder
½ t. orégano
1 c. cooking water from soybeans

1. Soak soybeans in 3 c. boiling water 3 to 4 hours; drain in sieve.
2. Put soybeans and 6 c. water in large saucepan, cover, and boil 90 minutes.
3. Heat fat in frying pan. Cook beef, stirring three or four times, until light brown; add onion and cook until golden, stirring one or two times. Remove beef mixture.
4. Cook beans in same fat until light brown, stirring occasionally.
5. Add meat, onion, purée, seasonings, and 1 c. water to beans; simmer for 45 minutes.

Meat Balls and Spaghetti

½ lb. ground beef
¼ c. soybean grits
¼ c. soft bread crumbs
⅓ c. water
½ t. salt
⅛ t. pepper
2 T. shortening
2 t. chopped onion
1 c. cooked spaghetti (p. 366)
1 recipe Tomato Sauce (p. 424)

1. Mix beef, grits, crumbs, water, and seasonings together; form into 1½- to 2-inch-diameter balls.
2. Heat shortening in frying pan. Add meat balls and cook until light brown, turning once. Remove from pan.
3. Add onion to shortening, cook until golden, stirring.
4. Put meat balls into baking dish fitted with a cover; add onion, cooked spaghetti, and tomato sauce.
5. Cover dish; bake at 350° F. for 20 to 25 minutes.

Meat Nests

1 lb. ground beef
⅓ c. dry bread crumbs
2 T. soybean flour
¾ c. milk
1¼ t. salt
⅛ t. pepper
⅛ t. marjoram, if desired
6 T. grated cheese
2 T. chopped pimento

1. Mix beef, crumbs, flour, milk, and seasonings together.
2. Line ungreased muffin tins with beef mixture to ¼-inch thickness. Add grated cheese to each nest.
3. Fill meat nests with creamed potatoes (below); sprinkle pimento on top. Bake at 350° F. for 25 to 30 minutes.

Creamed-Potato Filling for Meat Nests

4 medium potatoes, diced
1 c. milk
½ t. salt
Pepper to taste

1. Wash, pare, and dice potatoes.
2. Put potatoes into saucepan; add milk and seasonings.
3. Simmer potatoes, covered, for 30 minutes.

VARIATIONS: Use recipe for *Meat Nests*.

–1–

2 c. chopped leftover meat substi-
    tuted for ground beef

–2–

1 egg for each meat nest substituted
    for creamed potatoes
Omit pimento.

Break an egg into each meat nest the last 10 to 15 minutes
of baking period.

Meat Loaf

6 to 8 servings

$\frac{3}{4}$ lb. ground beef
$\frac{1}{4}$ lb. ground pork
$\frac{3}{4}$ c. bread
   or cracker crumbs
2 eggs
1 T. table fat
2 T. chopped onion
1 c. chopped fresh
   or canned tomatoes
$1\frac{1}{2}$ t. salt
$\frac{1}{8}$ t. pepper
1 T. Worcestershire Sauce
Few grains of cayenne pepper
$\frac{1}{2}$ c. chopped peanuts
1 T. garlic butter

1. Mix meats and crumbs.
2. Beat eggs until mixed; add to meat mixture.
3. Heat fat in frying pan; add onion and cook until golden,
   stirring once or twice.
4. Remove onion to large bowl. Add tomatoes, seasonings,
   meat mixture, and peanuts; mix.
5. Shape meat mixture into loaf; put into $8\frac{1}{2}$ to 9-inch loaf
   pan and bake at 350° F. for 50 to 60 minutes.
6. Dot with garlic butter; serve.

Stuffed Peppers

4 servings

3 T. shortening
$1\frac{1}{2}$ lb. ground beef
1 medium onion, chopped
1 clove garlic
1 egg
$\frac{1}{4}$ c. soybean flour
$2\frac{1}{3}$ T. nonfat dried milk
$1\frac{1}{2}$ T. chopped parsley
$\frac{1}{4}$ c. milk
$\frac{1}{2}$ t. salt
$\frac{1}{8}$ t. pepper
$\frac{1}{8}$ t. thyme, if desired
$\frac{1}{8}$ t. basil, if desired
4 green peppers
$\frac{1}{2}$ c. water

1. Heat shortening in frying pan; add beef and onion;
   cook until beef is light brown, stirring two or three times.
2. Rub inside of mixing bowl with garlic. Add beef mixture,
   egg, flour, nonfat dried milk, parsley, milk, and seasonings; mix.
3. Wash peppers and remove stems and seeds. Fill with
   beef mixture.
4. Place peppers in a shallow, 6- to 8-inch baking dish. Add
   water; cover. Cook at 350° F. for 45 to 50 minutes.
   Broil 3 inches from heat unit for 3 minutes.

Stuffed Onions

6 servings

6 large Bermuda onions
¾ c. boiling water
½ t. salt
½ lb. sausage
½ c. cooked navy beans
½ t. salt
⅛ t. pepper
½ t. dry mustard
½ c. bread crumbs
2 T. finely chopped celery tops
1 T. brown sugar

1. Cook onions in boiling, salted water for 20 minutes. Drain and cool.
2. Cook sausage in frying pan until lightly browned. Drain off fat.
3. Remove centers of onions. Set aside.
4. Add beans, onion centers, and seasonings to sausage; mix.
5. Stuff onions; place in a shallow 6- to 8-inch baking dish.
6. Mix bread crumbs, celery, and brown sugar together; sprinkle on each onion.
7. Bake onions at 350° F. for 30 minutes.

Sausage-Stuffed Acorn Squash

4 servings

Two 1½-lb. acorn squashes
1 lb. sausage
1 small onion, grated
1½ c. soft bread crumbs
1 t. salt
⅛ t. pepper

1. Cut each squash in half; remove seeds and stem. Place cut side down in 1 inch of water in a covered frying pan. Cook until tender.
2. Cook sausage in frying pan until light brown. Drain off fat.
3. Add onion, crumbs, and seasonings to sausage.
4. Fill centers of squash with sausage mixture; bake in a shallow, 10-inch baking dish at 375° F. for 25 minutes.

Mock Sausages

4 servings

1½ c. cooked lima beans
¼ c. bread crumbs
1 egg
2 t. melted table fat
½ t. salt
Few grains of cayenne pepper
⅔ c. corn meal
3 T. shortening
½ c. tomato sauce, if desired

1. Force beans through a coarse sieve.
2. Add crumbs, egg, fat, and seasonings to bean purée, mixing well.
3. Shape bean mixture into flat cakes; turn in corn meal.
4. Heat fat in frying pan. Cook bean cakes until golden brown, turning once.
Serve with tomato sauce.

Hamburg Steak

4 servings

¾ lb. ground beef
¼ c. soft bread crumbs
½ c. milk
½ t. salt
⅛ t. pepper
½ t. Worcestershire sauce

1. Mix beef, crumbs, milk, and seasonings together.
2. Heat shortening in frying pan. Add meat mixture by tablespoonfuls and flatten into thin cakes.
3. Cook cakes until golden brown, turning once; remove and keep hot in oven or on low heat.

432

Frankfurter Casserole

6 servings

8 frankfurters
1½ c. water, boiling
½ t. salt
⅛ t. pepper
1 t. Worcestershire sauce
1 T. finely chopped onion
1½ c. diced potatoes
2 c. medium white sauce
½ c. grated sharp cheese
  or bread *or* cracker crumbs, buttered

1. Add frankfurters to boiling water and simmer for 5 minutes. Cool slightly. Cut into 1-inch rounds.
2. Mix frankfurters, seasonings, onion, and potatoes with white sauce. Put into 8-inch baking dish; top with cheese or crumbs.
   (If cheese is used, add to casserole last 5 minutes of baking.)
3. Bake casserole at 365° F. for 20 to 25 minutes.

Potato-Pork Pie

4 to 5 servings

2 T. shortening
½ lb. pork, cubed
¼ c. chopped onion
1½ c. cubed white *or* sweet potatoes
¾ c. fresh *or* canned peas
1 t. salt
⅛ t. pepper
1 T. flour
2 T. water
½ recipe Drop Biscuits (p. 381)

1. Heat shortening in frying pan; add pork and cook until light brown, stirring two or three times.
2. Add onion to pork and cook until golden, stirring occasionally.
3. Add hot water to cover pork; cover tightly and simmer 1 hour.
4. Add potatoes, peas, and seasonings to pork mixture. (Add peas, if canned, last 5 minutes of cooking.)
5. Cover pork mixture and cook 15 minutes or until vegetables are tender.
6. Mix flour and water together; combine with pork mixture; pour into 8- to 9-inch baking dish.
7. Top with teaspoonfuls of biscuit dough; bake at 425° F. for 12 to 15 minutes.

Meat Pie

4 servings

½ recipe Baking-Powder Biscuits (p. 381)
1 c. diced, cooked meat
½ c. diced celery
½ c. meat stock
  or 1 beef bouillon cube in ½ c. water
⅛ t. marjoram, if desired
¼ t. onion salt
1 c. grated cheese

1. Place dough on lightly floured board and roll to ⅜-inch thickness. Put into an 8- to 9-inch baking dish, covering the bottom and sides as for pie.
2. Add meat, celery, meat stock, and seasonings to dough-lined dish.
3. Bake pie at 425° F. for 15 minutes.
4. Reduce heat to 350° F. Add grated cheese to pie; bake 5 minutes.

Veal and Vegetables with Noodles

6 servings

$\frac{1}{2}$ lb. veal shoulder
$\frac{1}{4}$ c. shortening
$\frac{1}{2}$ c. sliced onions
1 c. stock
   or 1 c. water and 1 beef bouillon
   cube
$\frac{1}{4}$ c. diced celery
$\frac{1}{2}$ c. diced carrots
2 T. chopped green pepper
$\frac{1}{2}$ c. green peas
1 t. salt
1 c. cooked noodles (p. 366)
Parsley sprigs

1. Cut veal into 1-inch cubes.
2. Heat shortening in large frying pan. Add veal and cook until light brown; add onions and cook until golden, stirring once or twice.
   (Rub pan with a garlic bud first if desired.)
3. Add stock and salt to veal mixture.
4. Heat veal mixture to boiling; then reduce to low heat for 45 minutes.
5. Arrange vegetables and noodles on top of meat.
6. Cover pan tightly; cook mixture on moderate heat for 15 minutes.
7. Arrange noodles on platter with veal and vegetables in center. Garnish with parsley.

Lamb Stew

6 servings

$1\frac{1}{2}$ lb. lean, uncooked lamb *or* mutton
$1\frac{1}{2}$ t. salt
$\frac{1}{8}$ t. pepper
2 T. flour
2 T. shortening
$\frac{1}{4}$ c. chopped onions
3 potatoes, diced
3 carrots, diced
1 turnip, diced
2 T. chopped parsley

1. Cut lamb in 1-inch cubes; add seasonings, and sprinkle with flour.
2. Heat shortening in frying pan; add lamb and cook until light brown, stirring two or three times; add onion and cook until golden, stirring occasionally.
3. Add water to cover lamb; simmer 90 minutes.
   (Mutton will require another hour.)
4. Add vegetables to stew; cook 20 minutes or until tender. Garnish with parsley.

For thicker mixture:

2 T. flour
1 T. cold water

Brown flour in oven at 400° F. or in heavy skillet.
Mix flour and water; add 2 to 3 T. liquid from stew, stirring.
Add paste to stew when vegetables are tender, stirring.
Cook until thickened.

VARIATION: Use recipe for *Lamb Stew.*

Beef Stew

$1\frac{1}{2}$ lb. beef chuck substituted for lamb

434

American Chop Suey

4 servings

3 T. table fat
½ lb. veal, cut in ½-inch cubes
¼ c. coarsely cut onion
¾ c. hot water
½ t. salt
⅛ t. freshly ground peppercorns
¾ c. coarsely chopped celery
2 T. chopped green pepper
1½ T. cornstarch
1½ t. molasses
1 T. water
1 package (5 oz.) quick-cooking rice

1. Heat fat in large frying pan. Add veal and onion; cook until onion is golden, stirring two or three times.
2. Add water, seasonings, and vegetables to veal mixture. Cook, covered for 25 minutes or until veal is tender.
3. Mix cornstarch, molasses, and water. Add to veal mixture, stirring. Cook for 5 more minutes.
4. Cook rice, following directions on package. Serve veal mixture with rice.

Pan-Fried Liver

4 servings

¾ lb. liver
⅜ c. flour
½ t. salt
⅛ t. pepper
3 T. shortening

1. Remove veins and membrane from liver. Cut edges at several points to a ⅜-inch depth.
2. Mix flour and seasonings together. Dip slices of liver into flour mixture, coating each piece.
3. Heat shortening in frying pan. Add liver and cook until golden brown, or until each piece is just tender, turning once.
4. Drain liver on absorbent paper. May be served with broiled bacon or with onions.

Braised Heart

4 to 5 servings

1 beef *or* calf heart
½ recipe Fruit Stuffing (p. 450)
½ c. flour
½ t. salt
⅛ t. pepper
2 T. shortening
¾ c. water

1. Remove veins and arteries from beef heart; wash.
2. Fill cavity of heart with stuffing. Close opening with skewers or by sewing.
3. Mix flour and seasonings together; roll heart in flour mixture.
4. Heat shortening in deep frying pan; cook heart until light brown on all sides.
5. Add water to heart, cover, and simmer 2½ to 3 hours.

Braised Tongue

4 servings

1 calf, beef, lamb, *or* pork tongue
1 t. salt
Water to cover

1. Wash tongue in warm water and cut away bony part.
2. Simmer tongue in salted water for 1 to 3 hours or until tender.
3. Drain off liquid and add cold water to cover tongue.
4. Remove tongue when cool and peel.

Serve sliced for sandwiches or as main meat dish with horse-radish sauce (p. 425).

Creole Kidney

4 to 5 servings

1 medium beef kidney
$\frac{1}{4}$ c. flour
3 small bacon slices, chopped
$\frac{1}{4}$ c. chopped onion
2 T. chopped green pepper
2 c. tomatoes
1 t. salt
Few grains of cayenne pepper

1. Wash and remove outer skin from kidney; split through center and remove fat and large veins.
2. Soak kidney in cold water 30 minutes, changing water three or four times.
3. Cut kidney into $\frac{1}{2}$-inch slices. Dip into flour.
4. Cook bacon in large frying pan until it barely begins to crisp. Add kidney and onion; cook until bacon is crisp, stirring two or three times.
5. Add green pepper, tomatoes, and seasonings; simmer for 60 minutes. (Add water if needed.)

Sweetbreads and Mushrooms

4 to 5 servings

1 t. salt
1 T. vinegar
$\frac{1}{2}$ to $\frac{3}{4}$ lb. sweetbreads
4 c. water
$\frac{1}{2}$ lb. mushrooms, fresh
   or $\frac{1}{2}$ c., canned
$2\frac{1}{2}$ T. table fat
$1\frac{1}{2}$ c. medium white sauce
$\frac{1}{2}$ t. salt
$\frac{1}{8}$ t. pepper

1. Add salt, vinegar, and sweetbreads to water; simmer for 15 minutes.
2. Drain sweetbreads in sieve; place in bowl and cover with cold water. Change water two or three times.
3. Remove membranes from sweetbreads.
4. Clean mushrooms, if fresh, with soft brush and water.
5. Slice mushrooms, including the stems if tender.
6. Heat fat in medium frying pan; add mushrooms and cook until light brown, stirring two or three times.
7. Add white sauce, seasonings, and sweetbreads to mushrooms. Heat and serve on toast or with rice.

Deep-Fat-Fried Brains

3 to 4 servings

1 set brains—veal, beef, *or* pork
$\frac{1}{2}$ t. salt
2 c. cold water
$\frac{1}{2}$ t. salt
1 T. vinegar
2 c. hot water
Shortening
1 egg
1 c. cracker crumbs
$\frac{1}{4}$ c. tomato sauce

1. Remove veins and membrane from brains.
2. Add salt to cold water and soak brains 10 minutes. Drain in sieve.
3. Add brains, salt, and vinegar to hot water and simmer 15 minutes; drain.
4. Add enough shortening to fill a deep, heavy pan $\frac{1}{2}$ to $\frac{2}{3}$ full when melted; heat to 360° F.
5. Beat egg until mixed.
6. Divide brains into about 1-inch-square pieces; roll in crumbs, dip into egg, and again roll in crumbs.
7. Cook brains in shortening for 2 to 3 minutes or until golden brown, turning once.
8. Drain brains on absorbent paper.
Serve with tomato sauce.

VARIATION: Use recipe for *Deep-Fat-Fried Brains.*

Deep-Fat-Fried Sweetbreads

$\frac{1}{2}$ to $\frac{3}{4}$ lb. sweetbreads (p. 436) substituted for brains

Broiled Club Steak

4 to 6 servings

1 to 1$\frac{1}{2}$ lb. club steak, 1-inch thick
$\frac{1}{2}$ to 1 t. salt

1. Wipe steak with a damp cloth.
2. Slash outer edge of meat at 1-inch intervals to depth of
   $\frac{1}{2}$-inch.
3. Place meat on broiler rack with top surface 2 to 3 inches
   from heat unit. Cook until of desired doneness on one
   side; turn and cook (pp. 207–208). Season.
   Serve with garlic butter, if desired.

VARIATIONS: Use recipe for *Broiled Club Steak.*

Broiled Rib Steak

Rib steak substituted for club steak,
    1$\frac{1}{2}$ inches thick

Increase total cooking time 5 minutes.

Broiled Ham Slice

1$\frac{1}{2}$- to 2-lb. ham slice, $\frac{1}{2}$-inch thick,
    not tenderized

Refer to pp. 207–208.

Roast Lamb Shoulder

6 to 8 servings

3 to 5$\frac{1}{2}$ lb. lamb shoulder
1 t. salt
$\frac{1}{2}$ t. rosemary

1. Wipe lamb shoulder with a damp cloth; rub with seasonings.
2. Place shoulder on rack in open pan. Insert thermometer
   so that bulb reaches center of lamb shoulder.
3. Cook at 300° F. until thermometer registers 175° to
   180° F. (p. 429).

VARIATIONS: Use recipe for *Roast Lamb Shoulder.*

Roast Pork Loin

3 to 4 lb. pork loin, shoulder end
1 t. salt
$\frac{1}{2}$ t. thyme substituted for rosemary

Refer to pp. 207, 429.

Rolled Rib Roast of Beef

3 to 4 lb. rolled rib roast
1 t. salt
$\frac{1}{2}$ t. basil substituted for rosemary

Refer to pp. 207, 429.

Pot Roast of Beef   6 to 8 servings

4 lb. beef, chuck or round
3 T. flour
1½ t. salt
¼ t. pepper
⅛ t. marjoram
⅛ t. savory, if desired
¼ c. shortening
   or ⅛ lb. salt pork, sliced
½ to ¾ c. water, boiling

1. Wipe beef with a damp cloth.
2. Mix flour and seasonings together and rub into beef.
3. Heat shortening in heavy kettle or skillet. Add beef and cook slowly until golden brown on all sides, turning.
4. Place rack under beef (to prevent burning and hardening). Add water, cover, and cook slowly for 3 hours or until evenly cooked and tender. Add additional water if necessary.
5. Prepare gravy (p. 450).

VARIATION: Use recipe for *Pot Roast of Beef*.

6 to 8 small onions, carrots, potatoes, celery stalks
¾ t. salt

Add last hour of cooking.

Sauerbraten   4 servings

2 lb. beef, chuck
1 c. vinegar
2 bay leaves
5 to 6 peppercorns
6 to 8 cloves
¼ t. allspice
¼ c. flour
¾ t. salt
3 T. shortening
2 t. sugar

1. Wipe beef with a damp cloth. Place in a 10-inch-deep container.
2. Add vinegar and seasonings to beef. Add enough water to cover. Place in refrigerator, covered, for 12 to 18 hours.
3. Drain beef; save 1 c. liquid.
4. Mix flour and salt together and sprinkle over beef.
5. Heat shortening in heavy kettle or skillet. Add beef and cook until lightly browned on all sides, turning.
6. Place rack under beef; add ½ c. of the liquid. Cover and cook slowly for 3 hours or until tender. Add additional liquid if necessary.
7. Prepare gravy, adding sugar with flour (p. 450).

Swiss Steak   4 to 5 servings

1 slice round steak
   or chuck steak, about 1½ lb., 1½-inches thick
⅜ c. flour
¾ t. salt
⅛ t. celery salt
2 to 3 T. shortening
1 medium onion, sliced
1½ to 3 c. tomatoes
   or tomato juice
   or tomato soup

1. Wipe steak with a damp cloth. Cut into serving portions.
2. Mix flour and seasonings. Pound flour mixture into steak with meat pounder or edge of heavy saucer.
3. Heat shortening in frying pan. Add onion and cook until golden, stirring two or three times. Remove onion and set aside.
4. Add steak and cook until golden brown, turning once. Return onion to pan.
5. Pour tomatoes over steak, cover and simmer for 20 minutes or until tender.

Stuffed Flank Steak

1 large flank steak
  or 2 small ones
½ recipe Bread Stuffing (p. 449)
½ t. thyme
2 T. shortening

1. Wipe steak with a damp cloth. Spread stuffing on steak and sprinkle with thyme; working from one side, roll like a jelly roll.
2. Tie a string securely around roll in three or four places.
3. Heat shortening in frying pan. Add flank roll and brown on all sides.
4. Put roll on rack in roasting pan. Bake at 350° F. for 75 minutes.
5. Remove string and carve. Each serving will be a round slice with stuffing in center.
   Serve with beef-stock gravy.

"Dixie" Pork Chops

6 servings

1 T. shortening
6 lean pork chops
1 T. finely chopped onion
1 t. salt
½ t. sage
3 tart apples, cored and cut into rings
¼ c. sifted brown sugar
2 T. flour, browned
1 c. hot water
1 T. vinegar
⅛ t. peppercorn, freshly ground

1. Heat shortening in frying pan; add chops and cook until lightly browned, turning once. Add onion and seasonings; cook until onion is golden, stirring two or three times.
2. Remove chops to baking dish; set frying pan aside.
3. Place apple rings on chops and sprinkle with sugar.
4. Pour drippings from frying pan, measure 1½ T. and return to frying pan on low heat.
5. Add flour to drippings, stirring.
6. Add water and vinegar slowly to drippings mixture, stirring. Add peppercorn and cook until bubbling.
7. Pour gravy over chops. Bake at 350° F. for 45 to 50 minutes.

Corning Glass Works

Baked ham slice

Fish

Simmered or Poached Fish

3 to 4 servings

¼ t. basil, if desired
1 t. salt
2 T. vinegar
  or lemon juice
4 c. hot water
1½ lb. small fish fillets *or* steaks

1. Add seasonings and vinegar to simmering water.
2. Add fish (pp. 224–225) and simmer for 5 to 8 minutes, or bake in oven at 300° F. for 10 minutes or until tender. Drain fish.
   Serve with Lemon Butter.

Lemon Butter

¼ cup

3 T. table fat, softened
1 T. lemon juice
2 t. finely chopped parsley
⅛ t. salt
Few grains of pepper

Mix fat, lemon juice, parsley, and seasonings together.

Fried Fish

6 servings

2 lb. fish fillets *or* steaks *or* split fish
1 t. salt
½ c. corn meal
¼ to ⅜ c. shortening

1. Sprinkle fish with salt; turn in meal.
2. Heat shortening in frying pan until very hot (below smoking point).
3. Cook fish until golden brown, turning once. Drain on absorbent paper.

Broiled Halibut Steaks

6 servings

2 lb. halibut steaks *or* fillets
⅛ t. pepper
3 T. melted table fat
1 T. hot water
1 t. salt

1. Season fish with salt and pepper.
2. Combine fat and hot water; brush on fish.
3. Place fish with skin side up on greased broiler rack.
4. Broil fish 2 inches from heat unit for 3 to 7 minutes for each side; turn once and brush with fat and water. Serve with lemon wedge.

Baked Fish

6 servings

2½ to 3 lb. fish fillets *or* split fish
1 t. salt
⅛ t. pepper
½ t. marjoram, if desired
2 T. melted table fat
1 medium onion, sliced thinly
1 c. milk
Paprika
Watercress

1. Sprinkle fish with seasonings; brush with fat.
2. Place fillets skin side down in shallow, 8- to 10-inch baking dish. Add onion slices and milk.
3. Bake fillets at 325° F. for 20 to 25 minutes, basting two or three times with milk in dish. Broil 2 to 3 inches from heat unit until golden brown.
4. Sprinkle with paprika.
   Garnish with watercress.
   Serve.

VARIATION: Use recipe for *Baked Fish.*

Stuffed Fillets

½ recipe Bread Stuffing (p. 449)

Place stuffing between each two fillets.
Close sides with wooden picks or skewers.

Creamed Fish

4 to 5 servings

2 c. cooked fish flakes
1 c. medium white sauce, using cream *or* liquid from fish
2 t. grated onion
¼ t. mace
2 t. finely chopped parsley

1. Combine fish, sauce, onion, and mace.
2. Simmer fish mixture to serving temperature. Add parsley.
   May be served on toast, rice, or baked potato.

Deep-Sea Delight

8 servings

¼ lb. medium noodles
1 qt. water, boiling
½ t. salt
½ lb. mushrooms
2 T. table fat
1 can (7 oz.) tuna fish
2 c. thin white sauce (p. 423)
½ c. grated cheese

1. Add noodles to boiling salted water and cook for 15 minutes or until tender. Drain in sieve.
2. Wash mushrooms; slice thin.
3. Heat fat in frying pan and add mushrooms. Cook slowly until lightly browned, stirring three or four times.
4. Drain oil from tuna; flake with a fork.
5. Combine noodles, mushrooms, tuna, and white sauce.
6. Pour into 8-inch baking dish; sprinkle with cheese.
7. Bake tuna mixture at 350° F. for 20 minutes.

VARIATION: Use recipe for *Deep-Sea Delight.*

1 chopped pimento
3 chopped olives substituted for cheese

Fried Fish Cakes

4 servings

3 T. table fat *or* shortening
1 c. cooked fish flakes
1½ c. seasoned mashed potatoes
⅛ t. savory
1 egg, beaten with 1 T. water
Bread crumbs

1. Heat fat in frying pan.
2. Mix fish, potatoes, and savory. Mold into flat cakes, 2 inches in diameter.
3. Dip fish cakes in egg mixture, then in crumbs.
4. Cook cakes until golden brown, turning once. May be served with tomato sauce.

Salmon Loaf with Sauce

6 servings

2 c. salmon
1 c. soft bread crumbs
2 t. lemon juice
¼ t. salt
Few grains of cayenne pepper
2 eggs
2 c. very thick white sauce
½ c. cooked green peas
2 t. chopped parsley
2 hard-cooked eggs, chopped
1 c. thick white sauce (p. 423)

1. Flake salmon with a fork.
2. Combine salmon, crumbs, lemon juice, and seasonings.
3. Beat eggs slightly and add to salmon mixture. Add 2 c. white sauce, blending lightly with a fork.
4. Place salmon mixture in greased 8½- to 9-inch loaf pan. Bake at 350° F. for 25 minutes or until firm.
5. Combine peas, parsley, and eggs with 1 c. white sauce. Heat to serving temperature.
6. Pour sauce over salmon loaf and serve.

Fried Oysters

4 servings

18 large oysters
½ c. cracker *or* bread crumbs
1 t. salt
2 t. water
1 egg
½ c. shortening

1. Remove shell pieces from oysters; drain.
2. Mix crumbs with salt.
3. Roll oysters in crumb mixture. Set aside 10 minutes.
4. Add water to egg; beat slightly.
5. Dip oysters into egg mixture, and again roll in crumbs; set aside another 10 minutes.
6. Heat shortening in frying pan. Add oysters and cook until golden brown, turning once. Drain on absorbent paper.
   Garnish with sliced pickle or lemon, if desired.

VARIATION: Use recipe for *Fried Oysters*.

Fried Shrimp

Shrimp substituted for oysters

Scalloped Oysters

2 c. canned oysters
$\frac{1}{2}$ c. milk and oyster liquid
1$\frac{1}{2}$ c. cracker *or* bread crumbs
2 T. melted table fat
$\frac{1}{2}$ t. salt
$\frac{1}{8}$ t. pepper

4 servings

1. Remove shell pieces from oysters. Drain off liquid and add enough milk to make $\frac{1}{2}$ c.
2. Pour $\frac{1}{2}$ of the oysters into 6- to 8-inch baking dish.
3. Mix crumbs with fat and seasonings.
4. Sprinkle $\frac{1}{2}$ of the crumb mixture over the oysters.
5. Put in remaining oysters; sprinkle with remaining crumb mixture.
6. Pour milk mixture over oyster mixture; bake at 350° F. for 20 to 25 minutes.

French-Fried Shrimp

1 lb. shrimp
1 egg
$\frac{1}{2}$ c. milk
2 t. dry mustard
$\frac{1}{4}$ t. basil
$\frac{1}{8}$ t. pepper
Few grains of cayenne pepper
Few grains of garlic salt
1 t. finely chopped onion
Shortening
1 c. fine bread crumbs

6 to 8 servings

1. Remove shell and black vein from shrimp.
2. Beat egg until mixed and add milk and seasonings.
3. Put shrimp in egg mixture; marinate 45 minutes, stirring three or four times.
4. Add enough shortening to fill a deep, heavy pan $\frac{1}{2}$ to $\frac{2}{3}$ full when melted; heat to 400° F.
5. Drain shrimp; roll in crumbs. Cook for 3 minutes or until golden brown. Drain on absorbent paper.
   Serve with catchup or tartar sauce, if desired.

Shrimp Fondue

5 slices bread
3 t. melted table fat
1 c. finely cut shrimp
$\frac{3}{4}$ t. salt
$\frac{1}{8}$ t. pepper
3 eggs
2 c. milk
$\frac{3}{4}$ to 1 c. grated cheese

6 servings

1. Cut bread into 1$\frac{1}{2}$-inch cubes or make coarse crumbs.
2. Combine cubes with fat, shrimp, and seasonings.
3. Beat eggs until thick and add to bread-cube mixture. Add milk and cheese, tossing lightly.
4. Pour mixture into a deep, 6- to 8-inch baking dish; set in pan containing hot water to cover $\frac{2}{3}$ of dish.
5. Bake fondue at 350° F. for 50 to 55 minutes.

Fish Soufflé

1$\frac{1}{2}$ c. milk
1 c. finger shredded, dry (not hard) bread crumbs
1 t. table fat
2 c. cooked fish flakes
4 eggs, separated
$\frac{3}{4}$ t. salt
$\frac{1}{8}$ t. paprika
3 drops Tabasco sauce

6 servings

1. Heat milk over very low heat or in top of double boiler over hot water.
2. Add crumbs, fat, and fish to milk, stirring.
3. Beat yolks in large bowl until thick; add fish mixture, stirring.
4. Add salt to whites; beat to form softly rounded peaks.
5. Fold whites into fish mixture. Pour into a deep, 6- to 8-inch baking dish; set in pan containing hot water to cover $\frac{2}{3}$ of dish.
6. Bake soufflé at 350° F. for 50 to 55 minutes.
   Serve immediately.

443

Poultry

	TEMPERATURE AND TIME FOR COOKING POULTRY		
PRODUCT	READY-TO-COOK WEIGHT	TEMPERATURE (degrees Fahr.)	TOTAL COOKING TIME
CHICKEN			
Roasting	3–4½ lb.	325	3–3½ hr.
	4½–6 lb.	325	3½–4 hr.
Broiling	1½–2 lb.	Place 4 inches below heat unit	45 min.–1 hr.
Deep-fat frying	1½ lb.	365 beginning temperature	15–20 min.
		325 frying temperature	
Pan-frying	1½–3 lb.	Moderate heat	45–60 min.
TURKEY			
Roasting	4–8 lb.	325	3–4½ hr.
	8–12 lb.	325	3½–5 hr.
	12–16 lb.	325	5–6 hr.
	16–20 lb.	325	6–7 hr.
DUCK			
Roasting	3-5 lb.	325	2½–3 hr.
GOOSE			
Roasting	8–14 lb.	325	3½–5 hr.

Broiled Chicken

4 servings

1- to 1½-lb. chicken, cut into quarters
¼ c. melted shortening
½ to 1 t. salt
⅛ t. pepper
2 to 3 T. flour

1. Rub quarters with shortening and seasonings; roll in flour if desired.
2. Place quarters skin side down on broiling pan.
3. Broil 3 to 5 inches from heat unit for 40 to 60 minutes turning quarters three or four times.

VARIATIONS: Use recipe for *Broiled Chicken.*

–1–
¼ t. paprika

Rub into quarters with seasonings.

–2–
3 T. lemon juice

Sprinkle over quarters during broiling.

–3–
1 c. barbecue sauce (p. 424)

Baste quarters with sauce two or three times during broiling.

Southern Fried Chicken

4 to 6 servings

Shortening
1 to 2 t. salt
⅛ t. pepper
2½- to 3½-lb. chicken, cut into pieces
¼ to ⅜ c. flour
  or fine crumbs
  or equal parts of corn meal and
    flour mixed

1. Add enough shortening to fill a skillet ⅜- to ½-inch full when melted.
2. Season and roll pieces in flour.
3. Cook pieces in shortening until golden brown, turning one or two times.
4. Cover and cook pieces for 20 to 30 minutes; uncover last 5 minutes to crisp.
5. Use pan drippings for gravy (pp. 233, 450).

VARIATIONS: Use recipe for *Southern Fried Chicken.*

Italian Fried Chicken

Olive oil substituted for shortening

Country Fried Chicken

Table fat substituted for shortening

Oven-Fried Chicken

4 to 6 servings

½ c. flour
½ t. salt
3- to 3½-lb. frying chicken, cut into
  pieces
½ c. melted shortening

1. Sift flour and salt together.
2. Roll pieces in flour mixture. Place in shallow baking dish.
3. Pour shortening over pieces. Bake at 350° F. for 60 minutes, covered tightly, turning three or four times. Remove cover last 20 minutes.

445

Deep-Fat-Fried Chicken   *4 servings*

2½-lb. chicken, cut into pieces
1 recipe Batter for Fried Chicken
¾ to 1 c. bread crumbs
   or flour
Shortening

1. Dip pieces into batter. (See recipe for batter below.) Roll in crumbs; dry 10 minutes.
2. Add enough shortening to fill a deep, heavy pan ½ to ⅔ full when melted. Heat to 375° F.
3. Cook three or four pieces at a time until golden brown, turning once or twice.
4. Drain pieces on absorbent paper. Keep hot in oven at 300° F. until served.

Batter for Fried Chicken

1 egg
¾ c. milk
1 c. flour
½ t. salt
⅛ t. cinnamon, if desired

1. Beat egg slightly; add milk and blend.
2. Sift flour, salt, and cinnamon together.
3. Make a well in flour mixture; add egg mixture and blend.

Roast Chicken   *6 servings*

½ to 1 t. salt
4- to 5-lb. roaster, pullet,
   or capon, whole
1 recipe Bread Stuffing (p. 449)
2 to 2½ T. melted table fat
2 to 2½ T. flour

1. Rub salt over inside of bird.
2. Pile stuffing lightly into body cavity. Close opening by lacing with thread or skewers.
3. Rub outside of chicken with fat. Sprinkle with flour.
4. Place chicken, breast side down, on rack in roasting pan.
5. Bake at 325° F. for 35 minutes per pound, turning and basting three to four times. Remove lacing from chicken. Use drippings for gravy (pp. 233, 450).

Braised Chicken   *6 servings*

⅜ to ½ c. table fat
   or shortening
⅜ c. flour
1½ to 2 t. salt
¼ t. paprika
⅛ t. pepper
5-lb. fowl, cut into pieces
¾ to 1 c. water, milk, *or* thin cream
⅛ t. onion salt

1. Heat fat in skillet.
2. Sift flour and seasonings together.
3. Cook pieces until golden brown, turning once or twice.
4. Remove skillet from heat. Add water and onion salt; cover and simmer for 2 to 3 hours. Add additional water if needed. (Remove cover last 5 minutes of cooking to prevent curdling if cream is used.)

Serve chicken on warm platter. Use drippings for gravy (pp. 233, 450).

446

Stewed Chicken

6 servings

3- to 4-lb. fowl, cut into pieces
2 t. salt
$\frac{1}{4}$ c. chicken fat
$\frac{1}{4}$ c. flour
1 t. salt
$\frac{1}{8}$ t. pepper
Water, boiling, to cover

1. Cover and simmer chicken for $2\frac{1}{2}$ to 3 hours.
2. Remove chicken and skim excess fat from broth.
3. Blend fat with flour; stir in 3 to 4 T. broth. Add hot broth to fat mixture, blending, and cook until slightly thickened, stirring.
4. Add seasonings and chicken to gravy; heat to serving temperature.
   Serve with dumplings, if desired.

Dumplings for Stewed Chicken

$\frac{3}{4}$ c. sifted flour
$2\frac{1}{2}$ t. baking powder
$\frac{1}{2}$ t. salt
1 egg
$\frac{1}{3}$ c. milk

1. Sift flour, baking powder, and salt together.
2. Beat egg until mixed; add milk. Make a well in flour mixture; add egg mixture, blending.
3. Drop batter by teaspoons into boiling chicken broth. Cover tightly.
4. Cook for 15 minutes without lifting lid.

Chicken Croquettes

4 to 6 servings

$1\frac{1}{2}$ c. finely chopped cooked chicken
2 T. finely chopped onion
$\frac{3}{4}$ c. thick white sauce
$\frac{1}{8}$ t. pepper
1 t. salt
2 T. water
1 egg
$1\frac{1}{4}$ c. cracker crumbs
$\frac{1}{2}$ c. finely chopped blanched almonds, if desired
Shortening

1. Combine chicken, onion, white sauce, and seasonings. Shape uniform croquettes using 1 rounding T. chicken mixture.
2. Add water to egg; beat until mixed. Combine crumbs and chopped almonds.
3. Roll croquettes in crumb mixture, dip into egg and again roll in crumb mixture. Set aside 10 minutes to dry.
4. Add enough shortening to fill a deep, heavy pan $\frac{1}{2}$ to $\frac{2}{3}$ full when melted; heat to 375° F.
5. Cook croquettes for 2 minutes or until golden brown, turning once. Drain on absorbent paper.

Creamed Turkey

4 servings

2 T. table fat
1 T. chopped onion
2 T. chopped green pepper
2 T. flour
$1\frac{1}{2}$ c. turkey broth
$\frac{1}{2}$ c. cream
$\frac{1}{2}$ c. chopped celery, cooked
$\frac{1}{4}$ t. salt
$1\frac{1}{2}$ c. diced, cooked turkey

1. Heat fat in skillet. Cook onion and pepper in fat until onion is golden, stirring.
2. Blend flour into onion mixture. Add broth, cream, celery, and salt. Cook, stirring, until thickened.
3. Add turkey to onion mixture and heat to serving temperature.

May be served on rice, noodles, toast, or waffles, or in patty shells.

Chicken Pie

6 servings

½ recipe pie pastry (p. 476)
2 c. diced, cooked chicken
½ c. diced, cooked potatoes
¼ c. diced, cooked celery
½ c. cooked peas
2 T. chopped pimento
½ t. salt
⅛ t. pepper
¾ c. medium white sauce using chicken broth as liquid

1. Roll out pastry for top crust; cut slits as for top crust of fruit pie.
2. Place chicken, vegetables, seasonings, and white sauce in a 1-quart casserole. Cover with pastry.
3. Bake pie at 425° F. for 12 to 15 minutes.

Chicken Spaghetti

Buffet serving for 10

5-lb. fowl
   or roasting chicken
1 onion, quartered
Tops of one bunch of celery
1 t. salt
⅛ t. pepper
½ c. chicken fat
¼ c. flour
¾ c. chicken broth
1 c. diced celery
½ to ¾ c. sliced mushrooms
1 c. tomato juice
2 pimentos, diced
1 garlic clove
⅔ lb. spaghetti, cooked
½ c. grated **Parmesan** cheese

1. Cook chicken with onion, celery tops, and seasonings in pressure saucepan, following manufacturer's directions; or refer to Stewed Chicken recipe (p. 447).
2. Remove meat. Set broth aside until fat hardens; remove fat with a spoon.
3. Remove meat from bones and dice.
4. Mix 2 to 3 T. chicken fat with flour; add broth, blending. Cook until thickened, stirring.
5. Add celery, mushrooms, tomato juice, pimento, garlic, and chicken to sauce. Set aside 30 minutes.
6. Remove garlic from chicken mixture; add spaghetti and pour into a 2-quart casserole. Sprinkle chicken mixture with cheese; bake at 365° F. for 35 minutes.

Fried chicken for a buffet

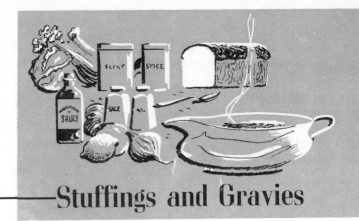

Stuffings and Gravies

Bread Stuffing

4 to 6 c. soft bread crumbs
$\frac{3}{8}$ to $\frac{1}{2}$ c. melted table fat
  or shortening
1 to $1\frac{1}{2}$ t. salt
$\frac{1}{8}$ t. pepper
1 to 2 T. finely chopped onion
Few grains garlic salt *or* sage to taste
2 eggs
Hot chicken *or* meat stock, *or*
  bouillon

5- to 7-pound bird

1. Mix crumbs, fat, and seasonings together.
2. Beat eggs well and toss lightly with crumb mixture.
3. Add enough hot stock to moisten crumb mixture, tossing.

VARIATIONS: Use recipe for *Bread Stuffing*.

Raisin Stuffing

$\frac{1}{4}$ c. raisins
$\frac{1}{2}$ c. chopped nuts

Add with seasonings.

Apple-and-Celery Stuffing

$\frac{1}{2}$ c. chopped celery
$\frac{1}{2}$ c. chopped apple
$\frac{1}{4}$ t. rosemary

Add with seasonings.

Mushroom Stuffing

10 to 12 mushrooms, sliced
$\frac{1}{4}$ t. thyme

Cook mushrooms in fat until light brown.
Add to moistened crumb mixture.

Oyster Stuffing

$1\frac{1}{2}$ c. chopped oysters, with liquid
2 t. finely chopped parsley

Add with seasonings.

Fruit Stuffing

2 cups

$\frac{3}{4}$ c. chopped, dried, tenderized prunes
Water to cover, boiling
$\frac{1}{2}$ c. chopped dried apricots
$\frac{1}{4}$ c. chopped raisins
$\frac{1}{4}$ c. table fat
3 c. dry bread cubes
$\frac{3}{4}$ t. salt

1. Wash fruits. Add prunes to water; cover, and simmer for 25 minutes or until softened.
2. Add apricots and raisins to prunes for last 15 minutes of simmering.
3. Drain fruits, saving liquid.
4. Remove stones and chop fruits coarsely.
5. Heat fat in frying pan; add bread and cook until light brown, stirring two or three times.
6. Toss fruits, bread, and salt together.
7. Add enough fruit liquid to moisten bread mixture, tossing.

Roast Beef Gravy

2 cups

4 T. drippings
4 T. flour, browned
1 c. liquid, made with 1 c. water and browned bits in roaster pan
1 t. salt
Pepper to taste

1. Pour fat drippings into skillet, add flour, stirring.
2. Cook fat and flour to light brown, stirring.
3. Add slowly the brown liquid from roasting pan to drippings and flour, stirring.
4. Add seasonings to mixture and boil 5 minutes, stirring 4 or 5 times.

Cream Gravy

2 T. drippings
1 to $1\frac{1}{2}$ T. flour, browned
$\frac{1}{8}$ to $\frac{1}{4}$ t. sugar, if desired
1 c. milk
  or chicken stock
$\frac{1}{2}$ t. salt
$\frac{1}{8}$ t. finely ground white peppercorns

1. Heat drippings in skillet; blend in flour and sugar, stirring until flour mixture is browned.
2. Add milk slowly to flour mixture and cook, stirring until thickened.
3. Add seasonings when gravy bubbles. Serve at once.

Giblet Gravy

$\frac{1}{4}$ lb. cleaned giblets
Water to cover, boiling
$\frac{1}{2}$ t. salt
2 T. table fat
1 T. finely chopped onion
2 T. flour, browned
$1\frac{1}{2}$ c. giblet stock

1. Simmer giblets in boiling water, in covered saucepan, until liver is tender; remove liver.
2. Continue cooking gizzards and heart until tender; remove them to cool. Set stock aside.
3. Chop giblets; set aside.
4. Heat fat in frying pan; add onion and cook until golden. Remove onion.
5. Add flour to fat, stirring.
6. Add stock slowly to flour mixture; cook until thickened, stirring. Add giblets and heat to serving temperature.

Yeast Breads

BAKING YEAST BREADS		
FOOD	TEMPERATURES (degrees Fahr.)	TIME (minutes)
Yeast-bread loaves	400	30–40
Yeast-bread rolls	400–425	15–25
Yeast-Sweet rolls	375	20–30

White Bread   2 loaves

$\frac{5}{8}$ c. milk
$1\frac{1}{2}$ T. sugar
2 t. salt
$1\frac{1}{2}$ T. melted table fat
1 cake compressed yeast
1 c. lukewarm water
$5\frac{1}{2}$ to 6 c. sifted flour

1. Scald milk in top of double boiler over hot water or over very low heat. Add sugar, salt, and fat.
2. Cool milk mixture to lukewarm; add crumbled yeast.
3. Add 1 c. lukewarm water and 1 c. flour to milk mixture; beat 85 strokes.
4. Add to batter as much of $3\frac{1}{2}$ c. remaining flour as needed for easy handling. (Dough should break away from bowl.)
5. Knead dough on lightly floured board for 10 minutes. (See p. 148.) Place in greased bowl; grease top; cover.
6. Let dough double in size.
7. Punch dough down and turn over. Grease top and cover; let dough double in size again for better texture.
8. Punch dough down again; let rest for 3 minutes.
9. Shape dough into loaves (p. 148). Put into $8\frac{1}{2}$- to 9-inch loaf pans. Brush top with fat and let double in size.
10. Bake loaves at 400° F. for 15 minutes; reduce heat to 375° F. and bake 35 to 45 more minutes.

VARIATIONS IN SHAPES: Use recipe for *White Bread*. (Bake variations on sheets, at 425° F. for 15 to 20 minutes.)

Braids

$\frac{1}{2}$ recipe

Cut 2- by 6-inch strips; roll between palms of hands. Pinch three strips together at one end and braid.

Bowknots

$\frac{1}{2}$ recipe

Cut 2- by 8-inch strips; roll between palms of hands. Tie each strip into a knot.

Crescents

$\frac{1}{2}$ recipe
3 T. melted table fat
Poppy seeds

Roll ball of dough into circular shape $\frac{1}{4}$-inch thick; grease. Cut into pie-shaped wedges; roll from wide edge to point. Place point side down on baking sheet; curve into crescent. Sprinkle with poppy seeds.

Whole-Wheat Bread

2 loaves

¾ c. milk
3 to 4 T. brown sugar
2 t. salt
1 cake compressed yeast
3 c. whole-wheat flour
1 c. sifted white flour
3 T. melted table fat
  or shortening

1. Scald milk in top of double boiler over hot water or over very low heat. Add sugar and salt; cool to lukewarm.
2. Add crumbled yeast to milk mixture.
3. Combine flours; add 1½ c. to milk mixture; beat 85 strokes.
4. Add more flour and 2 T. fat to batter; stir until blended into dough (should be moist).
5. Place dough on lightly floured board; let rest 3 minutes. Knead until elastic and velvety.
6. Place dough in greased bowl; grease top; cover and let double in size.
7. Punch dough down; divide into two parts. Let rest 3 minutes; mold into loaves.
8. Place loaves in 8½- to 9-inch loaf pans, brush with 1 T. fat and let double in size.
9. Bake loaves at 400° F. for 15 minutes. Lower temperature to 350° F.; bake 20 to 25 minutes longer.

VARIATIONS: Use recipe for *Whole-Wheat Bread*.

Date Bread

¾ c. chopped dates
2 t. grated orange rind

Add after beating.

Cheese Bread

1 c. grated cheese

Add during kneading process.

Yeast Biscuits

30 small biscuits

1 c. milk
½ c. lard *or* table fat
½ c. sugar
1 c. mashed potatoes
1 c. sifted flour
½ t. salt
1 t. baking soda
2 t. baking powder
1 package granular yeast, dissolved in 3 T. lukewarm milk
4 c. sifted flour
1 T. melted shortening

1. Scald milk in top of double boiler over hot water or over very low heat. Set aside.
2. Mix lard, sugar, and potatoes together.
3. Sift 1 c. flour, soda, salt, and baking powder together.
4. Add yeast to the fat mixture, and add flour mixture and lukewarm milk alternately. Beat 25 to 30 strokes. Add 4 c. flour, stirring until blended.
5. Place dough in greased bowl and grease top; cover.
6. Let dough rise 60 minutes.
7. Roll dough on lightly floured board; cut like biscuits and brush with shortening.
8. Place biscuits on baking sheet; let rise 15 minutes.
9. Bake biscuits at 420° F. for 12 to 15 minutes.

452

VARIATION: Use recipe for *Yeast Biscuits*.

Coconut Biscuits

¾ c. shredded coconut
1½ T. sugar

Add coconut and sugar after beating mixture.
Brush with melted table fat, heavy cream, or a mixture of ¼ c. milk and 1 T. sugar before baking for a glazed crust.

Refrigerator Rolls

24 rolls

1 c. milk
1 cake compressed yeast
¼ to ½ c. sugar
1 c. lukewarm water
1 egg
7 c. sifted flour
3 T. melted table fat
1 t. salt

1. Scald milk over hot water in top of double boiler or over very low heat. Cool to lukewarm.
2. Add crumbled yeast, sugar, water, and egg to milk; beat with a rotary beater until blended.
3. Add 3½ c. flour, fat, and salt to yeast mixture; stir until blended. Add remaining flour, stirring until blended.
4. Place dough in greased bowl; grease top; cover and store in refrigerator.
5. Remove dough from refrigerator and shape into rolls, place in 8- to 9-inch cake pan and brush top with fat. Let double in size.
6. Bake rolls at 425° F. for 15 to 20 minutes.

VARIATIONS IN INGREDIENTS: Use recipe for *Refrigerator Rolls*.

Cinnamon Rolls

½ recipe
2 T. melted table fat
¼ c. sugar
2 t. cinnamon
¼ c. currants
   or raisins

Roll dough on lightly floured board to oblong ¼-inch thick.
Brush with fat; sprinkle with sugar, cinnamon, and currants.
Roll like jelly roll and cut into 1-inch slices.
Place cut side down in muffin pans; let double in size.
Bake at 375° F. for 25 minutes.

Butterscotch Rolls

1 c. sifted brown sugar
2 T. corn sirup
1 T. table fat
½ c. broken nuts

Prepare dough as for cinnamon rolls.
Mix sugar, sirup, and fat in shallow 10-inch baking dish.
Heat slowly until sugar is dissolved.
Scatter nuts in dish; place rolls cut side down in sugar mixture.
Let double in size.
Bake at 375° F. for 25 minutes.

453

Clover Leaf Rolls

2 T. melted table fat

Form dough into small balls; place three balls in each muffin cup.
Brush tops with fat.

Parker House Rolls

2 T. melted table fat

Roll dough on lightly floured board to $\frac{3}{4}$-inch thickness.
Let rest 3 minutes.
Cut with floured biscuit cutter; crease each roll through center with table knife.
Brush with fat and fold in half.
Place on baking sheet.

Crullers

Jam

Cut 2- by 6-inch strips; roll between palms of hands.
Wrap each strip around a roll of foil.
Place on baking sheet.
Bake; remove the foil and fill with jam.

Pizza Pie

4 eight-inch pies

$\frac{3}{4}$ recipe Refrigerator Rolls (p. 453)
$1\frac{1}{2}$ to 2 lb. sausage
$\frac{1}{2}$ lb. sharp cheddar cheese
$\frac{1}{2}$ c. minced onion
$\frac{1}{8}$ t. salt
$\frac{1}{4}$ t. oregano
$\frac{1}{8}$ t. garlic salt
$\frac{1}{4}$ c. olive oil
1 can (8 oz.) tomato sauce
1 can (6 oz.) tomato paste
1 c. grated parmesan cheese
1 c. sliced mushrooms

1. Let dough rise until about double in size.
2. Pan fry sausage until pink color disappears; drain. If link sausage is used, brown lightly and slice.
3. Grate the cheese.
4. Sauté onions in 1 T. drippings. Add seasonings.
5. Divide dough in 4 parts; flatten each piece and line 4 pie pans; brush with olive oil.
6. Arrange $\frac{1}{2}$ of cheddar cheese on dough. Mix onion and tomato mixtures and cover dough. Add remaining $\frac{1}{2}$ lb. grated cheese and sausage to pies. Sprinkle each with grated parmesan cheese and add sliced mushrooms.
7. Bake immediately at 450° F. for 15 to 20 minutes.

Swedish Tea Ring

6 servings

$\frac{1}{2}$ recipe for Refrigerator Rolls (p. 453)
2 T. melted table fat
$\frac{1}{4}$ c. sugar
2 t. cinnamon
$\frac{1}{4}$ c. currants
or raisins
$\frac{1}{4}$ c. chopped nuts

1. Roll dough on floured board to oblong $\frac{1}{4}$-inch thick.
2. Brush dough with fat; sprinkle with sugar, cinnamon, and currants.
3. Roll dough like jelly roll. Seal by pinching edges of roll together.
4. Place sealed edge down on baking sheet. Join ends of roll to form ring; seal.
5. Make cuts $\frac{2}{3}$ through ring and 1 to 2 inches apart. Turn each section cut side up.
6. Let dough double in size.
7. Bake ring at 375° F. for 25 to 30 minutes.
   Ice with Confectioners' Icing, if desired (p. 473).

USING A HOT ROLL MIX

Mix according to directions on package and let rise until double in bulk

When the dough is ready, shape into a long roll on a floured board or pastry cloth. Divide evenly into the number of finished rolls needed

It is easy to divide each of the sections into three approximately equal parts. Mold each piece into a small ball and place three balls into each cup of a greased muffin tin. Brush the rolls with melted table fat. Let rise again

Bake until crusty and brown and serve at once

455

Sour-Cream Bread   2 loaves

2¼ c. sour cream
2 T. sugar
1 t. salt
1 package granular yeast, dissolved
    in 3 T. lukewarm water
5 c. sifted flour

1. Scald cream in top of double boiler over hot water or on very low heat. Add sugar and salt. Cool to lukewarm.
2. Add yeast and 3 c. flour to cream mixture; beat well.
3. Add remaining flour, stirring until dough forms ball, free from bowl.
4. Knead dough on lightly floured board until elastic and velvety. Place in greased bowl; grease top; cover.
5. Let dough double in size.
6. Punch dough down, gently form into two loaves, and put in 8½ to 9-inch loaf pans.
7. Let double in size again. Bake at 350° F. 40 minutes.

VARIATION: Use recipe for *Sour-Cream Bread*.

Christmas Stollen

½ c. chopped raisins
1 c. chopped, mixed candied fruits
1 c. chopped nuts
2 T. melted table fat
½ c. candied red cherries
½ c. candied citron
½ recipe Confectioners' Icing
    (p. 473)

Place dough on lightly floured board and flatten.
Sprinkle with fruits and nuts; fold and knead quickly.
Roll dough on lightly floured board to oblong 9 by 12 inches; fold the long way.
Place dough on baking sheet; form into crescent. Press folded edges firmly.
Brush top of dough with fat and let double in size.
Sprinkle stollen lightly with fruit and nuts.
Bake stollen at 375° F. for 30 to 35 minutes.
Top with Confectioners' Icing while warm.

Batter Muffins   9 or 10 medium muffins

½ c. milk, scalded
¾ t. salt
3 T. shortening
¼ c. water, lukewarm
2 t. to 1 T. sugar
1 pkg. yeast
1 egg
2 c. sifted flour

1. Combine milk, salt, and shortening; cool to lukewarm.
2. Measure lukewarm water into large-sized bowl; add sugar. Sprinkle or crumble yeast into water mixture.
3. Add milk mixture to yeast mixture when yeast is dissolved. Add egg; blend all with rotary beater.
4. Add flour to yeast mixture; stir only enough to dampen flour.
5. Fill well-greased muffin pans one-half full. Set muffins aside until double in bulk, about 50 minutes.
6. Bake muffins at 400° F. 15 to 20 minutes or until light brown.

456

Batter Oatmeal Bread

4 to 6 servings

1½ c. water
1 T. fat
1½ t. salt
⅓ c. brown sugar
1½ c. rolled oats
1 pkg. yeast
¼ c. water, lukewarm
3 c. sifted flour

1. Heat water in pan to boiling; add fat, salt, brown sugar, and oats to boiling water; cool to lukewarm.
2. Sprinkle or crumble yeast into ¼ c. lukewarm water.
3. Combine yeast mixture with oat mixture when yeast is dissolved.
4. Make a well in flour in large bowl and add oat and yeast mixture all at once; stir until flour is moistened.
5. Set dough to rise for about 1 hour.
6. Bake in 8½ to 9-inch loaf pan at 375° F. for 40 to 50 minutes.

Custards and Puddings

Baked Custard

4 servings

3 c. milk
3 eggs
⅜ c. sugar
¼ t. salt
½ t. vanilla
Nutmeg

1. Scald milk in top of double boiler over hot water or on very low heat.
2. Beat eggs until slightly mixed; add sugar and salt.
3. Add milk slowly to egg mixture, stirring. Add vanilla, stirring.
4. Pour custard into cups; sprinkle with nutmeg.
5. Set cups in pan containing hot water to cover ⅔ of cups. Bake at 350° F. for 30 to 45 minutes.
6. Insert silver knife in center of custard to ½-inch depth. If knife comes out clean, custard is done.

VARIATIONS: Use recipe for *Baked Custard*.

Coconut Custard

½ c. coconut

Add with vanilla.

Caramel Custard

½ c. sugar

Caramelize sugar (p. 426).
Pour sirup in bottom of custard cups.
Add custard.

Chocolate Custard

1½ sq. chocolate, finely cut

Add to scalded milk.

Pumpkin Custard

⅔ c. pumpkin, mashed

Add with vanilla.

Soft Custard

4 servings

2 c. milk
2 eggs
¼ c. sugar
⅛ t. salt
½ t. flavoring

1. Scald milk in top of double boiler over hot water or on very low heat.
2. Beat eggs in large bowl until slightly mixed; add sugar and salt.
3. Add milk slowly to egg mixture, stirring.
4. Place egg mixture over hot water. Cook slowly, stirring rapidly until mixture coats a metal spoon lightly and evenly.
5. Add flavoring to custard, stirring. Pour immediately into chilled bowl or serving dishes.

Top with coconut, nuts, fruits, whipped cream, or flavored gelatin cubes.

Junket

4 servings

1 junket tablet
1 T. cold water
3 T. sugar
1 t. vanilla
2 c. milk
Cinnamon
Nutmeg
⅜ c. chopped fruit

1. Put junket tablet in cold water and crush with a spoon.
2. Add sugar and vanilla to milk in saucepan. Heat to lukewarm.
3. Add dissolved junket to milk mixture, stirring quickly.
4. Pour milk mixture at once into serving dishes; sprinkle with spices; set aside until set. Chill.
5. Top each serving with chopped fruit.

Cornstarch Pudding

4 servings

2 c. milk
2⅓ T. cornstarch
¼ c. sugar
⅛ t. salt
1 t. vanilla
1 t. table fat

1. Scald milk in top of double boiler over hot water.
2. Sift cornstarch, sugar, and salt together in top of another double boiler.
3. Add milk slowly to cornstarch mixture, stirring.
4. Cook cornstarch mixture to rolling boil, stirring.
5. Place cornstarch mixture over hot water; cover and continue cooking 15 minutes. Stir two or three times. Add vanilla and fat last 2 minutes of cooking and blend in with last stirring.
6. Pour pudding into serving dishes. Chill.
   Serve with thin cream or fruit sauce.

Rice Pudding

6 servings

2 c. cooked rice
3 c. milk
¾ c. sugar
3 eggs
1 c. seedless raisins
Nutmeg

1. Mix rice, milk, and sugar together.
2. Beat eggs until slightly mixed; add to rice mixture. Add raisins and sprinkle with nutmeg; stir until blended.
3. Place pudding in 6-inch baking dish; set in pan containing hot water to cover ⅔ of dish. Bake at 350° F. for 20 minutes or until firm. (See Baked Custard, p. 457.)

Bread Pudding

4 servings

2 c. milk
1 T. table fat
1 c. bread crumbs
   or cubes
1 egg
   or 2 egg yolks
$\frac{1}{4}$ c. sugar
$\frac{1}{4}$ t. salt
$\frac{1}{2}$ t. vanilla
$\frac{1}{8}$ t. mace, if desired

1. Scald milk over hot water in top of double boiler or on very low heat. Add fat.
2. Add crumbs to milk mixture. Set aside 5 minutes.
3. Beat eggs until slightly mixed. Add sugar, salt, and flavorings, blending.
4. Add milk mixture slowly to egg mixture, stirring. Pour into a 6- to 8-inch baking dish; set in pan containing hot water to cover $\frac{2}{3}$ of dish.
5. Bake pudding at 350° F. for 45 minutes or until firm. (Test as for Baked Custard (pp. 168–170.) Serve with Hard Sauce (p. 426).

VARIATIONS: Use recipe for *Bread Pudding*.

Raisin-Honey Pudding

3 T. honey substituted for sugar
$\frac{1}{2}$ c. chopped raisins

Add raisins with vanilla.

Cocoa Pudding

$\frac{1}{4}$ c. cocoa
$\frac{1}{4}$ t. cinnamon
$\frac{1}{2}$ c. sugar substituted for $\frac{1}{4}$ c.

Mix cocoa and cinnamon with sugar.

Chocolate Cream Pudding

6 servings

4 c. milk
2 sq. chocolate, finely cut
$\frac{1}{4}$ c. cornstarch
1 c. sugar
$\frac{1}{8}$ t. salt
2 t. vanilla
2 t. table fat

1. Scald $3\frac{1}{2}$ c. milk in top of double boiler over hot water or on very low heat.
2. Melt chocolate in pan over hot water.
3. Sift cornstarch, sugar, and salt together.
4. Add $\frac{1}{2}$ c. cold milk to cornstarch mixture, blending together. Add to melted chocolate, stirring.
5. Add scalded milk slowly to cornstarch mixture, stirring. Bring to rolling boil, stirring.
6. Place cornstarch mixture over hot water; cover and continue cooking for 15 minutes. Stir two or three times. Add vanilla and fat last 2 minutes of cooking and blend in with last stirring.
7. Pour pudding into serving dishes. Chill.

Tapioca Pudding

4 servings

1 egg, separated
2 T. sugar
2 c. milk
3 T. tapioca (quick-cooking)
3 T. sugar
$\frac{1}{8}$ t. salt
$\frac{1}{2}$ t. vanilla

1. Beat white until foamy. Add 2 T. sugar, one at a time, beating until mixture forms softly rounded peaks.
2. Beat yolk with $\frac{1}{4}$ c. milk in saucepan. Add tapioca, remaining milk, sugar, and salt.
3. Cook yolk mixture to rolling boil, stirring. Remove from heat.
4. Pour small amount of tapioca mixture over beaten white; blend. Fold remaining tapioca mixture into whites. Cool.
5. Stir tapioca after 15 to 20 minutes. Add vanilla; chill. Garnish with fruit, coconut, whipped cream, or nuts, if desired.

Plum Pudding

6 to 8 servings

$\frac{1}{2}$ c. sifted flour
1 t. salt
2 t. baking powder
$\frac{1}{2}$ t. nutmeg
$\frac{3}{4}$ t. cinnamon
$\frac{1}{2}$ t. cloves
$\frac{1}{4}$ t. mace
2 c. chopped raisins
$\frac{1}{4}$ lb. citron, thinly sliced
2 c. currants
$\frac{1}{4}$ c. chopped nuts
1 c. milk
$2\frac{1}{2}$ c. soft bread crumbs
$\frac{1}{2}$ c. sugar
$\frac{1}{2}$ c. finely chopped suet
$\frac{1}{2}$ c. dark corn sirup
3 T. fruit juice
4 eggs

1. Sift flour, salt, baking powder, and spices together.
2. Combine fruits and nuts with flour mixture.
3. Scald milk over hot water in top of double boiler or on very low heat. Add crumbs to milk.
4. Mix sugar, suet, sirup, and fruit juice together.
5. Beat eggs until thick; add sugar mixture and milk mixture, blending. Add flour mixture, stirring until blended.
6. Place pudding in molds; cook in pressure saucepan, following directions of manufacturer. Or cover tightly and steam for 3 hours in a covered container, placed on a rack over boiling water.
Serve with Hard Sauce (p. 426) or Lemon Sauce (p. 426).

Brown Betty

4 servings

2 c. bread crumbs
3 T. melted table fat
$\frac{1}{2}$ c. sifted brown sugar
$\frac{1}{2}$ t. grated lemon rind
1 T. lemon juice
$\frac{1}{4}$ t. cinnamon
$\frac{1}{8}$ t. nutmeg
3 to 4 apples
$\frac{1}{3}$ c. hot water

1. Combine crumbs and fat; divide into thirds. Place $\frac{1}{3}$ of mixture in a 6-inch baking dish.
2. Combine sugar, rind, lemon juice, and spices.
3. Pare, core, and slice apples; lay $\frac{1}{2}$ of them over crumbs. Sprinkle with $\frac{1}{3}$ of crumb mixture and $\frac{1}{2}$ of sugar mixture.
4. Add remaining apples to dish. Add water. Sprinkle with remaining sugar and crumb mixtures.
5. Bake apple mixture at 375° F. for 30 to 40 minutes.

Apple Dumplings

4 servings

4 medium apples
$\frac{5}{8}$ c. sifted brown sugar
$2\frac{1}{2}$ T. table fat
$\frac{1}{4}$ t. salt
$\frac{1}{2}$ t. cinnamon
$\frac{1}{2}$ t. grated lemon rind
$\frac{1}{2}$ recipe pie pastry (p. 476)

1. Pare and core whole apples.
2. Mix sugar, fat, salt, cinnamon, and rind together.
3. Fill apple cavities with sugar mixture.
4. Roll pastry to $\frac{1}{8}$-inch thickness.
5. Cut squares of pastry to cover each apple. Place apples in center, bring corners to top, moisten, and pinch together.
6. Place dumplings in a 6- to 8-inch baking dish; bake at 350° F. for 30 minutes.
   Serve with thin cream or Lemon Sauce (p. 426).

Cherry Cobbler

6 servings

1 recipe pie pastry (p. 476)
2 cans (No. 2) sour red cherries
2 c. sugar
$\frac{3}{8}$ c. flour
$\frac{1}{8}$ t. salt
$\frac{1}{2}$ c. cherry juice
2 T. table fat
$\frac{1}{4}$ t. almond flavoring

1. Divide pastry in half; roll bottom crust and line a 9-inch baking dish (pp. 181–182). Return remaining crust to refrigerator.
2. Drain cherries; save juice.
3. Combine sugar, flour, salt, and juice in saucepan. Cook until thickened and clear, stirring two or three times.
4. Roll top crust.
5. Add fat, flavoring, and cherries to sugar mixture.
6. Pour cherry filling into dish. Add top crust.
7. Bake cobbler at 425° F. for 15 minutes. Reduce heat to 375° F.; bake 25 more minutes.

Cakes

Two-Egg Layer Cake

(Standard Mixing Method)

8 to 10 servings

3 c. sifted cake flour
 or $2\frac{1}{3}$ c. sifted all-purpose flour
1 T. baking powder
$\frac{1}{4}$ t. salt
$\frac{1}{2}$ c. table fat
 or shortening
1 t. vanilla
 or other flavoring
$1\frac{1}{2}$ c. sugar
2 eggs
1 c. milk
 or fruit juice (orange, grapefruit, pineapple, or apple)

1. Sift flour, baking powder, and salt together three times.
2. Blend fat and vanilla. Add sugar, $\frac{1}{4}$ c. at a time; cream until fluffy. Beat 200 strokes or 1 minute (medium speed).
3. Beat eggs until thick; add slowly to fat mixture, beating 300 strokes or $1\frac{1}{2}$ minutes with mixer at medium speed.
4. Add $\frac{1}{4}$ of flour mixture to fat mixture; stir 25 or 30 strokes. Add $\frac{1}{3}$ of milk; stir 10 to 12 strokes. Repeat processes until all flour mixture and milk are added (last addition flour). Stir 110 to 115 strokes. (With mixer, add milk and flour and beat 1 minute at medium speed. For all-purpose flour, cut time in half.)
5. Use 9-inch layer-cake pans; bake at 365° F. 25 to 30 min.

461

TEMPERATURE AND TIME FOR BAKING CAKES AND COOKIES

FOOD	TEMPERATURES (degrees Fahr.)	TIME (minutes)
Layer cake	350–375	20–35
Layer cake, chocolate	350	30
Cup cakes	350–375	15–25
Loaf cakes	350	45–60
Loaf cakes, chocolate	350	45–60
Pound cakes	325	60–75
Sponge cakes	350–375	35–45
Angel cakes	350–375	35–45
Drop cookies	350–400	8–15
Rolled cookies	375	8–10
Refrigerator cookies	400	5–8
Bar cookies	325–350	25–40

White Layer Cake

8 to 10 servings

(Standard-Sponge Mixing Method)

3 c. sifted cake flour
1⅓ T. baking powder
½ t. salt
½ c. table fat
  or shortening
1 t. vanilla
1½ c. sugar
1 c. milk
4 egg whites

1. Sift flour, baking powder, and salt together three times.
2. Add vanilla to fat; add ½ of the sugar (¾ c.); cream until fluffy.
3. Add 1 T. flour mixture to fat mixture; stir 15 strokes. Add 1 T. milk; stir 15 strokes. Repeat addition of 1 T. flour mixture and stir 15 strokes.
4. Add ½ of remaining flour mixture and ½ of remaining milk to fat mixture; stir 80 to 85 strokes.
5. Add remaining flour mixture and milk to batter; stir 80 to 85 strokes.
6. Beat whites until mounded in bowl. Add remaining sugar (¾ c.) ¼ c. at a time, beating to form stiffly pointed peaks.
7. Fold egg-white mixture into batter with 35 strokes; stir 10 to 12 strokes.
8. Pour batter into two 9-inch layer-cake pans; bake at 365° F. for 20 to 25 minutes.

Sour-Cream Cake

10 to 12 servings

1¾ c. sifted cake flour
1½ t. baking powder
¼ t. baking soda
⅛ t. salt
1 c. sifted sugar
1 c. sour cream
1 t. vanilla
2 eggs

1. Sift flour, baking powder, soda, and salt together twice.
2. Add sugar to sour cream, ¼ c. at a time, stirring until blended after each addition. Add vanilla with last sugar addition.
3. Add eggs, one at a time, to cream mixture; beat with rotary beater after each until blended.
4. Add flour mixture gradually to cream mixture; stir until blended. Beat 200 strokes.
5. Pour batter into 8½ to 9-inch loaf pan; bake at 365° F. for 35 to 40 minutes.

VARIATION: Use recipe for *Sour-Cream Cake.*

Sour-Cream Spice Cake

¼ t. nutmeg
½ t. cinnamon
⅛ t. allspice
⅛ t. mace, if desired
⅛ t. cloves, if desired

Sift spices with flour.
Use broken nuts or ground raisins in icing.

Devil's-Food Layer Cake √

8 to 10 servings

2¼ c. sifted cake flour
1½ t. baking soda
¾ t. baking powder
¾ t. salt
¾ c. water, boiling
3 sq. chocolate
¾ c. table fat
  or shortening
1½ t. vanilla
1⅞ c. sifted brown sugar
3 eggs
¾ c. sour milk

1. Sift flour, soda, baking powder, and salt together twice.
2. Pour boiling water over chocolate in saucepan; stir over low heat until thickened. Cool to room temperature.
3. Add vanilla to fat. Add sugar ¼ c. at a time, creaming after each addition until fluffy. Beat 200 strokes after all sugar is added.
4. Beat eggs until thick; add slowly to creamed mixture, stirring until blended.
5. Add chocolate to fat mixture, beating until stiffened.
6. Add ¼ of flour mixture to fat mixture; stir 25 to 30 strokes. Add ⅓ of milk; stir 10 to 12 strokes. Repeat processes until all flour mixture and milk are added. (Make last addition flour mixture.)
7. Stir batter 140 strokes after all flour mixture is added.
8. Pour batter into 9-inch layer-cake pan; bake at 350° F. for 30 to 35 minutes.

Spice Layer Cake ✓

2⅓ c. sifted cake flour
1⅓ T. baking powder
½ t. salt
½ c. table fat
1 t. cloves
1 t. nutmeg
1 t. cinnamon
1½ c. sifted brown sugar
1 T. water
4 egg yolks
1 c. milk

8 to 10 servings

1. Sift flour, baking powder, and salt together twice.
2. Blend fat and spices. Add sugar, ¼ c. at a time, creaming after each addition until fluffy.
3. Beat fat mixture 200 strokes after all sugar is added.
4. Add water to yolks; beat until foamy. Add gradually to fat mixture, stirring.
5. Add ¼ of flour mixture to fat mixture; stir 25 to 30 strokes. Add ⅓ of milk; stir 10 to 12 strokes. Repeat processes until all flour mixture and milk are added. (Make last addition flour mixture.)
6. Stir batter 110 to 115 strokes.
7. Pour batter into two pans; bake at 365° F. for 25 to 30 minutes.

Cocoa Layer Cake ✓

1¼ c. sifted cake flour
2 t. baking powder
⅛ t. salt
2 c. sugar
¾ c. cocoa
5 eggs, separated
½ c. cold water
1 t. vanilla

8 to 10 servings

1. Sift flour, baking powder, and salt together twice.
2. Mix sugar and cocoa in large bowl until blended.
3. Beat yolks until thick and add to sugar mixture; add water and vanilla, stirring.
4. Add ½ of flour mixture to sugar mixture; stir 25 strokes. Add remaining flour mixture; stir 50 strokes.
5. Beat whites to form stiffly pointed peaks.
6. Fold whites gently into batter using 20 to 25 folding strokes both clockwise and crosswise.
7. Pour batter into two 9-inch layer-cake pans; bake at 365° F. for 25 minutes.

Procter & Gamble

Devil's-food layer cake

Applesauce Cake

8 to 10 servings

1¾ c. sifted cake flour
½ t. baking powder
1 t. baking soda
½ t. salt
½ c. table fat
 or shortening
½ t. cloves
½ t. cinnamon
1 t. allspice
1 c. sugar
2 eggs
1 c. applesauce, unsweetened
¼ c. sifted cake flour
½ c. chopped nuts
1 c. raisins

1. Sift flour, baking powder, baking soda, and salt together twice.
2. Blend fat and spices. Add sugar, ¼ c. at a time, creaming after each addition until fluffy.
3. Add eggs, one at a time, to fat mixture; beat with rotary beater after each until blended.
4. Add applesauce to fat mixture, stirring.
5. Add flour mixture by fourths to fat mixture, stirring until blended after each addition.
6. Flour nuts and raisins by sifting ¼ c. flour over them. Add to batter. Stir until blended.
7. Pour batter into two 9-inch pans; bake at 365° F. for 30 to 35 minutes.

Pineapple Upside-Down Cake

6 servings

3½ T. table fat
½ c. brown sugar
1 can (No. 2) pineapple chunks
6 maraschino cherries
1¼ c. sifted flour
2 t. baking powder
¼ t. salt
⅓ c. shortening
 or table fat
1 t. vanilla
½ c. sugar
1 egg
½ c. pineapple juice

1. Melt fat in a 6 to 8-inch baking dish. Sprinkle sugar over fat.
2. Arrange pineapple chunks, cut to ½-inch thickness, in flower-shaped patterns on sugar mixture; place well-drained cherry in center of each flower.
3. Sift flour, baking powder, and salt together.
4. Add vanilla to shortening. Add sugar gradually, creaming until fluffy.
5. Add egg to fat mixture, beating with rotary beater until blended.
6. Add flour mixture and pineapple juice alternately to fat mixture, stirring until blended after each addition.
7. Spread batter over pineapple. Bake at 350° F. for 50 to 60 minutes.
8. Turn cake on flat plate immediately.

VARIATION: Use recipe for *Pineapple Upside-Down Cake.*

Apricot or Peach Upside-Down Cake

1 can (No. 2½) apricots
 or peach halves substituted for pineapple
½ c. chopped nuts
½ c. milk substituted for pineapple juice

Arrange on sugar mixture.

Banana Layer Cake ✓

2¼ c. sifted cake flour
½ t. baking powder
¾ t. baking soda
½ t. salt
½ c. table fat
1 t. vanilla
1½ c. sugar
2 eggs
1 c. bananas, lightly mashed
¼ c. buttermilk

1. Sift flour, baking powder, baking soda, and salt together twice.
2. Add vanilla to fat. Add sugar, ¼ c. at a time, creaming after each addition until fluffy.
3. Add eggs, one at a time, to creamed mixture; beat with rotary beater after each until blended.
4. Add flour mixture and bananas alternately to fat mixture, stirring after each addition until blended. Beat 200 strokes.
5. Add buttermilk to batter, stirring 20 to 25 times.
6. Pour batter into 9-inch layer-cake pans; bake at 350° F. for 30 to 35 minutes. Cool cake thoroughly before removing from pan.

Cheese Cake ✓

4 to 6 servings

12 graham crackers, rolled fine
¼ c. sifted confectioners' sugar
½ t. cinnamon
⅔ c. melted table fat
1 lb. cream cheese
4 to 6 T. sugar
4 eggs
1 c. sour cream
½ c. sugar

1. Mix cracker crumbs, confectioners' sugar, cinnamon, and fat together. Line bottom and sides of 3-inch-deep, square or round 8-inch cake pan with crumb mixture.
2. Blend cheese and sugar.
3. Add eggs, one at a time, to cheese mixture; beat with rotary beater after each until blended.
4. Pour cheese mixture into pan; bake at 400° F. for 20 minutes.
5. Mix cream and ½ c. sugar and pour on top of cheese cake; bake 5 minutes longer.
6. Turn off heat; open oven door, and leave cake in oven 30 minutes. Cut when cold.

Angel Cake

8 to 10 servings

1 c. sifted cake flour
1¼ c. sifted sugar
1 c. egg whites
¼ t. salt
1 t. cream of tartar
¾ t. vanilla
¼ t. almond extract

1. Sift flour and ½ c. sugar together four times.
2. Add salt to whites; beat until foamy. Sprinkle in cream of tartar; beat to form softly rounded peaks (should look moist).
3. Add remaining sugar to whites, ¼ c. at a time; fold in each addition with 10 strokes. Add flour mixture, ¼ c. at a time, to white mixture; fold in each addition with 15 strokes. After last addition, use 10 more folding strokes. Add flavorings, folding in with last strokes.
4. Push batter into ungreased 10-inch tube pan; bake at 350° F. for 50 to 60 minutes.

Sponge Cake

1 c. sugar
1 T. lemon juice
½ lemon rind, grated
2 T. water
⅛ t. salt
6 eggs, separated
1 c. sifted cake flour

1. Mix ½ c. sugar, juice, rind, water, and salt together in large bowl.
2. Add yolks to sugar mixture; beat with rotary beater until well blended.
3. Sift ¼ of flour over yolk mixture; fold in, using 15 strokes. Repeat process until all flour is added.
4. Beat whites until foamy in large bowl. Add remaining sugar, ¼ c. at a time; fold in after each addition. Beat to form softly rounded peaks.
5. Spread yolk mixture over whites, folding in gently only until blended.
6. Pour batter into ungreased 10-inch tube pan; bake at 325 F. for 40 to 45 minutes.

Sunshine Cake

1 c. sifted cake flour
10 egg whites
1 t. cream of tartar
1½ c. sifted sugar
6 egg yolks
1 t. lemon juice

1. Sift flour three times.
2. Beat whites until foamy. Sprinkle in cream of tartar; beat to form softly rounded peaks.
3. Add sugar, ¼ c. at a time, to whites; fold in each addition with 15 strokes.
4. Beat yolks until thick. Add lemon juice and beat.
5. Add flour, ¼ c. at a time, to whites alternately with yolks; fold in after each addition with 10 strokes. (Make last addition flour.)
6. Use 10 more folding strokes. Pour batter into ungreased 10-inch tube pan; bake at 350° F. for 50 minutes. Serve with Orange Sauce (p. 426), if desired.

Yellow Chiffon Cake

1⅛ c. sifted cake flour
¾ c. sugar
1½ t. baking powder
½ t. salt
¼ t. cream of tartar
4 egg whites
¼ c. vegetable oil
3 egg yolks
6 T. cold water
½ lemon rind, grated
1 t. vanilla

1. Sift flour, sugar, baking powder, and salt together three times.
2. Sprinkle cream of tartar over whites in large bowl. Beat until they form stiffly pointed peaks. (Rubber scraper, pulled through them, should leave a clean path.)
3. Make a well in flour mixture; add oil, yolks, water, rind, and vanilla. Beat, using both clockwise and crosswise strokes.
4. Pour batter gently over beaten whites; fold in until just blended. Push batter into ungreased 10-inch tube pan; bake at 350° F. for 50 to 55 minutes.

Christmas Fruit Cake

5 pounds

1 c. uncooked prunes, pitted
1 c. halved candied cherries
2 c. sliced citron
3 c. seedless white raisins
$\frac{1}{2}$ c. diced pineapple
$\frac{1}{2}$ c. ground candied orange peel
$\frac{1}{4}$ c. ground candied lemon peel
$1\frac{1}{2}$ c. broken walnut meats
2 t. grated orange rind
$\frac{1}{2}$ c. fruit juice
$2\frac{1}{2}$ c. sifted flour
$\frac{3}{4}$ t. salt
$1\frac{1}{2}$ t. baking powder
1 c. table fat
1 c. white sugar
$\frac{1}{2}$ c. brown sugar
$1\frac{1}{2}$ t. cinnamon
$\frac{1}{2}$ t. powdered clove
$\frac{1}{2}$ t. allspice
1 t. mace
5 eggs, well beaten
1 t. vanilla

1. Pour boiling water over prunes; cover, let stand 10 minutes.
2. Rinse, drain, and dry cherries and citron before slicing.
3. Rinse raisins, drain and dry on a towel.
4. Drain prunes, dry and cut from pits into very small pieces.
5. Combine prunes, cherries, citron, raisins, and pineapple in large bowl.
6. Add nuts and rinds to fruit mixture.
7. Pour fruit juice over combined fruits.
8. Sift flour, salt and baking powder together.
9. Blend fat and spices. Add sugar, $\frac{1}{4}$ c. at a time, creaming after each addition until fluffy.
10. Add beaten eggs to creamed mixture and beat thoroughly.
11. Add flour, prepared fruit mixture, and flavoring to creamed mixture and stir until fruits are well distributed.
12. Push batter into 10-inch tube pans, bake at 280° F. for $3\frac{3}{4}$ hours.

Cookies

For chart on temperatures and times for baking, see page 462. See also page 178.

Sugar Cookies

3 dozen

2 c. sifted flour
$\frac{1}{2}$ t. baking powder
$\frac{1}{4}$ t. salt
$\frac{1}{2}$ c. table fat
$\frac{1}{4}$ t. nutmeg
$\frac{3}{4}$ c. sugar
1 egg
1 T. milk

1. Sift flour, baking powder, and salt together.
2. Blend fat and nutmeg. Add sugar in fourths, creaming after each addition until fluffy.
3. Add egg and milk to fat mixture; stir until blended.
4. Add flour mixture gradually to fat mixture, stirring until blended. Chill about 15 minutes.
5. Place dough on lightly floured board; roll to $\frac{1}{4}$-inch thickness.
6. Cut cookies with a floured cutter; place on baking sheet. Bake at 375° F. for 12 to 15 minutes.

Cinnamon candies may be used for decoration.

VARIATIONS: Use recipe for *Sugar Cookies*.

Cookie Wreaths

Egg white
Cinnamon drops
Gumdrop strips

Cut dough into wreaths; brush with egg white.
Decorate with cinnamon drops and strips of gumdrops for leaves.

Santa Claus Cookies

Egg white
Red-colored sugar
Melted sweet chocolate

Cut dough with Santa Claus cutter.
Brush surface with egg white. Decorate suit with red-colored sugar and boots with chocolate.

Butterscotch Cookies

$3\frac{1}{2}$ *dozen*

3 c. sifted flour
3 t. baking powder
1 c. table fat
1 t. vanilla
2 c. brown sugar
2 eggs
1 c. finely chopped nuts

1. Sift flour and baking powder together.
2. Add vanilla to fat; add sugar by fourths, creaming after each addition until fluffy.
3. Beat eggs until thick; add gradually to fat mixture, stirring.
4. Add flour mixture gradually to fat mixture, stirring. Add nuts in last stirring strokes.
5. Shape dough into three or four rolls; wrap in waxed paper. Chill about 12 hours or longer.
6. Slice roll, using a sharp knife, into $\frac{1}{8}$-inch slices; turn roll as you slice and place slices on baking sheet.
7. Bake at 400° F. for 8 to 10 minutes.

Peanut-Butter Cookies

3 dozen

$1\frac{1}{8}$ c. sifted flour
1 t. baking soda
$\frac{1}{8}$ t. salt
$\frac{1}{2}$ c. table fat
  or shortening
$\frac{1}{2}$ c. sifted brown sugar
$\frac{1}{2}$ c. granulated sugar
$\frac{1}{2}$ c. peanut butter
1 egg

1. Sift flour, baking soda, and salt together.
2. Add sugars gradually to fat, creaming after each addition until fluffy. Add peanut butter and blend.
3. Add egg to fat mixture; beat with a rotary beater until blended.
4. Add flour mixture gradually to fat mixture, stirring until well blended.
5. Place dough on lightly floured board; roll to $\frac{1}{8}$-inch thickness and cut with a floured cutter.
6. Place cookies on baking sheet. Bake at 400° F. for 12 to 15 minutes.

Corn-Flakes Cookies

3 dozen

2 egg whites
1 c. sugar
2 c. corn flakes, rolled (will measure
    $\frac{1}{2}$ c. after rolling)
$\frac{1}{2}$ c. shredded coconut
$\frac{1}{2}$ c. chopped nuts

1. Beat whites to form stiffly pointed peaks.
2. Add sugar to whites, $\frac{1}{4}$ c. at a time, folding in each addition.
3. Gradually fold corn flakes, coconut, and nuts into whites.
4. Drop batter from teaspoon onto baking sheet. Bake at 300° F. for 15 to 20 minutes.

Molasses Cookies

3$\frac{1}{2}$ dozen

3 c. sifted flour
1 t. baking soda
$\frac{3}{4}$ t. salt
$\frac{1}{2}$ c. table fat
   or shortening
2 t. ginger
1 t. cinnamon
$\frac{1}{2}$ c. sugar
1 egg
1 c. molasses
1 T. vinegar
$\frac{1}{2}$ c. water, boiling
$\frac{1}{4}$ c. sugar, colored

1. Sift flour, baking soda, and salt together.
2. Blend fat and spices. Add sugar, creaming until fluffy.
3. Beat egg until thick. Add molasses, stirring.
4. Add egg mixture to fat mixture, stirring.
5. Add vinegar to boiling water and add alternately with flour mixture to fat mixture, stirring after each addition until blended.
6. Drop batter from tablespoon onto baking sheet; sprinkle with colored sugar. Bake at 375° F. for 12 to 15 minutes.

Sandies

3 dozen

1 c. table fat
2 t. vanilla
$\frac{1}{4}$ c. sifted confectioners' sugar
1 T. water
2 c. sifted flour
1 c. chopped pecan nuts
3 T. sifted confectioners' sugar

1. Add vanilla to fat. Add $\frac{1}{4}$ c. sugar, creaming until fluffy.
2. Add water to creamed mixture, stirring. Add flour and nuts gradually, stirring until blended.
3. Shape dough into small rolls, 1$\frac{1}{2}$ inches long.
4. Place rolls on ungreased baking sheet and bake at 300° F. for 20 minutes. Roll in confectioners' sugar.

Chocolate-Chip Oatmeal Cookies

3$\frac{1}{2}$ dozen

$\frac{1}{2}$ c. sifted flour
$\frac{1}{4}$ t. salt
1$\frac{1}{2}$ c. quick-cooking oats, uncooked
1 c. (6-oz. pkg.) chocolate chips
$\frac{1}{2}$ c. table fat
   or shortening
1 t. vanilla
1 c. sifted brown sugar
1 egg
3 T. evaporated milk

1. Mix flour, salt, oats, and chocolate chips together.
2. Add vanilla to fat; add sugar, creaming until fluffy.
3. Add egg and milk to fat mixture, stirring until blended. Add flour mixture gradually, stirring until mixed.
4. Drop batter from teaspoon onto baking sheet. Bake at 375° F. for 12 minutes.

Tea Cakes

2½ c. sifted cake flour
½ t. baking soda
¼ t. salt
1 c. table fat
1 t. almond
  or other flavoring
1 c. sugar
1 egg
Nut halves

1. Sift flour, baking soda, and salt together.
2. Add almond flavoring to fat; add sugar, ¼ c. at a time, creaming after each addition until fluffy.
3. Beat egg until thick; add slowly to fat mixture, stirring.
4. Add flour mixture gradually to fat mixture, stirring until blended.
5. Shape dough into 1-inch-diameter balls. Press nut on top of each.
6. Place cakes on baking sheet; bake at 350° F. for 30 minutes.

Tea Puffs
1½ dozen

½ c. table fat
1 t. vanilla
2 T. granulated sugar
1 c. chopped nuts
1 c. sifted flour
3 T. sifted confectioners' sugar

1. Add vanilla to fat; add 2 T. sugar, creaming until fluffy.
2. Add nuts and flour gradually to fat mixture, stirring until blended.
3. Shape dough into rolls 1½ inches long. Place on baking sheet; bake at 300° F. for 30 minutes.
4. Roll puffs in confectioners' sugar while hot.

Refrigerator Cookies
4 dozen

3⅝ c. sifted flour
½ t. baking soda
¼ t. salt
2 c. table fat
1½ t. vanilla
1¼ c. sugar
2 eggs
1½ T. dark sirup
1 c. chopped nuts

1. Sift flour, baking soda, and salt together.
2. Add vanilla to fat; add sugar, ¼ c. at a time, creaming after each addition until fluffy.
3. Add eggs, one at a time, to fat mixture; beat with rotary beater after each until blended. Add sirup and blend.
4. Add flour mixture and nuts gradually to fat mixture, stirring until blended. Shape dough into three rolls.
5. Wrap separately in waxed paper. Chill about 1 hour.
6. Slice rolls to ⅛-inch thickness. Place on ungreased baking sheet. Bake at 400° F. for 6 to 8 minutes.

Fruit Squares
2 dozen

½ lb. dried fruit (apricots or dates)
½ c. granulated sugar
½ c. water
¼ c. table fat
½ c. brown sugar
¾ c. sifted flour
¼ t. salt
⅞ c. quick-cooking oats, uncooked

1. Cook fruit, granulated sugar, and water in saucepan until thickened.
2. Add brown sugar to fat gradually, creaming until fluffy.
3. Add flour and salt gradually to fat mixture, stirring. Add oats; mix until crumbly.
4. Firmly press ½ of flour mixture into oblong 10- by 6-inch cake pan.
5. Spread fruit mixture evenly over flour mixture.
6. Add remaining crumbs to top and pat smooth; bake at 325° F. for 25 minutes. Cut into squares while warm.

Brownies

$\frac{3}{4}$ c. sifted flour
$\frac{1}{4}$ t. baking powder
$\frac{1}{4}$ t. salt
3 T. sugar
2 sq. unsweetened chocolate
$\frac{1}{2}$ c. table fat
1 t. vanilla
1 c. white corn sirup
2 eggs
$\frac{3}{4}$ c. chopped nuts
2 T. sifted confectioners' sugar

1. Sift flour, baking powder, salt, and sugar together.
2. Melt chocolate over hot water.
3. Add vanilla to fat; add sirup gradually, stirring.
4. Add melted chocolate and $\frac{1}{4}$ of flour mixture to fat mixture, stirring until blended.
5. Add eggs, one at a time, to fat mixture; beat with rotary beater after each until blended.
6. Add remainder of flour mixture and nuts to fat mixture, stirring until blended.
7. Push batter into a square 8-inch cake pan; bake at 350° F. for 35 to 40 minutes. Dust with confectioners' sugar. Cut into $1\frac{1}{2}$-inch squares immediately.

"Helene's Cookies"

$2\frac{1}{4}$ c. sifted flour
1 t. baking soda
$\frac{1}{2}$ t. salt
$\frac{1}{2}$ c. table fat
$\frac{1}{2}$ t. cinnamon
$\frac{1}{8}$ t. allspice
$\frac{1}{8}$ t. cloves
$\frac{1}{2}$ c. sifted brown sugar
2 eggs
2 T. flour
$\frac{1}{2}$ c. finely cut gumdrops
$\frac{1}{2}$ c. broken nuts
$\frac{1}{2}$ c. chopped dates

1. Sift flour, baking soda, and salt together.
2. Blend fat and spices. Add sugar, creaming until fluffy.
3. Add eggs, one at a time, to fat mixture; beat with rotary beater after each until blended.
4. Add flour mixture to fat mixture, stirring until blended. Add gumdrops, nuts, and dates, floured by sifting 2 T. flour over them and tossing lightly. Stir until blended.
5. Shape dough into two or three rolls; wrap each in waxed paper. Chill about 15 minutes.
6. Slice rolls into $\frac{1}{8}$-inch slices; place on sheet. Bake at 350° F. for 15 to 20 minutes.

Fruit Balls

$\frac{1}{2}$ lb. dried apricots
$\frac{1}{2}$ lb. dried prunes
2 slices candied pineapple
$\frac{1}{4}$ lb. candied cherries
1 c. nuts
$\frac{1}{2}$ lb. honey (in comb)
$\frac{3}{4}$ c. sifted confectioners' sugar

1. Put fruits and nuts through food grinder twice, using fine cutter.
2. Add honey to fruit mixture; stir until blended.
3. Shape mixture into balls; roll in confectioners' sugar.
4. Store balls in covered container in cool place.

Icings and Fillings

Confectioners' Icing

1 medium cake

½ c. table fat
1 t. vanilla
3 c. sifted confectioners' sugar
¼ c. thin cream
   or evaporated milk

1. Blend fat and vanilla.
2. Add sugar and cream alternately, blending after each addition.

VARIATIONS: Use recipe for *Confectioners' Icing.*

Mocha Icing

3 T. cocoa
¼ c. cold black coffee substituted for cream

Combine with confectioners' sugar.

Orange or Lemon Icing

1 T. grated rind
¼ c. juice substituted for cream
Omit vanilla.

Blend fat and rind.

Pineapple Icing

⅓ c. crushed pineapple substituted for cream
Omit vanilla.

Cream-Cheese Icing

1 medium cake

1 package (3 oz.) cream cheese
½ t. vanilla
   or maple flavoring
Few grains of salt
1 T. thin cream
2½ c. sifted confectioners' sugar

1. Blend cheese, vanilla, salt, and cream.
2. Add sugar gradually to cheese mixture, blending.

VARIATION: Use recipe for *Cream-Cheese Icing.*

½ t. cinnamon
Omit vanilla.

473

Seven-Minute Icing

1 medium cake

2 egg whites
1½ c. sugar
5 T. water
1½ t. light corn sirup
    or ¼ t. cream of tartar
1 t. vanilla
⅛ t. salt

1. Put whites, sugar, water, sirup, and salt in top of double boiler over boiling water.
2. Beat with rotary or electric beater 7 minutes or until white mixture stands in peaks.
3. Remove from heat, add vanilla, and beat icing until thick enough to spread.

Fudge Icing

1 medium cake

2 c. sugar
1 c. milk
    or water
¼ t. salt
2 sq. chocolate, finely cut
2 T. light corn sirup
2 T. table fat
1 t. vanilla

1. Mix sugar, milk, salt, chocolate, and sirup in saucepan.
2. Cook over low heat, stirring gently until sugar dissolves.
3. Cook sugar mixture, covered, for 2 to 3 minutes.
4. Continue cooking sugar mixture, uncovered, until soft ball forms in icy-cold water.
5. Set aside and cool pan to lukewarm.
6. Add vanilla and beat fudge until creamy (shiny appearance disappears). Spread quickly.

VARIATION: Use recipe for *Fudge Icing*.

Brown-Sugar Icing

1 c. sifted brown sugar substituted
    for 1 c. granulated sugar

"Quickie" Glaze Icing

1 medium cake

2½ T. flour
½ c. milk
1 c. sugar
¼ c. table fat
½ t. flavoring

1. Combine sugar and flour; add milk, stirring until blended.
2. Cook until very thick, stirring constantly.
3. Remove from heat, add table fat and vanilla; beat until thick enough to spread. (For thicker icing, add ¼ c. confectioners' sugar.)

Broiled Icing

Top of medium cake

2 T. table fat
½ c. sifted brown sugar
2 T. cream
½ c. chopped nuts
    or coconut
    or cut gumdrops

1. Mix fat, sugar, cream, and nuts together.
2. Spread over warm or cooled cake.
3. Broil 4 inches from heat unit for 2 minutes.

474

Lemon Filling

1 medium cake

$\frac{3}{4}$ c. sugar
1 T. cornstarch
$\frac{3}{4}$ c. cold water
2 t. grated lemon rind
2 egg yolks
$\frac{1}{3}$ c. lemon juice
1 T. table fat
$\frac{1}{8}$ t. salt

1. Mix sugar and cornstarch in top of double boiler; add water and rind.
2. Bring sugar mixture to a boil, stirring constantly. Set aside.
3. Beat yolks until thick. Add 2 to 3 T. sugar mixture, beating.
4. Add yolk mixture gradually to sugar mixture, stirring.
5. Cook over hot water until yolk mixture lightly coats a spoon, stirring two to three times. Remove from heat.
6. Add lemon juice, fat, and salt to yolk mixture, stirring. Cool.

Caramel Filling

1 medium cake

1 c. granulated sugar
1 c. sifted brown sugar
$\frac{1}{2}$ c. thin cream
$\frac{1}{4}$ c. table fat
$\frac{1}{4}$ c. dark sirup

1. Mix sugars, cream, fat, and sirup in saucepan.
2. Boil until mixture forms soft ball in icy-cold water. Cool pan to lukewarm.
3. Beat caramel mixture until creamy (shiny appearance disappears). Spread quickly.

Fruit-Nut Filling

1 medium cake

$\frac{1}{3}$ c. ground raisins
$\frac{1}{3}$ c. ground prunes
$\frac{3}{4}$ c. sugar
1 c. water
$\frac{1}{3}$ c. chopped nuts
1 T. lemon juice
1 t. grated lemon rind

1. Combine fruits, sugar, and water in saucepan. Simmer for 15 minutes, stirring two or three times.
2. Cool fruit mixture; add nuts, lemon juice, and rind, stirring. Spread between cake layers.
Use for Sour-Cream or Spice Cake.

VARIATION: Use recipe for *Fruit-Nut Filling.*

$\frac{2}{3}$ c. apricots substituted for raisins
and prunes

Pastry and Pies

Cold-Water Pastry

Two 9-inch crusts

2 c. sifted flour
1 t. salt
½ c. shortening, chilled
4 to 6 T. icy-cold water

1. Sift flour and salt together; cut in shortening with two knives or a pastry blender until the pieces are the size of small peas.
2. Sprinkle 1 T. water over flour mixture; toss lightly with a fork. Continue adding water gradually and tossing quickly until dough holds together.
3. Chill dough 5 minutes. Roll and place in pan (pp. 181–182).

VARIATION: Use recipe for *Cold-Water Pastry*.

Hot-Water Pastry

Hot water substituted for cold water

Add shortening to hot water; beat with a fork.
Pour into flour mixture and stir hard until dough follows fork.

Vegetable-Oil Pastry

Two 9-inch crusts

2 c. sifted flour
1¼ to 1½ t. salt
½ c. vegetable oil
¼ c. plus 2 to 3 T. icy-cold water

1. Sift flour and salt together.
2. Pour vegetable oil and water into measuring cup; beat until frothy.
3. Sprinkle 1 T. oil mixture over flour mixture; toss lightly with a fork. Continue adding oil mixture gradually and tossing quickly until dough holds together.
4. Divide dough in half; shape each half into a smooth ball.
5. Roll dough between two 12-inch squares of waxed paper. Remove top sheet of paper; place dough in pan; peel off bottom paper.
6. Roll dough for top crust between waxed paper.

476

VARIETIES OF CRUMB CRUSTS				
KIND	AMOUNT	TABLE FAT	CRUMBS	SUGAR
Graham crackers	12–14	$\frac{1}{3}$–$\frac{1}{2}$ c.	$1\frac{1}{2}$ c.	2 T.
Vanilla or chocolate wafers, or gingersnaps	20–22 two-inch cookies	$\frac{1}{3}$–$\frac{1}{2}$ c.	$1\frac{1}{2}$ c.	–
Corn flakes	3 c.	$\frac{1}{3}$–$\frac{1}{2}$ c.	$1\frac{1}{3}$ c.	2 T.

1. Place crackers, cookies, or flakes on waxed paper. Crush to fine crumbs.
2. Soften table fat; add with sugar to crumbs; mix well.
3. Press crumb mixture firmly into greased piepan with back of spoon. Bake at 400° F. for 8 to 10 minutes. Cool.

NOTE: To increase the nutritional value, add $\frac{1}{4}$ c. nonfat dried milk to crumbs.

Timbales or Patty Shells

2 eggs
1 t. sugar
$\frac{1}{4}$ t. salt
Shortening
1 c. sifted flour
1 c. milk

12 to 15 shells

1. Beat eggs until thick and add sugar and salt.
2. Add enough shortening to fill a deep kettle $\frac{1}{2}$ to $\frac{2}{3}$ full when melted; heat to 365° F.
3. Add flour and milk alternately to egg mixture, stirring after each addition.
4. Pour small amount of batter into small deep mixing bowl. Dip timbale iron into this.
5. Heat iron in the hot deep shortening; drain and tap off excess fat on absorbent paper.
6. Dip hot iron into batter until $\frac{2}{3}$ covered. Stir batter each time before dipping in the iron.
7. Place iron in hot shortening until case is delicately browned.
8. Remove iron, tip upside-down to drain. Push off case on absorbent paper.

Amber Pie

$\frac{1}{2}$ recipe pie pastry (p. 476)
2 eggs
$\frac{1}{2}$ c. sugar
1 t. cloves
1 t. cinnamon
$\frac{3}{4}$ c. buttermilk
1 T. flour
$\frac{1}{2}$ c. chopped raisins
1 T. table fat

9-inch pie

1. Roll out pastry; line pan.
2. Beat eggs until thick; add sugar and spices.
3. Blend buttermilk into egg mixture.
4. Sprinkle flour over raisins; add to egg mixture.
5. Pour pie filling into pastry-lined pan. Dot with fat.
6. Bake at 425° F. for 10 minutes; reduce heat to 325° F. and bake 25 more minutes.

Pumpkin Pie

Two 9-inch pies

1 recipe pie pastry (p. 476)
1½ c. sifted brown sugar
1 can (No. 2½) pumpkin
4 eggs
3 T. melted table fat
2 T. molasses
2 t. cinnamon
¾ t. ginger
½ t. nutmeg
1¼ t. salt
1½ c. milk

1. Roll out pastry; line pan.
2. Add sugar to pumpkin.
3. Beat eggs until thick and add with fat, molasses, seasonings, and milk to pumpkin mixture; stir.
4. Pour pumpkin mixture into pastry-lined pans. Bake at 425° F. for 10 minutes; reduce heat to 325° F. and bake 25 more minutes.

VARIATION: Use recipe for *Pumpkin Pie.*

Sweet-Potato Pie

2½ c. mashed sweet potatoes substituted for pumpkin
Omit ½ c. brown sugar

Custard Pie

9-inch pie

½ recipe pie pastry (p. 476)
2 c. milk
3 eggs
  or 6 egg yolks
½ c. sugar
¼ t. salt
¼ t. nutmeg
½ t. vanilla

1. Roll out pastry; line pan.
2. Scald milk over hot water in top of double boiler or on very low heat.
3. Beat eggs slightly; add sugar, salt, nutmeg, and vanilla.
4. Add scalded milk slowly to egg mixture, stirring.
5. Pour custard into pastry-lined pan. Bake at 425° F. for 10 minutes; reduce heat to 325° F. and bake 25 more minutes.

Raisin Pie

9-inch pie

1 recipe pie pastry (p. 476)
1½ c. raisins
Hot water
1 c. water, boiling
⅓ c. sugar
¼ t. salt
3 T. flour
2 t. table fat
¼ c. lemon juice
¼ c. orange juice

(¼ c. vinegar and ¼ c. water may be used to replace fruit juices.)

1. Roll out pastry; line pan. Roll top crust.
2. Place raisins in sieve; pour hot water over them. Cook in boiling water in saucepan for 5 minutes.
3. Mix sugar, salt, and flour together in a saucepan. Add raisins and liquid slowly; stir.
4. Cook raisin mixture until thickened, stirring two or three times. Add juices. (If mixture is thin, heat quickly to boiling point.)
5. Pour raisin mixture into pastry-lined pan, dot with fat, and cover with top crust.
6. Bake pie at 425° F. for 15 minutes. Reduce heat to 375° F.; bake for 30 to 35 more minutes.

Apple Pie

1 recipe pie pastry (p. 476)
6 c. apple slices
$\frac{5}{8}$ to $\frac{3}{4}$ c. sugar (more for tart apples)
$\frac{1}{8}$ t. salt
$\frac{1}{4}$ t. cinnamon
Ground cloves
Allspice
1 T. table fat

1. Roll out pastry; line pan. Roll top crust.
2. Put apples into pastry-lined pan; sprinkle with sugar and seasonings, and dot with fat.
3. Cover pie with top crust.
4. Bake pie at 425° F. for 15 minutes. Reduce heat to 375° F.; bake for 20 more minutes.
Wedges of Cheddar cheese may be served with the pie, if desired.

Berry Pie

1 recipe pie pastry (p. 476)
3 c. berries, fresh
$\frac{2}{3}$ to 1 c. sugar
2 T. cornstarch
  or $\frac{1}{4}$ c. flour
$\frac{1}{8}$ t. salt
1 T. table fat

1. Roll out pastry; line pan. Roll top crust.
2. Mix sugar, cornstarch, and salt.
3. Put berries in pastry-lined pan; sprinkle with sugar mixture and dot with fat. Cover with top crust.
4. Bake pie 10 minutes at 450° F. Reduce heat to 375° F. and bake for 30 more minutes.

Lemon Pie

(Cooked Filling)

$\frac{1}{2}$ recipe pie pastry (p. 476)
$\frac{3}{8}$ c. cornstarch
$1\frac{1}{2}$ c. sugar
$\frac{1}{2}$ t. salt
2 c. water
3 eggs, separated
$1\frac{1}{2}$ T. table fat
$\frac{3}{8}$ c. lemon juice
2 t. grated lemon rind
3 T. sugar

1. Roll out pastry; line pan.
2. Mix cornstarch, sugar, and salt in top of double boiler. Add water, stirring.
3. Cook cornstarch mixture over hot water until clear, stirring.
4. Bake pastry at 425° F. for 12 to 15 minutes.
5. Beat yolks until thick.
6. Pour cornstarch mixture slowly into yolks, stirring.
7. Return yolk mixture to top of double boiler. Cover and cook over hot water until thickened, stirring two or three times. Continue to cook 3 minutes, stirring.
8. Blend fat, lemon juice, and rind into yolk mixture.
9. Pour lemon filling into crust.
10. Beat whites for meringue. (Use Meringue recipe directions, p. 480.) Spread meringue on pie; bake at 350° F. for 12 minutes.

Lemon Pie

(Uncooked Filling)

½ recipe pie pastry (p. 476)
2 eggs, separated
½ c. lemon juice
½ c. condensed milk
½ T. grated lemon rind
2 T. sugar

1. Roll out pastry; line pan.
2. Beat yolks until thick; add lemon juice and milk alternately, stirring.
3. Blend lemon rind into yolk mixture.
4. Bake pastry at 425° F. for 15 minutes.
5. Beat whites for meringue. (Use Meringue recipe directions below.)
6. Pour lemon filling into crust. Spread meringue on pie; bake at 350° F. for 12 minutes.

Meringue

9-inch pie

2 to 3 egg whites
3 to 4 T. confectioners' *or* granulated sugar

1. Beat whites until foamy. Add sugar, 1 T. at a time; beat until blended after each. Continue beating until meringue forms softly rounded peaks.
2. Spread meringue on pie, extending slightly onto crust. Bake at 350° F. for 12 minutes.

Butterscotch-Nut Pie

9-inch pie

½ recipe pie pastry (p. 476)
1 c. sifted, dark-brown sugar
2 T. cornstarch
2 c. milk
2 eggs, separated
1 T. table fat
½ c. broken nuts
2 T. sugar

For immediate serving, add 2 T. additional cornstarch

1. Roll out pastry; line pan.
2. Combine sugar, cornstarch, and ½ c. milk.
3. Heat sugar mixture in top of double boiler over hot water until sugar dissolves.
4. Beat yolks until thick; add remaining milk.
5. Combine yolk mixture with sugar mixture and cook until thickened, stirring. Continue cooking for 5 minutes, stirring two or three times.
6. Bake pastry at 425° F. for 12 to 15 minutes.
7. Remove sugar mixture from heat; stir in fat and nuts. Cool.
8. Beat egg whites for meringue. (Use Meringue recipe directions above.)
9. Pour filling into crust. Spread meringue on pie; bake at 350° F. for 12 minutes.

Chocolate Cream Pie

½ recipe pie pastry (p. 476)
2 c. milk
2 sq. unsweetened chocolate
1 c. sugar
½ t. salt
5 T. flour
3 eggs, separated
2 T. table fat
1½ t. vanilla
2 T. sugar

1. Roll out pastry; line pan.
2. Scald milk in top of double boiler over hot water.
3. Grate chocolate coarsely; add to milk. When melted, beat until blended.
4. Mix sugar, salt, and flour; add milk mixture, stirring.
5. Beat yolks until thick and add milk mixture, stirring.
6. Bake pastry at 425° F. for 12 minutes.
7. Cook milk mixture over hot water for 10 minutes, stirring two or three times.
8. Blend fat and vanilla into milk mixture; cool to lukewarm; stir occasionally.
9. Beat whites for meringue. (Use Meringue recipe directions, p. 480.)
10. Pour filling into crust. Spread meringue on pie; bake at 350° F. for 12 minutes.

Pineapple Chiffon Pie

½ recipe pie pastry (p. 476)
1 T. gelatin
½ c. cold water
1 c. unsweetened pineapple juice
1 T. lemon juice
½ t. salt
¾ c. sugar
3 eggs, separated
½ c. whipping cream

1. Roll out pastry; line pan.
2. Mix gelatin with cold water; set aside 5 minutes.
3. Blend juices, salt, and sugar together; heat, stirring until sugar dissolves.
4. Add softened gelatin to pineapple mixture; stir to dissolve.
5. Beat yolks until thick; add pineapple mixture.
6. Bake pastry at 425° F. for 12 to 15 minutes.
7. Chill pineapple mixture until partially set.
8. Beat whites in bowl to form softly rounded peaks.
9. Beat cream in chilled bowl (using same beater) to form softly rounded peaks.
10. Fold whites into chilled pineapple mixture; fold in cream.
11. Pour pineapple filling into crust and chill.

Gelatin Desserts, Ice Cream, and Fruits

Banana Sponge

1 T. gelatin
2 T. cold water
½ c. water, boiling
½ c. sugar
3 bananas, mashed
2 t. lemon juice
¼ t. salt
3 egg whites
¼ c. whipping cream
½ T. sugar

4 servings

1. Mix gelatin with cold water; set aside 5 minutes. Dissolve in boiling water.
2. Stir sugar into gelatin mixture until dissolved. Cool.
3. Add bananas and lemon juice to gelatin mixture. Chill until it begins to set.
4. Add salt to whites; beat to form softly rounded peaks.
5. Beat gelatin mixture until frothy.
6. Fold whites into gelatin mixture.
7. Beat cream in chilled bowl. Fold in sugar.
8. Pour gelatin mixture into chilled serving dishes. Top with whipped cream and serve.

Spanish Cream

2 t. gelatin
2 c. milk
⅓ c. sugar
2 eggs, separated
¼ t. salt
1 t. vanilla

Fresh, canned, or frozen fruit, sauces, or whipped cream may be used as a garnish.

4 to 5 servings

1. Mix gelatin with milk in top of double boiler; set aside 5 minutes.
2. Place pan over hot water; add sugar, stirring. Heat until gelatin and sugar dissolve, stirring.
3. Beat yolks in bowl until thick. Add gelatin mixture slowly to yolks, stirring.
4. Return gelatin mixture to top of double boiler; cook over hot water, stirring until metal spoon is lightly coated. Cool.
5. Add salt to whites in large bowl; beat to form softly rounded peaks.
6. Fold egg mixture and vanilla into whites. Chill until it begins to set.
7. Beat Spanish cream quickly with rotary beater until smooth; pour into chilled sherbet glasses. Serve.

Strawberry Bavarian Cream

6 servings

1 T. gelatin
¼ c. cold water
¾ c. sifted confectioners' sugar
1 c. crushed strawberries
1 c. whipping cream
Whole strawberries

1. Mix gelatin with cold water in top of double boiler; set aside 5 minutes.
2. Place pan over hot water until gelatin dissolves.
3. Remove gelatin from heat; cool until partially set.
4. Add sugar to strawberries.
5. Beat gelatin until frothy and add strawberry mixture.
6. Beat cream in chilled bowl to form softly rounded peaks; fold in strawberry mixture.
7. Pour Bavarian cream into chilled glasses. Garnish with whole berries. Serve.

Butterscotch Charlotte Russe

6 servings

2½ T. table fat
⅔ c. sifted brown sugar
2 eggs, separated
1½ c. milk
1 T. gelatin
¼ c. cold water
¼ t. salt
1 c. evaporated milk, chilled icy cold
½ t. vanilla
12 ladyfingers
   or strips of sponge cake

1. Cook fat and sugar until blended in top of double boiler over hot water.
2. Beat yolks until thick; gradually add fat mixture and milk, stirring.
3. Mix gelatin with cold water; set aside 5 minutes.
4. Return fat mixture to top of double boiler. Cook over hot water, stirring, until metal spoon is lightly coated.
5. Remove fat mixture from heat. Add gelatin and stir until dissolved. Chill until it begins to set.
6. Add salt to egg whites; beat to form softly rounded peaks.
7. Beat evaporated milk in chilled bowl to form softly rounded peaks.
8. Fold whites and vanilla into fat mixture. Fold in beaten milk.
9. Line mold with ladyfingers. Add butterscotch mixture; chill until firm.

Peach Velvet

6 servings

1 can (No. 2½) peach halves
1 T. gelatin
⅓ c. lemon juice
½ c. sugar
⅛ t. salt
1 t. grated lemon rind
1¾ c. evaporated milk, chilled icy cold
10 to 12 vanilla wafers

1. Drain peaches; save ¾ c. sirup.
2. Dice peaches to make 1½ c.; save remainder for garnish.
3. Mix gelatin with lemon juice; set aside 5 minutes.
4. Heat peach sirup, sugar, and salt to boiling. Add gelatin to hot sirup mixture. Add rind and cool.
5. Chill gelatin mixture until it begins to set.
6. Beat evaporated milk in chilled bowl to form softly rounded peaks.
7. Fold gelatin mixture into cream. Fold in diced peaches.
8. Alternate layers of vanilla wafers with gelatin mixture in a 1½-qt. mold. Chill until firm; unmold and garnish.

Peach halves, maraschino cherries, or mint leaves may be used as garnish.

Frozen Orange-Apricot Whip

4 servings

1 egg, separated
$\frac{5}{8}$ c. sugar
$\frac{3}{4}$ c. apricot pulp
$\frac{1}{2}$ c. orange juice
2 T. lemon juice
2 t. grated orange
  or lemon rind
1 c. evaporated milk, chilled icy cold,
  or whipping cream

1. Beat white to form softly rounded peaks. Gradually fold in sugar.
2. Fold apricot pulp into whites; blend in juices and rinds.
3. Beat evaporated milk in chilled bowl to form softly rounded peaks.
4. Fold apricot mixture into cream. Put into refrigerator tray; freeze to mush consistency.
5. Remove apricot mixture to chilled bowl; beat quickly with rotary beater until smooth. Return to tray; continue freezing (p. 258).

Apple Frappé

4 servings

3 c. diced apples
$\frac{1}{4}$ c. red cinnamon candies
$\frac{1}{3}$ to $\frac{2}{3}$ c. sugar
1 c. water

1. Cook apples, candies, sugar, and water, covered, until apples are tender.
2. Force apple mixture through sieve; cool.
3. Pour apple mixture into refrigerator tray; freeze to mush consistency.
4. Remove apple mixture to chilled bowl; beat quickly with rotary beater until smooth. Return to tray; continue freezing (p. 258).

Fruit Ice

6 servings

3 c. sugar
3 c. water, boiling
1 c. orange juice
$\frac{1}{2}$ c. lemon juice
1 T. grated lemon rind
1 T. grated orange rind
1 c. crushed pineapple
$\frac{1}{4}$ c. puréed strawberries

1. Add sugar to water in saucepan, stirring until sugar dissolves. Boil for 5 minutes. Cool.
2. Add juices, rinds, pineapple, and strawberries to sugar mixture.
3. Put fruit mixture into refrigerator tray; freeze to mush consistency.
4. Remove fruit mixture to chilled bowl; beat quickly with rotary beater until smooth. Return to tray and continue freezing.

Lemon Dessert Sherbet

8 servings

$2\frac{1}{4}$ c. sugar
1 c. water, boiling
$\frac{1}{8}$ t. salt
2 eggs, separated
1 T. white sirup
4 c. cold water
$\frac{3}{4}$ c. lemon juice

1. Add sugar to water in saucepan; cook, stirring, until sugar dissolves.
2. Boil this sirup without stirring until it spins a thread.
3. Add salt to whites; beat to form softly rounded peaks.
4. Pour hot sirup slowly into whites, beating continuously.
5. Beat white sirup, water, and lemon juice into hot sirup.
6. Pour sherbet into refrigerator tray; freeze to mush consistency.
7. Remove sherbet to chilled bowl; beat quickly with rotary beater until smooth. Return to tray; continue freezing.

Vanilla Ice Cream

6 servings

(Using Gelatin)

2 eggs, separated
1½ c. milk
½ c. sugar
2 t. gelatin
1 T. cold water
1 t. vanilla
¾ c. evaporated milk, chilled icy cold,
   or whipping cream

1. Beat yolks until thick in top of double boiler; add milk and sugar, stirring.
2. Mix gelatin with cold water; set aside 5 minutes.
3. Cook yolk mixture over hot water until metal spoon is lightly coated.
4. Add gelatin to yolk mixture; stir. Set aside to cool.
5. Beat whites to form softly rounded peaks; fold into cooled egg mixture. Fold in vanilla.
6. Pour egg mixture into refrigerator tray; freeze to mush consistency.
7. Beat evaporated milk in chilled bowl to form softly rounded peaks.
8. Remove egg mixture to chilled bowl. Beat quickly with rotary beater until smooth.
9. Fold cream into egg mixture. Return to tray and continue freezing.

VARIATIONS: Use recipe for *Vanilla Ice Cream.*

Chocolate Ice Cream

⅔ c. sugar substituted for ½ c.
¼ c. cocoa
   or 1 sq. chocolate, finely cut

Add to yolk mixture before cooking.

Grapenuts Ice Cream

¼ c. crisp grapenuts

Add after folding in whipped cream.

Banana Ice Cream

1 c. banana, mashed
1 T. lemon juice
Omit vanilla.

Add before folding in whipped cream.

Peanut-Brittle Ice Cream

½ c. peanut brittle, crushed

Add after folding in whipped cream.

Peppermint Ice Cream

¼ c. sugar substituted for ½ c.
½ lb. (1 c.) peppermint candy, crushed
Omit vanilla.

Add to yolk mixture before cooking.

485

Pineapple Ice Cream

(Using Cornstarch or Flour)

6 servings

$\frac{1}{2}$ c. sugar
1 T. cornstarch
   or 2 T. flour
2 eggs, separated
1$\frac{3}{4}$ c. milk
$\frac{1}{2}$ c. crushed pineapple
$\frac{1}{2}$ c. whipping cream

1. Mix sugar and cornstarch together.
2. Beat yolks in top of double boiler until thick. Add milk and sugar mixture; stir.
3. Place yolk mixture over hot water. Cook until metal spoon is lightly coated, stirring. Set aside.
4. Beat whites to form softly rounded peaks. Fold yolk mixture and pineapple into whites.
5. Pour yolk mixture into refrigerator tray; freeze to mush consistency.
6. Beat cream in chilled bowl to form softly rounded peaks.
7. Remove yolk mixture to chilled bowl. Beat quickly with rotary beater until smooth. Fold in cream and return to tray; continue freezing.

Chocolate Sundae

4 servings

1 qt. vanilla ice cream
$\frac{1}{2}$ c. chocolate sirup
$\frac{1}{4}$ c. chopped nuts
   or toasted coconut
   or crushed peppermint candy

1. Serve ice cream in chilled dishes.
2. Top with sirup; sprinkle with nuts. Serve.

Cranberry Mousse

6 to 8 servings

2$\frac{1}{2}$ c. cranberries
1$\frac{1}{4}$ c. water
1$\frac{1}{4}$ c. sugar
1 c. evaporated milk, chilled icy cold,
   or whipping cream
2 T. lemon juice
$\frac{1}{4}$ c. orange juice

1. Wash berries in saucepan; add water and cook till soft.
2. Force berries through sieve. Return to saucepan, add sugar, and simmer for 10 minutes. Cool.
3. Beat evaporated milk in chilled bowl to form softly rounded peaks; add lemon juice and continue beating to form pointed peaks.
4. Combine cranberry mixture and orange juice; fold into cream mixture.
5. Pour into refrigerator tray and freeze (p. 258).

Chocolate Parfait

6 servings

$\frac{3}{4}$ c. sugar
$\frac{3}{4}$ c. water
3 eggs, separated
$\frac{1}{8}$ t. salt
3 sq. unsweetened chocolate
2 c. evaporated milk, chilled icy cold,
   or whipping cream
2 t. vanilla

1. Heat sugar and water slowly to boiling point; cook until soft ball forms in icy-cold water.
2. Add salt to whites; beat to form softly rounded peaks.
3. Pour sirup slowly over whites, beating constantly.
4. Melt chocolate over hot water; blend with sirup mixture.
5. Beat evaporated milk in chilled bowl to form softly rounded peaks. Add vanilla.
6. Fold sirup mixture into beaten milk. Serve in chilled dishes.

486

Broiled Fruit Halves

2 servings

2 fruit halves (grapefruit, orange, peach, *or* pear)
4 t. sugar
  or honey
2 t. table fat

1. Place fruit halves in shallow, 8-inch pan. Sprinkle with sugar and dot with fat.
2. Broil 3 to 4 inches from heat unit for 3 to 4 minutes.

Raspberry Purée

6 servings

2 c. raspberries
$\frac{3}{8}$ c. quick-cooking tapioca,
  or $\frac{1}{2}$ c. if frozen berries are used
$\frac{1}{2}$ c. sugar
1 c. orange *or* apple juice
3 c. water
$\frac{1}{2}$ c. whipping cream

1. Sort fresh raspberries for quality; wash. Force through sieve.
2. Add tapioca, sugar, and orange juice to water in saucepan. Cook, stirring two or three times, until tapioca is transparent.
3. Add raspberries to tapioca mixture and set aside 10 minutes. Chill.
4. Beat cream in chilled bowl to form softly rounded peaks.

Serve purée in chilled sherbet glasses. Top with whipped cream.

VARIATIONS: Use recipe for *Raspberry Purée.*

Strawberry-Pineapple Purée

$1\frac{1}{4}$ c. crushed strawberries substituted for raspberries
$\frac{3}{4}$ c. crushed pineapple

Add fruits to tapioca mixture.

Rhubarb-Apple Purée

$1\frac{1}{4}$ c. cooked rhubarb substituted for raspberries
$\frac{3}{4}$ c. unpeeled, raw, finely chopped apple

Add fruits to tapioca mixture.

Surprise Cocktail

6 servings

3 oranges
1 banana, sliced
3 slices pineapple, diced
$\frac{3}{4}$ c. fruit juice
$\frac{3}{4}$ c. fruit sherbet

1. Separate orange segments; cut each into two or three pieces (p. 354).
2. Combine oranges, banana, and pineapple; pour juice over fruit mixture. Chill.
3. Place sherbet in bottom of chilled dishes; add fruit.

VARIATION: Use recipe for *Surprise Cocktail.*

Melon Cocktail

$\frac{3}{4}$ c. honeydew-melon balls
$\frac{1}{2}$ c. watermelon balls substituted for pineapple

Prepare melon balls by shaping with teaspoon measure or ball cutter.

487

Compote of Cherries, Grapefruit, and Pears

Buffet serving for 8 to 10

1 can (No. 2) sour red cherries
1 can (No. 2½) pears
⅓ c. red-raspberry jelly
2 T. finely cut candied ginger
2 medium grapefruits
Mint leaves

1. Drain cherries and pears; save juices. Place pears in dish; pour cherry juice over them. Chill for 3 hours; turn two or three times.
2. Melt jelly and add with ginger to cherries; chill.
3. Section grapefruit (p. 354). Chill.
4. Place cherry mixture in center of chilled platter. Surround with grapefruit sections and pear halves, cut side down. Place mint leaves between pears.

Candies

Fruit-Jelly Candy

½ pound

1 c. fruit juice *or* purée
½ c. liquid pectin
¾ c. sugar
¾ c. corn sirup
½ c. sugar

1. Mix juice and pectin together in saucepan. Add sugar and sirup, stirring.
2. Heat juice mixture to boiling, stirring.
3. Cook until sirup drops in a sheet from spoon. Remove from heat.
4. Pour sirup to ¾-inch depth in shallow pan. Set aside overnight.
5. Cut fruit jelly into squares; place on waxed paper and set aside 24 hours. Roll in sugar.

VARIATIONS: Use recipe for *Fruit-Jelly Candy*.

–1–
¼ c. chopped nuts

Add nuts after removing from heat.

–2–
1 c. chopped dried fruit

Add fruit after removing from heat.

–3–
Peppermint flavoring and green vegetable coloring

Add after removing from heat.

488

Fondant

1 pound

2 c. sugar
1 c. water
⅛ t. cream of tartar
   or 2 T. crystal corn sirup
⅛ t. salt

1. Combine sugar, water, cream of tartar, and salt in saucepan.
2. Cook sugar mixture until sugar is dissolved, stirring.
3. Cover sirup and cook 2 minutes. Uncover and cook until soft ball forms in icy-cold water.
4. Pour fondant sirup on platter without scraping pan. When cool enough to handle, beat; then knead until creamy.
5. Store in covered container in refrigerator. Soften to room temperature and knead 15 times or until creamy before using.

VARIATIONS: Use recipe for *Fondant.*

Bonbons

1 drop food color—yellow, red, *or* green
2 to 3 drops flavoring—peppermint *or* wintergreen

Add to fondant before kneading.
Shape fondant into balls, cubes, patties, or diamonds.
Set aside to dry several hours.

Chocolate-Covered Fondant

3 sq. chocolate (p. 75)
¼ c. nut halves

Shape fondant and set aside to dry 30 minutes.
Melt chocolate over hot water.
Dip pieces into chocolate.
Top with nut halves.
Set aside to dry.

Fruit Bars

¼ c. chopped cherries, pineapple, and nuts
2 T. coconut

Add fruits, nuts, and coconut with last kneading.
Shape into bars ¾ by 2 inches.

Stuffed Dates

1 lb. apricot halves
1 lb. dates
Cherries, coconut, *or* nuts

Wash, dry, and fill with fondant.
Remove stones from dates and fill with fondant.
Top each with cherries, coconut, or nuts.

Chocolate Drops

¼ *pound*

4 sq. sweet chocolate
1 c. ready-to-eat flaked cereal

1. Heat chocolate in top of double boiler over hot water until melted.
2. Add cereal to chocolate, tossing lightly with fork until cereal is coated.
3. Drop by teaspoon onto waxed paper. Cool until firm.

Cocoa Fudge   1½ pounds

2 c. sugar
¼ c. cocoa
⅛ t. cream of tartar
⅔ c. milk
2 T. table fat
1 t. vanilla

1. Mix sugar and cocoa together in saucepan. Add cream of tartar and milk; stir.
2. Cook sugar mixture slowly, stirring until sugar dissolves.
3. Cover sirup and cook 2 minutes. Uncover and cook until soft ball forms in icy-cold water. Remove from heat.
4. Add fat to fudge sirup; do not stir. Cool to lukewarm.
5. Add vanilla and beat fudge until creamy (shiny appearance disappears and shape is held when dropped from spoon).
6. Pour fudge into shallow 8-inch pan; mark into squares when almost cool.

VARIATION: Use recipe for *Cocoa Fudge.*

½ c. chopped nuts
½ c. mixed, chopped, dried fruit

Add during the last beating strokes.

Panocha   1½ pounds

1½ c. light-brown sugar
1 c. sugar
Few grains of salt
1 c. medium cream
 or evaporated milk
½ t. maple flavoring

1. Combine sugars and salt in saucepan; add ½ cream. Cook, stirring until sugars dissolve.
2. Cover sugar mixture and cook 2 minutes. Remove cover; stir constantly, and add remaining cream gradually so sugar mixture never stops boiling.
3. Cook panocha sirup until soft ball forms in icy-cold water. Remove from heat; cool to lukewarm.
4. Add flavoring and beat until panocha is creamy (shiny appearance disappears and shape is held when dropped from spoon).
5. Pour panocha into shallow 8-inch pan; mark into squares when almost cool.

Pralines   1½ pounds

1 c. brown sugar
2 c. granulated sugar
2 T. corn sirup
¾ c. evaporated milk
½ c. water
2 t. maple flavoring
1½ c. nut halves

1. Mix sugars, sirup, milk, and water together in saucepan. Cook slowly until sugar dissolves, stirring.
2. Boil sugar mixture slowly, stirring two or three times, until soft ball forms in icy-cold water.
3. Remove praline sirup from heat; add flavoring and beat until it begins to hold shape. Add nuts during last beating strokes.
4. Drop candy rapidly by tablespoons on waxed paper to form 4-inch patties.

490

Caramels

$1\frac{1}{2}$ pounds

2 c. sugar
1 c. light corn sirup
$\frac{1}{4}$ t. salt
3 T. table fat
3 c. milk

1. Boil sugar, sirup, and salt together in saucepan until thickened. Add fat.
2. Add milk gradually so sugar mixture never stops boiling; stir constantly.
3. Stir caramel sirup constantly and cook rapidly until firm ball forms in icy-cold water.
4. Pour caramel sirup quickly into shallow 8-inch pan without scraping saucepan. Cool.
5. Cut candy into 1-inch squares. Wrap each in waxed paper.

VARIATION: Use recipe for *Caramels*.

Date Caramels

$\frac{3}{4}$ c. finely chopped dates

Fold in chopped dates before pouring sirup into pan.

Caramels

$1\frac{1}{2}$ pounds

2 c. sugar
2 c. white corn sirup
$\frac{1}{8}$ t. salt
$\frac{1}{2}$ c. table fat
1 can (14 oz.) evaporated milk
1 c. broken nut meats

1. Mix sugar, sirup, and salt together. Cook slowly, stirring constantly until clear.
2. Add bit by bit the table fat and drop by drop the milk while cooking sugar mixture very slowly.
3. Continue cooking sugar mixture until a soft ball forms in icy-cold water.
4. Add nut meats to candy; pour into a shallow, 8-inch greased pan. Cut when cool.

Caramel Apples

8 to 10 servings

2 c. sugar
1 c. brown sugar
$\frac{2}{3}$ c. light corn sirup
$\frac{2}{3}$ c. table fat
1 c. cream
  or evaporated milk
$\frac{1}{2}$ t. salt
2 t. vanilla
8 to 10 medium apples
$\frac{1}{2}$ c. chopped nuts
  or coconut

1. Mix sugars, sirup, fat, cream, and salt in 2-qt. saucepan. Cook, stirring until firm balls form in icy-cold water.
2. Remove sirup from heat; cool until slightly thickened. Add vanilla and stir.
3. Place wooden stick in stem end of each apple and dip apple into caramel sirup.
4. Drain apples on waxed paper. Roll in chopped nuts.

Divinity

$1\frac{1}{2}$ pounds

$2\frac{1}{2}$ c. sugar
$\frac{2}{3}$ c. corn sirup
$\frac{1}{2}$ c. water
1 t. salt
2 egg whites
$\frac{1}{2}$ t. vanilla

1. Combine sugar, sirup, water, and salt. Cook over low heat until sugar is dissolved, stirring.
2. Cover sirup and cook for 2 minutes. Uncover and continue cooking sirup without stirring until hard ball forms in icy-cold water.
3. Beat whites to form stiffly pointed peaks.
4. Pour divinity sirup gradually into whites, beating constantly. Add vanilla.
5. Continue beating until a small amount of divinity dropped from a spoon holds its shape.
6. Drop divinity by teaspoons onto waxed paper or greased pan.

Popcorn Balls

Fifteen 3-inch balls

2 c. light corn sirup
3 t. vinegar
1 t. salt
2 t. vanilla
3 qt. popped corn

1. Combine sirup, vinegar, and salt in saucepan.
2. Cook, stirring three or four times, until hard ball forms in icy-cold water.
3. Add vanilla, blending quickly.
4. Add sirup to popcorn, tossing with a fork. Form into balls with lightly greased hands. Slice balls with a sharp knife. (Popcorn mixture may be pressed into cans for shaping.)

VARIATIONS: Use recipe for *Popcorn Balls*.

Festive Popcorn Balls

$1\frac{1}{2}$ c. chopped candied fruit

Mix with popcorn before adding sirup.

Cheese Popcorn Balls

1 c. grated cheese

Mix with popcorn before adding sirup.

Candied Orange Rinds

$1\frac{1}{2}$ pounds

3 orange rinds (enough to make 2 c. orange-rind strips after cooking)
4 c. water
1 T. salt
2 c. sugar
$\frac{1}{2}$ c. water
$\frac{1}{2}$ c. sugar

1. Place orange rinds in saucepan and cover with the 4 c. water. Add salt.
2. Place saucer on top to weight rinds under water. Set aside 10 to 12 hours.
3. Drain rinds and wash thoroughly. Using same pan, cover rinds with cold water. Heat to boiling point; drain. Repeat this process three times.
4. Cut rinds into petal-shaped strips. Place again in same saucepan. Add 2 c. sugar and $\frac{1}{2}$ c. water.
5. Cook rinds slowly for 30 minutes. Drain. Roll in sugar. Dry on cake rack.

Taffy

1 pound

1 c. sugar
1 c. light molasses
½ c. water
2 t. vinegar
2 T. table fat
⅛ t. salt
¼ t. baking soda
½ t. vanilla

1. Combine sugar, molasses, water, and vinegar in large, heavy saucepan.
2. Cook slowly until sugar dissolves, stirring.
3. Cover sirup and cook for 2 minutes. Uncover and cook, stirring three or four times toward end of cooking period.
4. Remove from heat when sirup forms into threads which are hard but not brittle in icy-cold water.
5. Add fat, salt, baking soda, and vanilla, blending quickly. Pour immediately onto shallow pan; do not scrape saucepan.
6. Cool sirup, lifting edges with a spatula and pulling them toward center.
7. Form into ball when cool enough to handle. Pull with lightly greased hands until light colored and porous. Cut into pieces, using kitchen shears.

VARIATION: Use recipe for *Taffy.*

Peppermint Taffy

½ t. peppermint flavoring substituted
   for vanilla

Peanut Brittle

1 pound

2 T. table fat
½ c. water, boiling
2 T. molasses
1½ c. sugar
1 c. roasted peanuts
1 t. baking soda

1. Heat fat in large skillet; add water and molasses.
2. Sift sugar into skillet and stir until dissolved.
3. Boil until sirup forms into hard and brittle threads in icy-cold water. Remove from heat; quickly add peanuts and baking soda, stirring.
4. Pour candy onto baking sheet. Spread quickly into thin sheet. When cool, break into pieces.

VARIATION: Use recipe for *Peanut Brittle.*

Pecan Brittle

1 c. chopped pecans substituted for
   peanuts
1 t. vanilla

Add with baking soda.

Salted Almonds

½ pound

2 c. water
½ lb. almonds, shelled
¼ t. salt
2 T. melted table fat
  or olive oil
  or peanut oil

1. Boil water in saucepan; remove from heat.
2. Immediately add almonds to hot water. Cover and let stand 2 minutes or until skins slip easily.
3. Drain almonds in sieve. Slip almond skins off with fingers.
4. Put almonds in shallow pan. Add salt and fat; mix well.
5. Bake almonds at 350° F. for 15 to 20 minutes; stir two or three times.
6. Remove almonds and cool quickly in another pan.

Sugared Walnut Slices

½ pound

2 c. water
½ lb. walnuts
2 T. orange juice
¼ c. granulated *or* confectioners' sugar
  (Confectioners' sugar may be tinted.)

1. Boil water in saucepan; remove from heat.
2. Immediately add walnuts to hot water. Cover and let stand 3 minutes.
3. Drain walnuts in sieve.
4. Slice nuts into thin pieces.
5. Moisten slices slightly with orange juice. Roll in sugar. Dry thoroughly for several days.

Spiced Nuts

1 pound

1 c. sugar
½ t. cinnamon
⅓ c. evaporated milk
1½ c. nut halves
½ t. vanilla

1. Combine sugar, cinnamon, and milk in saucepan. Cook and stir until sugar dissolves.
2. Boil sirup slowly, stirring two or three times, until soft ball forms in icy-cold water.
3. Add nuts and vanilla, stirring until very thick.
4. Drop tablespoons of sugar mixture onto waxed paper.

Fruit Balls

¾ pound

2 doz. dried apricots
  or peaches
1½ c. coconut
2 t. lemon juice
2 T. confectioners' sugar
⅜ c. sugar

1. Put apricots and coconut through food grinder, using medium blade.
2. Add juice and sugar to apricot mixture, blending.
3. Shape fruit mixture into balls. Roll in sugar.

494

Canning Fruit

SELECTION: Select fully ripened, sound fruit.

PREPARATION: Wash and sort for quality and size; stem or hull, pit or core. Cut into pieces, halve, or leave whole, depending upon the fruit.

PACKING: Hot-pack: boil in sirup or with sugar for specified time; pack into hot jars. Cover with sirup. Process.
Cold-pack: pack into hot jars. Cover with boiling sirup. Process.

PROCESSING: Hot-water bath.

FRUIT	PREPARATION	AMOUNT OF SUGAR OR SIRUP	Hot-Water-Bath Processing Time (minutes) Quarts	Pints
APPLES	HOT PACK Boil in sirup 5 minutes.	Thin or medium sirup	20	15
APPLE SAUCE		Sweetened to taste or unsweetened	10	10
APRICOTS	COLD PACK	Thin or medium sirup	30	25
	HOT PACK Simmer 3 to 5 minutes in sirup	Thin or medium sirup	25	20
BERRIES, except strawberries	COLD PACK	Thin or medium sirup	20	20
	HOT PACK Add sugar; bring to boil.	½ c. sugar to each quart of fruit	15	10
CHERRIES	COLD PACK	Medium or heavy sirup	25	20
	HOT PACK Add sugar; boil 2 minutes.	½ to 1 c. sugar to each quart of cherries	15	10
FRUIT JUICES	Remove pits and crush fruits. Heat to simmering. Strain through cloth bag. Add sugar. Reheat to simmering. Fill jars. Process.	1 c. sugar to each gallon	5	5
PEACHES, PEARS	Plunge into boiling water, then into cold water, to loosen skins; peel. COLD PACK	Thin or medium sirup	30	25
	HOT PACK Simmer 3 to 5 minutes in sirup.	Thin or medium sirup	25	20

METHOD AND TIMETABLE FOR CANNING FRUIT

495

METHOD AND TIMETABLE FOR CANNING FRUIT

FRUIT	PREPARATION	AMOUNT OF SUGAR OR SIRUP	Hot-Water-Bath Processing Time (minutes) Quarts	Pints
PLUMS	Prick each plum.			
	COLD PACK	Medium or heavy sirup	25	20
	HOT PACK Simmer in sirup 5 minutes.	¼ to ½ c. sugar to each quart	15	15
RHUBARB	Cut in short lengths. Boil in water or sirup until soft.	½ c. sugar to each quart	10	10
STRAWBERRIES	Add ½ to 1 c. sugar to each quart of berries. Heat slowly to boiling point. Remove from heat. Let stand several hours or overnight. Bring quickly to boil. Pack into jars.	½ to 1 c. sugar to each quart	15	15
TOMATOES	Plunge into boiling water then into cold water, to loosen skins. Remove cores and skin. **COLD PACK** Add ½ t. salt to each pint. Add juice leaving 1-inch head space. Set in boiling water and heat through; partially seal. Process.		35	35
	HOT PACK Heat slowly to boiling. Boil 2 minutes.		10	10
TOMATO JUICE	Remove core and cut tomatoes into small pieces. Simmer until soft; rub through strainer. Bring pulp to boiling point; fill jars. Add 1 t. salt to each quart.		10	10

SELECTION: Choose fresh, firm, tender vegetables.

PREPARATION: Wash and sort for quality and size; peel, trim, shell, or husk. Cut into pieces, halve, or leave whole. Cover vegetables with boiling water; precook.

PACKING: Pack hot vegetables into hot jars quickly. Cover with boiling water leaving $\frac{1}{2}$- to 1-inch head space. Add 1 t. salt to each quart or $\frac{1}{2}$ t. to each pint. Work out bubbles by running knife blade around inside of the jar.

PROCESSING: Use water bath, steam-pressure cooker, or pressure saucepan.

COOLING: Set jars 2 or 3 inches apart on heavy cloth; cool in upright position. Jars are not to be set in draft or on cold wet surface and are not to be covered.

STORING: Test glass jars for leaks by tapping lids with a spoon. A clear ringing sound indicates a seal. Wipe jars, label, and store in dark, cool, dry place.

METHODS AND TIMETABLE FOR CANNING VEGETABLES

VEGETABLES	HOW TO PREPARE	Minutes in Pressure Canner at 10-lb. Pressure, 240° F.	
		Quarts	Pints
Asparagus	Tie in bundles; stand upright in boiling water; cover and boil 2 to 3 minutes. Cut in 1 inch pieces; add boiling water and boil 2 to 3 minutes.	30	25
Beans Lima	Bring to boil. Leave 1-inch head space.	50	40
Snap	Boil 5 minutes.	25	20
Beets	Cut off tops, leaving 1 inch of stem. Steam 15 to 20 minutes; skin and trim. Pack. Cover with boiling water. (Add 1 t. vinegar to each pint.)	40	25
Carrots	Bring to boil.	30	25

All these canned foods should be opened and boiled 10 minutes before they are tasted or served.

METHODS AND TIMETABLE FOR CANNING VEGETABLES

VEGETABLES	HOW TO PREPARE	Minutes in Pressure Canner at 10-lbs. Pressure, 240°F.	
		Quarts	Pints
Corn Cream-style	Husk, remove silk; wash. Cut corn from cob at about center of kernel. Scrape cob with back of knife to obtain juice. Add ½ as much boiling water as corn. Heat to boiling point.	—	95
Whole-kernel	Cut kernels from cob at about ⅔ depth of kernel. Add 1 pt. boiling water to 1 qt. corn; heat to boiling point. Leave 1-inch head space.	85	55
Greens	Do not add water. Heat 5 minutes or until wilted.	70	45
Peas	Bring to a boil. Leave 1-inch head space.	40	40
Pumpkin, strained	Steam until tender or about 25 minutes; strain. Simmer until heated, stirring to prevent sticking. Pack without addition of liquid or salt.	90	55
Squash Winter, strained	Prepare as for pumpkin, above.	40	30
Summer	Prepare as for pumpkin. Bring to boil.	40	30
Sweet potatoes	Boil or steam 20 to 30 minutes; skin. Pack. Add no liquid.	90	55

All these canned foods should be opened and boiled 10 minutes before they are tasted or served.

Freezing Fruits

SELECTION: The fruits suggested in the following table for freezing have been found to give best results. Fresh, fully ripened, sound fruits should be selected.

PREPARATION: Wash fruit carefully; drain; pare, core, stem, seed, or pit fruit; sort fruit according to size. Slice, halve, crush, or leave fruits whole. Fruits to be served uncooked or whole are best when packaged in sirup. If sirup is made with hot water, cool before using. Fruits to be cooked may be sugar-packed or packed without sugar. In the sugar pack, fruits should be mixed with sugar until sugar is dissolved before packaging. Ascorbic acid is used to prevent the darkening of fruits.

PACKING: To pack with sirup put fruit into containers, add sirup to cover; or slice fruit directly into sirup in container, and add sirup to cover. Leave $\frac{1}{2}$- to $\frac{3}{4}$-inch head space from top of pint container and 1- to $1\frac{1}{2}$-inch head space for quart containers. Seal and quick-freeze. If you use the sugar pack, mix fruits with sugar until sugar is dissolved, before packaging. Dry packs should have $\frac{1}{2}$-inch space from top of containers. Seal and quick-freeze. Ascorbic acid is added to the sirup in sirup pack, or sprinkled over the fruit before adding the sugar in sugar pack.

LABELING: Label each container with the name of the fruit and the date on which it was prepared for freezing.

STORING: Store fruits at 0° F. or below.

SIRUPS FOR FREEZING FRUITS*

TYPE OF SIRUP	SUGAR†	WATER	YIELD	TYPE OF SIRUP	SUGAR†	WATER	YIELD
30% sirup	2 c.	4 c.	5 c.	**50% sirup**	$4\frac{3}{4}$ c.	4 c.	$6\frac{1}{2}$ c.
35% sirup	$2\frac{1}{2}$ c.	4 c.	$5\frac{1}{3}$ c.	**60% sirup**	7 c.	4 c.	$7\frac{3}{4}$ c.
40% sirup	3 c.	4 c.	$5\frac{1}{2}$ c.	**65% sirup**	$8\frac{3}{4}$ c.	4 c.	$8\frac{2}{3}$ c.

*Bureau of Human Nutrition and Home Economics, United States Department of Agriculture, Home and Garden Bulletin No. 10, p. 10.

†Dissolve sugar in hot or cold water. If hot water is used, cool sirup before adding to fruit. Completely cover fruit with sirup when packing to freeze. Corn sirup may be substituted for $\frac{1}{4}$ of sugar.

FRUITS	HOW TO PACK	HOW TO SWEETEN*
APPLES	**SIRUP-PACK** Slice into cold sirup in container.	40% sirup, ½ t. ascorbic acid per quart of sirup
	SUGAR-PACK Slice apples into solution of 2 T. salt to 1 gal. water during preparation to keep from darkening. Drain. Add sugar.	1 c. sugar to 4 c. fruit
APRICOTS	**SUGAR-PACK** Sprinkle fruit with acid solution of ¼ t. ascorbic acid in ¼ c. cold water per quart of fruit.	½ c. sugar to 4 c. fruit
	SIRUP-PACK Slice apricots directly into sirup.	40% sirup, ¾ t. ascorbic acid per quart of sirup
CHERRIES, sour, whole	**SIRUP-PACK**	60-65% sirup
	SUGAR-PACK	¾ c. sugar to 4 c. fruit
CHERRIES, sweet, whole	**SIRUP-PACK**	40% sirup, ½ t. ascorbic acid per quart of sirup
CRANBERRIES, whole	**SIRUP-PACK**	50% sirup
	SUGAR-PACK	¾ c. sugar to 4 c. fruit
	PACK WITHOUT SUGAR	
FIGS, whole or sliced	**SIRUP-PACK**	35% sirup, ¾ t. ascorbic acid per quart of sirup
	PACK WITHOUT SUGAR Sprinkle each quart of fruit with acid solution of ¼ t. ascorbic acid in ¼ c. cold water per quart of fruit	

*For types of sirup see table on page 499, "Sirups for Freezing Fruits."

FRUITS	HOW TO PACK	HOW TO SWEETEN*
PEACHES, halves or slices	**SIRUP-PACK** Halve or slice directly into sirup in container.	40% sirup, ½ t. ascorbic acid per quart of sirup
	SUGAR-PACK Sprinkle fruit with acid solution of ¼ t. ascorbic acid in ¼ c. cold water per quart of fruit.	⅔ c. sugar to 4 c. fruit
	WATER-PACK Cover peaches with cold water containing 1 t. ascorbic acid per quart of water.	
PINEAPPLE	**SIRUP-PACK** Dice or cut in wedges	30% sirup
	PACK WITHOUT SUGAR	
PLUMS and PRUNES	**SIRUP-PACK**	40–50% sirup, ½ t. ascorbic acid per quart of sirup
	PACK WITHOUT SUGAR	
RASPBERRIES, whole	**SIRUP-PACK**	40% sirup
	SUGAR-PACK	¾ c. sugar to 4 c. berries
	PACK WITHOUT SUGAR	
RHUBARB	**SIRUP-PACK** Cut into 1- or 2-inch pieces. Heat in boiling water for 1 minute and cool by plunging in cold water.	40% sirup
	PACK WITHOUT SUGAR	
STRAWBERRIES, whole	**SIRUP-PACK**	50% sirup
	SUGAR-PACK	¾ c. sugar to 1 qt. fruit
	PACK WITHOUT SUGAR	

*For types of sirup see table on page 499, "Sirups for Freezing Fruits."

501

Freezing Vegetables

SELECTION: All of the vegetables in the following table are suitable for freezing. Fresh, young, tender, sound vegetables should be selected.

PREPARATION: Wash; trim; shell or cut; sort vegetables according to size. Soaking in a solution of 4 t. salt to 1 gal. water will rid vegetables of insects.

BLANCHING: Use 1 gal. boiling water for each pound of vegetables; add vegetables and return to boiling; then time for blanching according to directions.

CHILLING: Blanched vegetables should be chilled in a large quantity of icy-cold water (60° F. or below) as quickly as possible before packaging.

PACKAGING: Drain vegetables quickly and dry-pack in appropriate containers. Leave $\frac{1}{2}$-inch head space for expansion. Seal packages, label, and quick-freeze immediately.

STORING: Store at 0° F. or below.

DIRECTIONS FOR FREEZING VEGETABLES

VEGETABLE	SELECTION AND PREPARATION	BLANCHING TIME
ASPARAGUS	Pack with tips down, or alternate tips with stem ends.	Small stalk, 2 min. Medium stalk, 3 min. Large stalk, 4 min.
BEANS **Green, snap, or wax**	Use stringless beans that snap when broken. Cut in 1- or 2-inch pieces.	Cut, 3 min. Whole, 5 min.
Lima	Select well-filled pods.	Small beans, 2 min. Medium beans, 3 min. Large beans, 4 min.
BEETS	Mature beets not more than 3 inches across may be used. Trim tops leaving $\frac{1}{2}$ inch of stems.	Small beets 25 to 30 min. Medium beets 45 to 50 min.
BROCCOLI	Select tight, compact, dark-green heads. Soak heads down $\frac{1}{2}$ hr. in salt-water solution made of 4 t. salt to 1 gal. cold water. Split heads lengthwise so pieces are $1\frac{1}{2}$ inches across. In packaging leave no head space.	Steam 5 min. or put in boiling water for 3 min.

502

DIRECTIONS FOR FREEZING VEGETABLES

VEGETABLE	SELECTION AND PREPARATION	BLANCHING TIME
BRUSSELS SPROUTS	Select compact heads. In packaging, leave no head space.	Small heads, 3 min. Medium heads, 4 min. Large heads, 5 min.
CAULIFLOWER	Choose snow-white heads. Break or cut into pieces about 1 inch across. (If necessary to remove insects, soak 30 min. in salt solution. Drain.)	3 to 4 min. (Add 4 t. salt to 1 gal. water.)
CORN **On the cob**	Select ears with plump kernels and thin sweet milk. Husk and remove silk. Heat. Cool. Pack ears into containers or wrap in moisture-vapor-resistant material.	Small ears ($1\frac{1}{4}$ inches in diameter), 7 min. Medium ears ($1\frac{1}{4}$ to $1\frac{1}{2}$ inches in diameter), 9 min. Large ears (over $1\frac{1}{2}$ inches in diameter), 11 min.
Whole-kernel and cream-style	After chilling, cut off kernels. For whole-kernel corn, cut kernels from cob at about $\frac{2}{3}$ of the depth of the kernels. If milk is thick and starchy, use for cream-style corn. For cream-style cut kernels off cob at about center of the kernels. Scrape cobs with back of knife to obtain milk and heart of kernel.	Same as for Corn on the cob
OKRA	Select tender green pods; cut off stems.	Small pods, 3 min. Large pods, 4 min.
PEAS, green	Select bright-green, plump, firm pods. Shell.	1 to $1\frac{1}{2}$ min.
PEPPERS, green	Select crisp, thick-walled peppers. Cut away seeds; slice or halve. Or, freeze without blanching.	Slices, 2 min. Halves, 3 min.
TURNIPS	Select small to medium turnips. Peel and cut into $\frac{1}{2}$-inch cubes.	2 min.

Freezing Meat, Poultry, and Fish

SELECTION: Select sound high-quality meat, plump poultry, and fresh fish.

PREPARATION: Handle meat carefully to keep clean. Place amount of meat for a meal in one package. Wrap meat in airtight, moistureproof material.

LABELING: Label.

FREEZING: Freeze at 0° F. or lower temperature.

STORING: Store at 0° F. or lower. Keep record of meats put in freezer, including the date.

STORAGE TIME LIMITS FOR MEAT

CUTS OF MEAT	STORAGE TIME LIMITS (months)	CUTS OF MEAT	STORAGE TIME LIMITS (months)
Veal (all cuts)	3–4	Pork (all cuts)	3–4
Beef (all cuts)	6–8	Sausage (with salt)	1–3
Ground meats	1–3	Poultry (cut up or whole)	6–12
Lamb (all cuts)	6–8	Fish (cut up or whole)	3–4

Jellies, Preserves, and Pickles

Apple Butter

3 to 4 pints

4 lb. apples
2 c. water
   or cider vinegar
Sugar
2 t. cinnamon
1 t. cloves
½ t. allspice
1 T. grated lemon rind
2 T. lemon juice, if desired

1. Wash apples, remove stems, and quarter.
2. Simmer apples in water until soft.
3. Force apples through sieve. Add ½ c. sugar for each cup of pulp. Add seasonings tied in cheesecloth bag.
4. Heat apple mixture slowly; then boil rapidly until thick, stirring.
5. Add lemon rind and juice last 2 minutes of cooking.
6. Put apple butter in sterilized jars; seal.

Pineapple Marmalade

1 to 1½ pints

4 c. water
3½ c. finely shredded pineapple
1 lemon, thinly sliced
1 orange, thinly sliced
4 c. sugar

1. Add water to fruits; set aside overnight.
2. Cook fruit mixture for 25 minutes.
3. Add sugar to fruit mixture; stir until sugar dissolves. Cook until jelly drops in a sheet from spoon (p. 306).
4. Pour marmalade into hot sterilized glasses; cover with melted paraffin and seal.

Grape Conserve

4 to 5 pints

7 c. grapes, stemmed
2 c. nuts
2 c. raisins
7 c. sugar

1. Wash grapes; slip off skins and set aside.
2. Cook grape pulp for 10 minutes, crushing with a wooden spoon.
3. Force grape pulp through sieve to remove seeds.
4. Chop grape skins, nuts, and raisins, and combine with grape-pulp mixture.
5. Heat grape-pulp mixture slowly until sugar dissolves, stirring. Boil for 20 minutes or until thick, stirring.
6. Remove conserve from heat; cover and let stand 2 minutes.
7. Skim foam from conserve; stir and pour into hot sterilized glass jars. Cover with melted paraffin and seal.

Strawberry Preserves

1½ to 2 pints

3½ c. sugar
½ c. water
4 c. stemmed strawberries

1. Add sugar to water in deep saucepan; simmer, stirring two or three times until sugar dissolves.
2. Boil sugar mixture until a 2-inch thread spins when dropped from side of spoon.
3. Add strawberries slowly; bring to a rolling boil and cook for 10 to 12 minutes. Set aside; skim if necessary.
4. Pour preserves into a shallow dish. Set aside, covered, for 24 hours. Shake the dish two or three times to move berries in the sirup. Pour into hot sterilized glass jars; cover with melted paraffin and seal.

VARIATIONS: Use recipe for *Strawberry Preserves*.

Cherry Preserves

4 c. stemmed and seeded cherries substituted for strawberries
4 c. sugar substituted for 3½ c.

Raspberry Preserves

4 c. raspberries substituted for strawberries

Grape Jelly

1 c. water
2 c. grape juice
1 package powdered pectin
3½ c. sugar

1. Add water to juice in saucepan.
2. Add pectin to juice mixture, stirring. Bring to boil over high heat, stirring.
3. Add sugar when mixture boils rapidly, stirring. Continue stirring juice mixture and bring to a rolling boil for ½ minute.
4. Remove juice mixture from heat; skim. Pour into hot sterilized glasses; cover with melted paraffin and seal.

Pickled Peaches

6 pints

8 lb. peaches
2 T. whole cloves
8 two-inch pieces stick cinnamon
1 T. whole ginger
4 c. sugar
4 c. vinegar

1. Wash and pare peaches.
2. Put spices in cloth bag and tie securely.
3. Mix spices, sugar, and vinegar in saucepan. Simmer for 10 minutes.
4. Add peaches to spice mixture and cook slowly until tender but not broken. Set aside overnight.
5. Remove spice bag and drain peaches.
6. Boil sirup rapidly until thickened.
7. Pack peaches in hot sterilized jars. Pour sirup over peaches and seal tightly.

Pepper-Onion Relish

3 to 4 pints

4 c. finely chopped onion
2 c. finely chopped green pepper
2 c. finely chopped sweet red pepper
1 c. sugar
4 c. vinegar
1⅓ T. salt

1. Combine onion, peppers, sugar, vinegar, and salt in saucepan. Bring slowly to boiling point.
2. Boil mixture until slightly thickened.
3. Pack relish into hot sterilized jars; seal tightly.

Bread-and-Butter Pickles

3 to 4 quarts

18 medium unpeeled cucumbers
6 c. sliced onions
1½ c. vinegar
1½ c. brown sugar
1 t. tumeric
1 t. celery seed
1 t. mustard seed

1. Slice cucumbers. Set aside overnight in weak salt solution to cover (1 T. salt to 4 c. water).
2. Drain cucumbers; add onions, vinegar, sugar, and seasonings.
3. Simmer mixture for 20 minutes. Put in hot sterilized glass jars; seal tightly.

Ripe-Tomato Catchup

12 to 15 lb. ripe tomatoes
6 large onions
1⅓ T. salt
Parsley and celery leaves
2 to 3 t. cloves
2 to 3 t. cinnamon
5 c. sugar
½ t. red pepper
1 t. paprika
1 T. nutmeg
2 t. celery salt
6 c. vinegar
1 T. cornstarch

1. Core and quarter tomatoes; peel and quarter onions.
2. Combine tomatoes, onions, and vegetable leaves and cook until tender. Force through sieve.
3. Add seasonings and all but 1 T. vinegar to tomato mixture.
4. Mix 1 T. vinegar with cornstarch. Add to tomato mixture, stirring.
5. Simmer catchup in large kettle for 60 minutes. Pour into hot sterilized jars; seal tightly.

Appendix

TABLE I

WEIGHT–HEIGHT–AGE TABLE FOR GIRLS OF SCHOOL AGE

Table prepared by Bird T. Baldwin, Ph.D., Iowa Child Welfare Research Sta., State University of Iowa, and Thos. D. Wood, M.C., Columbia University. Reprinted by courtesy of the American Child Health Association, New York.

Height (inches)	Average weight for height (pounds)	5	6	7	8	9	10	11	12	13	14	15	16	17	18
38	33	33	33												
39	34	34	34												
40	36	36	36	36											
41	37	37	37	37											
42	39	39	39	39											
43	41	41	41	41	41										
44	42	42	42	42	42										
45	45	45	45	45	45	45									
46	47	47	47	47	48	48									
47	50	49	50	50	50	50	50								
48	52		52	52	52	52	53	53							
49	55		54	54	55	55	56	56							
50	58		56	56	57	58	59	61	62						
51	61			59	60	61	61	63	65						
52	64			63	64	64	64	65	67						
53	68			66	67	67	68	68	69	71					
54	71				69	70	70	71	71	73					
55	75				72	74	74	74	75	77	78				
56	79					76	78	78	79	81	83				
57	84					80	82	82	82	84	88	92			
58	89						84	86	86	88	93	96	101		
59	95						87	87	90	92	96	100	103	104	
60	101						91	95	95	97	101	105	108	109	111
61	108							99	100	101	105	108	112	113	116
62	114							104	105	106	109	113	115	117	118
63	118								110	110	112	116	117	119	120
64	121								114	115	117	119	120	122	123
65	125								118	120	121	122	123	125	126
66	129									124	124	125	128	129	130
67	133									128	130	131	133	133	135
68	138									131	133	135	136	138	138
69	142										135	137	138	140	142
70	144										136	138	140	142	144
71	145										138	140	142	144	154

AGE (years)		6	7	8	9	10	11	12	13	14	15	16	17	18
Average height (inches)	Short	43	45	47	49	50	52	54	57	59	60	61	61	61
	Medium	45	47	50	52	54	56	58	60	62	63	64	64	64
	Tall	47	50	53	55	57	59	62	64	66	66	67	67	67
Average annual gain (pounds)	Short	4	4	4	5	6	6	10	13	10	7	2	1	
	Medium	5	5	6	7	8	10	13	10	6	4	3	1	
	Tall	6	8	8	9	11	13	9	8	4	4	1	1	

508

TABLE II
WEIGHT–HEIGHT–AGE TABLE FOR BOYS OF SCHOOL AGE

Table prepared by Bird T. Baldwin, Ph.D., Iowa Child Welfare Research Sta., State University of Iowa, and Thos. D. Wood, M.C., Columbia University. Reprinted by Courtesy of the American Child Health Association, New York.

Height (inches)	Average weight for height (pounds)	5	6	7	8	9	10	11	12	13	14	15	16	17	18	19
38	34	34	34													
39	35	35	35													
40	36	36	36													
41	38	38	38	38												
42	39	39	39	39	39											
43	41	41	41	41	41											
44	44	44	44	44	44											
45	46	46	46	46	46	46										
46	48	47	48	48	48	48										
47	50	49	50	50	50	50	50									
48	53		52	53	53	53	53									
49	55		55	55	55	55	55	55								
50	58		57	58	58	58	58	58	58							
51	61			63	61	61	61	61	61							
52	64			64	64	64	64	64	64	64						
53	68			66	67	67	67	67	68	68						
54	71				70	70	70	70	71	71	72					
55	74				72	72	73	73	74	74	74					
56	78				75	76	77	77	77	78	78	80				
57	82					79	80	81	81	82	83	83				
58	85					83	84	84	85	85	86	87				
59	89						87	88	89	89	90	90	90			
60	94						91	92	92	93	94	95	96			
61	99							95	96	97	99	100	103	106		
62	104							100	101	102	103	104	107	111	116	
63	111							105	106	107	108	110	113	118	123	127
64	117								109	111	113	115	117	121	126	130
65	123								114	117	118	120	122	127	131	134
66	129									119	122	125	128	132	136	139
67	133									124	128	130	134	136	139	142
68	139										134	134	137	141	143	147
69	144										137	139	143	146	149	152
70	147										143	144	145	148	151	155
71	152										148	150	151	152	154	159
72	157											153	155	156	158	163
73	163											157	160	162	164	167
74	169											160	164	168	170	171

AGE (years)		6	7	8	9	10	11	12	13	14	15	16	17	18	19
Average height (inches)	Short	43	45	47	49	51	53	54	56	58	60	62	64	65	65
	Medium	46	48	50	52	54	56	58	60	63	65	67	68	69	69
	Tall	49	51	53	55	57	59	61	64	67	70	72	72	73	73
Average annual gain (pounds)	Short		3	4	5	5	5	4	8	9	11	14	13	7	3
	Medium		4	5	6	6	6	7	9	11	15	11	8	4	3
	Tall		5	7	7	7	7	8	12	16	11	9	7	3	4

The figures represent weight in pounds; age at nearest birthday; height at nearest inch; weight at nearest pound.

Table III
Recommended Daily Dietary Allowances[1]

Food and Nutrition Board, National Academy of Sciences—National Research Council, Revised 1963

Designed for the maintenance of good nutrition of practically all healthy persons in the U.S.A.

	Age[2] Years from to	Weight kg. (lbs.)	Height cm. (in.)	Calories	Protein gm.	Calcium gm.	Iron mg.	Vitamin A Value IU	Thiamine mg.	Riboflavin mg.	Niacin Equiv. mg.	Ascorbic Acid mg.	Vitamin D IU
MEN	18–35	70 (154)	175 (69)	2,900	70	0.8	10	5,000*	1.2	1.7	19	70	
	35–55	70 (154)	175 (69)	2,600	70	0.8	10	5,000	1.0	1.6	17	70	
	55–75	70 (154)	175 (69)	2,200	70	0.8	10	5,000	0.9	1.3	15	70	
WOMEN	18–35	58 (128)	163 (64)	2,100	58	0.8	15	5,000	0.8	1.3	14	70	
	35–55	58 (128)	163 (64)	1,900	58	0.8	15	5,000	0.8	1.2	13	70	
	55–75	58 (128)	163 (64)	1,600	58	0.8	10	5,000	0.8	1.2	13	70	
	Pregnant (2nd and 3rd trimester)			+200	+20	+0.5	+5	+1,000	+0.2	+0.3	+3	+30	400
	Lactating			+1,000	+40	+0.5	+5	+3,000	+0.4	+0.6	+7	+30	400
INFANTS[3]	0–1	8 (18)		kg.x115 ±15	kg.x2.5 ±0.5	0.7	kg.x1.0	1,500	0.4	0.6	6	30	400
CHILDREN	1–3	13 (29)	87 (34)	1,300	32	0.8	8	2,000	0.5	0.8	9	40	400
	3–6	18 (40)	107 (42)	1,600	40	0.8	10	2,500	0.6	1.0	11	50	400
	6–9	24 (53)	124 (49)	2,100	52	0.8	12	3,500	0.8	1.3	14	60	400
BOYS	9–12	33 (72)	140 (55)	2,400	60	1.1	15	4,500	1.0	1.4	16	70	400
	12–15	45 (98)	156 (61)	3,000	75	1.4	15	5,000	1.2	1.8	20	80	400
	15–18	61 (134)	172 (68)	3,400	85	1.4	15	5,000	1.4	2.0	22	80	400
GIRLS	9–12	33 (72)	140 (55)	2,200	55	1.1	15	4,500	0.9	1.3	15	80	400
	12–15	47 (103)	158 (62)	2,500	62	1.3	15	5,000	1.0	1.5	17	80	400
	15–18	53 (117)	163 (64)	2,300	58	1.3	15	5,000	0.9	1.3	15	70	400

[1] The allowance levels are intended to cover individual variations among most normal persons as they live in the United States under usual environmental stresses. The recommended allowances can be attained with a variety of common foods, providing other nutrients for which human requirements have been less well defined.

[2] Entries on lines for age range 18–35 years represent the 25-year age. All other entries represent allowances for the midpoint of the specified age periods, i.e., line for children 1–3 is for age 2 years (24 months); 3–6 is for age 4½ years (54 months), etc.

[3] The calorie and protein allowances per kg. for infants are considered to decrease progressively from birth. Allowances for calcium, thiamine, riboflavin, and niacin increase proportionately with calories to the maximum values shown.

* 1,000 IU from preformed Vitamin A and 4,000 IU from beta-carotene.

TABLE IV

NUTRITIONAL VALUE OF FOODS

Ca = Calcium
Cal. = Calories
CHO = Carbohydrate
diam. = diameter

Fe = Iron
Gm. = Gram
" = inches
I.U. = International Unit

Mg. = Millogram
oz. = ounce
P = Phosphorus
Pro. = Protein

T = Tablespoon
t = teaspoon
Tr. = Trace, or tiny amount
Vit. = vitamin

Taken from *Composition of Foods—Raw, Processed, Prepared,* Bureau of Home Nutrition and Home Economics, Agricultural Research Administration, United States Department of Agriculture, Handbook No. 8. (Parentheses with figures indicate estimated, not proved, value.)

Food	Measure	Food Energy Cal.	Pro. Gm.	Fat Gm.	CHO Gm.	Ca Mg.	P Mg.	Fe Mg.	Vit. A I.U.	Thiamine Mg.	Riboflavin Mg.	Niacin Mg.	Ascorbic Acid Mg.
Apples, fresh	1 medium, 2½" diam.	76	.4	.5	19.7	8	13	.4	120	.05	.04	.2	6
Applesauce, canned	1 cup	184	.5	.3	50.0	10	20	1.0	80	.05	.03	.1	3
Apricots, fresh	3 (114 gm.)	54	1.1	.1	13.8	17	25	.5	2,990	.03	.05	.9	7
Apricots, dried, cooked	1 cup	400	4.9	.3	102.7	78	110	4.6	6,860	.01	.13	2.9	10
Asparagus, fresh, cooked	1 cup cut spears	36	4.2	.4	6.3	33	93	1.8	1,820	.23	.30	2.1	40
Avocado (alligator pear), fresh	1 cup	372	2.6	40.1	7.8	15	58	.9	430	.10	.20	1.7	24
Bacon, cooked	2 slices	97	4.	8.8	.2	4	41	.5	(0)	.08	.05	.8	0
Bananas, fresh	1 medium	88	1.2	.2	23.	8	28	.6	430	.04	.05	.7	10
Beans, kidney, canned	1 cup	230	14.6	1.0	42.0	102	317	4.9	(0)	.12	.12	2.0	(0)
Beans, baked, canned, pork and molasses	1 cup	325	15.1	7.8	50.1	146	295	5.5	90	.13	.09	1.2	7
Beans, snap, cooked	1 cup	27	1.8	.2	5.9	45	29	.9	830	.09	.12	.6	18
Beans, Lima, green, shelled	1 cup	152	8.0	.6	29.3	46	123	2.7	290	.04	.09	.8	9
Beans, Lima, dried	1 cup	610	37.9	2.4	112.7	124	697	13.7	0	.88	.32	3.6	3
Beef, round, lean	3 ounces without bone	197	23.	11.	0.	9	191	2.9	(0)	.06	.19	4.7	0
Beef, rib roast	3 ounces without bone	266	20.	20.	0.	9	157	2.6	(0)	.05	.15	3.6	0
Beef, dried	1 cup	336	56.6	10.4	0.	33	667	8.4	(0)	(.12)	(.53)	(6.3)	0
Beef, stew, with veg.	1 cup	252	12.9	19.3	16.7	31	176	2.6	2,520	.12	.15	3.4	15
Beet greens	1 cup, cooked	39	2.9	.4	8.1	171	65	4.6	10,790	.07	.23	.6	22
Beets, cooked	1 cup diced	68	1.6	.2	16.2	35	51	1.2	30	.03	.07	.5	11
Biscuits, baking powder	1 biscuit, enriched flour	129	3.1	4.0	19.8	83	73	.7	30	.09	.09	.8	(0)
Blackberries, fresh	1 cup	82	1.7	1.4	18.0	46	46	1.3	280	.05	.06	.5	16
Blueberries, fresh	1 cup	85	.8	.8	21.1	22	18	1.1	400	(.04)	(.03)	(.4)	23
Bologna	1 piece (1 by 1½ inches diam.)	467	31.2	33.5	7.6	(19)	(236)	4.6	(0)	.37	.40	5.7	0
Bouillon cubes	1 cube	2	(.2)	.1	(0.)						.07	1.0	0
Bran	1 cup	145	7.2	2.0	44.5	56	787	6.2	(0)	.22	.23	11.5	(0)

511

Food	Measure	Food Energy Cal.	Pro. Gm.	Fat Gm.	CHO Gm.	Ca Mg.	P Mg.	Fe Mg.	Vit. A I.U.	Thiamine Mg.	Riboflavin Mg.	Niacin Mg.	Ascorbic Acid Mg.
Bread, cracked-wheat, unenriched	1 slice	60	2.0	.5	11.8	19	29	.2	0	.03	.02	.3	(0)
Bread, rye	1 slice	57	2.1	.3	12.1	17	34	.4	0	.04	.02	.4	(0)
Bread, white, enriched	1 slice	64	1.9	.8	12.0	15	19	.4	0	.06	.04	.5	(0)
Bread, whole-wheat	1 slice	55	2.1	.6	11.3	22	60	.5	0	.07	.03	.7	(0)
Broccoli, flower stalks	1 cup	44	5.0	.3	8.2	195	114	2.0	5,100	.10	.22	1.2	111
Brussels sprouts	1 cup	60	5.7	.6	11.6	44	101	1.7	520	.05	.16	.6	61
Butter	1 T	100	.1	11.3	.1	3	2	.0	460	Tr.	Tr.	Tr.	(0)
Buttermilk	1 cup	86	8.5	.2	12.4	(288)	227	.2	10	.09	.43	.3	3
Cabbage, chinese	1 cup, cooked	27	2.3	.6	4.6	82	78	1.7	490	.04	.06	.6	42
Cabbage, raw	1 cup	24	1.4	.2	5.3	46	31	.5	80	.06	.05	.3	50
Cabbage, cooked	1 cup	40	2.4	.3	9.0	78	53	.8	150	.08	.08	.5	53
Cake, plain	2" × 2" × 1"	81	1.6	2.0	14.2	39	34	.1	30	.01	.02	.1	(0)
Cake, angel food	2" sector	108	3.4	.1	23.5	2	10	.1	0	Tr.	.05	.1	(0)
Cantaloupes, raw	1 cup diced	30	.9	.3	6.7	25	23	.6	4,960	.07	.05	.7	47
Carrots, cooked	1 cup diced	44	.9	.7	9.3	38	38	.9	18,130	.07	.07	.7	6
Cauliflower, cooked	1 cup	30	2.9	.2	5.9	26	86	1.3	108	.07	.10	.6	34
Celery	1 large outer stalk	7	.5	.1	1.5	20	16	.2	108	.02	.02	.2	3
Chard, leaves only	1 cup, cooked	47	4.6	.7	8.4	184	63	4.4	16,960	.07	.28	.5	30
Cheese, cheddar	1 in. cube	113	7.1	9.1	.6	206	140	.3	400	.01	.12	Tr.	(0)
Cheese, cottage	1 ounce	27	5.5	.1	.6	27	54	.1	(10)	.01	.09	Tr.	(0)
Cherries, sweet	1 cup	94	1.7	.8	22.8	28	31	.6	960	.08	.09	.6	13
Chicken, broilers	½ bird, 8 oz.	332	44.4	15.8	0.	31	440	3.3	(0)	.18	.36	22.4	(0)
Chicken, stewed	4 oz.	342	20.4	28.3	0.	16	227	1.7	(0)	.09	.18	9.1	(0)
Chicken, roasters	4 oz.	227	22.9	14.3	0.	16	227	1.7	(0)	.09	.18	9.1	(0)
Chocolate, milk, bar	1 oz.	151	(2.3)	10.9	14.2	58	71	.8	40	.04	.14	(.3)	(0)
Chocolate, bitter	1 oz.	142	(1.6)	15.0	8.3	28	126	1.2	20	.01	.06	.3	(0)
Cocoa	1 T	21	(.6)	1.7	3.4	9	50	.8	Tr.	.01	.03	.2	(0)
Cocoa, beverage	1 cup	236	9.5	11.5	27.2	298	285	1.0	400	.10	.46	.5	3
Cod, fresh	4 oz.	84	18.7	.5	0.	11	220	.5	0	.07	.10	2.5	2
Cod, dried	1 oz.	106	23.2	.8	0.	(14)	253	1.0	0	.02	.13	3.1	(0)
Cookies, plain	3 in. diam.	109	1.5	3.2	18.8	6	16	.2	(0)	.01	.01	.1	(0)
Corn, sweet	1 cup	140	4.5	1.2	33.3	8	86	1.0	640	.18	.16	2.3	13
Corn bread	1 slice	103	3.5	2.7	16.7	68	104	.8	60	.07	.09	.4	(0)
Corn flakes	1 cup	96	2.0	0.1	21.2	3	14	0.3	(0)	0.01	0.02	0.4	(0)
Corn meal, cooked, enriched	1 cup	119	2.6	.5	25.5	2	33	1.0	100	.14	.09	1.1	(0)
Corn sirup	1 T	57	(0.)	(0.)	(14.8)	9	3	.8	0	(0)	Tr.	Tr.	(0)
Cornstarch	1 T	29	.0	.0	7.0	(0)	(0)	(0)	(0)	(0)	(0)	(0)	(0)
Cornstarch blancmange	1 cup	275	8.7	9.7	38.9	290	228	.2	390	.08	.40	.2	2
Crab, cooked	3 oz.	89	14.4	2.5	1.1	38	155	.8		(.04)	(.05)	(2.1)	2

Food	Measure	Calories	Protein (g)	Fat (g)	Carbohydrate (g)	Calcium (mg)	Phosphorus (mg)	Iron (mg)	Vitamin A (I.U.)	Thiamine (mg)	Riboflavin (mg)	Niacin (mg)	Ascorbic Acid (mg)
Crackers, graham	2 med.	55	1.1	1.4	10.4	3	28	.3	(0)	.04	.02	.2	(0)
Crackers, saltines	2 in. square	34	.7	.9	5.7	2	7	.1	(0)	Tr.	Tr.	.1	(0)
Cranberries, raw	1 cup	54	.5	.8	12.8	16	12	.7	50	(.03)	(.02)	.1	13
Cream, light	1 T	30	.4	3.0	.6	15	12	.0	120	Tr.	.02	Tr.	Tr.
Cream, whipped	1 T	49	.3	5.2	.5	12	9	.0	220	Tr.	.02	Tr.	Tr.
Cucumber	6 slices	29	.4	.1	7.1	13	11	.8	80	.01	.02	Tr.	4
Currants, raw	1 cup	60	1.3	.2	15.0	40	36	1.0	130	.04	.05	.2	40
Custard	1 cup	283	13.1	13.4	27.8	283	295	1.2	840	.11	.49	(1.3)	1
Dandelion greens	1 cup, cooked	79	4.9	1.3	15.8	337	126	5.6	27,310	.23	.22	3.9	29
Dates	1 cup	505	3.9	1.1	134.2	128	107	3.7	100	.16	.17	.4	(0)
Doughnuts	1 med.	136	2.1	6.7	16.9	23	92	(.2)	40	.05	.04	Tr.	0
Eggs, whole	1 med.	77	6.1	5.5	.3	26	101	1.3	550	.05	.14	Tr.	0
Egg, white	1 med.	15	3.3	0.	.2	2	5	.1	(0)	0	.08	Tr.	0
Egg, yolk	1 med.	61	2.8	5.4	.1	25	100	1.2	550	.05	.06	Tr.	0
Endive, raw	1 lb.	90	7.3	.9	18.2	359	254	7.7	13,600	.30	.53	1.8	49
Farina, cooked	1 cup, unenriched	104	3.1	.2	21.7	7	31	.2	0	.01	.02	.2	(0)
Figs, fresh	3 small	90	1.6	.5	22.3	62	36	.7	90	.06	.06	.6	2
Figs, dried	1 large	57	.8	.3	14.4	39	23	.6	20	.03	.02	.4	(0)
Flour, bread, enriched	1 cup	408	13.2	1.2	83.7	18	106	3.2	(0)	.49	.29	3.9	(0)
Flour, rye	1 cup	285	7.5	.8	62.3	18	148	.9	(0)	.12	.06	.5	(0)
Flour, whole-wheat	1 cup	400	16.0	2.4	85.2	49	446	4.0	(0)	.66	.14	5.2	(0)
Frankfurters	1 oz.	124	7.	10.	1.	3	25	.6	60	.08	.09	1.3	Tr.
Fudge, plain	1 T	116	.5	3.2	23.0	14	19	.1	(0)	Tr.	.02	Tr.	(0)
Gelatin, dry	1 T	34	8.6	.0	0.	(0)	(0)	(0)	(0)	(0)	(0)	(0)	(0)
Gelatin dessert, plain	1 cup	155	3.8	.0	36.3	(0)	(0)	(0)	(0)	(0)	(0)	(0)	(0)
Gingerale	1 cup	80			21.				(0)				(0)
Gingerbread	1 piece	180	2.1	6.6	28.4	63	39	1.4	50	.02	.05	.6	(0)
Grapes	1 cup	84	1.7	1.0	17.7	20	25	.7	90	.07	.05	.3	5
Grape juice	1 cup	170	1.0	.0	46.2	25	25	.8	10	.09	.12	(.6)	Tr.
Grapefruit	½ small	49	.6	.2	12.6	28	22	.7	20	.05	.02	.3	50
Grapefruit juice	1 cup fresh	87	1.2	.2	22.6	20	32	1.0	(0)	.09	.05	.5	99
Halibut, broiled	4" × 3" × ½"	228	32.8	9.8	0.	18	335	1.0	(0)	.08	.09	13.1	0
Ham, cooked	3 oz.	338	20.	28.	0.	9	202	2.6	(0)	.45	.20	4.0	0
Ham, smoked	3 oz.	339	20.	28.	(.3)	9	141	2.5	(0)	.46	.18	3.5	0
Heart, beef	3 oz.	92	14.4	3.1	.6	8	173	3.9	30	.50	.75	6.6	5
Hominy, cooked	1 cup, unenriched	62	2.9	.2	26.6	1	24	.2	(0)	.04	.01	.4	0
Honey	1 T	49	.1	0.	16.7	(26)	3	.2	(0)	Tr.	.04	Tr.	1
Honeydew	1 wedge	167	.8	0.	12.8	100	(24)	(.6)	60	.07	.01	.3	34
Ice cream, plain	1 slice	50	3.2	10.1	16.7	(2)	80	.1	420	.03	.15	.1	1
Jelly	1 T	45	.0	.0	13.0	248	(2)	.1	(Tr.)	Tr.	(Tr.)	(Tr.)	1
Kale, cooked	1 cup	89	4.3	.7	7.9	11	68	2.4	9,220	.08	.25	1.9	56
Kidney, veal	3 oz.	47	14.1	2.8	.9	71	202	7.8	(980)	.44	2.06	6.3	11
Kohlrabi, cooked	1 cup	356	3.3	.2	10.4	9	78	.9	Tr.	.06	.06	.3	57
Lamb, chops	3 oz.	293	20.	30.	0.	8	170	2.6	(0)	.12	.22	4.8	0
Lamb, roast	3 oz.	293	18.	24.	0.	8	160	2.2	(0)	.10	.19	3.9	0
Lemons	1 med.	20	.6	.4	5.4	25	14	.4	0	.03	Tr.	.1	31

513

Food	Measure	Food Energy Cal.	Pro. Gm.	Fat Gm.	CHO Gm.	Ca Mg.	P Mg.	Fe Mg.	Vit. A I.U.	Thiamine Mg.	Riboflavin Mg.	Niacin Mg.	Ascorbic Acid Mg.
Lemon juice	1 T	4	.1	.0	1.2	2	2	.0	0	.01	Tr.	Tr.	7
Lettuce, head	1 lb.	68	5.4	.9	13.2	100	114	2.3	2,470	.20	.38	.9	35
Lettuce, leaf	2 large	7	.6	.1	1.4	11	12	.2	270	.02	.04	.1	4
Liver, beef, cooked	2 oz.	118	13.4	4.4	5.5	5	276	4.4	30,330	.15	2.25	8.4	18
Liver, calves', uncooked	3 oz.	120	16.2	4.2	3.4	5	292	9.0	19,130	.18	2.65	13.7	30
Lobster, canned	3 oz.	78	15.6	1.1	.3	55	163	.7	(280)	(.03)	.06	(1.9)	
Loganberries	1 cup	90	1.4	.9	21.6	50	27	1.7	990	(.04)	(.10)	(.4)	34
Macaroni and cheese	1 cup, baked	464	17.8	24.2	43.3	420	372	1.1	(280)	.07	.35	.9	Tr.
Mararoni, cooked	1 cup, enriched	209	7.1	.8	43.2	13	91	1.5	(0)	.24	.15	2.0	(0)
Mackerel, canned	3 oz. Atlantic	155	16.4	9.4	0.	157	233	1.8	370	.05	.18	4.9	
	3 oz. Pacific	153	17.9	8.5	0.	221	245	1.9	20	.02	.28	7.4	
Marmalade	1 T	55	.1	.1	14.2	2	2	.1	Tr.	Tr.	Tr.	Tr.	1
Mayonnaise	1 T	92	.2	10.1	.4	2	8	.1	30	Tr.	Tr.	Tr.	0
Milk, whole	1 cup	166	8.5	9.5	12.0	288	227	.2	(390)	.09	.42	.2	3
Milk, skim	1 cup	87	8.6	.2	12.5	303	239	.2	(10)	.09	.44	.3	3
Milk, condensed, sweetened	1 cup	981	24.8	25.7	167.7	835	698	.6	(1,300)	.16	1.19	.3	3
Milk, evaporated	1 cup	346	17.6	19.9	24.9	612	491	.4	1,010	.12	.91	.6	3
Milk, malted, dry	1 oz.	115	4.1	2.4	20.0	81	107	.6	290	.09	.15	.5	3
Molasses, light	1 T	50			13.0	33	9	.9		.01	.01		(0)
Muffins, enriched	1	134	3.8	4.0	20.2	99	92	.8	50	.09	.10	.7	
Mushrooms, canned	1 cup	28	3.4	.5	9.0	(17)	(220)	(2.0)	0	.04	.60	4.8	(0)
Mustard greens	1 cup, cooked	31	3.2	.4	5.6	308	53	4.1	10,050	.08	.25	.8	63
Noodles, cooked	1 cup, enriched	107	3.5	1.0	20.5	6	56	.8	60	.22	.10	1.0	(0)
Oatmeal, cooked	1 cup	148	5.4	2.8	26.0	21	158	1.7	(0)	.22	.05	.4	(0)
Oil, salad	1 T	124	0.	14.	0.	0	0	0	0	0	0	0	(0)
Okra, cooked	8 pods	28	1.5	.2	6.3	70	53	.6	630	.05	.06	.7	17
Oleomargarine	1 T	101	.1	11.3	.1	3	2	.0	460	(0)	(0)	(0)	(0)
Olives, green	10	72	.8	7.4	2.2	48	9	.9	160	Tr.	Tr.	Tr.	
Olives, ripe	10	106	1.0	11.6	1.4	48	9	.9	40	Tr.	Tr.	Tr.	
Onions, cooked	1 cup	79	2.1	.4	18.3	67	92	1.0	110	.04	.06	.4	13
Onions, raw	1 T	4	.1	.0	1.0	3	4	.0	Tr.	Tr.	Tr.	Tr.	1
Onions, green	6 small	23	.5	.1	5.3	68	12	.4	(30)	Tr.	.06	(.1)	12
Oranges	1 med.	70	1.4	.3	17.4	51	36	.6	(290)	.04	.04	.4	77
Orange juice, fresh	1 cup	108	2.0	.5	27.1	47	39	.5	(460)	.12	.06	.6	122
Oysters, raw	1 cup	200	23.5	5.0	13.4	226	343	13.4	770	.19	.48	2.8	
Parsnips, cooked	1 cup	94	1.6	.8	21.5	88	124	1.1	0	.35	.16	.3	19
Peaches, fresh	1 med.	46	.5	.1	12.0	8	22	.6	880	.09	.05	.9	8
Peanut butter	1 T	92	4.2	7.6	3.4	12	63	.3	0	.02	.02	2.6	(0)
Peanuts, roasted	1 T	50	2.4	4.0	2.1	7	35	.2	0	.03	.01	1.5	(0)
Pears, fresh	1 med.	95	1.1	.6	23.9	20	24	.5	30	.03	.06	.2	6

Food	Measure	Calories	Protein	Fat	Carbohydrate	Calcium	Phosphorus	Iron	Vitamin A	Thiamine	Riboflavin	Niacin	Vitamin C
Peas, cooked	1 cup	111	7.8	.6	19.4	35	195	3.0	1,150	.40	.22	3.7	24
Peas, canned	1 cup	168	8.5	1.0	32.1	62	167	4.5	1,350	.28	.15	2.6	21
Peas, canned, drained	1 cup	145	7.2	1.0	27.5	51	123	3.4	1,070	.19	.10	1.6	15
Pecans	1 T	52	.7	5.5	1.0	6	24	.2	Tr.	.05	.01	.1	Tr.
Peppers, green	1 med.	16	.8	.1	3.6	7	16	.3	400	.02	.04	.2	77
Pie, apple	1 med. piece	331	2.8	12.8	53.3	9	32	.5	220	.04	.02	.3	1
Pie, lemon	1 med. piece	302	4.3	12.1	44.9	24	61	.6	210	.04	.10	.3	1
Pineapple, fresh	1 cup	74	.6	.3	19.2	22	15	.4	180	.12	.04	.3	33
Plums, fresh	1	29	.4	.1	7.4	10	11	.3	200	.04	.02	.3	3
Popcorn, popped	1 cup	54	1.8	0.7	10.7	(2)	(39)	(0.4)	(0)	(0.05)	(0.02)	(0.3)	(0)
Pork, chops	3 oz.	284	20.	22.	0.	9	200	2.6	(0)	.71	.20	4.3	0
Pork, sausage	4 oz.	510	12.2	50.8	0.	7	113	1.8	(0)	.49	.19	2.6	
Potato, white, baked	1 med.	97	2.4	.1	22.3	13	65	.8	20	.11	.05	1.4	17
Potato, white, boiled	1 med.	105	2.5	.1	24.1	14	71	.9	20	.12	.04	1.3	17
Potato, white, mashed	1 cup	240	4.1	11.7	31.0	52	115	1.2	500	.15	.10	1.6	13
Potato, french fried	8 pieces	157	2.2	7.6	20.8	12	61	.8	20	.07	.04	1.3	11
Potato chips	7 large	108	1.3	7.4	9.8	(6)	(30)	(.4)	(10)	(.04)	.02	(.6)	2
Potato, sweet, baked	1 med.	183	2.6	1.1	41.3	44	72	1.1	11,410	.12	.08	.9	28
Prunes, dried	4 med.	73	.6	.2	19.2	15	23	1.1	510	.03	.04	.5	1
Prune juice, canned	1 cup	170	1.0	0.	46.3	(60)	(96)	(4.3)		(.07)	(.19)	1.0	(2)
Puffed rice	1 cup	55	.8	.1	12.3	3	16	.3	(0)	.06	.01	.8	(0)
Puffed wheat	1 cup	43	1.3	.2	9.6	6	39	.5	(0)	.07	.02	.8	(0)
Pumpkin, canned	1 cup	76	2.3	.7	18.0	(46)	(82)	(1.6)	7,750	.04	.14	1.2	
Radishes	4 small	4	.2	.0	.8	7	6	.2	10	.01	Tr.	.1	5
Raisins, dried	1 T	26	.2	.0	7.1	8	13	.3	Tr.	.02	.01	Tr.	Tr.
Raspberries, black	1 cup	100	2.0	2.1	21.0	54	50	1.2	(0)	.03	(.09)	(.4)	(32)
Raspberries, red	1 cup	70	1.5	.5	17.0	49	46	1.1	160	.03	(.08)	(.4)	29
Rhubarb, cooked	1 cup	383	1.1	.3	97.9	112	54	1.1	70	.02	.01	.2	17
Rice, cooked	1 cup	201	4.2	.2	44.0	13	76	.5	(0)	.02	.03	.7	(0)
Rice, flakes	1 cup	118	1.8	.2	26.3	6	35	.5	(0)	.14	.11	1.6	(0)
Rutabagas, cooked	1 cup	50	1.2	.2	11.6	85	64	.6	540	.08	.03	1.1	33
Salad dressing	1 T, boiled	28	.8	1.7	2.6	15	17	.1	80	.01	(0)	Tr.	Tr.
Salad dressing, French	1 T	59	.1	5.3	3.0	(0)	(0)	(0)	(0)	(0)	.33	(0)	(0)
Salmon, cooked	1 steak	204	33.6	6.7	.2	220	500	1.4	200	.12	.14	9.8	(0)
Salmon, red, canned	3 oz.	147	17.2	8.2	0.	301	293	1.0		.03	(.12)	6.2	(0)
Sardines, Atlantic	3 oz. can	288	17.9	23.0	.9	(324)	369	(3.5)	(20)	(.01)	(.26)	(3.3)	(0)
Sardines, Pacific	3 oz. can	171	15.1	23.0	.6	85	42	(1.2)	80	(.01)	0.15	(6.3)	
Sauerkraut, canned	1 cup	39	2.6	11.5	8.0	48	38	.0	0	0.08	.07	0.3	38
Sherbet	½ cup	118	1.4	0.5	28.8	13	102	1.0	(0)	.02	.03	.0	(0)
Shredded wheat	1 large biscuit	102	2.9	.0	22.7				50	.06	.03	1.3	(0)
Shrimp, canned	3 oz., drained	108	22.8	.7		98	224	2.6		.01		1.9	(0)
Soup, pea	1 cup	141	6.4	1.2	25.0	32	98	1.5		.17	.07	1.2	5
Soup, tomato	1 cup	90	2.2	2.0	17.9	24	39	1.0	(440)	.02	.10	.7	10
Soup, vegetable	1 cup	82	4.2	2.2	14.5	32	50	.8	(1,230)	.05	.08	1.0	8
Spinach, cooked	1 cup	46	5.6	1.8	6.5	223	59	3.6	21,200	.14	.36	1.1	54
Squash, winter	1 cup, baked	97	3.9	.8	22.6	49	72	1.6	12,690	.10	.31	1.2	14

Food	Measure	Food Energy Cal.	Pro. Gm.	Fat Gm.	CHO Gm.	Ca Mg.	P Mg.	Fe Mg.	Vit. A I.U.	Thiamine Mg.	Riboflavin Mg.	Niacin Mg.	Ascorbic Acid Mg.
Strawberries, fresh	1 cup	54	1.2	0.7	12.4	42	40	1.2	90	0.04	0.10	0.4	89
Sugar, granulated	1 T	48	(0.)	(0.)	12.4				(0)	(0)	(0)	(0)	(0)
Sugar, powdered	1 T	31	(0.)	(0.)	8.0				(0)	(0)	(0)	(0)	(0)
Sugar, brown	1 T	51	(0.)	(0.)	13.1	10	5	.4	(0)	(0)	(0)	(0)	(0)
Swordfish, cooked	1 steak	223	34.2	8.5	0.	25	314	1.4	2,880	.06	.07	12.9	(0)
Tapioca, dry	1 cup	547	.9	.3	131.3	18	18	(1.5)	(0)	(0)	(0)	(0)	(0)
Tomato, raw	1 med.	30	1.5	.4	6.0	16	40	.9	1,640	.08	.06	.8	35
Tomato juice, canned	1 cup	50	2.4	.5	10.4	(17)	(36)	(1.0)	2,540	.12	.07	1.8	38
Tongue, beef	4 oz.	235	18.6	17.	.5	10	212	3.2	(0)	.14	.33	5.7	(0)
Tunafish, canned	3 oz.	247	20.2	17.8	0.	6	250	1.0	(180)	(0.04)	(0.08)	(9.1)	(0)
Turkey, raw	4 oz.	304	22.8	22.9	0.	26	363	4.3	Tr.	.10	.16	9.1	(0)
Turnip greens, boiled	1 cup	43	4.2	.6	7.8	376	72	3.5	15,370	.09	.59	1.0	87
Turnips, cooked	1 cup	42	1.2	.3	9.3	62	53	.8	Tr.	.06	.09	.6	28
Veal, cutlet	3 oz. cooked	184	24.	9.	0.	10	219	3.0	(0)	.07	.24	5.2	0
Veal, roast	3 oz.	193	24.	10.	0.	10	219	3.1	(0)	.11	.27	6.7	0
Waffles, baked	1 waffle, enriched	216	7.0	8.0	28.4	144	153	1.4	270	.14	.20	1.0	(0)
Walnuts, English	1 T	49	1.1	4.8	1.2	6	28	.2	Tr.	.04	.01	.1	Tr.
Watercress	1 lb.	84	7.7	1.4	15.0	885	209	9.1	21,450	.37	.71	3.6	350
Watermelon	½ slice	45	.8	.3	11.0	11	19	.3	950	.08	.08	.3	10
White sauce, med.	1 cup	429	10.6	33.1	23.3	305	252	.3	1,350	.09	.41	.3	1
Yeast, compressed	1 oz.	24	(3.0)	.1	3.7	7	172	1.4	(0)	.13	.59	8.0	(0)

Audio-Visual Aids

The use of audio-visual aids from the following compilation will add emphasis to the ideas presented in *Experiences with Foods*. The teacher will obtain best results through a discussion of the film both preceding and following its showing.

The motion pictures are 16 mm productions and the filmstrips are 35 mm, single-frame productions. You may find these aids available in a division of audio-visual education connected with a public school or with a university.

KEY TO SYMBOLS

min.	Minutes	c.	Color
sd.	Sound motion picture	sg.	Study guide
	fs.	Filmstrip	

UNIT ONE

Cooking: Kitchen Safety (YA: 11 min: sd: sg). Deals with handling kitchen implements safely.

Cooking: Measuring (YA: 11 min: sd: sg). Teaches how to measure accurately.

Food and Nutrition (EBF: 11 min: sd: sg). Food requirements and deficiencies resulting from lack of minerals and vitamins.

Making Ends Meet (DCSt.: sd: sg). Presents foods rich in minerals and vitamins.

UNIT TWO

Fundamentals of Diet (EBF: 11 min: sd: sg). Shows use of food in human body. Results of experiments with animals are used to illustrate food deficiencies.

Whenever You Eat (NDC: 12 min: sd: c). Deals with relation between food choices and consumption of foods and good health.

UNIT THREE

Home Management: Why Budget? (YA: 11 min: sd). Explains the importance of the budget to families on all income levels.

Let's Make a Meal in Twenty Minutes (SM: 5 min: sd: c). Deals with the value of intelligent marketing and the use of tools in preparing meals in a limited time.

Meal-time Can Be Magic (BC–GM: fs: c). Pointers on serving attractive meals.

Wise Buying (Cor: 10 min: sd: c). Discusses seasonal changes, quantity purchases, and product labels.

UNIT FOUR

Bread (SVE: fs: sg). New methods of preparation of bread and new ideas for its use.

Cooking: Planning and Organization (YA: 11 min: sd: sg). Presents values of organized planning in meal preparation.

Principles of Baking (EBF: 11 min: sd). Shows processes of baking bread, pastries, and cakes.

Way to a Man's Heart (UW: 30 min: sd). Foods needed for healthy bodies, and cooking of meats at low temperature.

UNIT FIVE

ABC's of Beef Cookery (A: 14 min: sd). Practical advice on preparing beef.

Can You Carve? (MTPS: 12 min: sd: c). How to carve assorted meats and poultry.

Home Cookery of Fish (EBF: 11 min: sd). Shows cookery of boiled cod, baked whitefish, and broiled halibut.

Pork 'Round the Clock (NL: 14 min: sd: c). How to cook various cuts of pork.

Principles of Cooking (EBF: 11 min: sd: sg). Advantages and disadvantages of methods of cooking: boiling, roasting, steaming, etc.

UNIT SIX

Baby Sitter, The (YA: 15 min: sd). Shows mutual responsibility of sitter and parents.

Children Growing Up with Other People (UW: 30 min: sd). Shows children learning to be independent, self-reliant, and co-operative.

Food and Nutrition (Pop. Sc.: fs: sg). Shows that health and energy depend largely upon eating right kinds and quantities of food.

UNIT SEVEN

Distribution of Foods (EBF: 11 min: sd). Shows how food preservation and transportation have made possible the distribution of perishable foods.

Freezing Fruits and Dairy Products (Pop. Sc.: fs). Shows steps in the freezing process.

Freezing Prepared Meals, Baked Goods, Leftovers (Pop. Sc.: 48 fs: sd: c). Shows ways of wrapping and storing products to be frozen.

Frozen Freshness (GM: 30 min: sd). Presents techniques in quick freezing a variety of foods.

UNIT EIGHT

Dinner Party (SM: 22 min: sd: c). Emphasis on table etiquette.

Good Manners When Visiting and Table Manners (E: fs: sg: c). These filmstrips show that real courtesy is consideration for others.

How Do You Do? (YA: 15 min: sd). Presents acceptable social introductions.

Over the Back-yard Grill (NL: 15 min: sd: c). How and what to cook outdoors.

What Makes a Good Party (Cor: 10 min: sd: c). Demonstrates the skills needed to give a successful party.

Words of Courtesy (YA: 11 min: fs). Dramatizes the why and when of good manners.

DISTRIBUTORS

A — Armour and Company, 401 N. Wabash Street, Chicago, Illinois.

BC–GM — Betty Crocker of General Mills, 9200 Wayzata Boulevard, Golden Valley, Minnesota.

Cor — Coronet Instructional Films, 65 E. South Water Street, Chicago 1, Illinois.

DCSt. — Dairy Council of St. Louis, 4030 Chouteau Avenue, St. Louis 10, Missouri.

E — Eyegate House, Inc., 330 W. 42d Street, New York 18, New York.

EBF — Encyclopaedia Britannica Films, 20 North Wacker Drive, Chicago 6, Illinois.

GM — General Motors Corp., Dept. of Public Relations, Film Section, 3044 W. Grand Blvd., Detroit 2, Michigan; 405 Montgomery St., San Francisco 4, California.

MTPS — Modern Talking Picture Service, 9 Rockefeller Plaza, New York 20, New York.

NDC — National Dairy Council, 11 N. Canal Street, Chicago, Illinois.

NL — National Livestock and Meat Board, 407 N. Dearborn Street, Chicago, Illinois.

Pop. Sc. — Popular Science Publishing Company, Audio-Visual Division, 353 Fourth Avenue, New York 10, New York.

SM — Simmel-Meservey, Inc., 9113 W. Pico Blvd., Los Angeles, California.

SVE — Society for Visual Education, Inc., 100 East Ohio Street, Chicago 11, Illinois.

UW — United World, 1445 Park Avenue, New York 29, New York.

YA — Young America Films, Inc., 18 East 41st Street, New York 17, New York.

Index

Abbreviations and measures, chart, 350

Accompaniments, salads as, 159; soup, 158

Activity, and body weight, 281, 284; and water, 18; as determinant of caloric needs, 5

Almonds, salted, 494

Amino acids, 9

Angel cake, 174; recipe: 466

Appetite, 2, 3, 292; in child, 276; of overweight, 285, 287; of underweight, 282

Apple butter, 504

Apple frappé, 484

Apple pie, 479

Apples, 38; cooking, 44; recipes: baked, 356; caramel, 491; cinnamon-candy, 356; dried, 357; fried, 356; glazed, 355; uses and varieties of, chart, 39

Applesauce, 355

Apricots, 38; recipes: baked, 357; dried, 357

Ascorbic acid, 16, 20, 239. *See also* Vitamin C

Avocado, 40

Babies, dietary needs of, 73, 273–274

Bacon, 70

Bacteria, 74, 277, 293, 304

Bakery, 143

Baking, of bread, 149; of cakes, 173, 174; of cookies, 178; of griddle cakes, 56; of vegetables, 251; temperatures for, 350

Baking powder, 53–54, 55

Baking soda, 54, 55

Banana sponge, 482

Bananas, 39

Banquets, 326

Barbecue sauce, 424

Barbecues, 344–345

Barley, 48

Basting, 206

Batter, for fried chicken, 446

Batters, 55–56

Bavarian cream, 255; recipe: strawberry, 483

Bean soup, 387; purée, 387

Beans, 137; recipe: goldenrod, 412

Beans, dried, value of, 20, 239

Beef, 193, 202–203, 205; carving, 212–213, 214; cooking, 207, 208; cuts, 194–195, chart, 194; recipes: pot roast, 438; rolled rib roast, 437; stew, 434

Beriberi, 15

Berries, 40

Beverage ice cubes, 362

Beverages, 72–73, 75–79; for young children, 274; in packed lunch, 126; serving, 314; recipes: 359–363

Biscuits, 56; recipes: bacon, 381; baking-powder, 381; cheese, 381; drop, 381; pigs-in-blanket, 381; scones, 381; sour-milk, 381; yeast, 452; yeast coconut, 453

Bisques, 155; recipes: clam, 389; shrimp, 389

Body, and food, 3; and calories, 4–5; nutrient needs of, 3–20

Boiling of vegetables, 249–250

Bonbons, 489

Bones, uses for, 205

Borsch, 390

Boston brown bread, 379

Botulism, 299

Bouillon, 155, 157

Brains, 209; recipe: deep-fat fried, 436

Braising, 210, 234

Bran, 49

Bread, 49; at dinner, 265–266; choice of, 143; cost of, 143; eating, 330; leavening, 142–143; luncheon, 143

Breads, quick, baking chart, 375; buying, 57–58; cooking, 55–56; cost of, 143; ingredients, 52–55; qualities of, 57, chart, 57; techniques for, 55–56; recipes: biscuits, 381; Boston brown, 379; buckwheat, 383; cheese straws, 383; coffee cake, 380; corn bread, 379; doughnuts, 382; gingerbread, 383; griddle cakes, 376; muffins, 378; nut bread, 380; orange-nut, 380; popovers, 375; Virginia corn bread, 379; waffles, 377–378

Breads, yeast, 144–152; baking, 149, chart, 451; ingredients, 146–147; kneading, 148; qualities, 144–146; rising, 148; shaping, 148; recipes: batter oatmeal, 457; bowknots, 451; braids, 451; cheese, 452; Christmas stollen, 456; crescents, 451; date, 452; sour-cream, 456; Swedish tea ring, 454; white, 451; whole-wheat, 452; yeast biscuits, 452–453

Breakfast, and luncheon balance, 185, 186; beverages for, 72, 79; breads for, 52, 58; cereals for, 48, 51, 52; cooking, 88–89; eggs and meats in, 60, 68–70; equipment for serving, 314; fruits for, 36, 42–43; need for, 34–35; planning, 82–87; types of, 34–35

Brine, 308

Broiling, of meats, 207–208; pan, 208; of poultry, 231–232; range, 207–208; of vegetables, 251

Brown Betty, 460

Brown bread, Boston, 379

Brownies, 472

Brunch, 83

Buckwheat, 48

Budget, family, and breakfast, 83, 87; and food management, 115–119; and luncheon planning, 187; and using purchases wisely, 119–120, 132; dinner costs in, 263–266

Buffet parties, 334–336

Bulk, 286

Buns party, 404

Butter, lemon, 440

Butter, as source of fat, 8; as vitamin A source, 14

Buttermilk. *See* Milk

Buying, economical, 114–119

Cabbage, 247

Cabinets, kitchen, 102–104

Café au lait, 360
Caffeine, 77
Cakes, chiffon, 174; icings, frostings, fillings, for, 174; making with shortening, 171–174; making without shortening, 174; mixes, frozen, 174; sponge, 174; storing, 178; recipes: angel, 466; applesauce, 465; apricot or peach upside-down, 465; banana layer, 466; cheese, 466; Christmas fruit, 468; cocoa, 464; devil's-food layer, 463; pineapple upside-down, 465; sour-cream, 463; sour-cream spice, 463; spice layer, 464; sponge, 467; sunshine, 467; two-egg layer, 461; white layer, 462; yellow chiffon, 467
Cakes and cookies, temperature and time for baking, chart, 462
Calcium, 10, 11–12, 14; and cereals, 49, 50; and cheese, 134; and vegetables, 240; and vitamin D, 14; function of, 12; in milk, 273
Calories, and choice of desserts, 255; and overweight, 285, 286–287; and underweight, 282–283; function of, 4; in breads, 144; in breakfast, 82, 83; in carbohydrates, 5–6; in cereals, 49; in eggs, 61; in fats, 8; in foods, chart, 284; in fruits, 37; in luncheon, 187; in proteins, 9; in sandwiches, 149–150; in snacks, 23; in sugar, 166
Canapes, 330; recipes: 408
Candies, 488–494
Candles, 326
Candling, of eggs, 61
Canned meats and poultry, 132; in salad, 162
Canned soups, 158
Canning, commercial, standards for, 41
Canning, home, containers for, 301–302; preparation of foods for, 299–301; processing methods, 302, 495–497
Canning fruit, method and timetable for, chart, 495–496
Canning vegetables, methods and timetable for, chart, 497–498

Cans, sizes of, chart, 41
Caramel pecan roll, 491
Caramels, 491; date, 491
Carbohydrates, 3, 4, 9, 18; and fats, 8; and overweight, 286; and underweight, 283; and vitamins, 16; function of, 5–7; in cereals, 49; in desserts, 166; in legumes, 138; in vegetables, 239, 240; needs for, 6–7
Carbon dioxide, 144
Caring for children, 272–278
Carotene, 14
Carrots, with orange sauce, 412
Carving, of meat, 211–216; of poultry, 216, 234–236
Carving set, 211
Casein, 133
Casseroles, economy of, 123; examples of, 123; types of, 123–124; recipes: cheese, 410; frankfurter, 433
Catchup, ripe tomato, 507
Cavities, see Tooth decay
Celery, stuffed, 421
Cellulose, 5, 42, 239, 249
Centerpieces, 325, 326
Cereal cookery chart, 365
Cereal grain, structure and composition of a, chart, 49
Cereal gruel, 366
Cereals, 83; as meat extenders, 139; care of, 50; choosing, 51–52; food value of, 48–50; history of, 48–49; structure of, 48; types of, 48; recipes: 364–367
Charlotte russe, 255; recipe: butterscotch, 483
Cheese, care and preparation of, 136; kinds, 133–134; nutrients in, 134; sandwiches, 150; selection and use of, 134–136
Cheese and rice, 409
Cheeseburgers, 405
Cheese dressing, 398
Cheese fondue, 411
Cheese loaf, 410
Cheese sandwiches, grilled, 403
Cheese soufflé, 410; and ham, 410; and tomato, 411
Cheese spread, 402
Cheese straws, 383; pastry, 383
Cherries, 39, 40
Chicken, 227–236; carving, 235–236; cooking, 231–234; mar-

ket classes of, chart, 228; three grades of, chart, 229; types of, 228–230; recipes: braised, 446; broiled, 445; country-fried, 445; deep-fat fried, 446; Italian fried, 445; oven-fried, 445; roast, 446; Southern-fried, 445; stewed, 447
Chicken croquettes, 447
Chicken pie, 448
Chicken-rice soup, 384
Chicken-salad sandwiches, 405
Chicken spaghetti, 448
Chicken stock, 384
Chiffon cake. See Cake
Children, caloric requirements of, 5; carbohydrate needs of, 6; desserts for, 166; eggs for, 61; fat needs of, 8; helping to enjoy food, 275–277; meeting food needs of, 272–275; milk for, 73; mineral needs of, 11–12; protein needs of, 10; taking responsibility for, 277–278; weight problems of, 280, 284
Chile con carne, 428; soybean, 430
China dinnerware, 320; examples of, 323–325
Chlorophyll, 239, 250
Chocolate, 74, 77; recipe: hot, 361
Chocolate drops, 489
Chocolate pie. See Pies
Chop suey, American, 435
Chowder, 155; recipes: corn, 389; fresh-fish, 389; seafood, 388
Chow mein, 139
Cider, hot spiced, 361
Cinnamon toast, 373
Clam appetizer dip, 402
Clam bisque, 389
Clams, 226
Cleaning, of kitchen, 109; of large equipment, 109–111; of small equipment, 112; of vegetables, 242
Cleanliness, in handling children's foods, 277; in handling convalescent's foods, 293; kitchen, 23–24
Climate, and vegetables, 238–239
Cobalt, 10–11

Cobblers, 178, 180; recipe: cherry, 461
Cocktail, surprise, 487; melon, 487
Cocoa, 27, 73, 75–77; recipes: 361
Cocoa butter, 75
Coconut sticks, 375
Codfish balls, 70
Cod-liver oil, 283
Coffee, 73, 78; recipes: 359–361
Coffee cakes, 56; recipe: quick, 380
Coffee-makers, 109
Cole slaw, 392
Compote, cherries, grapefruit, and pears, 488
Condensed milk. *See* Milk
Condensed-milk dressing, 400
Conserves, 305; recipe: grape, 505
Consommé, 154, 157; recipes: 385
Containers, for canning, 301–302
Convalescent, foods for, 291–292; importance of doctor's directions for, 291; preparing for meals, 292–293; preparing meals for, 293–294; serving, 294–296; special diets for, 292, 295–296
Cooked dressing, 162, 164; recipe: 400
Cookies, baking, 178; from mix, 27–28; storing, 178; types of, 177; recipes: butterscotch, 469; chocolate-chip oatmeal, 470; corn-flake, 470; fruit balls, 472; fruit squares, 471; "Helene's," 472; molasses, 470; peanut-butter, 469; refrigerator, 471; sandies, 470; Santa Claus, 469; sugar, 468; tea cakes, 471; tea puffs, 471; wreaths, 469
Cookies and cakes, temperature and time for baking, chart, 462
Cooking, and vitamin B., 15; of cakes, 171–174, 175; of cereals, 51–52, chart, 365; of cheese, 136; of custard, 168; of dried fruit, 45; of eggs, 66–68; of fish, 224–227; of fresh fruit, 43–45; of gelatin, 255–256; of luncheon meats, 133; of meat, 206–211; of meat-stock

soups, 155–158; of pickles, 308–309; of poultry, 231–234; of puddings, 170; of snacks, 23; of vegetables, 243, 249–252
Cooking utensils, 28, 107
Corn, 48, 49
Corn bread, 379; Virginia spoon, 379
Corn chowder, 389
Corn-meal mush, fried, 366
Corn pudding, 420
Cornstarch, 48, 49; puddings, 170; recipe: 458
Corn sirup, 48
Cornucopias, 405
Cost, of breads, 143; of dinner as guide to planning, 263–266
Courtesy. *See* Etiquette
Cover, table, 313–314, 319
Cream-cheese, jelly-nut sandwiches, 405
Cream fillings, 183
Cream soup. *See* Soup
Croutons, 374
Crusts, how to make, 179–182; varieties of, chart, 477
Culpeper, Nicholas, 289
Cupcakes, 173
Cured meats, 132
Custard, making, 168–170; recipes: baked, 457; caramel, 457; chocolate, 457; coconut, 457; pumpkin, 457; soft, 458
Custard pie, 183; recipe: 478

Daily Food Guide, 18
Dates, stuffed, 489
Demitasse, 360
Desserts, 165; cakes, 171–177; cookies, 177; custards, 168–170; frozen, 257–259, 330; fruit, 259–260; gelatins, 255–256; history of, 254–255; in packed lunches, 127; nutrients in, 166–167; pastry, 180–183; puddings, 170; salads, 159; selecting for dinner, 255
Dextrose. *See* Glucose
Diet, and convalescence, 290–296; and weight, 281–287; breakfast in, 81, 82, 83–84; of babies, 273–274; of children, 274–275; components of, 5–20; dinner in, 263; eggs in, 60; fish in, 219; fruits in, 36–37, 259; luncheon in, 186; meat in, 60,

193; milk in, 73; pastry in, 227; snacks in, 23; vegetables in, 239–240
Digestion, 3, 5, 8, 12, 61, 249; and inactivity, 292
Dining area, 102
Dinners, 185, 262; costs, 263–266; desserts for, 255; equipment for serving, 314; formal, 318–320, 326; importance of, 263; menus, 266–267; preparation of, 268–269; special, 343
Dishwashing, 30, 317
Divinity, 492
Doctor, 291
Dough, 55, 56; leavening, 48; making, 146–148; shaping, 148
Doughnuts, 382; chocolate, 382; drop, 382; glazed, 382; orange, 382; sugared, 382
Dressing. *See* Salad dressing
Dried beef, creamed, in toast cups, 428
Drinking tube, 295
Dry ingredients, measuring, 26
Duck, 230, 233
Dumplings, 178; recipes: apple, 461; for stewed chicken, 447

Earthenware, 324–325
Eating, and overweight, 284, 287; habits of, 36, 86; in children, 275–278; out, 330–332; preparing children for, 278
Economy, of food. *See* Food management
Education, of children, 272–273
Egg in toast cup, 23
Eggnog, 363
Eggplant, baked, 422
Eggs, 54–55, 83; beating whites, 65–66; cooking, 66–68; grades, 62–63; in cakes, 171; in custard, 168; selection and handling, 61–65; standard for freshness, chart, 62; substitutes, 63; value of, in diet, 60–61, 133; recipes: baked, 368; broiled, 368–369; creole, 372; deviled, 372; fried, 368; hard-cooked, 368; in omelets, 370–371; poached, 368; scalloped, 372; scrambled, 369; soft-cooked (two methods), 367
Electric kitchen equipment, 107–109

Electric mixers, 109, 267
Elimination, 4, 5, 17, 36
Emotions, and weight, 281, 285
Energy, and food, 3–5, 17; and carbohydrates, 5–7; and fats, 8; and minerals, 10; and proteins, 8–9; and weight, 286; needs, in luncheon planning, 187; value: of cereals, 48–49; of cheese, 134; of fruits, 37; of sugar, 166
Entertaining, 333–347; at home, 334–345; at school, 345–347
Equipment, kitchen, 102–112; picnic, 344; small, for kitchen, chart, 110
Etiquette, 312–313; at receptions, 346; at teas, 340–341; being seated, 327; being served, 329–330; eating out, 330–332; general, 327; in family dining, 316; napkin use, 328; serving, 329; using silverware, 328–329
Evaporated milk. See Milk
Exercise, and weight, 282, 286

Fats, 3, 4, 5, 9, 18; and cheese, 134; and nuts, 139; and overweight, 286; and underweight, 282; and vitamins, 16; function of, 7–8; in bread, 146; in cakes, 171; in desserts, 166; in fish, 219; in poultry, 227; individual needs for, 8
Federal Food, Drug, and Cosmetic Act, 118, 248
Federal Meat Inspection Act, 202
Fermentation, 144, 146
Fillets, of fish, preparation of, 226; 441
Filling, cake, 177; cream, 183; pie, 182–183; sandwich, 149–151; recipes: caramel, 475; creamed-potato, 430; for cinnamon-apple salad, 397; fruit-nut, 475; lemon, 475
Fin fish, 219, 220; cooking, 224–225
Finger bowls, 330
Fish, 140, 218; canned, 221; cooking, 224–226; dried, salted, smoked, 220; eating, 330; freezing, 504; fresh, 219–220; frozen, 221; importance of,

219; selection and care, 219–223; storage, 220; recipes: baked, 441; cakes, fried, 442; creamed, 441; deep-sea delight, 441; fried, 440; simmered or poached, 440; soufflé, 443
Flat-sour spoilage, 299
Flatwear, 313–314, 319, 322–323
Flavoring, 146
Flour, 48, 55; enriched, 49; in bread, 55, 56, 143, 146; in cakes, 171; storing, 50; types, 52–53
Flower containers, 326
Fluorine, 12
Fondant, 489
Food combinations, a guide to, chart, 264
Food equivalents, chart, 351
Food Guide, Daily, 18
Food habits, good, 272
Food management, good, 87, 114–120, 188
Food needs, of adolescents, 4, 5, 8, 9, 12, 186; of adults, 4–5, 6, 8, 10, 12, 186; of children, 4, 6, 8, 9, 12, 13, 272–275
Food plan for good nutrition, chart, 116
Food values. See Nutrients
Foods, and energy, 3–5; and overweight, 283–287; for children, 272–278; for convalescent, 293–294; foreign and unfamiliar, 330; groups of, 5–18; high, moderate, and low calorie, chart, 284; home preserving of, 116–117, 298–309; need for, 2–5; preparation of, in kitchen, 100–102
Frappés, 257, 259; recipe: 484
Freezer, home, 107, 116–117, 144, 267
Freezing, breads and sandwiches, 144, 151–152; fish, 504; fruits, 303, 304, 499, directions for, chart, 500–501; home, 303–304; ice cream, 257–259; meats, 504; pastry, 182; poultry, 504; protein food, 152; vegetables, 502, directions for, chart, 502–503
French dressing, 163; recipe: 398
French toast, 374

Fritters, apple, 358; banana, 358; corn, 420; peach, 358; pineapple, 358
Froebel, Friedrich, 273
Frosting. See Icing
Frozen breads, 144; and sandwiches, 151–152
Frozen cakes, 174
Frozen foods, economy of, 115
Frozen fruit juices, 79
Frozen fruit salad, 397
Frozen meat, optimum storage time for, chart, 304
Frozen vegetables, 243–246; timetable for cooking, chart, 419
Fructose, 5, 167
Fruit balls, 494; cookies, 472
Fruit bars, 489
Fruit butters, 305
Fruit canning, method and timetable for, chart, 495–496; sirups for, chart, 301
Fruit combination desserts, 178–180, 259
Fruit-filled spread, 401
Fruit halves, broiled, 487
Fruit ice, 484
Fruit jelly candy, 488
Fruit juices, 42, 78–79; concentrates, 79
Fruit pies, 182–183
Fruit plate luncheons, 125
Fruit punch, 362
Fruit rolls, 180
Fruit squares, 471
Fruit whips, 259–260
Fruits, 5, 83; canning, 301, 302, 495; care of, canned, 41; citrus, 37–38; cooking, 43–45; desserts, 259–260; dried, 42, 357, average yields, chart, 45; freezing, 303, 304, 499, directions for, chart, 500–501; sirups for, chart, 499; fresh, 37, average yields, chart, 44; frozen, 42; garden, 40–41; importance of, 20, 36–37; in breads, 55, 146; in jelly, 305–308; in packed lunches, 127; in salads, 160, 162; orchard, 38–39; small, 40; tropical, 39–40; uses of, 42–43; vine, 40; recipes: 354–358, 482–488
Frying, meats, 209; poultry, 231; vegetables, 251

Fudge, cocoa, 490
Fudge icing, 474

Garnishes, 150, 151, 158, 159, 166
Geese, 230, 233
Gelatin, 254–256; recipes: 482–483
Gels, 255
Gingerbread, 383; waffles, 378
Glassware, 320, 323; chart, 323
Glucose, 5, 167
Gluten, 49, 53, 54, 56, 144, 171
Goiter, 12–13
Goulash, 124
Government grades. See United States Government
Grain, history of, 47–48. See also Cereals
Grapefruit, 37, 38; recipes: 354
Grapes, 40
Gravy, roast beef, 450; cream, 450; giblet, 450
Green salad, 392
Greens, in salads, 159, 162, 241
Griddle cakes, 55; recipes: nut, 376; pineapple, 376; sour-milk, 376; sweet-milk, 376
Ground meats, care of, 205
Growth, body, and proteins, 9; and vitamins, 14; of babies, 273–274
Guests, 313, 346
Guineas, 230, 233

Halibut steaks, broiled, 440
Ham, 70, 197, 205; carving, 214, 216; cooking, 207, 208
Ham and cheese soufflé, 410
Hamburg steak, 432
Ham slice, broiled, 437
Hard sauce, 426
Health, 3; and foods, 4–20; and sugar consumption, 167
Heart, 210; recipe: braised, 435
Hemoglobin, 12
Herbs, 206
Hollandaise sauce, 425
Hollow ware, 322–323
Homemaking, 22
Home production, 116–117, 298–309
Hominy grits, baked, 367
Hors d'oeuvres, 408
Horse-radish dressing, No. 1, 398; No. 2, 399
Horse-radish sauce, 425

Hostess, 313, 314, 333–334; at buffet, 335–336; at school reception, 346; at teas, 340–341; seating place for, 327
Hot-water bath, 299, 302
Hunger, 2, 60
Hydrogenation, 8

Ice cream, 254, 257–259; freezing, 257–259; ingredients, 257; recipes: banana, 485; chocolate, 485; grapenuts, 485; peanut-brittle, 485; peppermint, 485; pineapple, 486; vanilla, 485
Ice cubes, beverage, 362
Ices, 257, 259
Icing, 174, 176–177; recipes: broiled, 474; brown-sugar, 474; confectioners', 473; cream-cheese, 473; fudge, 474; mocha, 473; orange, lemon, 473; pineapple, 473; "quickie" glaze, 474; seven-minute, 474
Illness, and food, 278
Iodine, 12–13, 219, 240
Iron, 10, 14; function of, 12; in cereals, 49, 50; in vegetables, 240

Jam, 305
Jellies, 304–308; recipe: grape, 506
Junket, 458

Kidney, Creole, 436
Kidneys, 210
Kindergarten, 273
Kitchen, 92; and family needs, 95–100; care of, 109–112; combination, 97–98; efficient, 93–95; equipment, 102–112; farm, 98–100; food receiving in, 100; for moderate family, 96; small, 95–96; small equipment for, chart, 110; work centers in, 100–102
Kitchen management, 23–25
Kitchen skills, 22
Kitchen utensils, suggested, chart, 108
Kneading dough, 148
Kumquats, 38

Labels, as help in purchasing food, 41, 118, 248

Lactose, 5, 167
Lamb, 193, 202–203, 205; carving, 213, 214; cooking, 207, 209; cuts, 198, 199, chart, 198; recipes: roast shoulder, 437; stew, 434
Laundry, place for, 97–98
Leavening, 48; egg whites as, 65; in cakes, 171; types, 53–54
Leftovers, and breakfast, 70, 83; in soup, 155; meats, 132, 211; poultry, 234
Legumes, 136–139
Lemon desserts, 480, 484
Lemonade, 362
Lemons, 37, 38
Limes, 38
Linens, 320, 321
Liquids, measuring, 26; use in cakes, 171
Liver, 209; recipe: pan-fried, 435
Liver spread, 401
Lobster, 226–227
Luncheon, as light meal, 185; breads for, 143, 144; casseroles for, 123–124; desserts for, 166; equipment for serving, 314; formal and informal, 341–342; importance of, 186; meats for, 132–133; packed, 125–127; planning of, 186–187; plate, 124–125; preparation of, 188–190; sandwiches for, 149–152; school, 127–129; soups for, 154

Macaroni and cheese, 409
Malnutrition, 3, 167
Maltose, 5
Marinating, of salads, 161
Market, standards for, 117, 118; suggested order form, chart, 267
Marketing order, 87, 118, 187, 267
Marmalade, 305; recipe: pineapple, 505
Mayonnaise, 163; recipe: 399
Meal, rich, modification of, chart, 286
Meals, and weight, 284, 286; etiquette for, 327–332; for children, 275, 276; for convalescent, 293–294; preparing convalescent for, 292–293; serving, 294–296; snacks as, 22–30; three, from one cut of meat, chart, 204

Measures and abbreviations, chart, 350

Measuring, baking powder, 353; flour, 352; liquids, 353; shortening, 353; utensils, 25–27

Meat balls and spaghetti, 430

Meat, frozen, optimum storage time for, chart, 304

Meat loaf, 431

Meat nests, 430–431

Meat pie, 124; recipe: 433

Meat plate luncheons, 124

Meat spread, 403

Meat, storage time limits for, chart, 504

Meats, alternates for, 133–139; breakfast, 68–70; care of, 205; carving, 211–216; cooking, 206–211; cost in dinner, 263, 265–266; extenders, 139–140; freezing, 303–304, 504; history of, 192; importance of, 60, 193; in sandwiches, 150; kinds, 193–199; luncheon, 132–133; preparation of, for canning, 301, 302; selection, 199–205; temperature and time for cooking, chart, 429; variety, 209; various cuts of, 199–202; recipes: 428–439

Meatstock soup, 155–156

Meat thermometer, 207

Meat, three meals from one cut of, chart, 204

Medicine, 289–290

Melba toast, 373

Melons, 40; recipes: 355

Menu chart for one day, 85

Menus, barbecues, 345; breakfast, 34, 82–87, 88, 89; buffet, 334–335; convalescent, 291–292, 294–296; dessert in, 167; dinner, 263, 266–267, 269; formal dinner, 318; holiday, 343; late supper, 343; luncheons, 187, 342; party, 344; planning, 87, for the sick, chart, 290; reception, 346–347; snack, 27, 30; tea, 336

Meringue, 183; recipe: 480

Milk, cooking, 75; importance in diet, 73; in bread, 146; in custard, 168; keeping safe, 74–75; market forms, 73; various forms, chart, 76

Milk shakes, 363; recipes: ba-

nana, 363; chocolate, 363; maple, 363; strawberry, 363

Millet, 48

Milling, 49

Minerals, 3, 17, 18; and overweight, 286; function of, 10–12; in bread, 143; in breakfast, 84; in dessert, 167; individual needs for, 11–13; in eggs and meat, 60; in fish, 219; in fruits, 36, 42, 43; in grains, 49; in legumes, 138; in poultry, 227; in soup, 155; in vegetables, 239–240, 265

Mixes, ready, breads, 58, 144; cake, 174; pastry, 181

Mousse, 257; cranberry, 486

Muffins, 56; recipes: bacon, 379; batter, 456; bran, 378; orange, 378; plain, 378; rich blueberry, 378; soybean, 378

Mushroom sauce, 423

Mutton, 193, 197, 203

Napkins, 322, 328

Nectarines, 38

Niacin, 14, 16, 144, 240; in cereals, 49, 50; in meats, 206. See also Vitamin B group

Night blindness, 13–14

Noodle ring, baked, 367

Noodles, French-fried, 366; veal and vegetables with, 434

Nutrients, 3, 18–20; and breakfast, 36, 86; and convalescence, 290–291, 294; and luncheon, 122–123, 124, 125; and weight, 281–287; balance of, in dinner, 263, 266; for babies, 73, 273–274; for children, 6, 8, 9, 12, 13, 274; in bread, 143, 144; in cereals, 48–50, 51; in cheese, 134; in custards, 168; in desserts, 166–167, 260; in eggs, 60, 61; in fruits, 36–37; in gelatin, 255; in jellies and preserves, 304–305; in meats, 60, 61, 193; in milk, 73; in pickles, 308; in soup, 154; in vegetables, 239–240, 246, 248–250; preserving, in cooking vegetables, 243, 249, 250

Nutrition, 3; and food economy, 115–116, 119–120; good, a food plan for, chart, 116

Nuts, 139, 146, 150; fuel value

of, chart, 137; recipe: spiced, 494

Oatmeal, 49, 51

Oats, 48, 49

Oils, in salad dressing, 163, 164

Okra creole, 420

Omelets, 370; recipes: cheese, 370; fluffy, 370–371; jelly, 370; nut, 370; plain, 370

Onion soup, cream, 386

Onions, scalloped, 419; stuffed, 432

Open House, 347

Orange-apricot whip, frozen, 484

Orange juice, 78; recipe: cocktail, 363

Orange rinds, candied, 492

Oranges, 37–38; recipes: 354

Oven, 24, 173

Overeating, 3, 283–286

Overweight, 283–287

Oxidation, 3; and minerals, 12, 13; and vitamins, 16; of fats, 8; of sugars, 6

Oyster stew, 390

Oysters, 226; recipes: fried, 442; scalloped, 443

Panocha, 490

Pans, for cakes, 173

Pantry, 100

Parfait, 257; recipe: chocolate, 486

Parties, at home, 343–344; at school, 345–347

Pastry, 180–184; rolling and shaping, 181–182; ways to make, 180–181; recipes: cold-water, 476; hot-water, 476; vegetable-oil, 476

Patient. See Convalescent

Patty shells, 477

Peaches, 38; recipes: baked canned, 357; pickled, 506

Peach velvet, 483

Peanut brittle, 493

Peanut-butter, special spread, 402; cookies, 469

Peanuts, 137

Pears, 38; recipe: baked, 357

Pea soup, with ham, 387

Peas, dried, 137

Pecan brittle, 493

Pectin, 305

Pellagra, 16

524

Pepper-onion relish, 506
Pepper pot soup, 388
Peppers, stuffed, 431
Persimmons, 39
Phosphorus, 10, 11, 14; function, 12; in cereals, 49, 50; in milk, 273; in vegetables, 239
Pickles, bread-and-butter, 506
Pickling, 308–309
Picnics, 344
Pies, 180, 181–183; eating, 330; recipes: amber, 477; apple, 479; berry, 479; butterscotch-nut, 480; chocolate-cream, 481; custard, 478; lemon, 479, 480; pineapple chiffon, 481; pumpkin, 478; raisin, 478; sweet-potato, 478
Pigeons, 230
Pigs-in-blanket, 381
Pineapple, 39–40; recipes: 354, 465, 481, 486
Pizza pie, 454
Placemats, 321
Plastic dishes, 324
Plate luncheons, fruit for, 125; meats or meat alternates in, 124; vegetable, 124–125
Plums, 38–39, 40
Popcorn balls, 492
Popovers, 55; recipe: 375
Pork, 197, 203; cooking, 206, 207, 208; cuts, 200–201, chart, 200; recipe: loin roast, 437
Pork chops "Dixie," 439
Potato chips, garlic buttered, 404
Potato-pork pie, 433
Potato salad, 395
Potato soup, cream, 386
Potato water, 146
Potatoes, mashed, 412; scalloped, 419; sweet, 412; sweet-potato pie, 478
Pot-roasting, 210
Pottery, 324–325
Poultry, 140, 218; carving, 216, 235–236; cooking, 231–234; freezing, 504; importance of, 227; selection and care, 227–231; storage, 231; temperature and time for cooking, chart, 444; types, 228–231; recipes: 445–448
Pralines, 490
Preserves, 304–308; recipes:

cherry, raspberry, strawberry, 505
Preserving, home, 298–309; canning, 299–302; freezing, 302–304; jellies and preserves, 304–308; pickles, 308–309
Pressure cookery, 211, 250–251; for canning, 299–302
Proteins, 3, 6, 18; and breakfast, 84; and dinner, 263; and luncheon, 125, 132, 133, 187; and overweight, 286; and underweight, 283; and vitamins, 16; freezing, 152; function of, 8–10; in bread flour, 53; in cheese, 133, 134, 136; in desserts, 166; individual needs for, 10; in eggs and meat, 60, 61, 68; in fish, 219; in gelatin, 255; in legumes, 136–137, 138; in main-dish sandwiches, 150; in meats, 193, 206; in milk, 273; in nuts, 139; in poultry, 227; in soybean products, 50, 240; in vegetables, 239
Prunes, stewed dried, 357
Puddings, 170; recipes: bread, 459; Brown Betty, 460; cherry cobbler, 461; chocolate-cream, 459; cocoa, 459; corn, 420; cornstarch, 458; junket, 458; plum, 460; raisin-honey, 459; rice, 458; tapioca, 460
Purée, bean soup, 387; raspberry, 487; rhubarb-apple, 487; strawberry-pineapple, 487

Quick breads, 52–59, 375–383; baking chart, 375; qualities of, chart, 57
Quinces, 39

Range, kitchen, 106, 111–112, 267
Rarebit, Spanish, 411; Welsh, 411
Receptions, 326, 345–347
Recipes, 354–507; accuracy in following, 25; dependable, 88; for dinner menu, 267; Introduction to, 350. See also specific recipes
Refreshments, 159, 344
Refrigerator, 107, 109–111, 117
Relish, pepper-onion, 506
Rhubarb, 40, 41
Ribbon sandwiches, 406

Riboflavin, 14, 15–16, 144; in cereals, 49, 50; in meats, 205; in milk, 273; in vegetables, 240. See also Vitamin B group
Rice, 48, 49, 50; recipes: curried, 366; cheese and, 409
Rickets, 14
Rising period, for breads, 148
Roaster, electric, 267; oven, 109
Roasting, meat, 206–207; poultry, 233
Roasts. See Meats
Rolled sandwiches, 406
Rolls, butterscotch, 453; cinnamon, 453; clover leaf, 454; crullers, 454; Parker house, 454; refrigerator, 453; stuffed, 404
Russian dressing, 399

Safety, in kitchen, 24–25
Salad dressing, care of, 164; cheese, 136, 162; for marinating, 161; kinds, 163; making, 163–164; recipes: cheese, 398; condensed-milk, 400; cooked, 400; French, 398; fruit salad, 400; horse-radish, 398, 399; mayonnaise, 399; Russian, 399; Thousand Island, 399; Thousand-Island French, 398
Salads, cheese in, 136; dessert fruit, 259; greens, 241; history of, 158–159; ingredients, 159–161; making and serving, 162; recipes: cart-wheel, 394; chef, 393; chicken, 395; chinese-cabbage, 391; cinnamon-apple, 397; cole slaw, 392; cranberry, 396; frozen fruit, 397; fruit chef, 397; green, 392; head-lettuce, 391; hot potato, 395; jellied tomato, 393; kidney-bean, 395; perfection, 393; potato, 395; salmon, 396; savory salmon, 396; spinach, 392; stuffed-tomato, 394; supreme, 394; tuna, 396; vegetable mold, 393; Waldorf, 396; wilted-leaf lettuce, 391
Salmon loaf with sauce, 442
Salt, 13, 146
Sandwiches, as accompaniments, 150–151; cheese in, 136; cold, 150; in packed luncheons, 126; main-dish, 149; making,

151; storing, 151–152; toasted, 150; recipes: checkerboard loaf, 406–407; chicken-salad, 405; cream-cheese, jelly-nut, 405; grilled cheese, 403; ribbon, 406; rolled, 406

Sanitation, 277

Sauces, for fish, 224; recipes: caramel, 426; cheese, 423; chocolate, 427; cranberry, 427; cucumber, 425; egg, 423; hard, 426; hollandaise, 425; horse-radish, 425; lemon, 426; mushroom, 423; orange, 426; raisin, 427; sea-food cocktail, 424; sweet-sour, 425; sweet spice, 427; tartar, 424; tomato, 424; vanilla, 426; white, 423

Sauerbraten, 438

Sausage, 70, 205–206

Sausages, mock, 432

Sausage-stuffed acorn squash, 432

Scales, 118

Scallops, French-fried, 443

School lunches, 127–129

School lunchrooms, 128

Scones, 381

Scurvy, 16

Seasonings, cake, 171; in salad dressing, 163; in soup, 158, chart, 157; on fish, 224; on meat, 206

Seasons, influence of, on planning meals, 83–86, 167

Seeds, 48, 146

Serving, at meal, 329

Shellfish, 219, 220, 225–227

Sherbet, 254, 257, 259; recipe: lemon dessert, 484

Shopping, 114, 118, 119

Shortcakes, 178

Shortening, 54; adding to breads, 55; measuring, 26

Shrimp, 226; recipes: French-fried, 443; fried, 442

Shrimp bisque, 389

Shrimp fondue, 443

Sick, planning menus for the, chart, 290

Silverware, 320; flatware and hollow ware, 322–323; placing of, 313–314, 319; using, 328–329, 330

Sink, kitchen, 104–106

Sirups, for freezing fruits, chart, 499; for fruit canning, chart,

301; recipes: brown-sugar, 427; chocolate, 427

Snacks, for children, 275; marketing for, 28; menus, 27, 30, 32; planning and serving, 22–30; work plan, 30–32

Snows, 255

Soufflés, cheese, 410–411; vegetable, 422

Soup, 153, 205; concentrated, dehydrated, canned, 158; eating, 330; kinds, 154–155; legume, 138–139; making, 155–158; recipes: bean, 387; borsch, 390; chicken-noodle, 385; chicken-rice, 384; chicken stock, 384; consommé, 385; cream-of-celery, 386; cream-of-corn, 386; cream-of-onion, 386; cream-of-potato, 386; cream-of-spinach, 386; cream-of-tomato, 385; jellied consommé, 385; oyster stew, 390; pea soup with ham, 387; pepper pot, 388; purée of bean, 387; vegetable, 388; vichyssoise, 390

Soups, seasonings for, chart, 157

Sour milk, 74

Soybeans, 137; flour and grits, 50, 139; nutrients in, 10, 240

Spaghetti and meat balls, 430; French-fried, 366; and cheese, 409

Spanish cream, 255; recipe: 482

Spanish rarebit, 411

Spending, and economical food use, 119–120; planned, 115–119

Spinach soup, cream, 386

Spoilage, types of, 299

Sponge method, 148

Spreads, bacon, 403; baked-bean, 403; cheese, 402; chopped-liver, 401; clam appetizer dip, 402; frankfurter, 402; fruit-filled, 401; meat, 403; peanut-butter, 402; sharp-flavored, 401

Squabs, 231

Squash, acorn, sausage-stuffed, 432

Stainless-steel flatware, 323

Starches, 5, 6; and cooking, 43; in cereals, 49, 51; in vegetables, 239, 249

Steak, broiled club, 437; broiled

rib, 437; hamburg, 432; stuffed flank, 439; Swiss, 438

Steaks, "quickie," 428

Stew, 124; recipes: beef, 434; lamb, 434

Stewing, 210, 234

Stock, soup, 154, 155–156; clearing, 384

Storage, 87, 96, 100; of bread, 144; of cakes and cookies, 178; of eggs, 63; of fish, 220; of frozen food, 246, 304; of jellies and preserves, 308; of meat, 132, 193, 202, 203, 205; of vegetables, 242–243, 246; time limits for meat, chart, 504

Straight-dough method, 148

Strawberries, 40

Stuffing, poultry, 233; recipes: apple-and-celery, 449; bread, 449; fruit, 450; mushroom, 449; oyster, 449; raisin, 449

Sucrose, 5, 167

Sugar, 5–6, 55, 56, 146; as preservative, 304; history of, 165–166; importance of, 167; in cakes, 171; in custards, 168; in fruits, 36; in pudding, 170; measuring, 26–27; need of, 166

Sundaes, and weight, 285; recipe: chocolate, 486

Sunshine, value of, 14

Supper, 185; late, 342–343; pot-luck, 343

Swedish tea ring, 454

Sweetbreads, 209; recipes: and mushrooms, 436; deep-fat fried, 437

Sweet potato pie, 478

Sweet potatoes, mashed, 412

Swell spoilage, 299

Table appointments, 320–325; china, earthenware, pottery, 323–325; glassware, 323; linens, 321–322; silverware, 322–323

Tablecloths, 322

Table decorations, 325–326; formal, 327; holiday, 325–326

Table service, 312–313, 321; American, 317; European, 318–320; without servants, 315–317

Table setting, 312–315, 318–319; additional equipment, 314–315;

for buffet party, 335; for tea, 337, 340, laying individual covers, 313–314

Taffy, 493; peppermint, 493

Tangerines, 37, 38

Tapioca, 460

Tartar sauce, 424

Tea, 73, 77–78; recipes: 359

Teas, 326; etiquette at, 340–341; foods for, 336–337; table for, 337, 340

Temperatures, for baking, 350; for cooking eggs, 66

Theine, 77

Theobromine, 75

Thiamine, 14, 15, 144, 240; cereals, 49, 50; in meats, 206; in milk, 273. *See also* Vitamin B group

Thickeners, 65

Thousand Island dressing, 399; French, 398

Timbales, 477

Toast, 58; recipes: bacon-and-cheese, 409; cheese, 374; cinnamon, 373; coconut sticks, 375; croutons, 374; French, 374; melba, 373; milk, 374; orange, 374; plain, 373; plain broiled, 373

Toasters, 109

Tomato beverage, chilled, 362

Tomato macaroni, 409

Tomatoes, 40–41; nutrients in, 239, 240, 248, 251; recipes: scalloped, 420; stuffed, 421

Tongue, 210; recipe: braised, 435

Tooth decay, 7

Topping, for coffee cake, 380

Trace elements, 10, 219; in vegetables, 239

Trays, 326; for bed-patient, 294

Trichina parasite, 206, 207, 208

Tuna boats, 27

Turkey, 227; carving, 235–236; market classes of, chart, 228; roasting, 233; types of, 230; recipe: creamed, 447

Undernourishment, 281

Underweight, 281–283

United States Government, canned vegetable grades, 248; chicken grades, chart, 229; fresh vegetable grades, 242; meat inspection and grading, 202–203

Variety meats, 205; preparing and cooking, 209–210

Veal, 193, 203, 205; cooking, 207, 208; cuts, 196–197, chart, 196

Veal and vegetables with noodles, 434

Vegetable juices, 78–79

Vegetable plate luncheons, 124–125

Vegetable soufflé, 422

Vegetable soup, 388

Vegetables, 6, 20; baked, chart, 416; canning, 301, 497, methods and timetable for, chart, 497–498; choice and care of, 240–248; cooking, 249–252, chart, 413–415; directions for freezing, chart, 502–503; for creamed soup, 157; for salads, 159–160, 162; freezing, 303, 304, 502; French-fried, chart, 417; frozen, 243–246, 251–252, timetable for cooking, chart, 419; history of, 238–239; in low-cost dinner, 265; in packed lunch, 127; in sandwiches, 150; kinds of, 239, chart, 244–245; nutrients in, 239–240; pan-fried, chart, 418; pickling, 308; preparation of, for canning, 299–302; with meat, 210; recipes, 412–422

Vichyssoise, 390

Vinegar, 163, 308

Vision, 13–14

Vitamin, A, 13–14, 49, 239; B group, 14–16, 240; C, 17, 37, 49, 239, 240, 251; D, 13–14, 49

Vitamins, 3, 8, 18, 20; and breakfast, 84; and overweight, 286; and underweight, 283; function of, 13–17; in breads, 143; in cereal grains, 49; in desserts, 167; individual needs for, 13–17; in fish, 219; in fruits, 36, 42, 43; in legumes, 138; in poultry, 227; in soup, 154–155; in vegetables, 239, 240, 250, 265

Waffle-bakers, 109

Waffles, 56; recipes: apple, 377; cheese, 377; chocolate, 377; coconut, 377; gingerbread, 378; nut, 377; pineapple, 377; plain, 377

Waitress, 317

Walnut slices, sugared, 494

Water, and overweight, 286; function of, 17; in bread, 146; in vegetables, 239

Weather, and caloric needs, 5

Wedding breakfasts, 326

Weight, body, 4–5, 7, 8; and sugar, 167; eating to control, 280–287

Welsh rarebit, 411

Wheat, 48, 49; flour, 52

White sauce, methods for making, 156–157, 422, chart, 156; recipes: cheese, 423; egg, 423; mushroom, 423; plain, 423

White sauces, chart, 423

Work plans, for snacks, 30–32; for breakfast, 88, 89; for luncheon, 188–190; for dinner, 268

Worry, and underweight, 281

Yeast, 48, 142; qualities and forms, 144–146

Yeast breads, 144–152, 451–457; baking, chart, 451